HB Publications

Regional Bus Datafile

No 10 - S

201

(6th edi

GW00776291

Researched & Updated by	Mike Pinder
Printed & Distributed by	HB Publications Ltd 3 Ingham Grove, Hartlepool TS25 2LH

Front Cover — Lothian Buses Wright Eclipse Gemini, SN59BGF (340), is seen on Princes Street in Edinburgh (Jeff Hall)

Rear Cover — Seen at the same location is KSK985 a Volvo B12B / Berkhof Axial 100 of Parks of Hamilton (Jeff Hall)

Contents

Introduction

Welcome to the sixth edition of the Scottish Regional Datafile.

Entries in this publication are prioritised in the order of Fleet Number then Registration Number.
If a Fleet contains vehicles, some of which do not carry Fleet Numbers, then the Vehicles with Fleet
Numbers are shown first, followed by the remainder of the Fleet.

The information in this book has been updated from information freely available in the public
domain, various Bus and Coach Operators, Buslists on the Web, the PSV Circle and Busdata
Computing Services to whom we would like to express our thanks.

Mike Pinder (December 2010) buses@hbpub.co.uk

Details of each entry are shown as follows

Column 1 **Fleet Number** - where Operators have only a few vehicles with fleet numbers, this is shown immediately before the Chassis Type

Column 2 **Registration Number** - * indicates Previous Registration history

Column 3 **Garage & status**
     a Ancillary Vehicle
     d For disposal
     l On Loan
     oo On Order
     p Preserved
     r Reserve Fleet
     t Training Vehicle
     u Un-registered
     w Withdrawn
     x Not PSV Registered
     y Used for spares
     z Owned but not used

Column 4 **Chassis Type**

Column 5 **Body Type**

Column 6 **Configuration**
The first letter(s) represent the type of bus
     A   Articulated Bus
     B   Single Decker Bus
     C   Coach
     DP   Dual Purpose Vehicle
     H   Double Decker Bus
     M   Minibus
     O   Open Topped Bus
     P   Partially Open Topped Bus
     T   Trolleybus

Next are numbers indicating the seating for Single Decked buses or the
Upper Deck seating on Double Decked Vehicles followed by the Lower Deck seating

The next entry signifies the type of access and egress on the bus
     C Centre
     D Dual
     F Front
     R Rear
     T Three or more
In addition there may also be an entry signifying the type of equipment
     L Wheelchair lift
     T Toilet
Where spaces are shown between the Type & Entrance letters, this indicates the seating is unknown
Where dashes are shown between the Type & Entrance letters, this indicates the vehicle has had the seating removed.

Some vehicles are shown as TV - Training Vehicles

Column 7 **Year vehicle was new into service**

AAA Coaches / L A Travel

AAA Coaches Ltd, Unit 7 Camps Industrial Estate, Kirknewton EH27 8DF
L Sutherland, 4 Murieston Walk, Murieston, Livingston EH54 9EW
Website www.aaacoaches.co.uk
Depot   Unit 7 Camps Industrial Estate, Kirknewton EH27 8DF
Licence   PM0002780 (AAA Coaches Ltd) / PM0002886 (L A Travel)

FJ06BNU	Volvo B12B	Sunsundegui Sideral	C53F	2006
FJ56KUH —	Volvo B7R	Jonckheere Mistral	C55F	2007
FJ58LSK —	Volvo B12B	Jonckheere Mistral	C53F	2008
FL02LSK	Volvo B12B	Berkhof	C51FT	2002
N74ESX	LDV 400	LDV	M16	2005
N792SJU	Dennis Javelin 12SDA	Marcopolo Viaggio	C53F	1996
NC56AYM	Ford Transit	Ford	M16	1905
PN06KSO	Irisbus EuroRider 357E.12.35	Marcopolo Viaggio	C70FL	2006
PN06TTE —	MAN 18.310	Marcopolo Viaggio	C70FL	2006
PN06TVV —	MAN 18.310	Marcopolo Viaggio	C70FL	2006
PN09CWO	Irisbus EuroRider 397E.12.43A	Beulas Cygnus	C56F	2009
PO58HRF —	Irisbus EuroRider 397E.12.43A	Beulas Cygnus	C55F	2009
PO60HZA —	MAN A91	Beulas	C57F	2010
SC53VOM	Ford Transit	Ford	M16	2004
SK57BEY	Mercedes-Benz Vario O.813D	Killbeggan Vehicle Converters	C24F	2007
SL07RVY	Ford Transit	Ford	M16	2007
SN02AAA	Mercedes-Benz Vario O.814D	Onyx	C24F	2002
SN09JUV	Volvo B12B	Van Hool Alizée	C49FT	2009
SN09JUW	Volvo B12B	Van Hool Alizée	C49FT	2009
SN09JUX —	Volvo B12B	Van Hool Alizée	C49FT	2009
SN55FEF —	MAN 18.310	Marcopolo Viaggio	C70F	2005
SN57EEP —	Bova FHD127-365	Bova Futura	C54FT	2007
WR04NDO	Setra S315GT-HD	Setra	C49FT	2004
Y744HWT	Volvo B10M-62	Plaxton Paragon	C48F	2001
YN05HUZ	Irisbus EuroRider 397E.12.35	Plaxton Paragon	C49FT	2005
YN07KHH	Volvo B7R	Plaxton Excalibur	C57F	2007
YN07KHK —	Mercedes-Benz Vario O.816D	Plaxton Cheetah	C33F	2007
YN09EZE	Mercedes-Benz Vario O.816D	Unvi	C33F	2009
YN57TVF	Mercedes-Benz Vario O.816D	Indcar	C51F	2007

A Trip In Time

A Trip in Time Ltd, 4 Bruce Street, Coatbridge ML5 2AL
Website
Depot   Unit 5A Greenhill Industrial Estate, Greenhill, Coatbridge ML5 2AG
Licence   PM1032966

N191EMJ	w	Mercedes-Benz 709D	Plaxton Beaver	B27F	1995
N371JGS		Mercedes-Benz 709D	Plaxton Beaver	B27F	1994
P215JKL		Mercedes-Benz 709D	Plaxton Beaver	B29F	1996
P218LKK		Mercedes-Benz 711D	Plaxton Beaver	B27F	1996
P334TGS		Mercedes-Benz 711D	Plaxton Beaver	DP24FL	1996
R84NNJ		Mercedes-Benz Vario O.814D	Plaxton Beaver 2	B27F	1997
R156UAL		Mercedes-Benz Vario O.814D	Alexander	B27F	1998
S132JSO		Mercedes-Benz 614D	Mellor	C21FL	1998

A & C Coaches

A&C Coaches Ltd, 3 Findlay Court, Motherwell ML1 1LA
Website
Depot   319 Orbiston Street, Motherwell ML1 1QN
Licence PM1081067

* J773HMX	Mercedes-Benz Vario O.814D	Crystals	DP28F	1991
* P896EEC	Volvo B10M-62	Plaxton Premiere 350	C53FT	1996
* R263JHL	Dennis Javelin 12SFD	Neoplan Transliner	C49FT	1997
SN03SWY	Mercedes-Benz 413CDI	Killbeggan Vehicle Converters	M16	2003
SN03SXJ	Mercedes-Benz Vario O.814D	Sitcar Beluga	C29F	2003
SN05FTK	Mercedes-Benz Vario O.814D	Euro Coach Builders	C28F	2005
SW03VCX	Ford Transit	Ford	M16	2003
* V86LYS	Volvo B10M-62	Plaxton Premiere 350	C53F	1999

Abbey Coaches

Abbey Coaches Ltd, 28 Glen Falloch Crescent, Neilston G78 3QY
Website
Depot   Kirktonfield Industrial Estate, Kirktonfield Road, Neilston G78 3NY
Licence PM0003055

FE02FBG	Volvo B10M-62	Plaxton Panther	C49FT	2002
* LKZ4453	Volvo B10M-62	Plaxton Premiere 350	C55F	1997
MV02UMG	Volvo B1M	Van Hool	C46FT	2002
N226HWX	Volvo B10M-62	Plaxton Premiere 350	C51F	1996
P55HMC	Volvo B10M-62	Plaxton Premiere 350	C49FT	1997
P645LFS	Mercedes-Benz Vario O.841D	Plaxton Beaver Coach	C33F	1996
SN53BKU	Iveco Daily 50-13	Iveco	M16	2003
W633MKY	Mercedes-Benz Vario O.814D	Plaxton Cheetah	C33F	2000
W851CWY	Volvo B7R	Plaxton Premiere 320	C57F	2000
YN55UDZ	BMC Probus 850RE	BMC	C35F	2005

ABC Travel

ABC Travel (Castle Douglas) Ltd, 36 Main Street, Kirkcowan, Newton Stewart DG8 0HG
Website
Depot   Clarebrand Industrial Estate, Clarebrand, Castle Douglas DG7 3AH
Licence PM1058933

* AM02NYC	MAN 18.310	Montana	C53F	2002
* ESK880	Volvo B10M-61	Van Hool Alizée	C53F	1987
F830XAJ	Volvo B10M-60	Van Hool Alizée	C55F	1989
* L188SUB	Volvo B10M-62	Plaxton Excalibur	C48FT	1994
M255UKX	Mercedes-Benz OH1416	Wright Urbanranger	B47F	1995
* M821YSC	Volvo B10M-48	Van Hool Alizée	C38F	1995
M996CYS	Mercedes-Benz 811D	Wadham Stringer	B33F	1994
N133GRE	Mercedes-Benz OH1416	Wright Urbanranger	B47F	1994
* P2KLT	Volvo B10M-62	Van Hool Alizée	C46FT	1997
P20JLS	Mercedes-Benz 711D	Plaxton Beaver Coach	C25F	1997
S582ACT	Mercedes-Benz Vario O.814D	Autobus Nouvelle	B33F	1999
V2AMS	Mercedes-Benz 614D	Onyx	C24F	1999
Y257KNB	Optare Solo M920	Optare	B33F	2001
YJ07VRN	Optare Solo M880SL	Optare	B25F	2007

Abbott Travel

M Cockell & Partners, 7/1 Edgefield Road Industrial Estate, Loanhead EH20 9TB
Website www.abbottravel.co.uk
Depot 7/1 Edgefield Road Industrial Estate, Loanhead EH20 9TB
Licence PM0002464

*	2767WF	Volvo B12B	Jonckheere Mistral	C53F	2004
*	B12ABT —	Volvo B12B	Jonckheere Mistral	C53F	2004
*	HIL2464	Volvo B10M-61	Van Hool Alizée	C49DT	1984
*	HIL6256—	Volvo B10M-62	Van Hool Alizée	C46F	1997
*	LCA381	Volvo B10M-62	Jonckheere Mistral	C53F	1997
*	MV08CNN	Volvo B12M	Jonckheere Mistral	C3F	2008
*	NM02AUJ	Volvo B12BT	Plaxton Excalibur	C49FT	2002
	S524LGA	Mercedes-Benz 614D	Adamson	C24F	1998
*	SF08VVE	Volvo B12M	Jonckheere Mistral	C53F	2008
*	SG03ZEL—	Volvo B12M	Jonckheere Mistral	C53F	2003
*	SW02VTP —	Volvo B12M	Jonckheere Mistral	C53F	2002

Aberfeldy Motor Services

J Stewart, Burnside Garages, The Square, Aberfeldy PH15 2DD
Website www.aberfeldycoaches.co.uk
Depot Burnside Garages, The Square, Aberfeldy PH15 2DD
Licence PM1007523

38	SP06EKA	Volvo B12B	Van Hool Alizée	C49FT	2006
39	SP06AEC	Bova HD120-340XF	Bova Magiq	C49FT	2006
41	* XSV893	Volvo B10M-62	Van Hool Alizée	C49F	2003
42	SP08ENL	Bova FHD120-365	Bova Futura	C49FT	2008
43	SP08ENK	Volvo B12B	Van Hool Alizée	C49FT	2008
44	SP08FJX	Mercedes-Benz Vario O.815D	Sitcar Beluga	C29F	2008
45	SP10DWV	Volvo B12B	Plaxton	C53F	2010
	SN54FBX	Mercedes-Benz Sprinter 413CDI	Killbeggan Vehicle Converters	M16	2004

Aberfoyle Coaches

Aberfoyle Coaches Ltd, The Garage, Main Street, Aberfoyle FK8 3UG
Website
Depot The Garage, Main Street, Aberfoyle FK8 3UG
Licence PM1090838

	BU06CUH	Mercedes-Benz Touro	Mercedes-Benz	C49FT	2006
	FJ07ABF	Volvo B12B	Volvo 9700	C49FT	2007
	MIB653	MAN 18.350	Neoplan Transliner	C48FT	2004
	MX10DXW	ADL Enviro Dart 8.9 SLF	ADL Enviro 200	B29F	2010
	SF58DHA	Iveco Daily 50C15		M16	2008
	SK07LFP	Mercedes-Benz O.814D	Killbeggan Vehicle Converters	C24F	2007

Ace Travel / McLean's Coaches

A McLean, 18 Woodhall Street, Chapelhall ML6 8SH
Website www.mcleancoaches.co.uk
Depot Unit 26 Brownsburn Industrial Estate, Airdrie ML6 9SE
Licence PM0002128

	EJR115W	Leyland Atlantean AN68A/2R	Alexander AL	H49/37F	1980
*	G5WJC	Dennis Condor DDA1702	D. McLean	H63/44F	1989
*	G7WJC	Dennis Condor DDA1702	D. McLean	H72/35D	1990
*	H223VKU	Leyland Olympian ON3R49C18Z4	Alexander RH	CH53/41F	1991
*	N18OVA	Bova FHD12-340	Bova Futura	C49F	2002
*	NX04MCL	Bova FHD13.340	Bova Futura	C55F	2004
	P322VWR	Volvo B10M-62	Plaxton Premiere 350	C48FT	1997

*	R261OFJ	Volvo B12T	Van Hool Astrobel	CH57/14CT	1998
	SF04WMY	Bova FHD13.340	Bova Futura	C55F	2004
*	SIL2292	DAF MB200DKFL600	Van Hool Alizée	C51FT	1983
	SJ54GBE	Bova FHD12-340	Bova Futura	C49FT	2004
	SP04AKG	Volvo B12B	Van Hool Alizée	C49FT	2004
*	T709UOS	Volvo B10M-62	Plaxton Premiere 350	C53F	1999
	VCU303T	Leyland Atlantean AN68A/2R	Alexander AL	H49/37F	1978
*	W8OVA	Bova FHD12-370	Bova Futura	C49FT	2000
	Y307KBN	Volvo B10M-62	Van Hool Alizée	C46FT	2000

Allan & Black

A Cameron & M Brown, Drumduan Depot, Dess, Aboyne AB34 5BN
Website www.allanandblackcoaches.co.uk
Depot Drumduan Depot, Dess, Aboyne AB34 5BN
Licence PM0000956

*	5397LJ	Scania K113CRB	Berkhof Excellence 2000HL	C51F	1994
*	BLZ8582	Setra S215HR	Setra Rational	C53F	1989
*	BVS118	Neoplan N516SHD	Neoplan Starliner	C48FT	2002
*	CKL1Y	Scania K113CRB	Berkhof Axial 50	C50FT	1996
	F694ACX	Volvo B10M-60	Van Hool Alizée	C53F	1989
	G369RTO	Scania N113DRB	Alexander RH	H47/33F	1990
*	K7SKY	Setra S250	Setra Special	C48FT	1997
*	P3KON	Peugeot Boxer	Crystals	M16	1997
	P6KET	Scania K113CRB	Van Hool	C70F	1996
	RAX19Y	Setra S215HD	Setra Tornado	C49FT	1982
*	VAV15	Setra S215HD	Setra Tornado	C53F	1989
	X508JGB	LDV Convoy	LDV	M16L	2000
*	Y603JSH	Scania K124IB4	Van Hool Alizée	C49FT	2001
	YN05UVL	Mercedes-Benz Sprinter 413CDI	Killbeggan Vehicle Converters	M16	2005

Allander Travel

Allander Coaches Ltd, Unit 19 Globerfield Estate, Milngavie G62 7LN
Website www.allandercoaches.co.uk
Depot Unit 19 Globerfield Estate, Milngavie G62 7LN
Licence PM0000035

AT 49	*	7726AT	Bova FHD10-370	Bova Futura	C48FT	2001
AT 88	*	7921AT	Bova FHD12-340	Bova Futura	C49FT	2005
AT 89	*	GIL1685	Mercedes-Benz 711D	Leicester Carriage Builders	B24F	1996
AT 91	*	4670AT	Bova FHD10-340	Bova Futura	C41F	2006
AT 92	*	9237AT	Bova FHD12-340	Bova Futura	C57F	2006
AT 93	*	8578AT	Bova FHD12-340	Bova Futura	C57F	2006
AT 94	*	4143AT	Bova FLC12-280	Bova Futura	C49FT	1998
AT 95		V691EWB	Bova FLC12-280	Bova Futura	C70F	1999
AT 96	*	B10MSC	MCW MetroBus 2 DR115/5	MCW	H63/43D	1988
AT 97	*	B10MSE	MCW MetroBus 2 DR115/5	MCW	H63/43D	1988
AT 98	*	B10MKF	Dennis Condor DDA1702	Duple Metsec	H63/43D	1989
AT100		PX07BEY	Bova FHD12-340	Bova Futura	C53F	2007
AT101		PX07BFA	Bova FHD12-340	Bova Futura	C53F	2007
AT102		PX07BFE	Bova FHD12-340	Bova Futura	C53F	2007
AT103	*	3289AT	Mercedes-Benz Sprinter 616CDI	Unvi	C22F	2007
AT108	*	AT2472	Bova FHD12-340	Bova Futura	C75FT	2002
AT109	*	2433AT	Bova FHD12-340	Bova Futura	C49F	2002
AT110	*	XAT11X	Bova FHD12-270	Bova Futura	C75F	2001
AT111	*	2367AT	Bova FHD12-340	Bova Futura	C49F	2002
AT112		T423TGA	Bova FHD12-340	Bova Futura	C57F	1999
AT114		Y218MYA	Bova FHD12-340	Bova Futura	C32FT	2001

Allander Travel

AT115		B9PRE	Mercedes-Benz 616CDI	Unvi	C22F	2007
AT116	*	RG03BVK	Bova FHD12.340	Bova Futura	C70F	2003
AT117	*	RG03BVW	Bova FHD12.340	Bova Futura	C70F	2003
AT118	*	RG03BSY	Bova FHD12.340	Bova Futura	C70F	2003

Allan's

D W Allan, Newtonloan Garage, Gorebridge EH23 4LZ
Website   www.allansgroup.com
Depot   Newtonloan Garage, Gorebridge EH23 4LZ
Licence   PM1016578

*	B11DWA	Mercedes-Benz 413CDI	Killbeggan Vehicle Converters	M16	2004
	B12DWA	Mercedes-Benz O.816D	Plaxton Cheetah	C29F	2009
	B13DWA	Scania K360EB4	Lahden	C51FT	2010
	B14DWA	Scania K360EB4	Lahden	C51FT	2010
	B15DWA	Scania K360EB4	Lahden	C51FT	2010
	—B17DWA	Scania K360EB4	Lahden	C51FT	2010
	B18DWA	Irisbus EuroRider 397E 12-35	Plaxton Panther	C61F	2009
	B19DWA	Irisbus EuroRider 397E 12-35	Plaxton Panther	C61F	2009
	B20DWA	Irisbus EuroRider 391.12.35	Plaxton Panther	C60F	2008
	~B21DWA	Irisbus EuroRider 391.12.35	Plaxton Panther	C60F	2008

Ann's Coaches

A Crawford, 1 Pit Road, Kirkintilloch G66 3ND
Website
Depot   1 Pit Road, Kirkintilloch G66 3ND
Licence   PM0000188

M1		H81PTG	Mercedes-Benz 811D	Optare StarRider	B33F	1991
M2	*	E444ANN	Mercedes-Benz 814D	Cunliffe	B34FL	1996
M3		N300SAS	Mercedes-Benz 811D	Autobus Classique	C29F	1996
M4		G89GOJ	Mercedes-Benz 811D	Optare StarRider	DP33F	1989
M5	*	3401AC	Mercedes-Benz Vario O.814D	Plaxton Cheetah	C33F	2002
PE1	*	410KGG	Leyland Leopard PSU4E/4R	Plaxton Paramount 3200 II	C45FT	1977
PT3	*	3935AC	Leyland Tiger TRCTL11/3RZ	Plaxton Paramount 3200 III	C53F	1988
D11	*	1709AC —	Dennis Javelin 10.5SFD	Plaxton Premiere 320	C41F	2000
	*	EIL584	Volvo B10M-60	Van Hool Alizée	C57F	1990
		G103KUB y	Mercedes-Benz 811D	Optare StarRider	C26F	1989

A Rays Travel

R & J Clarke, Shawrigg Nursery, Ayr Road, Shawsburn Larkhall ML9 2TZ
Website
Depot   Shawrigg Nursery, Ayr Road, Shawsburn Larkhall ML9 2TZ
              30 Reploch Street, Larkhall ML9 1AE
Licence   PM0001570

	A121GSA	Leyland Tiger TRBLXB/2RH	Alexander	B52F	1984
	F264YTJ	Leyland Olympian ONCL10/1RZ	Northern Counties	H47/30F	1988
	GN03PVT	Renault Master	Rohill	M15	2003
	H432EFT	Scania N113CRB	Alexander	B51F	1990
*	HOI364	Leyland LBM6T/2RA	Wadham Stringer Vanguard II	B34FL	1989
	R801JFS	Ford Transit	Ford	M16	1997
	R803JFS	Ford Transit	Ford	M16	1997
	S131JSO	Mercedes-Benz 614D	Mellor	B22FL	1998
	SF03PZC	Ford Transit	Ford	M16	2003

Arriva Scotland West
24 Greenock Road, Inchinnan, Renfrewshire PA4 9PG
Website www.arriva.co.uk
Depots As per list
Licence PM0001725

258	M109RMS	IN	Scania N113CRL	East Lancs European	B45F	1995
260	M112RMS	r	Scania N113CRL	East Lancs European	B45F	1995
261	M113RMS	IN	Scania N113CRL	East Lancs European	B45F	1995
262	M114RMS	IN	Scania N113CRL	East Lancs European	B51F	1995
263	M115RMS	IN	Scania N113CRL	East Lancs European	B51F	1995
265	M117RMS	IN	Scania N113CRL	East Lancs European	B51F	1995
266	M118RMS	r	Scania N113CRL	East Lancs European	B51F	1995
267	M119RMS	w	Scania N113CRL	East Lancs European	B51F	1995
268	M120RMS	IN	Scania N113CRL	East Lancs European	B51F	1995
270	L25LSX	IN	Scania N113CRL	East Lancs European	B42F	1993
1001	CX55EAA	J	Mercedes-Benz Citaro O.530	Mercedes-Benz	B39F	2005
1002	CX55EAC	J	Mercedes-Benz Citaro O.530	Mercedes-Benz	B39F	2005
1003	CX55EAE	J	Mercedes-Benz Citaro O.530	Mercedes-Benz	B39F	2005
1401	P962RUL	J	Dennis Dart 10.1 SLF	Alexander ALX200	B36F	1997
1402	P963RUL	J	Dennis Dart 10.1 SLF	Alexander ALX200	B36F	1997
1403	P964RUL	J	Dennis Dart 10.1 SLF	Alexander ALX200	B36F	1997
1404	P965RUL	J	Dennis Dart 10.1 SLF	Alexander ALX200	B36F	1997
1405	P966RUL	J	Dennis Dart 10.1 SLF	Alexander ALX200	B36F	1997
1406	P967RUL	J	Dennis Dart 10.1 SLF	Alexander ALX200	B36F	1997
1407	P968RUL	J	Dennis Dart 10.1 SLF	Alexander ALX200	B36F	1997
1408	* V311NGD	J	Dennis Dart 10.7 SLF	Plaxton Pointer 2	B36F	1999
1409	* V312NGD	J	Dennis Dart 10.7 SLF	Plaxton Pointer 2	B36F	1999
1410	* V313NGD	J	Dennis Dart 10.7 SLF	Plaxton Pointer 2	B36F	1999
1411	P801RWU	IN	Dennis Dart 10.1 SLF	Plaxton Pointer	B37F	1996
1412	P802RWU	IN	Dennis Dart 10.1 SLF	Plaxton Pointer	B37F	1996
1413	P803RWU	J	Dennis Dart 10.1 SLF	Plaxton Pointer	B37F	1996
1414	P804RWU	IN	Dennis Dart 10.1 SLF	Plaxton Pointer	B37F	1996
1415	P805RWU	IN	Dennis Dart 10.1 SLF	Plaxton Pointer	B37F	1996
1416	P806DBS	J	Dennis Dart 10.7 SLF	Alexander ALX200	B40F	1997
1417	P807DBS	J	Dennis Dart 10.7 SLF	Alexander ALX200	B40F	1997
1418	P808DBS	J	Dennis Dart 10.7 SLF	Alexander ALX200	B40F	1997
1419	P809DBS	J	Dennis Dart 10.7 SLF	Alexander ALX200	B40F	1997
1420	P810DBS	J	Dennis Dart 10.7 SLF	Alexander ALX200	B40F	1997
1421	P811DBS	J	Dennis Dart 10.7 SLF	Alexander ALX200	B40F	1997
1423	P813DBS	J	Dennis Dart 10.7 SLF	Alexander ALX200	B40F	1997
1424	P814DBS	J	Dennis Dart 10.7 SLF	Alexander ALX200	B40F	1997
1425	P815DBS	J	Dennis Dart 10.7 SLF	Alexander ALX200	B40F	1997
1426	P816GMS	IN	Dennis Dart 10.7 SLF	Plaxton Pointer	B39F	1997
1427	P817GMS	IN	Dennis Dart 10.7 SLF	Plaxton Pointer	B39F	1997
1428	P818GMS	IN	Dennis Dart 10.7 SLF	Plaxton Pointer	B39F	1997
1429	P819GMS	IN	Dennis Dart 10.7 SLF	Plaxton Pointer	B39F	1997
1430	P820GMS	J	Dennis Dart 10.7 SLF	Plaxton Pointer	B39F	1997
1431	P821GMS	IN	Dennis Dart 10.7 SLF	Plaxton Pointer	B39F	1997
1432	P822GMS	J	Dennis Dart 10.7 SLF	Plaxton Pointer	B39F	1997
1433	P823GMS	J	Dennis Dart 10.7 SLF	Plaxton Pointer	B39F	1997
1434	P824GMS	J	Dennis Dart 10.7 SLF	Plaxton Pointer	B39F	1997
1435	P825KES	IN	Dennis Dart 10.7 SLF	Plaxton Pointer	B39F	1997
1436	* HIL2148	IN	Dennis Dart 10.7 SLF	Plaxton Pointer	B39F	1997
1437	P827KES	J	Dennis Dart 10.7 SLF	Plaxton Pointer	B39F	1997
1438	P828KES	J	Dennis Dart 10.7 SLF	Plaxton Pointer	B39F	1997
1439	P829KES	IN	Dennis Dart 10.7 SLF	Plaxton Pointer	B39F	1997
1440	P830KES	IN	Dennis Dart 10.7 SLF	Plaxton Pointer	B39F	1997
1441	P831KES	IN	Dennis Dart 10.7 SLF	Plaxton Pointer	B39F	1997
1442	P832KES	J	Dennis Dart 10.7 SLF	Plaxton Pointer	B39F	1997
1443	P833KES	J	Dennis Dart 10.7 SLF	Plaxton Pointer	B39F	1997

1444	P834KES	J	Dennis Dart 10.7 SLF	Plaxton Pointer	B39F	1997
1445	P835KES	IN	Dennis Dart 10.7 SLF	Plaxton Pointer	B39F	1997
1446	P836KES	J	Dennis Dart 10.7 SLF	Plaxton Pointer	B39F	1997
1447	P837KES	J	Dennis Dart 10.7 SLF	Plaxton Pointer	B39F	1997
1448	P838KES	J	Dennis Dart 10.7 SLF	Plaxton Pointer	B39F	1997
1449	P839KES	J	Dennis Dart 10.7 SLF	Plaxton Pointer	B39F	1997
1450	P840KES	J	Dennis Dart 10.7 SLF	Plaxton Pointer	B39F	1997
1451	R381JYS	J	Dennis Dart 10.7 SLF	Alexander ALX200	B40F	1998
1452	R382JYS	J	Dennis Dart 10.7 SLF	Alexander ALX200	B40F	1998
1453	R383JYS	J	Dennis Dart 10.7 SLF	Alexander ALX200	B40F	1998
1454	R384JYS	J	Dennis Dart 10.7 SLF	Alexander ALX200	B40F	1998
1455	R385JYS	J	Dennis Dart 10.7 SLF	Alexander ALX200	B40F	1998
1456	S860OGB	J	Dennis Dart 10.7 SLF	Alexander ALX200	B37F	1998
1457	S861OGB	J	Dennis Dart 10.7 SLF	Alexander ALX200	B37F	1998
1458	S862OGB	J	Dennis Dart 10.7 SLF	Alexander ALX200	B37F	1998
1459	S863OGB	J	Dennis Dart 10.7 SLF	Alexander ALX200	B37F	1998
1460	S864OGB	J	Dennis Dart 10.7 SLF	Alexander ALX200	B37F	1998
1461	S865OGB	J	Dennis Dart 10.7 SLF	Alexander ALX200	B37F	1998
1462	S866OGB	J	Dennis Dart 10.7 SLF	Alexander ALX200	B37F	1998
1463	S867OGB	J	Dennis Dart 10.7 SLF	Alexander ALX200	B37F	1998
1464	S868OGB	J	Dennis Dart 10.7 SLF	Alexander ALX200	B37F	1998
1465	* S869OGB	J	Dennis Dart 10.7 SLF	Alexander ALX200	B37F	1998
1466	P210LKJ	J	Dennis Dart 10.7 SLF	Plaxton Pointer	B40F	1997
1467	P211LKJ	J	Dennis Dart 10.7 SLF	Plaxton Pointer	B40F	1997
1468	P212LKJ	J	Dennis Dart 10.7 SLF	Plaxton Pointer	B40F	1997
1471	V701LWT	J	Dennis Dart 10.7 SLF	Alexander ALX200	B31F	1999
1472	W602VGJ	J	Dennis Dart 10.7 SLF	Alexander ALX200	B32F	2000
1473	W603VGJ	J	Dennis Dart 10.7 SLF	Alexander ALX200	B32F	2000
1474	W604VGJ	J	Dennis Dart 10.7 SLF	Alexander ALX200	B32F	2000
1475	W605VGJ	J	Dennis Dart 10.7 SLF	Alexander ALX200	B32F	2000
1476	W606VGJ	J	Dennis Dart 10.7 SLF	Alexander ALX200	B32F	2000
1477	W607VGJ	J	Dennis Dart 10.7 SLF	Alexander ALX200	B32F	2000
1478	W608VGJ	J	Dennis Dart 10.7 SLF	Alexander ALX200	B32F	2000
1479	V609LGC	J	Dennis Dart 10.7 SLF	Alexander ALX200	B35F	1999
1480	V610LGC	J	Dennis Dart 10.7 SLF	Alexander ALX200	B35F	1999
1481	V611LGC	J	Dennis Dart 10.7 SLF	Alexander ALX200	B35F	1999
1482	V612LGC	J	Dennis Dart 10.7 SLF	Alexander ALX200	B35F	1999
1483	V613LGC	J	Dennis Dart 10.7 SLF	Alexander ALX200	B35F	1999
1484	V614LGC	J	Dennis Dart 10.7 SLF	Alexander ALX200	B35F	1999
1485	V615LGC	J	Dennis Dart 10.7 SLF	Alexander ALX200	B35F	1999
1486	V616LGC	J	Dennis Dart 10.7 SLF	Alexander ALX200	B35F	1999
1487	V617LGC	J	Dennis Dart 10.7 SLF	Alexander ALX200	B35F	1999
1488	V618LGC	J	Dennis Dart 10.7 SLF	Alexander ALX200	B35F	1999
1489	V619LGC	J	Dennis Dart 10.7 SLF	Alexander ALX200	B35F	1999
1490	V620LGC	J	Dennis Dart 10.7 SLF	Alexander ALX200	B35F	1999
1491	V621LGC	J	Dennis Dart 10.7 SLF	Alexander ALX200	B35F	1999
1492	V622LGC	J	Dennis Dart 10.7 SLF	Alexander ALX200	B35F	1999
1603	N681GUM	IN	Dennis Dart 9.8 SDL	Plaxton Pointer	B40F	1995
1605	P822RWU	IN	Dennis Dart 9.8 SFD	Plaxton Pointer	B40F	1996
1606	N672GUM	IN	Dennis Dart 9.8 SDL	Plaxton Pointer	B40F	1995
1607	N675GUM	IN	Dennis Dart 9.8 SDL	Plaxton Pointer	B40F	1995
1608	N677GUM	IN	Dennis Dart 9.8 SDL	Plaxton Pointer	B40F	1995
1609	N683GUM	IN	Dennis Dart 9.8 SDL	Plaxton Pointer	B40F	1995
1610	N685GUM	IN	Dennis Dart 9.8 SDL	Plaxton Pointer	B40F	1996
1614	N686GUM	IN	Dennis Dart 9.8 SDL	Plaxton Pointer	B40F	1996
1615	N687GUM	IN	Dennis Dart 9.8 SDL	Plaxton Pointer	B40F	1996
1619	N688GUM	IN	Dennis Dart 9.8 SDL	Plaxton Pointer	B40F	1996
1620	N691GUM	IN	Dennis Dart 9.8 SDL	Plaxton Pointer	B40F	1996
1624	S624KHN	J	Dennis Dart 10.7 SLF	Plaxton Pointer 2	B39F	1998
1642	S642KHN	J	Dennis Dart 10.7 SLF	Plaxton Pointer 2	B39F	1999

1643	S643KHN	IN	Dennis Dart 10.7 SLF	Plaxton Pointer 2	B39F	1999
1693	K543ORH	w	Dennis Dart 9 SDL	Plaxton Pointer	B34F	1992
1780	N710GUM	J	Dennis Dart 9 SDL	Plaxton Pointer	B34F	1995
1781	N711GUM	J	Dennis Dart 9 SDL	Plaxton Pointer	B34F	1995
1782	N712GUM	J	Dennis Dart 9 SDL	Plaxton Pointer	B34F	1995
1783	P913PWW	J	Dennis Dart 10.1 SFD	Plaxton Pointer	B34F	1996
1784	P914PWW	r	Dennis Dart 10.1 SFD	Plaxton Pointer	B34F	1996
1785	P915PWW	J	Dennis Dart 10.1 SFD	Plaxton Pointer	B34F	1996
1786	N708GUM	IN	Dennis Dart 9 SDL	Plaxton Pointer	B34F	1995
1787	N709GUM	r	Dennis Dart 9 SDL	Plaxton Pointer	B34F	1995
1918	W78PRG	IN	DAF DE12CSSB120	Wright Cadet	B39F	2000
1919	W79PRG	IN	DAF DE12CSSB120	Wright Cadet	B39F	2000
1921	W82PRG	IN	DAF DE12CSSB120	Wright Cadet	B39F	2000
1951	YJ54CKG	IN	DAF DE12CSSB120	Wright Cadet	B30F	2004
1952	YJ54CKK	IN	DAF DE12CSSB120	Wright Cadet	B30F	2004
1955	YJ07JSU	IN	VDL SB120	Plaxton Centro	B40F	2007
1956	YJ07JSV	IN	VDL SB120	Plaxton Centro	B40F	2007
1957	YJ07JSX	IN	VDL SB120	Plaxton Centro	B40F	2007
1958	YJ07JSY	IN	VDL SB120	Plaxton Centro	B40F	2007
1959	YJ07JSZ	IN	VDL SB120	Plaxton Centro	B40F	2007
2001	YJ09CVH	IN	VDL SB120	Wright Pulsar 2	B44F	2009
2002	YJ09CVK	IN	VDL SB120	Wright Pulsar 2	B44F	2009
2003	YJ09CVL	IN	VDL SB120	Wright Pulsar 2	B44F	2009
2004	YJ09CUV	IN	VDL SB120	Wright Pulsar 2	B44F	2009
2005	YJ09CVM	IN	VDL SB120	Wright Pulsar 2	B44F	2009
2006	YJ09CVN	IN	VDL SB120	Wright Pulsar 2	B44F	2009
2007	YJ09CVO	IN	VDL SB120	Wright Pulsar 2	B44F	2009
2008	YJ09CVR	IN	VDL SB120	Wright Pulsar 2	B44F	2009
2009	YJ09CUW	IN	VDL SB120	Wright Pulsar 2	B44F	2009
2010	YJ09CUX	IN	VDL SB120	Wright Pulsar 2	B44F	2009
2011	YJ04HJC	IN	DAF SB200	Wright Commander	B44F	2004
2012	YJ04HJD	IN	DAF SB200	Wright Commander	B44F	2004
2013	YJ04HJE	IN	DAF SB200	Wright Commander	B44F	2004
2014	YJ04HJF	IN	DAF SB200	Wright Commander	B44F	2004
2601	MV02XYJ	IN	Mercedes-Benz Vario O.814D	Plaxton Beaver 2	B27F	2002
2602	MV02XYK	IN	Mercedes-Benz Vario O.814D	Plaxton Beaver 2	B27F	2002
2603	MK52XNS	IN	Mercedes-Benz Vario O.814D	Plaxton Beaver 2	B27F	2002
2632	P632FHN	J-a	Optare MetroRider MR35	Optare	B25F	1997
2741	N804BKN	IN-a	Optare MetroRider MR15	Optare	B29F	1996
2801	SF09LOD	J	Renault Master		B15F	2009
2802	YX09EVG	J	Volkswagen	Bluebird	M14	2009
2803	YX09EVH	J	Volkswagen	Bluebird	M14	2009
3001	* GSU347	J	DAF SB3000WS601	Van Hool Alizée	C49FT	1994
3002	* WSU476	J	DAF SB3000WS601	Van Hool Alizée	C49FT	1995
4401	SF57NPK	J	Volvo B7RLE	Wright Eclipse Urban	B37F	2007
4402	SF57NPN	J	Volvo B7RLE	Wright Eclipse Urban	B37F	2007
4403	SJ57DDZ	J	Volvo B7RLE	Wright Eclipse Urban	B37F	2007
4404	SJ57DDY	J	Volvo B7RLE	Wright Eclipse Urban	B37F	2007
4405	SJ57DDX	J	Volvo B7RLE	Wright Eclipse Urban	B37F	2007
4406	SJ57DDV	J	Volvo B7RLE	Wright Eclipse Urban	B37F	2007
4407	SJ57DDU	J	Volvo B7RLE	Wright Eclipse Urban	B37F	2007
4408	SF57NMO	J	Volvo B7RLE	Wright Eclipse Urban	B37F	2007
4409	SF57NMM	J	Volvo B7RLE	Wright Eclipse Urban	B37F	2007
4410	SJ57DDO	J	Volvo B7RLE	Wright Eclipse Urban	B37F	2007
4411	SJ57DDN	J	Volvo B7RLE	Wright Eclipse Urban	B37F	2007
4531	L201TKA	J-t	Volvo B6-50	Plaxton Pointer	B38F	1994
4532	L210TKA	r	Volvo B6-50	Plaxton Pointer	B38F	1994
4533	L216TKA	w	Volvo B6-50	Plaxton Pointer	B38F	1994
4534	L306HPP	r	Volvo B6-50	Northern Counties Paladin	B40F	1994
4537	L235TKA	J-t	Volvo B6-50	Plaxton Pointer	B38F	1994

			Arriva Scotland West			
4665	YR58SUH	IN	Scania K230UB4	Scania OmniCity	B45F	2008
4666	YR58SUO	IN	Scania K230UB4	Scania OmniCity	B45F	2008
4667	YR58SUU	IN	Scania K230UB4	Scania OmniCity	B45F	2008
4668	YR58SUV	IN	Scania K230UB4	Scania OmniCity	B45F	2008
4669	YR58SUX	IN	Scania K230UB4	Scania OmniCity	B45F	2008
4670	YR58SUY	IN	Scania K230UB4	Scania OmniCity	B45F	2008
7214	D187FYM	w	Leyland Olympian ONLXB/1RH	Eastern Coach Works	H42/26D	1986
7264	M159GRY	J	Scania N113DRB	East Lancs Cityzen	H47/33F	1995
7265	M160GRY	J	Scania N113DRB	East Lancs Cityzen	H47/33F	1995
7266	M165GRY	J	Scania N113DRB	East Lancs Cityzen	H47/33F	1995
7267	M831SDA	J	Scania N113DRB	East Lancs Cityzen	DPH43/29F	1995
7268	M832SDA	J	Scania N113DRB	East Lancs Cityzen	DPH43/29F	1995
7269	M833SDA	J	Scania N113DRB	East Lancs Cityzen	DPH43/29F	1995
7273	L273FVN	IN	Leyland Olympian ON2R50C13Z4	Alexander RH	H45/29F	1993
7274	L274FVN	IN	Leyland Olympian ON2R50C13Z4	Alexander RH	H45/29F	1993

Arthurs Coaches

T D Arthur, The Willows, 20 West Canal Street, Coatbridge ML1 5PR
Website
Depot 22 Drumgelloch Street, Airdrie ML6 7EW
Greenfield House, Mollinsburn Road, Glenmavis, Airdrie ML6 0NG
Licence PM0000568

A236GHN	Leyland Olympian ONLXB/1R	Eastern Coach Works	H45/32F	1984
* BIG6153	DAF SBR3000D	Plaxton Paramount 4000	CH55/19CT	1990
C122CAT	Dennis Dominator DDA	East Lancs	H45/30F	1984
C128CAT	Dennis Dominator DDA	East Lancs	H45/30F	1986
C672GET	Leyland Olympian ONLXB/1R	Eastern Coach Works	H45/32F	1985
F89GGC	Mercedes-Benz 811D	Robin Hood	C29F	1989
F95XEM	Dennis Dominator DDA	East Lancs	H51/37F	1989
F96XEM	Dennis Dominator DDA	East Lancs	H51/37F	1989
F97XEM	Dennis Dominator DDA	East Lancs	H51/37F	1989
F99XEM	Dennis Dominator DDA	East Lancs	H51/37F	1989
F104XEM	Dennis Dominator DDA	East Lancs	H51/37F	1989
G115NGN	Volvo B10M-50	Northern Counties	H47/38F	1989
G135PGK	Volvo B10M-50	Northern Counties	H47/38F	1990
H201LOM	Scania N113DRB	Alexander RH	H45/31F	1990
H207LOM	Scania N113DRB	Alexander RH	H45/31F	1990
* H617LNA	Leyland Olympian ONCL10/5RZ	Alexander RH	CH53/41F	1989
* K14BUS	Dennis Javelin 12SDA	Wadham Stringer	C53F	1994
P253PSX	Volvo Olympian OLY-56	Alexander Royale	H51/30D	1997
P254PSX	Volvo Olympian OLY-56	Alexander Royale	H51/30D	1997
SHE622Y	Leyland Olympian ONLXB/1R	Eastern Coach Works	H45/32F	1982
* T609DGD	Volvo B10M-62	Van Hool Alizée	C46FT	1999

Austin Travel / Capital Coaches

J&D Austin, Station Road, Earlston, Borders TD4 6BZ
Website
Depot Station Road, Earlston, Borders TD4 6BZ
Licence PM0000985

* BX56VUM	Setra S416GT-HD	Setra TopClass	C49FT	2007
ESU974	Bova FHD127.365	Bova Futura	C55FT	2010
KNL665	Setra 415HD	Setra TopClass	C49FT	2008
* KSU175	Bova FHD127.365	Bova Futura	C50FT	2009
* MKZ7183	Iveco EuroRider 391E.12.35	Beulas Cygnus	C53F	2007
* N536SJF	Volvo B10M-62	Jonckheere	C49FT	1996
* UGE471	Mercedes-Benz Atego 1523L	Unvi Cimo	C33F	2007
* USU643	Mercedes-Benz 512D	Mercedes-Benz	C30FT	2008

	Austin Travel / Capital Coaches			
YN08OWY	Irisbus EuroRider 391E.12.35	Plaxton Panther	C61F	2008
YN08OWZ	Irisbus EuroRider 391E.12.35	Plaxton Paragon	C61F	2008

Avondale Coaches

Avondale Coaches Ltd, 189 Dumbarton Road, Clydebank G81 1UF
Website 9 Dock Street
Depot 189 Dumbarton Road, Clydebank G81 1UF
Licence PM0002912

F311DET	Mercedes-Benz 709D	Reeve Burgess Beaver	B25F	1988
G293TSL	Mercedes-Benz 709D	Alexander Sprint	B23F	1990
J10WBT	Dennis Dart 8.5 SDL	Northern Counties Paladin	B31F	1991
K151LGO	Dennis Dart 8.5 SDL	Plaxton Pointer	B28F	1992
K153LGO	Dennis Dart 8.5 SDL	Plaxton Pointer	B20F	1992
K221VTB	Dennis Dart 9 SDL	Northern Counties Paladin	B35F	1992
K222VTB	Dennis Dart 9 SDL	Northern Counties Paladin	B35F	1992
K223VTB	Dennis Dart 9 SDL	Northern Counties Paladin	B35F	1992
K224VTB	Dennis Dart 9 SDL	Northern Counties Paladin	B35F	1992
K225VTB	Dennis Dart 9 SDL	Northern Counties Paladin	B35F	1992
* K244SUS	Mercedes-Benz 709D	Alexander Sprint	B23F	1993
K581MGT	Dennis Dart 9 SDL	Plaxton Pointer	B32F	1993
K583MGT	Dennis Dart 9 SDL	Plaxton Pointer	B32F	1993
K593MGT	Dennis Dart 9 SDL	Plaxton Pointer	B32F	1993
L139XDS — y	Mercedes-Benz 709D	Wadham Stringer	B29F	1994
* L374BGA	Mercedes-Benz 709D	Eurocoach (Bunbeg)	B23F	1994
* L375BGA	Mercedes-Benz 709D	Eurocoach (Bunbeg)	B23F	1994
* L376BGA	Mercedes-Benz 709D	Eurocoach (Bunbeg)	B23F	1994
* L395BGA	Mercedes-Benz 709D	Eurocoach (Bunbeg)	B23F	1993
* L416BGA	Mercedes-Benz 709D	Eurocoach (Bunbeg)	B23F	1993
* L464BGA	Mercedes-Benz 709D	Eurocoach (Bunbeg)	B23F	1994
* L465BGA	Mercedes-Benz 709D	Eurocoach (Bunbeg)	B23F	1994
* L481BGA	Mercedes-Benz 709D	Eurocoach (Bunbeg)	B23F	1994
* L493BGA	Mercedes-Benz 709D	Alexander Sprint	B23F	1993
M211EGF	Dennis Dart 9 SDL	Plaxton Pointer	B35F	1995
M213EGF	Dennis Dart 9 SDL	Plaxton Pointer	B35F	1995
M271URC	Mercedes-Benz 811D	Wright NimBus	B31F	1995
M362LAX	Mercedes-Benz 709D	Alexander Sprint	B25F	1995
M363LAX	Mercedes-Benz 709D	Alexander Sprint	B25F	1995
M364LAX	Mercedes-Benz 709D	Alexander Sprint	B25F	1995
M365LAX	Mercedes-Benz 709D	Alexander Sprint	B25F	1995
M367LAX	Mercedes-Benz 709D	Alexander Sprint	B25F	1995
M371LAX	Mercedes-Benz 709D	Alexander Sprint	B25F	1995
M701EDD	Mercedes-Benz 709D	Alexander (Belfast)	B25F	1995
M704JDG	Mercedes-Benz 709D	Alexander (Belfast)	B25F	1995
M815JKU	Mercedes-Benz 709D	Plaxton Beaver	B27F	1995
N178DWM	Mercedes-Benz 811D	Plaxton Beaver	B31F	1996
N416CBU	Mercedes-Benz 709D	Plaxton Beaver	B27F	1996
N511BJA	Mercedes-Benz 709D	Alexander Sprint	B23F	1996
P180GND	Mercedes-Benz 811D	Plaxton Beaver	B31F	1996
P227EJW	Mercedes-Benz 811D	Marshall C16	B27F	1997
P228EJW	Mercedes-Benz 811D	Marshall C16	B27F	1997
P530PNE	Mercedes-Benz Vario O.810D	Plaxton Beaver 2	B27F	1997
P822BNR	Mercedes-Benz 709D	Plaxton Beaver	B27F	1996
R103NTA	Mercedes-Benz Vario O.814D	Alexander Sprint	B29F	1998
R105NTA	Mercedes-Benz Vario O.814D	Alexander Sprint	B29F	1998
R114NTA	Mercedes-Benz Vario O.814D	Alexander Sprint	B29F	1998
R116NTA	Mercedes-Benz Vario O.814D	Alexander Sprint	B29F	1998
R804YJC	Mercedes-Benz Vario O.814D	Plaxton Beaver 2	B27F	1998
SN03LFV	TransBus Dart 8.8 SLF	TransBus Mini Pointer	B29F	2003

R816 YJC
R811 YJC
R804 YJC

16   *HB10 - Scotland*

Avondale Coaches

SN03LFW		TransBus Dart 8.8 SLF	TransBus Mini Pointer	B29F	2003
SN03LFX —		TransBus Dart 8.8 SLF	TransBus Mini Pointer	B29F	2003
VU02TSO		Optare Solo M920	Optare	B33F	2002
VU02TTO		Optare Solo M920	Optare	B33F	2002
* X626DYB		Optare Solo M850	Optare	B30F	2001
YJ05XNP		Optare Solo M850	Optare	B19F	2005
YJ05XNR		Optare Solo M850	Optare	B19F	2005
YJ05XNS		Optare Solo M850	Optare	B19F	2005

Ayrways

Ayrways Coach Travel Ltd, 19 Monkton Road, Prestwick KA9 1AP
Website www.ayrways.net
Depot Saltpans Road, Ayr KA8 8BZ
Licence PM1005616

A227LFX		Volvo B10M-61	Duple Carribean	C51F	1984
AE54GKJ		LDV Convoy	LDV	M16	2004
AE54PSY		LDV Convoy	LDV	M16	2004
* B19WCS		Volvo B10M-61	Jonckheere Jubilee P599	C28FT	1988
C793USG		Volvo B10M-50	Alexander RV	H47/33F	1986
C801USG		Volvo B10M-50	Alexander RV	H47/33F	1986
C807USG		Volvo B10M-50	Alexander RV	H47/33F	1986
F122PHM		Volvo B10M-50	Alexander RV	H46/29D	1998
F135PHM		Volvo B10M-50	Alexander RV	H46/29D	1998
F427DUG	r	Volvo B10M-60	Plaxton Premiere 350	C51FT	1989
F481WFX		Volvo B10M-60	Duple 320	C57F	1989
FJ58LSC		Volvo B9R	Sunsundegui Sideral	C33F	2008
H224LOM		Scania N113DRB	Alexander RH	H47/33F	1990
* H912JVR		Volvo B10M-60	Plaxton Paramount 3500 III	C49FT	1991
J500CCH		Volvo B10M-60	Berkhof Excellence 2000	C50FT	1992
* K70AYR		Volvo B10M-55	Van Hool Alizée	C49FT	2002
* K100AYR		Volvo B10M-62	Berkhof Axial 50	C51FT	1997
* K200AYR		Volvo B10M-62	Berkhof Axial 50	C49FT	1998
* K222AYR		Volvo B10M-62	Van Hool Alizée	C53F	1998
* K300AYR		Volvo B12BT	Jonckheere Deauville	C49FT	1996
* K333AYR		Volvo B10M-62	Jonckheere	C53F	1996
* K400AYR		Volvo B12BT	Van Hool Astrobel	CH57/14CT	1995
* K500AYR		Volvo B12BT	Jonckheere Monaco	C57/15CT	1994
* K600AYR		Volvo B10M-62	Van Hool Alizée	C53F	1995
K655VNF		Mercedes-Benz 609D	Made to Measure	C24F	1992
* K700AYR		Volvo B10M-62	Jonckheere Deauville	C49F	1995
* K800AYR		Volvo B12BT	Van Hool Astrobel	CH57/20CT	1994
* KXI599		Volvo B10M-48	Plaxton Paramount 3200 II	C43F	1987
L452HOE		Fiat Daily 49-10	Jubilee	M16	1994
P655VWX		Scania L113CRL	East Lancs	B49F	1997
* PIL7835		Volvo B10M-60	Caetano Algarve II	C49FT	1993
* PIL9740		Volvo B10M-62	Plaxton Paramount 3500 II	C51FT	1985
* RIL3998		Volvo B10M-61	Jonckheere Jubilee P599	C49FT	1987
SF54ORC		Optare Solo M850	Optare	B20F	2004
SF54ORL		Optare Solo M850	Optare	B20F	2004
SJ52XJF		Ford Transit	Ford	M16	2002
SK03ZXU		Optare Solo M850	Optare	B27F	2003
SN05DMV		Mercedes-Benz Atego 1223L	Unvi Cimo	C30FT	2005
SP57FZZ		Volvo B12B	Van Hool Alizée	C49FT	2007
T420UUB		Optare Solo M920	Optare	B25F	1999
VU02TTE		Optare Solo M920	Optare	B33F	2002
W699PTN		LDV Convoy	Crest	M16	2000
* WIL7215		Volvo B10M-61	Van Hool Alizée	C49FT	1986

Bain's Coaches

D Bain, Station Garage, Oldmeldrum AB51 0EZ
Website
Depots   The Chalet, Station Garage, Station yard, Oldmeldrum AB51 0EZ
             Station Yard, Inverurie AB51 4TN
Licences PM0000657 (Bains Coaches)
             PM0001603 (ABC Travel)
             PM0001377 (Bains Chauffeur Drive)

	Reg	Chassis	Body	Layout	Year
*	611LFM	Neoplan N122/3	Neoplan Skyliner	CH53/18CT	1984
*	6292SC	Volvo B10M-60	Plaxton Premiere 350	C53F	1993
*	A20HOF	Scania K93CRB	Plaxton Premiere 320	C53F	1992
*	AIG6240	Mercedes-Benz Vario O.814D	Plaxton Cheetah	C29F	1999
*	BMC2T	BMC 750	BMC	C29F	2009
	BU05EHB	BMC Falcon 1100FE	BMC	B40F	2005
	BX06OCZ	BMC Falcon 1100FE	BMC	B55FL	2006
	BX54VNV	BMC Falcon 1100FE	BMC	B37F	2004
	BX56XAE	King Long XMQ6127	King Long	C47FT	2006
	E132YUD	DAF MB230LT625	Plaxton Paramount 3500 III	C53F	1988
*	JIL2949	Scania K93CRB	Plaxton Paramount 3200 III	C53F	1990
*	JIL7656	Volkswagen LT46	Volkswagen	M	2001
	LX58BZO	Mercedes-Benz 515CDI	Tawe	M16	2008
	N14FUG	Mercedes-Benz 711D	Wadham Stringer	B24FL	1995
	N120WBR	Dennis Dart 9.8 SDL	Marshall Dartline	B40F	1996
*	P80BMC	BMC Probus 850	BMC	C35F	2005
	P580WWO	LDV Convoy	LDV	M16	1997
	R18BLU r	Mercedes-Benz O.810D	UVG	B27F	1998
*	R376DJN	Optare Excel L1150	Optare	B35F	1998
	S306KNW r	DAF DE02GSSB220	Optare Delta	B49F	1998
	S471HOK	Toyota Coaster BB50R	Caetano Optimo	C26F	1998
	SV06ESG	BMC Falcon 1100FE	BMC	B40F	2006
	SV06ESN	BMC Falcon 1100FE	BMC	B40F	2006
	SV10CUK	BMC Falcon 1100FE	BMC	B F	2010
	SV58JJZ	King Long XMQ6127	King Long	C49FT	2008
*	UIW2135	Volvo B10M-61	Van Hool Alizée	C49FT	1987
	VO02VHN	Vauxhall Movano	Vauxhall	M14	2002
	W781PTN	Ford Transit	Ford	M14	2000
	Y147RSS	Toyota Coaster BB50R	Caetano Optimo	C26F	2001

Bee-Line Travel

G Dallas, Ravensneuk Farm, Peeble Road, Penicuik EH26 8PL
Website
Depot   Ravensneuk Farm, Peeble Road, Penicuik EH26 8PL
Licence PM1024435

	Reg	Chassis	Body	Layout	Year
*	BHZ8809	Volvo B10M-61	Jonckheere	C51FT	1985
*	C212PPE	Leyland Tiger TRCTL11/3R	Plaxton Paramount 3500 II	C46FT	1985
	EJR109W	Leyland Atlantean AN68A/2R	Alexander AL	H49/37F	1980
*	F73GYB	Setra S215HD	Setra Tornado	C49FT	1988
*	G7BUS	Setra S215HD	Setra Tornado	C49FT	1989
	K121CSG	Dennis Dart 9 SDL	Alexander AM	B35F	1992
	K122CSG	Dennis Dart 9 SDL	Alexander AM	B35F	1992
	K209OHS	Mercedes-Benz 709D	Dormobile Routemaker	B29F	1992
	N436WKL	Ford Transit	Dormobile Routemaker	M16	1995

Bennetts of Kilwinning

J Bennett, 4 Dalry Road, Kilwinning KA13 7HD
Website
Depots Building B4, Nobel Business Park, Stevenston KA20 3LN
6A Dalry Road, Kilwinning KA13 7HD
3 Byrehill Drive, West Byrehill Industrial Estate, Kilwinning K13 6HN
Licence PM1067056

	BU05HFN	Dennis Dart 8.8 SLF	Alexander	B29F	2005
	C641KDS	Volvo C10M-70	Ramseier Janzer	C49FT	1986
*	JIB82	Scania K113TRB	Irizar Century	C36FT	1995
*	JIB292	Volvo C10M-70	Ramseier Janzer	C48FT	1986
*	JIB3032	Volvo B12M	Sunsundegui Sideral	C49FT	2003
	K440HWY	Optare MetroRider MR03	Optare	DP33F	1993
	M498XSP	Mercedes-Benz 709D	Mellor	B27F	1995
*	PDZ6277	Leyland National 11351A/12 (Volvo)	East Lancs Greenway (1994)	DP49F	1978
	R990EWU	Optare Excel L1000	Van Hool	B33F	1998
*	RUI9480	Optare Excel L1000	Optare	B33F	1998
*	RUI9481	Optare Excel L1000	Optare	B33F	1998
	S639RJA	LDV Convoy	LDV	M16	1998
*	SIB2284	Mercedes-Benz 512D	Onyx	C20F	2000
*	SIB6297	Mercedes-Benz 709D	Alexander Sprint	DP23F	1987
*	SIB7357	Scania K124EB6	Irizar	C52FT	2004
	T443KAW	LDV Convoy	LDV	M16	1999

Blue Bus / Go by Bus

Blue Bus Ltd, 3 River View, Lanark ML11 8TJ
D Law, 34 Burnbrae Road, Shotts ML7 5DW
Website
Depots 34 Burnbrae Road, Shotts ML7 5DW
300 Mill Road, Allanton, Shotts ML7 5DG
Licences PM1029105 (Go by Bus)
PM1032689 (Blue Bus)

*	HIG7793	Mercedes-Benz Vario O.814D	Plaxton Cheetah	DP33FL	2007
	K112XHG	Mercedes-Benz 709D	Alexander Sprint	B25F	1993
	K618UFR	Mercedes-Benz 709D	Alexander Sprint	B25F	1992
	K619UFR	Mercedes-Benz 709D	Alexander Sprint	B25F	1992
*	KUI2759	Volvo B10M-60	Plaxton Paramount 3500 III	C53F	1989
	L34ULA	Mercedes-Benz 709D	Alexander Sprint	B28FL	1994
	L278JAO	Volvo B6-50	Alexander Dash	B40F	1993
	L630BFV	Mercedes-Benz 709D	Alexander Sprint	B25F	1993
	L635BFV	Mercedes-Benz 709D	Alexander Sprint	B25F	1993
	L665MSF	Volvo B6-50	Alexander Dash	DP40F	1994
	M748PRS	Volvo B6-50	Alexander Dash	DP40F	1994
	NXI6842	Mercedes-Benz 709D	Wright NimBus	B25F	1989
	SF04ZXD	Mercedes-Benz Vario O.814D	Plaxton Beaver 2	B31F	2004
*	SF54KHP	Mercedes-Benz Vario O.814D	Plaxton Welfare Beaver 2	B31F	2004
	SF54OUO	Mercedes-Benz Vario O.814D	Mellor	C28F	2004
*	SF54OVB	Mercedes-Benz Vario O.814D	Plaxton Beaver	B31F	2002
	SF54OVC	Mercedes-Benz Vario O.814D	Plaxton Beaver	B31F	2005
	T919OWB	Mercedes-Benz Vario O.814D	Plaxton Cheetah	C29F	1999
	Y557KSC	Mercedes-Benz Vario O.814D	Plaxton Beaver 2	DP33F	2001

S751LGA -

Blyth Coaches

Blyth Coaches Ltd, Balmain Farm, Leven KY8 5QL
Website
Depot Houston's Yard, Langdykes, Kennoway KY8 5SQ
Licence PM1041251

*	361EKH	Scania K113CRB	Berkhof Excellence 1000L	C49FT	1993
	A203RUR	Leyland Tiger TRCTL11/3R	Plaxton Paramount 3200 I	C53F	1984
*	CAZ6833	Scania K113CRB	Plaxton Paramount 3500 III	C50FT	1989
	G315TKO	Fiat Daily 49-10	Dormobile Routemaker	B25F	1990
	G470CEH	Ford Transit	Dormobile Routemaker	B20F	1990
	K797PLM	Mercedes-Benz 609D	Mellor	B15FL	1992
	L404LHE	Scania K113CRB	Van Hool Alizée	C53F	1994
*	LIL2173	Scania K113CRB	Van Hool Alizée	C49FT	1991
*	LUI7857	Leyland Lynx LX112TL11ZR1	Leyland Lynx	B49F	1987
*	MKZ7184	Iveco EuroRider 391E.12.35	Beulas Stergo E	C49FT	1998
	P393NSC	Mercedes-Benz 212D	Prestonhall	M12	1996
	R849HSC	Iveco Daily 49E10	Mellor	B15FL	1998
	T408BSS	LDV Convoy	Mellor	B12FL	1999
*	VJI1995	Volvo B10M-60	Plaxton Paramount 3500 III	C53FT	1990
*	YIL8799	Volvo B10M-61	Caetano Algarve II	C57F	1996

Bowman Coaches (Mull)

Bowman Coaches (Mull) Ltd, Scallcastle, Craignure, Isle of Mull PA65 6BA
Website www.bowmantours.co.uk
Depot Scallcastle, Craignure, Isle of Mull PA65 6BA
Licence PM0000453

	BP54WYH	Volvo B7RLE	Wright Eclipse Urban	B51F	2005
	FX03GKV	Mercedes-Benz Atego 1223L	Optare Solera	C39F	2003
	M627RCP	DAF DE33WSSB3000	Van Hool Alizée	C51FT	1995
	N38FWU	DAF DE33WSSB3000	Van Hool Alizée	C51FT	1996
	P696BRS	Volvo B10M-62	Van Hool Alizée	C53F	1996
	R591USJ	Volvo B10M-62	Van Hool Alizée	C49FT	1998
*	SA04AGT	Volvo B7RLE	Wright Eclipse Urban	B51F	2004
	SF03ABX	Volvo B7R	Plaxton Profile	C57F	2003
	SP04EUZ	Bova FHD12.340	Bova Futura	C49FT	2004
	SP04CXX	Bova FHD12.340	Bova Futura	C49FT	2005
*	T608DGD	Volvo B10M-62	Van Hool Alizée	C46FT	1999
	YN06RVX	Mercedes-Benz Vario O.814D	Plaxton Beaver	DP29FL	2006
	YN06RVY	Mercedes-Benz Vario O.814D	Plaxton Beaver	DP29FL	2006
	YX04FYF	Mercedes-Benz Atego 1223L	Optare Solera	C39F	2004

Brownings

Brownings (Whitburn) Ltd, 22 Longridge Road, Whitburn EH47 0DE
Website www.browningscoaches.co.uk
Depot Croftmalloch Inn, 22 Longridge Road, Whitburn EH47 0DE
Licence PM0000101

*	A286LLS	Volvo B10M-61	Van Hool Alizée	C50FT	1984
*	L82RHL	Dennis Javelin 12SDA	Wadham Stringer	DP70F	1995
*	L942LBV	Volvo B10M-62	Jonckheere	C53F	1994
*	M760ASL	Dennis Javelin 12SDA	Wadham Stringer	DP70F	1995
*	MIL3725	Volvo B10M-60	Van Hool Alizée	C46FT	1989
*	OBA695	Volvo B10M-62	Caetano Enigma	C53FT	1998
*	OJI5506	Volvo B10M-61	Van Hool Alizée	C57F	1987
	P222GSM	Volvo B10M-62	Berkhof Axial 50	C51FT	1997
	P444GSM —	Volvo B10M-62	Berkhof Axial 50	C51FT	1997
*	TJI4022	Volvo B10M-61	Van Hool Alizée	C53F	1985

*	V91LYS	Volvo B10M-62	Plaxton Premiere 350	C53F	1999
*	V93LYS	Volvo B10M-62	Plaxton Premiere 350	C53F	1999
*	WUH704	Dennis Javelin 12SDA	Wadham Stringer	DP70F	1995

Bruce Coaches

Bruce Coaches Ltd, 40 Main Street, Salsburgh ML7 4LW
Website
Depot 40 Main Street, Salsburgh ML7 4LW
Licence PM1043724

SC31		FJ57KGY	Scania K340EB6	Caetano Levante	C61FLT	2007
SC34		FJ57KHB	Scania K340EB6	Caetano Levante	C61FLT	2007
		CX06LKE	Ford Transit	Ford	M16	2006
	*	DBZ696 —	Bova FHD12-370	Bova Futura	C49FT	2001
		FJ57KHU —	Scania K340EB6	Caetano Levante	C61FLT	2007
		FJ57KJF	Scania K340EB6	Caetano Levante	C61FLT	2007
		FJ58AKK	Scania K340EB6	Caetano Levante	C51FT	2008
		FJ58AKY	Scania K340EB6	Caetano Levante	C53FT	2008
		FT10KUP	Mercedes-Benz 613D	Onyx	C24F	2010
	*	JXI317 —	Bova FHD12-340	Bova Futura	C49FT	2002
	*	KXI244 —	Bova FHD12-370	Bova Futura	C49FT	2001
		M58LBB	Volvo B10M-62	Plaxton Premiere 350	C46FT	1995
	*	M59LBB	Volvo B10M-62	Plaxton Premiere 350	C46FT	1995
		SJ54CCN—	Bova FHD12-340	Bova Futura	C49FT	2004
		X2PCC	Mercedes-Benz Vario O.814D	Plaxton Beaver 2	DP33F	2000

Bryans Coaches

Bryans Coaches Ltd, Whitehill Farm, Myothill Road, Head of Muir, Denny FK6 5NA
Website
Depot Whitehill Farm, Myothill Road, Head of Muir, Denny FK6 5NA
Licence PM1066160

*	FC04UZK	Volvo B12M	Sunsundegui Sideral	C51FT	2004
	FP53JYO	Volvo B12M	Jonckheere Mistral	C53F	2003
	P695RWU	Dennis Dart 10.1 SLF	Plaxton Pointer	B35F	1997
	P806GBA —	Volvo B10M-62	Van Hool Alizée	C49FT	1997
*	PDZ5772	Volvo B10M-60	Van Hool Alizée	C52FT	1992
	S461LGN ~	Dennis Dart 8.8 SLF	Plaxton Mini Pointer	B29F	1998
*	SF08VVG	Volvo B12M	Jonckheere	C53F	2008
	SL52CPE	Mercedes-Benz Sprinter 413CDI	Killbeggan Vehicle Converters	M16	2003
	SN10CAO	ADL Enviro Dart 8.9 SLF	ADL Enviro 200	B29F	2010
	SN59DCE	Bova FLD120.365	Bova Futura	C70F	2009
	X439JHS ~	Dennis Dart 8.8 SLF	Plaxton Mini Pointer	B29F	2000
*	YAZ6510	Volvo B10M-60	Plaxton Paramount 3500 III	C53F	1991
	YN05HVF —	Mercedes-Benz Vario O.814D	Plaxton Cheetah	C33F	2005

Burns of Tarves

J & M Burns, Dinneswood, Tarves, Ellon AB41 0LR
Website www.burnscoaches.co.uk
Depot Dinneswood, Tarves, Ellon AB41 0LR
Licence PM0000806

*	B10MBC	Volvo B10M-60	Van Hool Alizee	C53F	1989
	MK02GAU	Mercedes-Benz Sprinter 413CDI	Onyx	M16	2002
	P161RWR	DAF DE33WSSB3000	Ikarus Blue Danube 350	C70F	1997
	P716RWU	DAF DE33WSSB3000	Ikarus Blue Danube 350	C70F	1996
*	P720ESA	Mercedes-Benz 310D	Minibus Options	M12	1997

Burns of Tarves					
SK07FZV	Mercedes-Benz Sprinter 616CDI	Unvi	C22F	2007	
SV07AZZ	Setra S415GT-HD	Setra TopClass	C489FT	2007	
T981WPN	Mercedes-Benz 412CD	Constable	M14	1999	
V958DSO	Mercedes-Benz 614D	Onyx	C24F	1999	
W941OSA	DAF DE33WSSB3000	Van Hool Alizée	C53F	2000	
YCZ4486	Mercedes-Benz Vario O.814D	Euro Coach Builders	C29F	2004	
YJ05PYY	VDL DE40XSSB4000	Van Hool Alizée	C51FT	2005	
* YSU921	Volvo B10M-62	Van Hool Alizée	C46FT	1996	

Bus Na Cormhairle

Comhairle Nan Eilan Siar, Technical Services Department, Marybank Depot, Stornoway HS1 2QP

Website
Depots 10 Aignish,Point,Isle Of Lewis,HS2 0PB
Bus Station,South Beach,Stornoway,HS1 2BW
Bus Car Park,Island Road,Stornoway,HS1 2RD
52 North Tolsta,Isle Of Lewis,HS2 0NW
24 Sheshader,Point,Isle Of Lewis,HS2 0EW
Marybank Depot,Stornoway,HS1 2XH
Marybank Quarry,Stornoway,HS1 2BW
27 Upper Bayble,Point,Isle Of Lewis,HS2 0QH
64 Lochside,North Tolsta,Isle Of Lewis,HS2 0NF
41 Back,Isle Of Lewis,HS2 0LQ
Commercial Operations Unit,Market Stance Depot,Benbecula,
Isle Of Benbecula,Balavanich,HS7 5LA
Licence PM0002859

B114	R777GSM	Dennis Javelin 12SFD	Plaxton Premiere 320	C57F	1998
B115	M365AMA	Dennis Javelin 12SDA	Plaxton Premiere 350	C53F	1995
B116	M366AMA	Dennis Javelin 12SDA	Plaxton Premiere 350	C49FT	1995
B117	M602BCA	Dennis Javelin 12SDA	Plaxton Premiere 350	C46FT	1995
B118	M6SEL	Dennis Javelin 12SDA	Plaxton Premiere 350	C53F	1994
B120	YU04HJD	Mercedes-Benz Vario O.814D	TransBus Beaver 2	DP31F	2004
B121	YU04HJE	Mercedes-Benz Vario O.814D	TransBus Beaver 2	DP31F	2004
B122	YU04HJF	Mercedes-Benz Vario O.814D	TransBus Beaver 2	DP31F	2004
B123	YU04HJK	Mercedes-Benz Vario O.814D	TransBus Beaver 2	DP31F	2004
B125	YN54XYK	Mercedes-Benz Vario O.814D	Plaxton Beaver 2	DP33F	2004
B126	R917HTW	Dennis Javelin 12SFD	Plaxton Premiere 320	C53	1998
B128	YU07KGU	VDL SB200	Plaxton Centro	B42F	2007
B131	X174BNA	Mercedes-Benz Vario O.814D	Plaxton Beaver	B28FL	2000
	M7SEL	Dennis Javelin 12SDA	Plaxton Premiere 320	C53F	1994

Caber Coaches

Caber Coaches Ltd, Chapel Street Garage, Aberfeldy PH15 2AS
Website
Depot Chapel Street Garage, Aberfeldy PH15 2AS
Licence PM0002284

BJ59CWM	Ford Transit	Ford	M16	2009	
CV55FTY	Ford Transit	Ford	M16	2005	
* D349ESC	Leyland Tiger TRBTL11/2R	Alexander	C49F	1986	
* DFC568	DAF MB230LT615	Van Hool Alizee	C49FT	1989	
DY56LYZ	Ford Transit	Ford	M14	2006	
* FHJ83Y	DAF MB200DKFL600	Van Hool	C48FT	1982	
* L619SES	Mercedes-Benz 711D	Plaxton Cheetah	C25F	1993	
R898WOC	Mercedes-Benz Vario O.814D	Leicester Carriage Builders	C33F	1996	
* R971XBC	LDV Convoy	LDV	M16	1997	
SJ53AWW	Mercedes-Benz Vario O.814D	TransBus Beaver 2	B33F	2003	
SP05AUV	LDV Convoy	Excel	M16	2005	

John Campbell Coaches
Campbell Coaches Ltd, 7 Dundas Place, East Kilbride G74 4JQ
Website
Depot 7 Dundas Place, East Kilbride G74 4JQ
Licence PM1066414

* 832DVV	w	Volvo B10M-62	Van Hool Alizée	C48FT	1995
* FIL7615	w	DAF SB2300DHTD585	Plaxton Paramount 3200 I	C57F	1984
H558GKX	w	Leyland Olympian ON2R50C13Z4	Leyland Olympian	H47/31F	1991
H562GKX	w	Leyland Olympian ON2R50C13Z4	Leyland Olympian	H47/31F	1991
* IIL3481	w	Volvo B10M-61	Jonckheere Jubilee P599	C49FT	1988
* JIL2159	w	Leyland National 11351A/1R (Volvo)	East Lancs Greenway (1994)	B49F	1977
* JIL2165	w	Leyland National 11351A/1R (Volvo)	East Lancs Greenway (1994)	B49F	1976
* TIB7836	w	Volvo B10M-50	Van Hool Alizée	C49FT	1990
X807KBO	w	LDV Convoy	LDV	M16	2000
* XIL1257	w	Volvo B10M-61	Plaxton Paramount 3500 III	C48FT	1988
* XIL6215	w	Setra S228DT	Setra Imperial	CH54/20CT	1986
* XIL7241	w	Volvo B6R	Caetano Algarve II	C35F	1993

Campbells Coaches
Campbells Coaches Ltd, Clydeway House, 813 South Street, Glasgow G14 0BX
Website
Depot 813 South Street, Glasgow G14 0BX
Licence PM1039043

* P20GSG	Volvo B10M-62	Van Hool Alizée	C49FT	1998
* P22GSG	Volvo B10M-62	Berkhof Axial 50	C49FT	1998
* PIL6351	Volvo B10M-62	Jonckheere Deauville	C53F	1995
* VIL9330	Volvo B10M-60	Van Hool Alizée	C53F	1993
* VIL9332	Mercedes-Benz 614D	Crystals	C24F	1998

P Canavan Co
J & G Canavan, 4 Arches, Auchinstarry Road, Kilsyth, Glasgow G65 9SG
Website
Depot 4 Arches, Auchinstarry Road, Kilsyth, Glasgow G65 9SG
Licence PM1002235

H122MOB	Dennis Dart 8.5 SDL	Carlyle Dartline	B28F	1990
H890LOX	Dennis Dart 8.5 SDL	Carlyle Dartline	B28F	1990
K119SRH	Dennis Dart 9 SDL	Plaxton Pointer	B34F	1993
L9NCP	Dennis Dart 9 SDL	Plaxton Pointer	B37F	1993
L136VRH	Dennis Dart 9 SDL	Plaxton Pointer	B34F	1993
L142VRH	Dennis Dart 9 SDL	Plaxton Pointer	B34F	1993
L143VRH	Dennis Dart 9 SDL	Plaxton Pointer	B34F	1993
* L270ULX	Dennis Dart 9 SDL	Plaxton Pointer	B23D	1994
L656MYG	Mercedes-Benz 711D	Plaxton Beaver	B27F	1993
L701AGA	Mercedes-Benz 709D	Wadham Stringer	B29F	1994
M261GUS	Dennis Dart 9.8 SDL	Plaxton Pointer	B40F	1995
M547GNS	Dennis Dart 9.8 SDL	Plaxton Pointer	B40F	1995
N868MSU	Dennis Dart 9.8 SDL	Plaxton Pointer	B40F	1996
N869MSU	Dennis Dart 9.8 SDL	Plaxton Pointer	B40F	1996
* T272RMY	Dennis Dart 8.8 SLF	Marshall Capital	B28F	1999
* T403EGD	Volvo B10BLE	Alexander ALX300	DP44F	1999
* T404EGD	Volvo B10BLE	Alexander ALX300	DP44F	1999
T428AGP	Dennis Dart 8.8 SLF	Marshall Capital	B30F	1999
W809BGB	Dennis Dart 8.8 SLF	Plaxton Mini Pointer	B29F	2000
W811BGB	Dennis Dart 8.8 SLF	Plaxton Mini Pointer	B29F	2000

Central Coaches

W, V & W Smith, Central Garage, Church Road, Keith AB55 3BR
Website www.centralcoaches.co.uk
Depot Central Garage, Church Road, Keith AB55 3BR
Licence PM0001221

*	CCZ2221	Volvo B10M-60	Plaxton Paramount 3500 III	C57F	1992
	E559MSE	Mercedes-Benz 609D	Reeve Burgess	C21F	1987
	E643KCK	DAF MB230LT615	Plaxton Paramount 3500 III	C49FT	1988
*	EIG4966	Volvo B10M-62	Van Hool Alizée	C46FT	1996
	G999OKK	DAF MB230LT615	Caetano Algarve	C53F	1989
	L64GSE	Volvo B10M-60	Plaxton Premiere 350	C53F	1993
	M406KOA	Mercedes-Benz 609D	AMC	C20FL	1994
	M537JRY	Mercedes-Benz 709D	Leicester Carriage Builders	B24FL	1995
*	M994HHS	Volvo B10M-62	Jonckheere Deauville	C53F	1995
*	N93HSJ	Volvo b10M-62	Van Hool Alizée	C49FT	1996
	N347WPT	Volvo B10M-62	Van Hool Alizée	C49FT	1996
	P813OET	Optare Excel L1070	Optare	B40F	1997
*	SIL9637	Bova FHD12-340	Bova Futura	C48FT	1995
*	TJI3140	Volvo B10M-60	Plaxton Paramount 3500 III	C51FT	1987

Cheyne's Coaches

W Cheyne & Partners, Allandale, Oldmeldrum, Daviot, Inverurie AB51 0EJ
Website
Depot Allandale, Oldmeldrum, Daviot, Inverurie AB51 0EJ
Licence PM0001225

*	C3CHT	Bova FHD12-340	Bova Futura	C49FT	1999
	CU03LXH	Ford Transit	Ford	M16	2003
*	DSV707	Volvo B10M-62	Van Hool Alizée	C53F	1996
	DX04WKT	BMC Probus 850RE	BMC	C35F	2004
*	KSV803	Leyland Tiger TRCTL11/3RZ	Plaxton Derwent	B70F	1987
*	LEZ9446	Leyland Tiger TRCTL11/3RZ	Plaxton Derwent	B70F	1987
*	NUI2420	Dennis Javelin 12SDA	Plaxton Premiere 320	C53F	1996
*	OTC950	Volvo B10M-62	Van Hool Alizée	C70f	1997
	SJ53LTU	Ford Transit	Ford	M16	2003
*	WAY877	Volvo B10M-62	Van Hool Alizée	C70F	1996
	X224USC	Mercedes-Benz Vario O.814D	Plaxton Beaver 2	C33F	2000
	YX55ABF	Mercedes-Benz Vario O.814D	Autobus Nouvelle	C29F	2005
	YX55ABU	Mercedes-Benz Vario O.814D	Autobus Nouvelle	C29F	2005

City Circle

City Circle UK Ltd, 7 Bulls Bridge Centre, North Hyde Gardens, Hayes UB3 4QT
Website www.citycircleuk.com
Depot Unit 4, Butterfield Industrial Estate, Bonnyrigg EH19 3JQ
Licence PM1067311

7	BU04EZA	BG	Setra S415HD	Setra TopClass	C49FT	2004
8	BU04EZB	BG	Setra S415HD	Setra TopClass	C49FT	2004
9	BU04EZC	BG	Setra S415HD	Setra TopClass	C49FT	2004
11	BU04EZE	BG	Setra S415HD	Setra TopClass	C49FT	2004
12	BX05UVL	BG	Setra S415HD	Setra TopClass	C49FT	2005
14	BX05UVM	BG	Setra S415HD	Setra TopClass	C49FT	2005
15	BX05UVN	BG	Setra S415HD	Setra TopClass	C49FT	2005
16	YN57AEZ	BG	Neoplan N2216SHD	Neoplan Skyliner	C49FT	2007
17—	YJ08DXC	BG	Van Hool T911	Van Hool Alicron	C36FT	2008
18	YJ08DXD	BG	Van Hool T911	Van Hool Alicron	C36FT	2008
19	YJ08DXE	BG	Van Hool T911	Van Hool Alicron	C36FT	2008
20	YJ08DXF	BG	Van Hool T911	Van Hool Alicron	C36FT	2008

City Circle						
22	YN58OKU	BG	Neoplan N2216SHD	Neoplan Skyliner	C49FT	2008
24	YN58OKW	BG	Neoplan N2216SHD	Neoplan Skyliner	C49FT	2008
	YJ09CZY	BG	VDL DE40PSSB4000	Van Hool Alizée	C53F	2009
	AX10 DFK	*BG*	*Neoplan*			

City Sightseeing Glasgow

City Sightseeing Glasgow Ltd, 739 South Street, Barclay Curle Industrial Estate, Glasgow G14 0BX
Website   www.scotguide.com
Depot   739 South Street, Barclay Curle Industrial Estate, Glasgow G14 0BX
Licence   PM1016015

A156FPG	Leyland Olympian ONTL11/1R	Roe	O43/29F	1984
A983SYF	MCW MetroBus DR101/17	MCW	O43/28D	1984
C52JVO	MCW MetroBus DR130/22	MCW	O63/22F	1985
E309MSG	Leyland Olympian ONCL10/2RZ	Alexander RH	PO47/28F	1988
E310MSG	Leyland Olympian ONCL10/2RZ	Alexander RH	PO47/28F	1988
P479MBY	Volvo Olympian YN2RV18Z4	Alexander R	PO43/25D	1996
P480MBY	Volvo Olympian YN2RV18Z4	Alexander R	PO43/25D	1996
P481MBY	Volvo Olympian YN2RV18Z4	Alexander R	PO43/25D	1996
P485MBY	Volvo Olympian YN2RV18Z4	Alexander R	PO43/25D	1996
P487MBY	Volvo Olympian YN2RV18Z4	Alexander R	PO43/25D	1996
P491MBY	Volvo Olympian YN2RV18Z4	Alexander R	PO43/25D	1996
SN09FFA	Scania N230UD	Optare Olympus	O80F	2009
SN09FFB	Scania N230UD	Optare Olympus	O80F	2009
YN07LHR	Scania N230UD	East Lancs	H45/23D	2007
YN07LHY	Scania N230UD	East Lancs	H45/23D	2007

City Sightseeing Stirling

City Sightseeing Stirling, 120 Claremont, Alloa FK10 2EG
Website   www.citysightseeing.com
Depot   12 Hamilton Street, Clydebank G81 1LY
Licence   PM1068682

A514VKG	Leyland Olympian ONLXB/1R	East Lancs	O43/31F	1984
A949SUL	MCW MetroBus DR101/16	MCW	PO43/28D	1983
G567PRM	Mercedes-Benz 709D	Alexander	DP25F	1990

City Sprinter / S&A Coaches

S&A Coaches Ltd, 24 Parkinch, Erskine PA8 7HZ
Website
Depot   Unit 1B, Meadowside Complex, Meadowside Street, Renfrew PA4 8LF
Licence   PM1052552

F484CAL		Mercedes-Benz 709D	Plaxton Beaver	B27F	1996
G21KVH		DAF SB2305DHTD585	Plaxton Paramount 3200 III	C53F	1990
J627KCU		Dennis Dart 9.8 SDL	Wright Handybus	B40F	1992
J635KCU		Dennis Dart 9.8 SDL	Wright Handybus	B40F	1992
J638KCU		Dennis Dart 9.8 SDL	Wright Handybus	B40F	1992
K132XRE		Mercedes-Benz 709D	Dormobile Routemaker	B29F	1992
K242SFJ		Mercedes-Benz 709D	Plaxton Beaver	B25F	1992
L26LSG		Mercedes-Benz 709D	Alexander Sprint	B25F	1993
* L125DRN	w	Mercedes-Benz 709D	Alexander Sprint	B25F	1993
L501OAL		Volvo B6-50	Alexander Dash	B40F	1994
L502OAL		Volvo B6-50	Alexander Dash	B40F	1994
L505OAL		Volvo B6-50	Alexander Dash	B40F	1994
L508OAL		Volvo B6-50	Alexander Dash	B40F	1994
L741LWA	w	Mercedes-Benz 709D	Alexander Sprint	B25F	1993
L745LWA	w	Mercedes-Benz 709D	Alexander Sprint	B25F	1993

		City Sprinter			
L881SDY	Mercedes-Benz 709D	Alexander Sprint	B25F	1993
M103BLE	Dennis Dart 9.8 SDL	Plaxton Pointer	B39F	1994
M124VAK	Volvo B6-50	Alexander Dash	B44F	1995
M208EGF	Dennis Dart 9 SDL	Plaxton Pointer	B35F	1995
M208EUS	Volvo B6-50	Alexander Dash	B40F	1995
M209EGF	Dennis Dart 9 SDL	Plaxton Pointer	B35F	1995
M506ALP	Dennis Dart 9.8 SDL	Plaxton Pointer	B40F	1995
M677SSX	Volvo B6-50	Alexander Dash	B40F	1994
M719BCS	Volvo B6-50	Alexander Dash	DP40F	1994
M721BCS	Volvo B6-50	Alexander Dash	DP40F	1994
M736BSJ	Volvo B6-50	Alexander Dash	DP40F	1994
N249PGD	Mercedes-Benz 709D	UVG CityStar	B29F	1996
N250PGD	Mercedes-Benz 709D	UVG CityStar	B29F	1996
N842LGA	Mercedes-Benz 709D	Wadham Stringer	B16FL	1995
P294MLD	Dennis Dart 9.8 SDL	Plaxton Pointer	B39F	1996
P483CAL	Mercedes-Benz 709D	Plaxton Beaver	B27F	1966
P488CAL	Mercedes-Benz 709D	Plaxton Beaver	B27F	1996
R49SCH	Mercedes-Benz 711D	Plaxton Beaver	B27F	1997
R107NTA	Mercedes-Benz Vario O.814D	Alexander Sprint	B29F	1998
R110NTA	Mercedes-Benz Vario O.814D	Alexander Sprint	B29F	1998
R276RAU	Mercedes-Benz Vario O.814D	Plaxton Beaver	B31F	1997
R283RAU	Mercedes-Benz Vario O.814D	Plaxton Beaver	B31F	1997
T298LCH	Mercedes-Benz Vario O.814D	Plaxton Beaver	B31F	1999
T299LCH	Mercedes-Benz Vario O.814D	Plaxton Beaver	B31F	1999
* TJI1700	Volvo B10M-61	Plaxton Paramount 3500 III	C49FT	1989

Clan Travel
M Docherty, 115 Jerviston Street, New Stevenston, Motherwell ML1 4HT
Website
Depot   1 Petersburn Road, Airdrie ML6 8RD
Licence   PM0003085

* CKZ8186	Mercedes-Benz 709D	Plaxton Beaver	B23F	1994
F644XMS	Mercedes-Benz 811D	Alexander	B31F	1988
* F737FDV	Mercedes-Benz 709D	Reeve Burgess Beaver	DP25F	1988
M59WKA	Mercedes-Benz 709D	Alexander	B25F	1994
* P331LCC	Mercedes-Benz O.814D	Wadham Stringer	C25F	1996
T460JRH	Mercedes-Benz O.814D	Plaxton Beaver	B27F	1999
* XIB2453	Volvo B10M-60	Jonckheere	C51FT	1989

Clyde Coast
D H Frazer & K G McGregor, 55 Montgomerie Street, Ardrossan KA22 8HR
Website   www.clydecoast.com
Depot   55 Montgomerie Street, Ardrossan KA22 8HR
Licence   PM0003040

D614ASG	Leyland Tiger TRBTL11/3RH	Alexander P	B61F	1987
FJ58LSD	Volvo B9R	Sunsundegui Sideral	C53F	2008
* GIL2754	Volvo B10M-61	Van Hool Alizée	C53F	1987
M198ASJ	Mercedes-Benz 308D	Devon Conversions	M8	1994
SF57FZZ	Volvo B12B	Van Hool Alizée	C49FT	2007
SF59BXM	Mercedes-Benz O.816D	Plaxton Cheetah	C33F	2009
* XJF448	Volvo B12M	Sunsundegui Sideral	C49FT	2004

Coakley
Coakley Bus & Coach Ltd, 19 Newhut Road, Braidhurst Industrial Estate, Motherwell ML1 3ST
Website
Depot 19 Newhut Road, Braidhurst Industrial Estate, Motherwell ML1 3ST
Licence PM1024045

F357TSX	Mercedes-Benz Vario O.814D	Alexander	C33F	1988
F572SMG	Leyland Olympian ONLXB/1RZ	Alexander RL	H47/32F	1988
F575SMG	Leyland Olympian ONLXB/1RZ	Alexander RL	H47/32F	1988
* G504SFT	Leyland Olympian ONCL10/1RZ	Northern Counties	H47/30F	1989
G808GSX	Leyland Olympian ON2R56C13Z4	Alexander RH	H51/30D	1990
G812GSX	Leyland Olympian ON2R56C13Z4	Alexander RH	H51/30D	1990
G815GSX	Leyland Olympian ON2R56C13Z4	Alexander RH	H51/30D	1990
G820GSX	Leyland Olympian ON2R56C13Z4	Alexander RH	H51/30D	1990
G821GSX	Leyland Olympian ON2R56C13Z4	Alexander RH	H51/30D	1990
G823GSX	Leyland Olympian ON2R56C13Z4	Alexander RH	H51/30D	1990
G824GSX	Leyland Olympian ON2R56C13Z4	Alexander RH	H51/30D	1990
G825GSX	Leyland Olympian ON2R56C13Z4	Alexander RH	H51/30D	1990
H242MUK	Dennis Dart 9.8 SDL	Carlyle Dartline	B40F	1991
H533XGK	Dennis Dart 8.5 SDL	Plaxton Pointer	B20F	1991
H916XYT	Volvo B10M-55	East Lancs EL2000	B41F	1990
H921XYT	Volvo B10M-55	East Lancs EL2000	B41F	1990
H922XYT	Volvo B10M-55	East Lancs EL2000	B41F	1990
J316XVX	Dennis Dart 9 SDL	Wright Handybus	B35F	1994
J612XHL	Dennis Dart 9 SDL	Plaxton Pointer	B34F	1991
K98SAG	Dennis Dart 9 SDL	Plaxton Pointer	B28F	1993
K114SRH	Dennis Dart 9 SDL	Plaxton pointer	B34F	1992
K433OKH	Dennis Dart 9 SDL	Plaxton Pointer	B34F	1992
K470SKO	Dennis Dart 9.8 SDL	Plaxton Pointer	B40F	1992
K538ORH	Dennis Dart 9 SDL	Plaxton Pointer	B34F	1992
K540ORH	Dennis Dart 9 SDL	Plaxton Pointer	B34F	1992
K871LGN	Dennis Dart 9 SDL	Plaxton Pointer	B34F	1992
K947SGG	Dennis Dart 9.8 SDL	Plaxton Pointer	B35F	1993
KDZ5801	Dennis Dart 9 SDL	Wright Handybus	B39F	1991
L114YVK	Dennis Dart 9 SDL	Northern Counties Paladin	B35F	1994
L129YVK	Dennis Dart 9 SDL	Northern Counties Paladin	B35F	1994
L149YVK	Dennis Dart 9 SDL	Northern Counties Paladin	B35F	1994
L151WAG	Dennis Dart 9 SDL	Plaxton Pointer	B34F	1994
L152YVK	Dennis Dart 9 SDL	Northern Counties Paladin	B35F	1994
L166YAT	Dennis Dart 9 SDL	Plaxton pointer	B28F	1994
L228SWM	Dennis Dart 9 SDL	Northern Counties Paladin	B35F	1993
L229SWM	Dennis Dart 9 SDL	Northern Counties Paladin	B35F	1993
L230SWM	Dennis Dart 9 SDL	Northern Counties Paladin	B35F	1993
L231TKA	Volvo B6-50	Plaxton Pointer	B38F	1994
L232SWM	Dennis Dart 9 SDL	Northern Counties Paladin	B35F	1994
L233SWM	Dennis Dart 9 SDL	Northern Counties Paladin	B35F	1994
L234SWM	Dennis Dart 9 SDL	Northern Counties Paladin	B35F	1994
L308AUT	Mercedes-Benz 709D	Alexander (Belfast)	B25F	1994
L416UNJ	DAF SB220LC550	Ikarus Citibus	B48F	1994
L417UUF	DAF SB220LC550	Ikarus Citibus	B48F	1994
L504BNX	Dennis Dart 9 SDL	East Lancs EL2000	B33F	1994
L508BNX	Dennis Dart 9 SDL	East Lancs EL2000	B33F	1994
L605BNX	Dennis Dart 9 SDL	East Lancs EL2000	B33F	1994
L870LFS	Mercedes-Benz 711D	Plaxton Beaver	B25F	1994
* L906ANS	Mercedes-Benz 811D	Dormobile Routemaker	B33F	1994
M65FDS	Dennis Dart 9.8 SDL	Plaxton Pointer	B40F	1995
M67FDS	Dennis Dart 9.8 SDL	Plaxton Pointer	B40F	1995
M106RMS	Scania L113CRL	Alexander Strider	B51F	1995
M107RMS	Scania L113CRL	Alexander Strider	B51F	1995
M108RMS	Scania L113CRL	East Lancs	B45F	1995
M101RMS	Scania L113CRL	Alexander Strider	B45F	1995

		Coakley			
M115KBO		Optare MetroRider MR15	Optare	B31F	1994
M121KBO		Optare MetroRider MR15	Optare	B31F	1995
M121RMS		Scania L113CRL	Alexander Strider	B51F	1995
M132KBO		Optare MetroRider MR15	Optare	B31F	1995
M201EGF		Dennis Dart 9 SDL	Plaxton Pointer	B35F	1995
M202EGF		Dennis Dart 9 SDL	Plaxton Pointer	B35F	1995
M205EGF	y	Dennis Dart 9 SDL	Plaxton Pointer	B35F	1995
M206EGF		Dennis Dart 9 SDL	Plaxton Pointer	B35F	1995
M207EGF		Dennis Dart 9 SDL	Plaxton Pointer	B35F	1995
M215EGF		Dennis Dart 9 SDL	Plaxton Pointer	B35F	1995
M216EGF		Dennis Dart 9 SDL	Plaxton Pointer	B35F	1995
M236YKD		Dennis Dart 9 SDL	Plaxton Pointer	B35F	1995
M237YKD		Dennis Dart 9 SDL	Plaxton Pointer	B35F	1995
M248SPP		Dennis Dart 9.8 SDL	Wright Handybus	B40F	1994
M249SPP		Dennis Dart 9.8 SDL	Wright Handybus	B40F	1994
M250SPP		Dennis Dart 9.8 SDL	Wright Handybus	B40F	1994
M251SPP		Dennis Dart 9.8 SDL	Wright Handybus	B40F	1994
M409TCK		Optare MetroRider MR37	Optare	B25F	1995
M410TCK		Optare MetroRider MR37	Optare	B25F	1995
M742UUA		Optare MetroRider MR15	Optare	B31F	1994
M743UUA		Optare MetroRider MR15	Optare	B31F	1994
M744UUA		Optare MetroRider MR15	Optare	B31F	1994
M745UUA		Optare MetroRider MR15	Optare	B31F	1994
M791EUS	a	Mercedes-Benz 709D	TBP	B27F	1995
M880DDS		Mercedes-Benz 709D	Wadham Stringer	B29F	1994
N26KYS		Mercedes-Benz 811D	Plaxton Beaver	B31F	1995
N27KYS		Mercedes-Benz 811D	Plaxton Beaver	B31F	1995
N81PUS		Mercedes-Benz 811D	Marshall C16	B33F	1996
N142PTG		Optare MetroRider MR15	Optare	B31F	1996
N431GBV		Optare MetroRider MR17	Optare	B28F	1996
N439GHG		Dennis Dart 9.8 SDL	Northern Counties Paladin	B39F	1995
N440GHG		Dennis Dart 9.8 SDL	Northern Counties Paladin	B39F	1995
N473MUS		Dennis Dart 9.8 SDL	Northern Counties Paladin	B39F	1995
N631CDY		DAF SB220LC550	Ikarus Citibus	B49F	1996
NDZ7927		Mercedes-Benz 811D	Wright NimBus	B26F	1993
NDZ7928		Mercedes-Benz 811D	Wright NimBus	B26F	1993
NDZ7930		Mercedes-Benz 811D	Wright NimBus	B26F	1993
P30BLU		Dennis Dart 10.1 SLF	Wright Crusader	B32F	1997
P40BLU		Dennis Dart 10.1 SLF	Wright Crusader	B32F	1997
P50BLU		Dennis Dart 10.1 SLF	Wright Crusader	B32F	1997
P105OLX		Dennis Dart 9.3 SLF	Plaxton Pointer	B32F	1997
P106OLX		Dennis Dart 9.3 SLF	Plaxton Pointer	B32F	1997
P107OLX		Dennis Dart 9.3 SLF	Plaxton Pointer	B32F	1997
P203OLX		Dennis Dart 10.1 SLF	Plaxton Pointer	B36F	1997
P204OLX		Dennis Dart 10.1 SLF	Plaxton Pointer	B36F	1997
P205OLX		Dennis Dart 10.1 SLF	Plaxton Pointer	B36F	1997
P206OLX		Dennis Dart 10.1 SLF	Plaxton Pointer	B36F	1997
P207OLX		Dennis Dart 10.1 SLF	Plaxton Pointer	B36F	1997
P208OLX		Dennis Dart 10.1 SLF	Plaxton Pointer	B36F	1997
P210OLX		Dennis Dart 10.1 SLF	Plaxton Pointer	B36F	1997
P211OLX		Dennis Dart 10.1 SLF	Plaxton Pointer	B36F	1997
P226SGB		Optare MetroRider MR17	Optare	B29F	1996
P291MLD		Dennis Dart 9.8 SFD	Plaxton Pointer	B39F	1996
P295MLD		Dennis Dart 9.8 SFD	Plaxton Pointer	B39F	1996
P301MLD		Dennis Dart 9.8 SFD	Plaxton Pointer	B39F	1996
P318MLD		Dennis Dart 9.8 SFD	Plaxton Pointer	B39F	1996
P511RYM		Dennis Dart 9.3 SLF	Plaxton Pointer	B29F	1996
P528UGA		Mercedes-Benz 709D	Plaxton Beaver	B29F	1997
P529UGA		Mercedes-Benz 709D	Plaxton Beaver	B29F	1997
P736FMS		Dennis Dart 10.7 SLF	UVG Urbanstar	B43F	1997

			Coakley		
P737FMS	Dennis Dart 10.7 SLF	UVG Urbanstar	B43F	1997
P738FMS	Dennis Dart 10.7 SLF	UVG Urbanstar	B43F	1997
P931YSB	Mercedes-Benz 709D	Plaxton Beaver	B29F	1997
P937YSB	Mercedes-Benz 811D	Mellor	B33F	1997
* PEZ4338	Mercedes-Benz Vario O.814D	Plaxton Beaver 2	B27F	1998
* PEZ4562	Mercedes-Benz Vario O.814D	Plaxton Beaver 2	B22F	1998
* PEZ4563	Mercedes-Benz Vario O.810D	Plaxton Beaver 2	B27F	1998
R113RLY	Dennis Dart 10.1 SLF	Plaxton Pointer	B36F	1997
R114VLY	Dennis Dart 10.1 SLF	Plaxton Pointer	B36F	1997
R115RLY	Dennis Dart 10.1 SLF	Plaxton Pointer	B36F	1997
R116RLY	Dennis Dart 10.1 SLF	Plaxton Pointer	B36F	1997
R118RLY	Dennis Dart 10.1 SLF	Plaxton Pointer	B36F	1997
R119RLY	Dennis Dart 10.1 SLF	Plaxton Pointer	B36F	1997
R120RLY	Dennis Dart 10.1 SLF	Plaxton Pointer	B36F	1997
R121RLY	Dennis Dart 10.1 SLF	Plaxton Pointer	B36F	1997
R176VLA	Dennis Dart 10.1 SLF	Plaxton Pointer 2	B36F	1998
R178VLA	Dennis Dart 10.1 SLF	Plaxton Pointer 2	B36F	1998
R179VLA	Dennis Dart 10.1 SLF	Plaxton Pointer 2	B36F	1998
R180VLA	Dennis Dart 10.1 SLF	Plaxton Pointer 2	B36F	1998
R183VLA	Dennis Dart 10.1 SLF	Plaxton Pointer 2	B35F	1998
R184VLA	Dennis Dart 10.1 SLF	Plaxton Pointer 2	B36F	1998
R185VLA	Dennis Dart 10.1 SLF	Plaxton Pointer 2	B35F	1998
* R484GNB	Dennis Dart 10.1 SLF	Wright Crusader	B32F	1997
R682OYS	Dennis Dart 10.7 SLF	Marshall Capital	B37F	1997
R692OYS	Dennis Dart 10.7 SLF	Marshall Capital	B37F	1997
* R694OYS	Dennis dart 10.7 SLF	Marshall Capital	B37F	1997
R703MHN	Optare MetroRider MR15	Optare	B31F	1997
R707MHN	Optare MetroRider MR15	Optare	B31F	1997
R797OYS	Dennis Dart 10.7 SLF	Marshall Capital	B37F	1997
S775RNE	Dennis Dart 10.7 SLF	Plaxton Pointer 2	B39F	1998
S778RNE	Dennis Dart 10.7 SLF	Plaxton Pointer 2	B39F	1998
SF55HBD	ADL Enviro Dart 8.8 SLF	ADL Enviro 200	B29F	2005
V898DNB	Dennis Dart 8.8 SLF	Plaxton Mini Pointer	B29F	1999
* WIB9256	Mercedes-Benz 811D	Reeve Burgess Beaver	B31F	1990
Y191KNB	Dennis Dart 10.7 SLF	Alexander ALX200	B30F	2001
Y192KNB	Dennis Dart 10.7 SLF	Alexander ALX200	B30F	2001
Y193KNB	Dennis Dart 10.7 SLF	Alexander ALX200	B30F	2001

Colchri

Colchri Ltd, 29 Don Drive, Paisley PA2 0AF
Website
Depot   Bay 3, Block F, Westway Development, Porterfield Road, Renfrew PA4 8DJ
Licence   PM0002978

* E937XSB	Volvo B10M-61	Van Hool Alizée	C53F	1988
H101HDV	Mercedes-Benz 811D	Carlyle C19	B25F	1991
J512FPS	Dennis Dart 9.8 SDL	Alexander Dash	B41F	1992
K106XHG	Dennis Dart 9.8 SDL	Alexander Dash	B40F	1993
KX07KNY	Enterprise Bus Plasma EB01	Plaxton Primo	B28F	2007
KX07UGE	Enterprise Bus Plasma EB01	Plaxton Primo	B28F	2007
KX07UGF	Enterprise Bus Plasma EB01	Plaxton Primo	B28F	2007
L316JSA	Mercedes-Benz 709D	Alexander Sprint	DP25F	1993
L740PUA	Optare MetroRider MR15	Optare	B31F	1994
* MBZ9374	Mercedes-Benz 408D		M15	1989
N308AMC	Dennis Dart 9.8 SDL	Alexander	B36F	1995
N472RVK	Mercedes-Benz 709D	Alexander Sprint	B23F	1996
N642VSS	Mercedes-Benz 709D	Alexander Sprint	B25F	1996
N930NAP	Mercedes-Benz 709D	Alexander Sprint	B23F	1996
N931NAP	Mercedes-Benz 709D	Alexander Sprint	B23F	1996

N932NAP	Mercedes-Benz 709D	Alexander Sprint	B23F	1996
* SIB4458	Volvo B10M-61	Plaxton Paramount 3500 II	C53F	1986
SN56AYA	ADL Enviro Dart 8.9 SLF	ADL Enviro 200	B29F	2006
Y924SVV	Mercedes-Benz 311CDI		M15	2001

Courtney Travel
J Gaw, 21 Braemore Road, Stewarton KA3 3HL
Website
Depots 21 Braemore Road, Stewarton KA3 3HL
Workshop, Burnhouse, Beith KA15 1LF
Licence PM0002333

BD04XVU	X	Mercedes-Benz 313CDI		M8	2004
CS06CTS		Mercedes-Benz Atego 1223L	Unvi Cimo	C30F	2006
CS08CTS		Mercedes-Benz 515CDI		M16	2008
CT53CTS		Mercedes-Benz 413CDI	Killbeggan Vehicle Converters	M16	2003
* CTO5T		Mercedes-Benz Atego 1223L	Unvi Cimo	C41F	2004
* J249LLB		Mercedes-Benz Vario O.814D	North West Coach Sales	C24F	1991
* N296YOA		Mercedes-Benz 412CD	AMC	M12L	1995
P188AJU		Mercedes-Benz 412D	Frank Guy	M13L	1996
* SK07FYO		Mercedes-Benz 616CDI	Unvi	C16FL	2007
* SN54GWV		Mercedes-Benz Atego 1223L	Unvi Cimo	C34FT	2004
SN55JZR		Mercedes-Benz 311CDI		M16	2005
SN57EZP		Mercedes-Benz 515CDI	Killbeggan Vehicle Converters	M16	2007
T200OCT		Mercedes-Benz Atego O.1120L	Optare Solera	C32F	1999
V100OJW		Mercedes-Benz 410D	Frank Guy	C16FL	1999
X163ENJ		Mercedes-Benz 311CDI	Frank Guy	M8	2000

Henry Crawford
Henry Crawford Coaches Ltd, Shillford Mill, Neilston, Glasgow G78 3BA
Website www.henrycrawfordcoaches.co.uk
Depot Shillford Mill, Neilston, Glasgow G78 3BA
Licence PM0001193

* 935BRU	Volvo B12B	Van Hool Alizée	C53F	2006
* 937BUS	Volvo B12B	Van Hool Alizée	C57F	2004
* HCC100	Volvo B12B	Van Hool Alizée	C53F	2002
* HCC296 —	Volvo B10M-62	Van Hool Alizée	C57F	2001
* HCC440	Volvo B10M-55	Van Hool Alizée	C49FT	2000
* HCC551	Volvo B10M-62	Van Hool Alizée	C53F	1998
* HCC882	Volvo B10M-62	Van Hool Alizée	C53F	1998
JH54BUS	Bova FHD12.340	Bova Futura	C53F	2004
* L98WSW	Mercedes-Benz 609D	Onyx	C24F	1994
N702FLN	MAN 11.190	Optare Vecta	B42F	1995
* NNF922	Mercedes-Benz Vario O.814D	Onyx	C24F	2007
* NSK919	Mercedes-Benz Sprinter 413CDI	Ferqui	M16	2001
* NSK920	Mercedes-Benz Vario O.814D	Indcar	C25F	2005
* NSK921 —	Mercedes-Benz Vario O.815D	Unvi	C29F	2006
* OO03HCC	Volvo B12B	Van Hool Alizée	C53F	2003
* OO04HCC	Bova FHD12.340	Bova Futura	C49FT	2005
* OO5HCC	Bova FHD120-340	Bova Futura	C49FT	2005
OO06HCC	Bova FHD10-340	Bova Futura	C38FT	2006
OO07HCC	Bova FHD120-365	Bova Futura	C38FT	2007
OO08HCC —	Bova FHD120-365	Bova Futura	C38FT	2008
* R478SSA	Mercedes-Benz 614D	Crystals	C24F	1998

Crieff Travel

D Myles, Glenheath, Lodge Street, Crieff PH7 4DW
Website
Depot South Bridgend Industrial Estate, Muthill Road, Crieff PH7 4HQ
Licence PM0002633

K118CSG	Dennis Dart 9 SDL	Alexander Dash	B35F	1992
K120CSG	Dennis Dart 9 SDL	Alexander Dash	B35F	1992
K123CSG	Dennis Dart 9 SDL	Alexander Dash	B35F	1992
S353CSF	Mercedes-Benz Vario O.810D	Plaxton Beaver	C31F	1999
SF04EWL	Mercedes-Benz Vario O.810D	TransBus Beaver 2	DP33F	2004
SM06VJN	Citroen Relay	Advanced Vehicle Builders	M11	2006
T676ASN	Volvo B10M-62	Plaxton Excalibur	C49FT	1999
* T798FRU	Volvo B10M-62	Plaxton Premiere 350	C49FT	1999
V172FFS	Dennis Dart 11.3 SLF	Plaxton Pointer 2	B42F	2000
V173FFS	Dennis Dart 11.3 SLF	Plaxton Pointer 2	B42F	2000
W511PSF	Mercedes-Benz Vario O.814D	Plaxton Beaver 2	DP31F	2000
Y506BSF	Mercedes-Benz 614D	Onyx	C24F	2001
YN03NJF	Mercedes-Benz Vario O.814D	Plaxton Beaver	C33F	2003
YN56ORW	VDL DE12BSSB120	Plaxton Centro	B40F	2007
YN56ORX	VDL DE12BSSB120	Plaxton Centro	B40F	2007

D B Travel

D Bishop, 14 Lennox Road, Milton, Dumbarton G82 2TL
Website
Depot 14 Lennox Road, Milton, Dumbarton G82 2TL
Licence PM0002385

F219DCC	Mercedes-Benz 709D	Robin Hood	B27F	1988
F427EJC	Mercedes-Benz 709D	Robin Hood	DP25F	1989
F428GAT	Mercedes-Benz 811D	Reeve Burgess Beaver	B31F	1989
F624XMS	Mercedes-Benz 811D	Alexander AM	B28F	1988
K438XRF	Mercedes-Benz 709D	Plaxton Beaver	C25F	1992
K446XRF	Mercedes-Benz 709D	Plaxton Beaver	C25F	1992
L123DRN	Mercedes-Benz 709D	Alexander Sprint	B25F	1993
* L128DRN	Mercedes-Benz 709D	Alexander Sprint	B25F	1993
L202ONU	Optare MetroRider MR15	Optare	B30F	1994
L203ONU	Optare MetroRider MR15	Optare	B30F	1994
L509OAL	Volvo B6-50	Alexander Dash	B40F	1994
L730MWW	Optare MetroRider MR15	Optare	B31F	1993
L733MWW	Optare MetroRider MR15	Optare	B31F	1993
L738PUA	Optare MetroRider MR15	Optare	B31F	1994
N203LTN	Volvo B10M-55	Alexander PS	B49F	1995
N204LTN	Volvo B10M-55	Alexander PS	B49F	1995
N796PDS	Mercedes-Benz 814D	Mellor	C33F	1996

D J International

DJ International Ltd, 15 Carlibar Road, Barrhead G78 1AA
Website
Depot 15 Carlibar Road, Barrhead G78 1AA
Fairlie Quay Enterprise Park, Fairlie KA29 0AS
Kingston Yard, Ardgowan Street, Port Glasgow PA15 5DG
Licence PM0002680

G195PAO	Mercedes-Benz 709D	Alexander	DP25F	1990
G203PAO	Mercedes-Benz 709D	Alexander	DP25F	1990
* IUI9890	Toyota Coaster HB31R	Caetano Optimo	C19F	1989
K714DAO	Volvo B10M-55	Alexander PS	B49F	1992
K719DAO	Volvo B10M-55	Alexander PS	B53F	1992

K724DAO	Volvo B10M-55	Alexander PS	B49F	1993
K732DAO	Volvo B10M-55	Alexander PS	B53F	1993
* M10DVS	MAN 11.190	Optare Vecta	B42F	1995
N221MUS	Mercedes-Benz 709D	UVG CityStar	B29F	1996
P520RDS	LDV Convoy	LDV	M16	1996
* PJI7756	Leyland Leopard PSU5C/4R	Plaxton Supreme	C51F	1981
* RIL2576	Volvo B10M-62	Van Hool Alizée	C48FT	1995
* RIL3690	Leyland Tiger TRCTL11/3RZ	Plaxton Paramount 3500 II	C50FT	1986
* RIL3693	Bedford YMP	Plaxton Paramount 3200 III	C28FT	1987
* TSV677	Volvo B10M-62	Jonckheere Deauville	C53F	1995
W733DCS x	LDV Convoy	LDV	M8	2000

D & E Coaches

D&E Coaches Ltd, 39 Henderson Drive, Inverness IV1 1TR
Website www.decoaches.co.uk
Depot 39 Henderson Drive, Inverness IV1 1TR
Licence PM1031094

* B1YST	Volvo B10M-62	Van Hool Alizée	C46FT	1995
* B2YST	Bova FHD12-340	Bova Futura	C49FT	2003
* B3YST	Bova FHD12-340	Bova Futura	C51FT	1997
* B5YST —	Bova FHD12-340	Bova Futura	C51FT	1999
* B6YST	Bova FHD12-370	Bova Futura	C53F	1999
* B7YST	Bova FHD12-340	Bova Futura	C53F	1996
* B8YST	Dennis Lance 11SLF	Berkhof 2000NL	B40F	1994
* B9YST	Bova FHD127-365	Bova Futura	C57F	2007
* B10YST	Bova FHD12-340	Bova Futura	C49FT	1997
* B12YST	DAF MB230LT615	Van Hool Alizée	C51FT	1992
* B13YST	Volvo B10M-50	Alexander RV	H47/29D	1989
* B14YST	Volvo B10M-50	Alexander RV	H47/29D	1989
* B15YST	Dennis Lance 11SLF	Berkhof 2000NL	B40L	1994
* B17YST	Mercedes-Benz Vario O.814D	Plaxton Beaver	B31F	1999
* BU51DEC	Mercedes-Benz Vario O.816D	Plaxton Cheetah 2	C29F	2009
* BU53DEC	Mercedes-Benz 515CDI	Killbeggan Vehicle Converters	M16	2008
BU56DEC	Mercedes-Benz Vario O.814D	Plaxton Beaver 2	B31F	2006
BU58DEC	Mercedes-Benz Vario O.813D	Plaxton Beaver	B27FL	2008
DE08DEC	Mercedes-Benz Vario O.816D	Unvi	C29F	2008
P543MSF	Mercedes-Benz 711D	UVG CityStar	B16FL	1996
* S1YST	Bova FHD12.340	Bova Futura	C49FT	2002
* SIL4860	Mercedes-Benz 709D	Plaxton Beaver	C25F	1993
* SK07FCF	Toyota Coaster BB50R	Caetano Optimo	C26F	2007
YA10CFX	Mercedes-Benz 515CDI		M16	2010
YN09AOP	Mercedes-Benz Vario O.814D	Plaxton Cheetah	C33F	2009

Billy Davies Executive Coaches

W Davies, Unit 1, Plean Industrial Estate, Plean FK7 8BJ
Website
Depot Unit 1, Plean Industrial Estate, Plean FK7 8BJ
Licence PM0001509

* D453DWP	Van Hool T815	Van Hool Acron	C51FT	1987
G901ANR	Van Hool T815	Van Hool Acron	C49FT	1990
* H699PVW	Volvo Olympian ON2R50C13Z4	Alexander RH	H47/29F	1991
* H708PVW	Volvo Olympian ON2R50C13Z4	Alexander RH	H47/29F	1991
* H709PVW	Volvo Olympian ON2R50C13Z4	Alexander RH	H47/29F	1991
* H718PVW	Volvo Olympian ON2R50C13Z4	Alexander RH	H47/29F	1991
* HF53GVJ	Ayats A52E/AT	Ayats Atlantis	C53F	2003
R56EDW	Bova FLC12-280	Bova Futura	C53F	1998

* RIB6563	Volvo B10M-62	Plaxton Paramount 3500 III	C51F	1986
SF06OEA —	Mercedes-Benz Vario O.814D	Plaxton Cheetah	C33F	2006
SN10CAE —	ADL Enviro Dart 8.9 SLF	ADL Enviro 200	B29F	2010
Y965RKW	Irisbus EuroRider 397E.12.35A	Beulas Stergo E	C51FT	2001

Deveron Coaches

Deveron Coaches Ltd, 6 Union Road, Macduff AB44 1UJ

Website

Depot 6 Union Road, Macduff AB44 1UJ
1 March Lane, Buckie AB56 4BB

Licence PM1022563

* C892WKS		Volvo B10M-61	Van Hool Alizée	C49F	1986
* D146ENV		Volvo B10M-61	Duple 320	C53F	1987
* DJZ4676 —		Leyland Tiger TRCTL11/3RZ	Plaxton Derwent	DP70F	1987
F727VAC		Volvo B10M-60	Plaxton Paramount 3500 III	C53F	1989
* HIL5184	w	DAF MB200DKTL600	Plaxton Paramount 3200 I	C53F	1983
* K498PGN —		Mercedes-Benz 609D	Devon Conversions	C21F	1993
* L17ATS —		Volvo B6-45	Caetano Algarve II	C34F	1994
* M321RAW		Volvo B10M-62	Plaxton Premiere 350	C53F	1995
* M534CEY—		Volvo B10M-62	Jonckheere Deauville	C51FT	1995
MX05EMF		Optare Solo M850	Optare	B28F	2005
MX05OTE		Optare Solo M880	Optare	B26FL	2005
MX06ABV		Optare Solo M850	Optare	B30F	2006
MX53ZWE		Mercedes-Benz Vario O.810D	Onyx	C24F	2003
* N728HSX		Mercedes-Benz 811D	Leicester Carriage Builders	B33F	1995
* N781PEC		Volvo B10M-62	Plaxton Premiere 350	C49FT	1996
* N993THO		Volvo B10M-62	Plaxton Premiere 320	C45FT	1996
NC04NHG		Ford Transit	Ford	M16	2004
NK02EXB		Ford Transit	Ford	M14	2002
NV56WVH		Ford Transit	Ford	M14	2006
* OIL5315		Scania K112CRS	Van Hool Alizée	C49FT	1987
P314CVE		Volvo B10M-62	Plaxton Premiere 350	C52F	1996
* P364JJU		Volvo B10M-62	Plaxton Premiere 350	C53F	1997
P413TNG		Volvo B10M-62	Jonckheere Mistral	C53F	1997
* PIW2633		Volvo B10M-62	Plaxton Premiere 350	C53F	1997
R59DJS		Mercedes-Benz Vario O.810D	Plaxton Beaver 2	B33F	1998
R160TCH —		Mercedes-Benz Vario O.814D	Leicester Carriage Builders	C32FL	1997
R629VYB		Bova FHD12.340	Bova Futura	C49FT	1997
R901WEC		Volvo B10M-62	Plaxton Premiere 350	C70F	1998
S588ACT		Mercedes-Benz Vario O.814D	Autobus Nouvelle	C33F	1998
SF04HXN—		TransBus Dart 8.8 SLF	TransBus Mini Pointer	B29F	2004
SF53KUR —		TransBus Dart 8.8 SLF	TransBus Mini Pointer	B29F	2003
* SIW1940		Leyland Tiger TRCTL11/3R	Plaxton Paramount 3200 I	C46FT	1983
SJ52XLC		Ford Transit	Ford	M14	2002
SN03JWG		Mercedes-Benz Vario O.817L	Leinster	C33F	2003
* T12DEV —		Mercedes-Benz Vario O.814D	Frank Guy	C24FL	1999
* T802FRU		Volvo B10M-62	Plaxton Premiere 350	C49FT	1999
* UIL7816		Volvo B10M-61	Jonckheere Jubilee P50	C49FT	1987
V350EKY		Mercedes-Benz Vario O.814D	Plaxton Cheetah	C33F	1999
* VIB9485		Scania K112CRB	Van Hool Alizée	C51F	1996
W317OSA		Ford Transit	Ford	M14	2000
X223HCD		Mercedes-Benz Vario O.814D	Plaxton Cheetah	C25F	2001
Y313KDP		Volvo B6BLE	East Lancs Spryte	B36F	2001
Y342AUT		Volvo B10M-62	Berkhof Axial 50	C51FT	2001
Y797HPG		Volvo B10M-62	Berkhof Axial 50	C51FT	2001
YN53VBL		Mercedes-Benz Vario O.814D	TransBus Mini Pointer	C29F	2004
YR52XPA		Mercedes-Benz 311CDI	Mercedes-Benz	M14	2002

Dewar Coaches
D Dewar, 1 Antonine Street, Camelon, Falkirk FK1 4NX
Website www.dewarcoaches.com
Depot Unit 8, Merchiston Industrial Estate, Falkirk FK2 7PD
Licence PM1036940

P622TGE	Volvo B10M-62	Van Hool Alizée	C53F	1996
SN10AOA	Volvo B12B	Van Hool Alizée	C51FT	2010
* T6DOF	Mercedes-Benz Vario O.814D	Plaxton Cheetah	C29F	2004
* T7DOF	Volvo B10M-55	Van Hool Alizée	C49FT	1999
* T8DOF	Volvo B12M	Van Hool Alizée	C51F	2003
* T9DOF	Volvo B10M-62	Van Hool Alizée	C46FT	2002
Y369TGE	Mercedes-Benz Vario O.814D	Plaxton Cheetah	C33F	2001

Dicksons of Erskine
Stewart Dickson, 27 Broomlands Gardens, Erskine PA8 7BL
Website
Depot Unit 13, 13 Scotts Road, Paisley PA2 7AN
Licence PM0001887

G288TSL	Mercedes-Benz 709D	Alexander Sprint	B23F	1990
K807DJN	Mercedes-Benz O.811D	Plaxton Cheetah	C33F	1992
K866ODY	Mercedes-Benz 709D	Alexander Sprint	B25F	1993
K949OEM y	Mercedes-Benz 811D	Marshall C16	B27F	1993
L258YOD	Mercedes-Benz 709D	Plaxton Beaver	B25F	1993
L642DNA	Mercedes-Benz 709D	Plaxton Beaver	B27F	1993
L703AGA — y	Mercedes-Benz 709D	Wadham Stringer	B29F	1994
L748LWA	Mercedes-Benz 709D	Alexander (Belfast)	B25F	1993
M275FNS	Mercedes-Benz 811D	Wadham Stringer	B33F	1995
M877DDS	Mercedes-Benz 709D	Wadham Stringer	B26FL	1994
M943UDT	Mercedes-Benz 711D	Plaxton Beaver	B25F	1994
N207GCS —	Mercedes-Benz 709D	Wadham Stringer	B28F	1995
N744LUS	Mercedes-Benz 811D	Wadham Stringer	B33F	1995
N746YVR	Mercedes-Benz 711D	Marshall C19	B27F	1995
N798FSD	Mercedes-Benz 709D	Wadham Stringer	B16FL	1995
N812KHW	Mercedes-Benz Vario O.814D	TBP	C24F	1996
N881AVV	Mercedes-Benz 709D	Alexander Sprint	B25F	1996
N949MGG	Mercedes-Benz 709D	Wadham Stringer	B29F	1995
N950MGG	Mercedes-Benz 709D	Wadham Stringer	B29F	1995
P179FNF —	Mercedes-Benz 709D	Alexander Sprint	B23F	1996
P180FNF	Mercedes-Benz 709D	Alexander Sprint	B23F	1996
R35WDA	Mercedes-Benz Vario O.814D	Autobus Nouvelle	C33F	1997
R955FYS	Mercedes-Benz Vario O.810D	Plaxton Beaver 2	B31F	1998
V217DSS	Mercedes-Benz Vario O.814D	Keillor	DP25F	1999

T & E Docherty
H Tait, 40 Bank Street, Irvine KA12 0LP
Website
Depot 40 Bank Street, Irvine KA12 0LP
5 Corsehill Mount Road, Dreghorn, Irvine KA11 4JL
Mossculloch, Old Glasgow Road, Kilwinning KA13 7QJ
Licence PM0002276

* 2625ED		Volvo B10M-46	Caetano Algarve	C41FT	1986
* 5909D	a	Volvo B58-61	Plaxton Supreme	C46FT	1978
* 6491ED	w	Volvo B58-56	Duple Dominant	C51F	1979
H202LRF		Mercedes-Benz 814D	Wright NimBus	B33F	1991
NTF9	p	Leyland PD2/15	Leyland	H30/26R	1951
S268RBC		LDV Convoy	LDV	M16	1998
* WSD827	p	Leyland PD3/2	Alexander	H41/31F	1962

Dochertys Midland Coaches Ltd
J&E Docherty, Priory Park, Auchterarder, Perthshire PH3 1GB
Website www.dochertysmidlandcoaches.co.uk
Depot Priory Park, Auchterarder, Perthshire PH3 1GB
Licence PM1078265

AS07JDS	Volvo B12B	Jonckheere Mistral	C49FT	2007
AS09JDS	Bova FHD127.365	Bova Futura	C55F	2009
AS60JDS	Volvo B12B	Volvo 9700	C51FT	2010
BS07JDS	Volvo B12B	Jonckheere Mistral	C49FT	2007
BS09JDS	Scania K340EB4	Irizar Century	C49FT	2009
BS60JDS	Volvo B12B	Volvo 9700	C51FT	2010
CS07JDS	Scania K380EB	Irizar Century	C49FT	2007
JA5515 p	Leyland TS7	Windover	C32FL	1936
* JDS77J	Mercedes-Benz Vario O.814D	Plaxton Beaver Coach	C33F	1993
M785PRS	Volvo B10M-55	Alexander PS	DP48F	1995
M793PRS	Volvo B10M-55	Alexander PS	DP48F	1995
MX57CCJ	Optare Solo M950	Optare	B32F	2007
* N77JDS	Volvo B10B-58	Wright Endurance	DP47F	1997
N205EFS	Mercedes-Benz Vario O.814D	Plaxton Beaver Coach	C33F	1996
P565PNE	Mercedes-Benz O.810D	Plaxton Beaver	B27F	1997
P566PNE	Mercedes-Benz O.810D	Plaxton Beaver	B27	1997
SF04LKG	Volvo B12M	Van Hool Alizée	C49FT	2004
SN05FHM	Volvo B12M	Van Hool Alizée	C49FT	2005
SN57BJU	Scania K340EB4	Irizar Century	C49FT	2007
SN57BKL	Scania K230UB4	Wright Solar	B44F	2007
SN57BLK	Scania K230UB4	Wright Solar	B44F	2007
SN60AOF	Mercedes-Benz O.815D	Sitcar Beluga	C33F	2010
SN60CNU	Volvo B7RLE	Wright Eclipse Urban	B44F	2010
SP06DFZ	Volvo B12M	Van Hool Alizée	C49FT	2006
SP06DGE	Mercedes-Benz Vario O.815D	Sitcar Beluga	C29F	2006
SP06DGF	Scania K124EB	Irizar Century	C49FT	2006
SP09CWK	Optare Solo M950	Optare	B33F	2009
* W7JDS	Mercedes-Benz 410D	Olympus	M16	2000

Dodds of Troon
Dodds of Troon Ltd, 4 East Road, Ayr KA8 9BA
Website www.doddscoachholidays.com
Depot 4 East Road, Ayr KA8 9BA
Licence PM0000011

* AA05DOT	Volvo B12M *Stena Line livery*	Jonckheere Mistral	C51FT	2007
* BB05DOT	Volvo B12B	Jonckheere Mistral	C51FT	2007
CC06DOT	Volvo B12B	Jonckheere Mistral	C51FT	2006
* D5DOT	Volvo B10M-60	Van Hool Alizée	C53F	1994
* D11DOT	Volvo B10M-62	Van Hool Alizée	C46FT	1995
* D20DOT	Volvo B10M-62	Van Hool Alizée	C46FT	1995
DD06DOT	Volvo B12B	Jonckheere Mistral	C51FT	2006
FJ10EZX	Toyota Coaster BB50R	Caetano Optimo	C22F	2010
FJ10EZZ	Toyota Coaster BB50R	Caetano Optimo	C22F	2010
* GIL5407	Volvo B10M-61	Van Hool Alizée	C49FT	1989
* JEZ4096	Leyland Tiger TRBTL11/2RP	Alexander Q	DP53F	1985
* JEZ8980	Leyland Tiger TRBTL11/2RP	Alexander Q	DP53F	1985
M70TCC w	Toyota Coaster HZB50R	Caetano Optimo	C18F	1995
PXI5517	Leyland Tiger TRCTL11/3ARZA	Alexander (Belfast)	C53F	1990
PXI5523	Leyland Tiger TRCTL11/3ARZA	Alexander (Belfast)	C53F	1990
SF10DJJ	Volvo B12B	Volvo 9700	C49FT	2010
SF10DJK	Volvo B12B	Volvo 9700	C49FT	2010
SJW515 p	Guy Wulfrunian *Wotdor*	Burlingham	C41F	1957
* T3DOT	Volvo B12B	Jonckheere Mistral	C51FT	2005

* TJI5392	Volvo B10M-61	Van Hool Alizée	C53F	1988
* TJI5393	Volvo B10M-61	Plaxton Paramount 3200 II	C53F	1986
* TJI5394	Volvo B10M-61	Plaxton Paramount 3200 II	C53F	1986
* V9DOT	Volvo B12B	Jonckheere Mistral	C51FT	2005
V671EDK	Mercedes-Benz 614D	Minibus Options	B16FL	2000
* YXI7906	Volvo B10M-61	Van Hool Alizée	C53F	1989

Doigs of Glasgow

Doigs Ltd, Transport House, 7 Summer Street, Glasgow G40 3TB
Website   www.doigs.com
Depot   Transport House, 7 Summer Street, Glasgow G40 3TB
Licence   PM1055247

FJ07ACV	Volvo B7R	Sunsundegui Sideral	C57F	2007
FJ07ADV	Volvo B7R	Sunsundegui Sideral	C57F	2007
FJ08FYD	Volvo B12B	Sunsundegui Sideral	C49FT	2008
FN09AOC	Volvo B7R	Sunsundegui Sideral	C36F	2009
FN09AOD	Volvo B7R	Sunsundegui Sideral	C36F	2009
FN09AOE	Volvo B9R	Sunsundegui Sideral	C36F	2009
FN09AOF	Volvo B9R	Sunsundegui Sideral	C36F	2009
PN10FNP	Volvo B9TL	Optare Olympus	CH61/39F	2010
SJ06CBV	Volvo B12M	Sunsundegui Sideral	C53F	2006
SJ51LPA	Scania L94UA	Wright Solar	AB58D	2001
SK07FYP	Mercedes-Benz Sprinter 616CDI	Unvi	C17F	2007
SK07NKN	Scania K230EB4	Irizar Century	C49FT	2007
SN06KHO	Mercedes-Benz Sprinter 413CDI	Killbeggan Vehicle Converters	M16	2006
* SN08CNJ	Scania K114EB4	Irizar Century	C70F	2008
SN58DVZ	Scania KIB4	Irizar Century	C59FLT	2008
YP09NRF	Scania KIB4	Irizar Century	C49FT	2009
YX08AOP	Mercedes-Benz Sprinter 515CDI	Ferqui	M16	2008
YX08AUA	Mercedes-Benz Sprinter 515CDI	Ferqui	M16	2008
YX08HGD	Mercedes-Benz Sprinter 515CDI		M16	2008

S J Douglas / SD Travel

S J Douglas, 53 Glebe Road, Whitburn EH47 0HZ
Website
Depot   Yard 3, Inchcross, Standhill, Bathgate EH48 2HS
Licence

* CKZ8184	Dennis Dart 9 SDL	Plaxton Pointer	DP35F	1991
E701GCU	Scania N112DRB	Alexander	H47/31F	1987
* E711CDS	Mercedes-Benz 609D	Alexander (Belfast)	B24F	1987
J388GKH	Dennis Dart 8.5 SDL	Plaxton Pointer	B28F	1991
M955USC	Mercedes-Benz 609D	Onyx	C24F	1994
N189GFR	Iveco Daily 59.12	Mellor	B27F	1995
P123HCH	Mercedes-Benz Vario O.814D	Alexander	B29F	1996
R934AMB	Mercedes-Benz Vario O.814D	Plaxton Beaver	B29F	1997
SN56NSD	Optare Solo M850	Optare	B28F	2006
SN57EFG	ADL Enviro Dart 8.9 SLF	ADL Enviro 200	B29F	2007
T572GSL	Ford Transit	Ford	B12FL	1999
W262EWU	Optare Solo M850	Optare	B23F	2000

Dunns Coaches

Dunns Coaches Ltd, WIndyridge, 560 Stirling Road, Riggend, Airdrie ML6 7SS
Website
Depot   560 Stirling Road, Riggend, Airdrie ML6 7SS
Licence   PM1014807

	Reg	Chassis	Body	Seating	Year
*	DEZ4259	Volvo B10M-62	Plaxton Premiere 350	C53F	1996
	E156XHS	Volvo B10M-56	Plaxton Verde	B54F	1988
	E555UHS	Volvo B10M-61	Plaxton Paramount 3500 III	C53F	1987
*	F357MGB	Volvo B10M-60	Van Hool Alizée	C52FT	1989
	F945PFW	Volvo B10M-60	Plaxton Paramount 3200 III	C53F	1989
	G504XLO	Leyland Swift LBM6T/2RA	Reeve Burgess Harrier	B41F	1989
	G647ONH	Volvo B10M-60	Jonckheere Deauville	C51FT	1990
*	J119DUV	Dennis Dart 8.5 SDL	Plaxton Pointer	B24F	1992
*	K1WGD	Volvo B10M-62	Plaxton Premiere 350	C48FT	1996
	TND423X	DAF MB200DKFL600	Plaxton Supreme V	C47FT	1982
*	W333NOB	Mercedes-Benz Vario O.814D	Plaxton Beaver 2	B31F	2000
	W566JVV	Dennis Dart 10.7 SLF	Plaxton Pointer 2	B37F	2000
	YD02RBY	DAF DE12BSSB120	Wright Cadet	B39F	2002

Dunn's Coaches / C&M Coaches

C&M Dunn, 194 Inverkip Road, Greenock PA16 9EX
Website
Depot   13-21 Ingleton Street, Greenock PA15 4UD
Licence   PM0002209

	Reg	Chassis	Body	Seating	Year
*	A19NCR	Mercedes-Benz Vario O.814D	Plaxton Cheetah	C33F	2000
	E205YGC	Mercedes-Benz 709D	Reeve Burgess Beaver	C25F	1988
	E564YBU	Mercedes-Benz 709D	Reeve Burgess Beaver	B25F	1988
	F69LNU	Mercedes-Benz 709D	Robin Hood	B29F	1989
	F189RRF	Mercedes-Benz 709D	Robin Hood	B29F	1988
	F281GNB	Mercedes-Benz 609D	Made to Measure	B24F	1988
	G233FJC	Mercedes-Benz 709D	Robin Hood	B27F	1989
	GBZ7212	Mercedes-Benz 811D	Wright, Wishaw	B29F	1992
*	J55BUS	Volvo B10M-62	Jonckheere Mistral	C49FT	1997
*	K226BJA	Mercedes-Benz 709D	Plaxton Beaver	B27F	1992
	K322BTM	Volvo B10M-60	Plaxton Premiere 350	C53F	1993
	K593BEG	Mercedes-Benz 709D	Marshall C19	B27F	1992
	L500WEN	Volvo B10M-60	Plaxton Premiere 350	C53F	1993
	L644VCV	Mercedes-Benz 709D	Plaxton Beaver	C25F	1994
	L715WCC	Mercedes-Benz 709D	Marshall C19	B27F	1993
	L717WCC	Mercedes-Benz 709D	Marshall C19	B27F	1993
	M62WKA	Mercedes-Benz 709D	Alexander Sprint	B25F	1994
	N362AVV	Mercedes-Benz 709D	Alexander Sprint	B23F	1996
	N380PNY	Mercedes-Benz 709D	Alexander Sprint	B24F	1996
	N465RVK	Mercedes-Benz 709D	Alexander Sprint	B23F	1996
	N495RVK	Mercedes-Benz 709D	Alexander Sprint	B23F	1996
	N957NAP	Mercedes-Benz 709D	Alexander Sprint	B23F	1996
	N959NAP	Mercedes-Benz 709D	Alexander Sprint	B23F	1996
	P150HBG	Mercedes-Benz 711D	Onyx	C24F	1996
*	PIL3750	Mercedes-Benz 811D	Alexander AM	C33F	1988
*	PIL3752	Mercedes-Benz 709D	Alexander Sprint	B25F	1988
	R878FGE	Mercedes-Benz Vario O.810D	Plaxton Beaver 2	B29F	1997
	W563JVV	Dennis Dart 10.7 SLF	Plaxton Pointer 2	B29F	2000
	W869BOH	Mercedes-Benz 410D	Jubilee	M16	2000
*	XAM826A	DAF MB200DKFL600	Van Hool Alizée	C49FT	1983
*	XIL4668	Volvo B10M-60	Jonckheere Deauville	C51FT	1990

Earnside Coaches
D, E & F Rutherford, Earnside Coaches, Greenbank Road, Glenfarg PH2 9NW
Website www.earnside.com
Depot Greenbank Road, Glenfarg PH2 9NW
Licence PM0001643

*	7722SR	Neoplan N316SHD	Neoplan Euroliner	C53F	2003
*	B10MGR	Volvo B10M-62	Plaxton Premiere 320	C53F	1994
	B12BGR	Volvo B12B	Plaxton Panther	C49FT	2006
	G907PKK	Volvo B10M-60	Plaxton Paramount 3500 III	C53F	1989
*	N11JCR	Ford Transit	Ford	M16	2005
*	~~NHG550~~	~~Scania K114EB4~~	~~Irizar Century~~	~~C49FT~~	~~2002~~
*	NHG551	Volvo B12B	Jonckheere	C51FT	2005
*	T13GDR	Volvo B12B	Plaxton Panther	C49FT	2006
	TVS619	Neoplan N2216SHD	Neoplan Euroliner	C49FT	2009
	WSV490	Volvo B12B	Berkhof Axial 50	C49FT	2005

NHG550 — Neoplan N2216SHD — Neoplan — C49FT — 2011 (handwritten)

Easter Ross Coach Company
Easter Ross Coach Co, 3 The Old Granary, East Soulton Farm, Pencaitland, Tranent EH34 5BF
Website
Depot 3 The Old Granary, East Soulton Farm, Pencaitland, Tranent EH34 5BF
Licence PM1037267

DAZ1565	Volvo B10M-62	Plaxton Premiere 320	C53F	1994
FX51BVF	Mercedes-Benz Vario O.814D	Autobus Classique	C25F	2001
J414PRW	Mercedes-Benz 811D	Wright NimBus	B33F	1991

Edinburgh Coach Lines
Edinburgh Coach Lines Ltd, 81 Salamander Street, Edinburgh EH6 7JZ
Website www.edinburghcoachlines.com
Depot 81 Salamander Street, Edinburgh EH6 7JZ
Licence PM0000103

603	*	YSU196	Scania K124IB4	Irizar Century	C49FT	2000
705	*	PSU698	Scania K114EB4	Irizar Century	C49FT	2005
		FJ10DPY	Volvo B13R (T)	Volvo 9700	C44FT	2010
		FJ10DPZ	Volvo B13R (T)	Volvo 9700	C44FT	2010
	*	K764CSG	Mercedes-Benz 410D	Eurocoach (Bunbeg)	M15	1993
	*	M611YSF	Mercedes-Benz 410D	Eurocoach (Bunbeg)	M15	1995
	*	PSU610	MAN 12.220	Indcar Magu 2	C39FT	2002
	*	PSU611	Scania K124IB4	Van Hool Alizée	C49FT	2003
	*	PSU612	Scania K114EB4	Irizar Century	C50F	2006
	*	PSU613	Scania K124IB4	Van Hool Alizée	C49FT	2001
	*	PSU614	Scania K124IB4	Van Hool Alizée	C49FT	2003
	*	PSU615	Scania K114EB4	Irizar Century	C49FT	2003
	*	PSU616	Mercedes-Benz 413CDL		M16	2006
	*	PSU617	Scania K114EB4	Irizar Century	C51FT	2004
	*	PSU618	Scania K124IB4	Van Hool Alizée	C49F	2003
	*	PSU619	Scania K114EB4	Van Hool Alizée	C49FT	2003
	*	PSU620	Scania K114EB4	Van Hool Alizée	C49FT	2005
	*	PSU621	Scania K114EB4	Van Hool Alizée	C49FT	2005
	*	SK03FDL	Scania K14IB4	Irizar Century	C49FT	2003
		SN08KBY	Scania K340EB4	Van Hool Alizée	C53F	2008
		SN08KBZ	Scania K340EB4	Van Hool Alizée	C53F	2008
		SN09FUW	MAN 12.240	Plaxton Centro	B38F	2009
		SN09FUY	MAN 12.240	Plaxton Centro	B38F	2009
	*	T13ECL	Dennis Dart 10.7 SLF	Plaxton Pointer 2	B31D	1999

Elite Transportation / North Fife Travel / St Andrews Executive Travel

G Donaldson, Brownhills Garage, Brownhills, St Andrews KY16 8PL
Travel Link Scotland, 7 Pilmour Links, St Andrews KY16 9JG
C Hunter & Partners, 19 Mid Street, Largoward, Leven KY9 1HY

Website	
Depot	Unit 2, Tom Stewart Lane, St Andrews KY16 8YB
	Brownhills Garage, Brownhills, St Andrews KY16 8PL
	c/o Ravenscraig Motors, Junction Road, Kirkcaldy KY1 2BH
Licence	PM0001846 (North Fife Travel)
	PM0002977 (Travel Link Scotland)
	PM1045910 (Elite Transportation)

* K434DRW	Mercedes-Benz Vario O.814D	Cunliffe	DP24FL	1993
N264DSF	Mercedes-Benz 711D	Onyx	C24F	1995
SK07FBB —	Mercedes-Benz Atego 1523L	Unvi Cimo	C37F	2007
SK07FXV	Mercedes-Benz Atego 1018L	Unvi Cimo	C33F	2007
SK57BHX —	Mercedes-Benz Atego 1523L	Unvi Cimo	C26F	2007
SN04GUE	Mercedes-Benz Sprinter 413CDI	Killbeggan Vehicle Converters	M16	2004
SN05HSY	Mercedes-Benz Atego 1223L	Unvi Cimo	C39F	2005
SN06AEY	Mercedes-Benz Atego 1223L	Unvi Cimo	C32F	2006
SN06KAA	Mercedes-Benz Sprinter 616CDI	Unvi	C8F	2006
SN08GYH	Mercedes-Benz Atego 1524L	Unvi Cimo	C32F	2008
SN10EMP	Mercedes-Benz O.813D	EVM	C16F	2010
SN57EOD	Mercedes-Benz Atego 1018L	Unvi Cimo	C35F	2008
YN06AYL	Mercedes-Benz Sprinter 413CDI	VDL Kusters	M2FL	2006

Essbee Coaches

Essbee Coaches Ltd, 7 Hollandhurst Road, Coatbridge ML5 2EG

Website	www.essbeecoaches.com
Depots	7 Hollandhurst Road, Coatbridge ML5 2EG
	87 Drumgelloch Street, Airdrie ML6 7EZ
	1 Lochbuie Lane, Airdrie ML6 0QE
	19 Range Street, Motherwell ML1 2HT
	6 Elgin Place, Coatbridge ML5 4JG
Licence	PM0002854

7		TVP863S	Leyland National 11351A/1R	Leyland National	B50F	1978
8		XOV748T	Leyland National 11351A/1R	Leyland National	B49F	1979
9		NTC640M	Leyland National 1151/1R	Leyland National	B52F	1974
11		SA02BOU	Mercedes-Benz Vario O.814D	Essbee	C24F	2002
20	*	MIL6676	Leyland National 11351/1R	Leyland National	B50F	1974
	*	408UFC	Volvo B10M-61	Plaxton Paramount 3500 II	C49FT	1986
	*	A8AAA	Volvo B10M-62	Van Hool Alizée	C53F	1988
	*	E949JJN	Volvo B10M-61	Duple 320	C53F	1988
	*	EIG1435	Leyland National 10351A/2R	East Lancs	B41F	1979
	*	EIG1436	Leyland National 10351A/2R	East Lancs	B41F	1979
	*	EIG1437	Leyland National 10351/1R/SC	East Lancs	B41F	1979
		J420JBV	Volvo B10M-55	East Lancs EL2000	DP51F	1991
		J422JBV	Volvo B10M-55	East Lancs EL2000	B51F	1991
	*	JIL2161 —	Leyland National 11351/1R	East Lancs Greenway (1994)	B49F	1974
	*	KKG109W	Leyland National 116AL11/1R	Leyland National	B52F	1980
	*	MIL7620	Leyland National 11351/1R	Leyland National	B50F	1974
	*	MIL7622	Leyland National 11351/1R	Leyland National	B50F	1974
	*	NIB2796	Mercedes-Benz Vario O.814D	Plaxton Cheetah	C33F	2000
	*	NIB6535 —	Volvo B10M-61	Jonckheere Jubilee P50	C51FT	1983
	*	NIL7707	Volvo B10M-61	Duple 340	C49FT	1988
	*	PAZ6344	DAF MB230DKFL615	Duple 340	C53FT	1986
		SF08FDK	Mercedes-Benz Sprinter 515CDI	Essbee	M16	2008
		SF08FDL	Mercedes-Benz Vario O.813D	Essbee	C24F	2008

Essbee Coaches

SF56LUP	Mercedes-Benz 413CDI	Essbee	M16	2006
SF59KUW	Mercedes-Benz O.813D	Essbee	C24F	2009
SF60AAX	Mercedes-Benz 515CDI	Essbee	M16	2010
SJ57FYL	Mercedes-Benz Vario O.814D	Essbee	C24F	2007
T796BGD	Mercedes-Benz Vario O.814D	Crystals	C29F	1999
TOF694S	Leyland National 11351A/1R	East Lancs	B49F	1978
UHG741R	Leyland National 11351A/1R	Leyland National	B49F	1976
* VIB3264	Volvo B10M-61	Duple 320	C49FT	1987
X441JHS	Mercedes-Benz Vario O.814D	Plaxton Cheetah	C33F	2000
X442JHS —	Mercedes-Benz Vario O.814D	Plaxton Cheetah	C33F	2000
* XCS961	Volvo B10M-60	Duple 320	C57F	1989
YEV317S —	Leyland National 11351A/1R	East Lancs Greenway (1995)	B49F	1978
YEV324S	Leyland National 11351A/1R	East Lancs Greenway (1995)	B49F	1978

Eve Coaches

Eve Coaches Ltd, Spott Road Industrial Estate, Dunbar EH42 1RR
Website   www.eveinfo.co.uk
Depot   Spott Road Industrial Estate, Dunbar EH42 1RR
Licence   PM1036880

* EUE512	Volvo Olympian YN2RV18Z4	Alexander Royale	CH49/27F	1996
* EV07EVE	VDL DE40XSSB4000	Hispano Carrocera	C49F	2007
* EV08EVE	Irisbus EuroRider 397E.12.35A	Plaxton Panther	C61F	2008
* EVE4	Mercedes-Benz Vario O.816D	Plaxton Cheetah	C29F	2007
* G107NGN	Volvo B10M-50	Northern Counties	H47/39F	1989
* GS54EVE	Scania K94IB4	Irizar InterCentury	C70F	2005
* GSU370	Volvo Olympian YN2RV18Z4	Alexander Royale	CH49/27F	1996
H470KSG	Ford Transit	Williams Deansgate	M15	1990
* K10EVE	Toyota Coaster BB50R	Caetano Optimo	C21F	1997
L98PTW	Toyota Coaster HZB50R	Caetano Optimo	C21F	1994
MX51VCT	Mercedes-Benz Sprinter 413CDI	Olympus	M16	2001
OO05EVE	Scania K94IB4	Irizar InterCentury	C70F	2005
* OO06EVE	Mercedes-Benz Vario O.814d	Plaxton Cheetah	C33F	2007
OO56EVE	Mercedes-Benz Vario O.814D	Plaxton Cheetah	C33F	2006
* S400EVE	Mercedes-Benz Vario O.814D	Plaxton Cheetah	C33F	2006
SC09ALL	Volvo B9TL	Optare Olympus	CH61/39F	2009
SK07MMV	ADL Enviro Dart 8.9 SLF	ADL Enviro 200	B29F	2007
* Y10EVE —	Scania K124IB4	Van Hool Alizée	C49F	2001
YJ57EJA —	Optare Solo M880SL	Optare	B26F	2007
YJ59GHZ	Optare Solo M950SL	Optare	B31F	2009
YN57DXH	Irisbus EuroRider 397E.12.31	Plaxton Panther	C57F	2007

Fairline Coaches / Airport Express

Fairline Coaches Ltd, 331 Charles Street, Glasgow G21 3QA
Website   www.fairlinecoaches.co.uk
Depot   331 Charles Street, Glasgow G21 3QA
Licence   PM0001106

* EGB60T	Bova FHD12.340	Bova Futura	C49FT	2006
* EPK1V	Bova FHD12-370	Bova Futura	C49FT	2000
* GSO84V	Bova FHD12-340	Bova Futura	C49FT	2004
* OBX51 —	Bova FHD12-340	Bova Futura	C49FT	2004
* OOB32X —	Bova FHD12-340	Bova Futura	C49FT	2002
RX03HNN	Volkswagen LT35		M14	2003
S445OGB	Ford Transit	Ford	M14	1998
SF05BEJ	Mercedes-Benz Sprinter 311CDI	Mercedes-Benz	M16	2005
SF08FTA —	Mercedes-Benz O.816D	Plaxton Cheetah	C33F	2008
SF57JRX	Mercedes-Benz Vario O.814D	Plaxton Cheetah	C33F	2007

SN03NLJ	Mercedes-Benz 614D	Onyx	C24F	2003
SV06CEN	Bova FHD12.340	Bova Futura	C49FT	2006
T280TSF	Bova FHD12-340	Bova Futura	C49FT	1999
* TSJ61S	Bova FHD12.340	Bova Futura	C49FT	2004
W592PFS	Mercedes-Benz 614D	Onyx	C24F	2000
* YC02DHV	Volvo B12M	Jonckheere Mistral	C48FT	2002
YJ56YOD	Mercedes-Benz 616D	Onyx	C24F	2007
YN06CYV	Mercedes-Benz Vario O.814D	Plaxton Cheetah	C33F	2006
YT57EJC	Optare Solo M950	Optare	B33F	2007
SN10ENR —	Mercedes Benz	Feigui	C33F	

Festival Travel

Festival Travel (Scotland) Ltd, 12 Kirklands Park Grove, Kirkliston EH29 9EU
Website
Depot Trailerdec Ltd, Loaninghall, Uphall EH52 5NT
Trailerdec Ltd, Unit 6, Whitecross Industrial Park, Whitecross, Linlithgow EH46 6LH
Licence PM1036025

H171EJF	MAN 10.180	Caetano Optimo	C35F	1990
* JIL3757	Volvo B10M-61	Van Hool Alizée	C49FT	1987
M134SKY —	Volvo B10M-62	Van Hool Alizée	C51F	1994
* T52MOA —	Volvo B10M-62	Berkhof	C49FT	1999
* WIB7186 w	Volvo B10M-61	Jonckheere Jubilee P599	C49FT	1986
* WRC751 —	Iveco Euro Rider 391E 12.35	Beulas Stergo E	C51FT	2002
* YIJ351	Volvo B10M-62	Van Hool Alizée	C46FT	1994
* YOI890	Irisbus EuroRider 391E 12.35	Beulas Stergo E	C51FT	2001
R26GNW —	DAF SB220	Optare	B52F	
AK02 LSS —				

First Scotland

First Aberdeen Ltd / G E Mairs Hire Services Ltd, 395 King Street, Aberdeen AB24 5RP
Midland Bluebird Ltd / First Scotland East Ltd,   Carmuirs House, 300 Stirling Road, Larbert FK5 3NJ
First Glasgow No 1 / First Glasgow No 2, 197 Victoria Road, Glasgow G42 7AD

Website	www.firstgroup.co.uk
Depot	As above
Licence	PM0000631 (First Aberdeen) / PM0001340 (Mairs Coaches)
	PM0000003 (Midland Bluebird) / PM0000923 (First Scotland East)
	PM0000001 (First Glasgow No 1) / PM0000006 (First Glasgow No 2)

10015	Y151ROT	SC	Volvo B7LA	Wright Eclipse Fusion	AB56D	2001
10016	Y152ROT	SC	Volvo B7LA	Wright Eclipse Fusion	AB56D	2001
10033	W116CWR	r	Volvo B7LA	Wright Eclipse Fusion	AB56D	2000
10034	W117CWR	SC	Volvo B7LA	Wright Eclipse Fusion	AB56D	2000
10044	V601GGB	SC	Volvo B10LA	Wright Fusion	ADP55D	1999
10045	V602GGB	SC	Volvo B10LA	Wright Fusion	ADP55D	1999
10047	W2FAL	AB	Volvo B7LA	Wright Eclipse Fusion	AB56D	2000
10048	W3FAL	AB	Volvo B7LA	Wright Eclipse Fusion	AB56D	2000
10049	W4FAL	AB	Volvo B7LA	Wright Eclipse Fusion	AB56D	2000
10050	W5FAL	AB	Volvo B7LA	Wright Eclipse Fusion	AB56D	2000
10051	W6FAL	AB	Volvo B7LA	Wright Eclipse Fusion	AB56D	2000
10052	W7FAL	AB	Volvo B7LA	Wright Eclipse Fusion	AB56D	2000
10103	V603GGB	r	Volvo B10LA	Wright Fusion	ADP55D	1999
10104	V604GGB	SC	Volvo B10LA	Wright Fusion	ADP55D	1999
10105	V605GGB	r	Volvo B10LA	Wright Fusion	ADP55D	1999
10106	V606GGB	r	Volvo B10LA	Wright Fusion	ADP55D	1999
10107	V607GGB	r	Volvo B10LA	Wright Fusion	ADP55D	1999
10108	V608GGB	SC	Volvo B10LA	Wright Fusion	ADP55D	1999
10109	V609GGB	SC	Volvo B10LA	Wright Fusion	ADP55D	1999
10110	V610GGB	SC	Volvo B10LA	Wright Fusion	ADP55D	1999
10131	W131WPO	r	Volvo B7LA	Wright Eclipse Fusion	AB56D	2000
10132	W132WPO	r	Volvo B7LA	Wright Eclipse Fusion	AB56D	2000
10133	W133WPO	SC	Volvo B7LA	Wright Eclipse Fusion	AB56D	2000
10134	X134FPO	SC	Volvo B7LA	Wright Eclipse Fusion	AB56D	2000
10136	X136FPO	SC	Volvo B7LA	Wright Eclipse Fusion	AB56D	2000
10137	X137FPO	r	Volvo B7LA	Wright Eclipse Fusion	AB56D	2000
10138	X138FPO	r	Volvo B7LA	Wright Eclipse Fusion	AB56D	2000
10139	X139FPO	SC	Volvo B7LA	Wright Eclipse Fusion	AB56D	2000
10141	X141FPO	SC	Volvo B7LA	Wright Eclipse Fusion	AB56D	2000
10142	X142FPO	SC	Volvo B7LA	Wright Eclipse Fusion	AB56D	2000
10143	X143FPO	r	Volvo B7LA	Wright Eclipse Fusion	AB56D	2000
10144	X144FPO	SC	Volvo B7LA	Wright Eclipse Fusion	AB56D	2000
10146	X146FPO	SC	Volvo B7LA	Wright Eclipse Fusion	AB56D	2000
10147	Y147ROT	SC	Volvo B7LA	Wright Eclipse Fusion	AB56D	2001
10148	Y148ROT	SC	Volvo B7LA	Wright Eclipse Fusion	AB56D	2001
10149	Y149ROT	SC	Volvo B7LA	Wright Eclipse Fusion	AB56D	2001
10154	SV05DXA	AB	Volvo B7LA	Wright Eclipse Fusion	AB56D	2005
10155	SV05DXC	AB	Volvo B7LA	Wright Eclipse Fusion	AB56D	2005
10156	SV05DXD	AB	Volvo B7LA	Wright Eclipse Fusion	AB56D	2005
10157	SV05DXE	AB	Volvo B7LA	Wright Eclipse Fusion	AB56D	2005
10158	SV05DXF	AB	Volvo B7LA	Wright Eclipse Fusion	AB56D	2005
10159	SV05DXG	AB	Volvo B7LA	Wright Eclipse Fusion	AB56D	2005
10160	SV05DXH	AB	Volvo B7LA	Wright Eclipse Fusion	AB56D	2005
10161	SV05DXJ	AB	Volvo B7LA	Wright Eclipse Fusion	AB56D	2005
10162	SV05DXK	AB	Volvo B7LA	Wright Eclipse Fusion	AB56D	2005
10163	SV05DXL	AB	Volvo B7LA	Wright Eclipse Fusion	AB56D	2005
10164	SV05DXM	AB	Volvo B7LA	Wright Eclipse Fusion	AB56D	2005
10165	SV05DXO	AB	Volvo B7LA	Wright Eclipse Fusion	AB56D	2005
10166	SV05DXP	AB	Volvo B7LA	Wright Eclipse Fusion	AB56D	2005
10167	SV05DXR	AB	Volvo B7LA	Wright Eclipse Fusion	AB56D	2005

10168	SV05DXS	AB	Volvo B7LA	Wright Eclipse Fusion	AB56D	2005
10169	SV05DXT	AB	Volvo B7LA	Wright Eclipse Fusion	AB56D	2005
10170	SV05DXU	AB	Volvo B7LA	Wright Eclipse Fusion	AB56D	2005
10171	SV05DXW	AB	Volvo B7LA	Wright Eclipse Fusion	AB56D	2005
10172	SV05DXX	AB	Volvo B7LA	Wright Eclipse Fusion	AB56D	2005
10173	SV05DXY	AB	Volvo B7LA	Wright Eclipse Fusion	AB56D	2005
10183	SF05KUH	SC	Volvo B7LA	Wright Eclipse Fusion	AB56D	2005
20008 *	542GRT	AB	Scania K124IB4	Irizar Century	C49FT	1998
20011 *	2GRT	AB	Volvo B10M-62	Plaxton Premiere 350	C49FT	1994
20012 *	N1GRT	AB	Volvo B10M-62	Plaxton Premiere 350	C48FT	1996
20013	J11GRT	AB-t	Volvo B10M-60	Jonckheere Deauville	C53F	1992
20014 *	LSK570	AB	Volvo B10M-60	Jonckheere Deauville	C49FT	1993
20015 *	LSK571	AB-t	Volvo B10M-60	Jonckheere Deauville	C47FT	1993
20016 *	PSU627	AB	Scania K124IB4	Irizar Century	C49FT	1998
20017 *	PSU628	AB	Scania K113CRB	Irizar Century	C49FT	1997
20018 *	PSU629	AB	Scania K113CRB	Irizar Century	C49FT	1997
20021	FC52AFC	AB	Volvo B12B	Jonckheere Mistral	C53F	2003
20036 *	PSU314	AB-a	Scania K113CRB	Plaxton Paramount 3500 III	C4DL	1990
20112	N612APU	GS	Volvo B10M-62	Plaxton Premiere 320	C53F	1996
20116	N616APU	GS	Volvo B10M-62	Plaxton Premiere 320	C53F	1996
20204 *	WSU487	AB	Volvo B12BT	Plaxton Excalibur	C51F	1999
20205 *	WSU489	AB	Volvo B12BT	Plaxton Excalibur	C51F	1999
20206 *	HSU247	AB	Volvo B12BT	Plaxton Excalibur	C51F	1999
20207 *	FSU382	AB	Volvo B12BT	Plaxton Excalibur	C51F	1999
20354	CU05LGJ	LN	Volvo B7R	Plaxton Profile	C46FTL	2005
20355	CU05LGK	LN	Volvo B7R	Plaxton Profile	C45FL	2005
20356	CV55ABN	LN	Volvo B7R-63	Plaxton Profile	C45FL	2005
20357	CV55ABK	LN	Volvo B7R-63	Plaxton Profile	C45FTL	2005
20364	CV55AFE	LN	Volvo B7R-63	Plaxton Profile	C45FL	2005
20366	CV55AFF	BF	Volvo B7R-63	Plaxton Profile	C45FTL	2005
20369	CV55AMU	LT	Volvo B7R	Plaxton Profile	C46FTL	2005
20370	CV55ACY	GS	Volvo B7R-63	Plaxton Profile	C46FTL	2005
20371	CV55AMX	GS	Volvo B7R	Plaxton Profile	C46FTL	2005
20404	R304JAF	LN	Volvo B10M-62	Plaxton Premiere 350	C44FT	1998
20405	R305JAF	BK	Volvo B10M-62	Plaxton Premiere 350	C44FT	1998
20438	M413DEU	LN	Volvo B10M-62	Plaxton Premiere 350	C44FT	1994
20462	X192HFB	AB	Volvo B10M-62	Plaxton Premiere 350	C49FT	2000
20502	AO02RBZ	BT	Volvo B12M	Plaxton Paragon	C53F	2002
20503	AO02RCF	BT	Volvo B12M	Plaxton Paragon	C53F	2002
20504	AO02RCU	BT	Volvo B12M	Plaxton Paragon	C53F	2002
20505	AO02RCV	BT	Volvo B12M	Plaxton Paragon	C53F	2002
20506	AO02RCX	BT	Volvo B12M	Plaxton Paragon	C53F	2002
20507	AO02RCY	BT	Volvo B12M	Plaxton Paragon	C53F	2002
20508	AO02RCZ	BT	Volvo B12M	Plaxton Paragon	C53F	2002
20509	AO02RDU	BT	Volvo B12M	Plaxton Paragon	C53F	2002
23330	SV58ASZ	AB	Scania K340EB	Irizar Century	C??FT	2009
23401	SV54FRZ	AB	Scania K114IB4	Irizar Century	C??FT	2004
23402	SV54FTA	AB	Scania K114IB4	Irizar Century	C??FT	2004
30107 *	K174EUX	r	Volvo Olympian YN2RV18V3	Alexander Royale	H42/32F	1994
30216	K601LAE	D	Leyland Olympian ON2R56C16Z4	Northern Counties Palatine I	H47/29F	1993
30220	K605LAE	w	Leyland Olympian ON2R56C16Z4	Northern Counties Palatine I	H47/29F	1993
30222	K888ELR	w	Leyland Olympian ON2R50C13Z4	Northern Counties Palatine	H47/30F	1992
30226	K888BFG	w	Leyland Olympian ON2R50C13Z4	Northern Counties Palatine	H47/30F	1992
30358	G281OGE	M	Volvo B10M-50	Alexander RV	H47/37F	1989
30740	P192TGD	BK	Volvo Olympian YN2RV18V3	Alexander RL	H47/32F	1996
30741	P193TGD	BK	Volvo Olympian YN2RV18V3	Alexander RL	H47/32F	1996
30742	P194TGD	D	Volvo Olympian YN2RV18V3	Alexander RL	H47/32F	1996
30743	P195TGD	BK	Volvo Olympian YN2RV18V3	Alexander RL	H47/32F	1996
30744	P196TGD	DBK	Volvo Olympian YN2RV18V3	Alexander RL	H47/32F	1996
30745	P197TGD	BK	Volvo Olympian YN2RV18V3	Alexander RL	H47/32F	1996

30746	P198TGD	D 6u	Volvo Olympian YN2RV18V3	Alexander RL	H47/32F	1996
30747	P199TGD	BK	Volvo Olympian YN2RV18V3	Alexander RL	H47/32F	1996
30748	P201TGD	BF	Volvo Olympian YN2RV18V3	Alexander RL	H47/32F	1996
30749	P202TGD	LT	Volvo Olympian YN2RV18V3	Alexander RL	H47/32F	1996
30750	P203TGD	D	Volvo Olympian YN2RV18V3	Alexander RL	H47/32F	1996
30751	P204TGD	BK	Volvo Olympian YN2RV18V3	Alexander RL	H47/32F	1996
30826	R646HYG	LT	Volvo Olympian OLY-56	Alexander Royale	H43/29F	1998
30827	R647HYG	M	Volvo Olympian OLY-56	Alexander Royale	H43/29F	1998
30828	R648HYG	LT	Volvo Olympian OLY-56	Alexander Royale	H43/29F	1998
30829	R649HYG	NB	Volvo Olympian OLY-56	Alexander Royale	H43/29F	1998
30830	R650HYG	NB	Volvo Olympian OLY-56	Alexander Royale	H43/29F	1998
30831	R651HYG	w	Volvo Olympian OLY-56	Alexander Royale	H43/29F	1998
30832	R652HYG	M	Volvo Olympian OLY-56	Alexander Royale	H43/29F	1998
30833	R653HYG	D	Volvo Olympian OLY-56	Alexander Royale	H43/29F	1998
31200	R152EHS	BT	Volvo Olympian OLY-56	Alexander Royale	H42/29F	1997
31421	M834DUS	BT	Volvo Olympian YN2RV18Z4	Alexander Royale	H47/32F	1994
31422	M835DUS	BT	Volvo Olympian YN2RV18Z4	Alexander Royale	H47/32F	1994
31423	M836DUS	w	Volvo Olympian YN2RV18Z4	Alexander Royale	H47/32F	1994
31425	M838DUS	C	Volvo Olympian YN2RV18Z4	Alexander Royale	H47/32F	1994
31426	M839DUS	L	Volvo Olympian YN2RV18Z4	Alexander Royale	H47/32F	1994
31427	M840DUS	C	Volvo Olympian YN2RV18Z4	Alexander Royale	H47/32F	1994
31428	M841DUS	C	Volvo Olympian YN2RV18Z4	Alexander Royale	H47/32F	1994
31429	M939EYS	L	Volvo Olympian YN2RV18V3	Alexander Royale	H45/29F	1995
31430	M940EYS	SC	Volvo Olympian YN2RC16V3	Alexander Royale	H45/29F	1995
31431	M941EYS	L	Volvo Olympian YN2RC16V3	Northern Counties Palatine II	H47/30F	1995
31432	M942EYS	w	Volvo Olympian YN2RC16V3	Northern Counties Palatine II	H47/30F	1995
31433	N944SOS	SC	Volvo Olympian YN2RV18V3	Alexander RL	H47/32F	1996
31434	N945SOS	SC	Volvo Olympian YN2RV18V3	Alexander RL	H47/32F	1996
31435	N946SOS	C	Volvo Olympian YN2RV18V3	Alexander RL	H47/32F	1996
31436	N947SOS	C	Volvo Olympian YN2RV18V3	Alexander RL	H47/32F	1996
31437	N948SOS	C	Volvo Olympian YN2RV18V3	Alexander RL	H47/32F	1996
31438	N949SOS	SC	Volvo Olympian YN2RV18V3	Alexander RL	H47/32F	1996
31439	N950SOS	wGS	Volvo Olympian YN2RV18V3	Alexander RL	H47/32F	1996
31440	N951SOS	SC	Volvo Olympian YN2RV18V3	Alexander RL	H47/32F	1996
31441	N952SOS	SC	Volvo Olympian YN2RV18V3	Alexander RL	H47/32F	1996
31442	N953SOS	SC	Volvo Olympian YN2RV18V3	Alexander RL	H47/32F	1996
31443	N954SOS	SC	Volvo Olympian YN2RV18V3	Alexander RL	H47/32F	1996
31444	N955SOS	SC	Volvo Olympian YN2RV18V3	Alexander RL	H47/32F	1996
31445	N956SOS	SC	Volvo Olympian YN2RV18V3	Alexander RL	H47/32F	1996
31446	N957SOS	SC	Volvo Olympian YN2RV18V3	Alexander RL	H47/32F	1996
31447	N958SOS	SC	Volvo Olympian YN2RV18V3	Alexander RL	H47/32F	1996
31448	N959SOS	SC	Volvo Olympian YN2RV18V3	Alexander RL	H47/32F	1996
31449	N960SOS	SC	Volvo Olympian YN2RV18V3	Alexander RL	H47/32F	1996
31450	N961SOS	w	Volvo Olympian YN2RV18V3	Alexander RL	H47/32F	1996
31468	P595WSU	SC	Volvo Olympian OLY-56	Alexander Royale	H42/29F	1997
31469	P596WSU	L	Volvo Olympian OLY-56	Alexander Royale	H42/29F	1997
31470	P597WSU	L	Volvo Olympian OLY-56	Alexander Royale	H42/29F	1997
31471	P598WSU	L	Volvo Olympian OLY-56	Alexander Royale	H42/29F	1997
31472	P599WSU	BT	Volvo Olympian OLY-56	Alexander Royale	H42/29F	1997
31473	P601WSU	L	Volvo Olympian OLY-56	Alexander Royale	H42/29F	1997
31474	P602WSU	L	Volvo Olympian OLY-56	Alexander Royale	H42/29F	1997
31475	P603WSU	SC	Volvo Olympian OLY-56	Alexander Royale	H42/29F	1997
31476	P604WSU	SC	Volvo Olympian OLY-56	Alexander Royale	H42/29F	1997
31477	P605WSU	L	Volvo Olympian OLY-56	Alexander Royale	H42/29F	1997
31478	P606WSU	SC	Volvo Olympian OLY-56	Alexander Royale	H42/29F	1997
31479	P607WSU	SC	Volvo Olympian OLY-56	Alexander Royale	H42/29F	1997
31480	P608WSU	C	Volvo Olympian OLY-56	Alexander Royale	H42/29F	1997
31481	P617WSU	C	Volvo Olympian OLY-56	Alexander Royale	H42/29F	1997
31482	P618WSU	C	Volvo Olympian OLY-56	Alexander Royale	H42/29F	1997
31483	P619WSU	BT	Volvo Olympian OLY-56	Alexander Royale	H42/29F	1997

31484	P620WSU	C	Volvo Olympian OLY-56	Alexander Royale	H42/29F	1997
31485	R139EHS	SC	Volvo Olympian OLY-56	Alexander Royale	H42/29F	1997
31486	R143EHS	SC	Volvo Olympian OLY-56	Alexander Royale	H42/29F	1997
31487	R144EHS	L	Volvo Olympian OLY-56	Alexander Royale	H42/29F	1997
31488	R145EHS	BT	Volvo Olympian OLY-56	Alexander Royale	H42/29F	1997
31489	R146EHS	L	Volvo Olympian OLY-56	Alexander Royale	H42/29F	1997
31490	R147EHS	L	Volvo Olympian OLY-56	Alexander Royale	H42/29F	1997
31491	R148EHS	BT	Volvo Olympian OLY-56	Alexander Royale	H42/29F	1997
31492	R149EHS	BT	Volvo Olympian OLY-56	Alexander Royale	H42/29F	1997
31493	R150EHS	L	Volvo Olympian OLY-56	Alexander Royale	H42/29F	1997
31494	R151EHS	L	Volvo Olympian OLY-56	Alexander Royale	H42/29F	1997
31495	R153EHS	BT	Volvo Olympian OLY-56	Alexander Royale	H42/29F	1997
31496	R654DUS	L	Volvo Olympian OLY-56	Northern Counties Palatine II	H43/29F	1997
31497	R655DUS	L	Volvo Olympian OLY-56	Northern Counties Palatine II	H43/29F	1997
31498	R656DUS	L	Volvo Olympian OLY-56	Northern Counties Palatine II	H43/29F	1997
31499	R657DUS	L	Volvo Olympian OLY-56	Northern Counties Palatine II	H43/29F	1997
31500	R658DUS	L	Volvo Olympian OLY-56	Northern Counties Palatine II	H43/29F	1997
31501	R659DUS	L	Volvo Olympian OLY-56	Northern Counties Palatine II	H43/29F	1997
31503	R661DUS	BT	Volvo Olympian OLY-56	Northern Counties Palatine II	H43/29F	1997
31504	R662DUS	L	Volvo Olympian OLY-56	Northern Counties Palatine II	H43/29F	1997
31505	R663DUS	L	Volvo Olympian OLY-56	Northern Counties Palatine II	H43/29F	1997
31506	SA52DVR	L	Volvo B7L	East Lancs Nordic	H55/40F	2002
31507	SA52DVT	L	Volvo B7L	East Lancs Nordic	H55/40F	2002
31508	SA52DVU	L	Volvo B7L	East Lancs Nordic	H55/40F	2002
31509	SA52DVV	L	Volvo B7L	East Lancs Nordic	H55/40F	2002
31510	SA52DVW	L	Volvo B7L	East Lancs Nordic	H55/40F	2002
31511	SA52DVX	L	Volvo B7L	East Lancs Nordic	H55/40F	2002
31512	SA52DVY	L	Volvo B7L	East Lancs Nordic	H55/40F	2002
31513	SA52DVZ	L	Volvo B7L	East Lancs Nordic	H55/40F	2002
31514	SA52DWC	L	Volvo B7L	East Lancs Nordic	H55/40F	2002
31515	SA52DWD	L	Volvo B7L	East Lancs Nordic	H55/40F	2002
31516*	M846DUS	BT	Volvo Olympian YN2RV18Z4	Alexander Royale	DPH47/28F	1994
31517*	WLT408	w	Volvo Olympian YN2RV18Z4	Alexander Royale	H47/32F	1994
31520*	WLT741	BT	Volvo Olympian YN2RV18Z4	Alexander Royale	DPH47/28F	1994
31528	URS318X	w	Leyland Atlantean AN68C/1R	Alexander AL	O45/29D	1982
31529	CRG325C	AB	Daimler CVG6	Alexander	H37/29R	1965
31558	X132NSS	AB	Volvo B7L	Alexander ALX400	H49/29F	2000
31559	X771NSO	AB	Volvo B7L	Alexander ALX400	H49/29F	2000
31560	X103NSS	AB	Volvo B7L	Alexander ALX400	H49/29F	2000
31561	X104NSS	AB	Volvo B7L	Alexander ALX400	H49/29F	2000
31562	X136NSS	C	Volvo B7L	Alexander ALX400	H49/29F	2000
31563	X137NSS	C	Volvo B7L	Alexander ALX400	H49/29F	2000
31569	R301LKS	D	Volvo Olympian OLY-56	Alexander Royale	H42/29F	1998
31570	R422YMS	LT	Volvo Olympian OLY-56	Alexander Royale	H42/29F	1998
31571	P589WSU	LT	Volvo Olympian OLY-56	Alexander Royale	H42/29F	1997
31572	P594WSU	LT	Volvo Olympian OLY-56	Alexander Royale	H42/29F	1997
31577	XSS344Y	AB-a	Leyland Atlantean AN68C/1R	Alexander AL	H / F	1983
31634	R302LKS	D	Volvo Olympian OLY-56	Alexander Royale	H42/29F	1998
31635	R303LKS	r	Volvo Olympian OLY-56	Alexander Royale	H42/29F	1998
31636	R304LKS	D	Volvo Olympian OLY-56	Alexander Royale	H42/29F	1998
31637	R305LKS	M	Volvo Olympian OLY-56	Alexander Royale	H42/29F	1998
31638	R206LKS	D	Volvo Olympian OLY-56	Alexander Royale	H42/29F	1998
31639	R307LKS	D	Volvo Olympian OLY-56	Alexander Royale	H42/29F	1998
31640	R308LKS	D	Volvo Olympian OLY-56	Alexander Royale	H42/29F	1998
31641	R309LKS	w	Volvo Olympian OLY-56	Alexander Royale	H42/29F	1998
31642	R310LKS	LT	Volvo Olympian OLY-56	Alexander Royale	H42/29F	1998
31643	R311LKS	D	Volvo Olympian OLY-56	Alexander Royale	H42/29F	1998
31644	R312LKS	GS	Volvo Olympian OLY-56	Alexander Royale	H42/29F	1998
31645	R313LKS	LN	Volvo Olympian OLY-56	Alexander Royale	H42/29F	1998
31646	R314LKS		Volvo Olympian OLY-56	Alexander Royale	H42/29F	1998

31647	R315LKS	LT	Volvo Olympian OLY-56	Alexander Royale	H42/29F	1998
31648	R416YMS	LN LT	Volvo Olympian OLY-56	Alexander Royale	H42/29F	1998
31649	R417YMS	LT	Volvo Olympian OLY-56	Alexander Royale	H42/29F	1998
31650	R418YMS	GS	Volvo Olympian OLY-56	Alexander Royale	H42/29F	1998
31651	R419YMS	D	Volvo Olympian OLY-56	Alexander Royale	H42/29F	1998
31652	R420YMS	D	Volvo Olympian OLY-56	Alexander Royale	H42/29F	1998
31653	R421YMS	D	Volvo Olympian OLY-56	Alexander Royale	H42/29F	1998
31654	R423YMS	LT	Volvo Olympian OLY-56	Alexander Royale	H42/29F	1998
31655	S924AKS	GS	Volvo Olympian OLY-5639	Alexander Royale	H43/29F	1998
31656	S925AKS	LN	Volvo Olympian OLY-5639	Alexander Royale	H43/29F	1998
31657	S926AKS	LN	Volvo Olympian OLY-5639	Alexander Royale	H43/29F	1998
31659	S928AKS	LN	Volvo Olympian OLY-5639	Alexander Royale	H43/29F	1998
31660	S929AKS	GS	Volvo Olympian OLY-5639	Alexander Royale	H43/29F	1998
31661	S930AKS	M	Volvo Olympian OLY-5639	Alexander Royale	H43/29F	1998
31662	S931AKS	M	Volvo Olympian OLY-5639	Alexander Royale	H43/29F	1998
31663	S932AKS	M	Volvo Olympian OLY-5639	Alexander Royale	H43/29F	1998
31664	S933AKS	M	Volvo Olympian OLY-5639	Alexander Royale	H43/29F	1998
31665	S934AKS	M	Volvo Olympian OLY-56	Alexander Royale	H43/29F	1999
31666	S935AKS	M LT	Volvo Olympian OLY-56	Alexander Royale	H43/29F	1999
31667	S936AKS	M	Volvo Olympian OLY-56	Alexander Royale	H43/29F	1999
31668	S937AKS	M	Volvo Olympian OLY-56	Alexander Royale	H43/29F	1999
31669	S938AKS	M LT	Volvo Olympian OLY-56	Alexander Royale	H43/29F	1999
31670	R140EHS	M	Volvo Olympian OLY-56	Alexander Royale	H42/29F	1997
31671	R141EHS	NB	Volvo Olympian OLY-56	Alexander Royale	H42/29F	1997
31672	R142EHS	r	Volvo Olympian OLY-56	Alexander Royale	H42/29F	1997
31675	P611WSU	LT	Volvo Olympian OLY-56	Alexander Royale	H42/29F	1997
31678	P614WSU	LN	Volvo Olympian OLY-56	Alexander Royale	H42/29F	1997
31679	P615WSU	LT	Volvo Olympian OLY-56	Alexander Royale	H42/29F	1997
31680	P616WSU	LT	Volvo Olympian OLY-56	Alexander Royale	H42/29F	1997
31681	P585WSU	LN	Volvo Olympian OLY-56	Alexander Royale	H42/29F	1997
31682	P586WSU	LT	Volvo Olympian OLY-56	Alexander Royale	H42/29F	1997
31684	P588WSU	GS	Volvo Olympian OLY-56	Alexander Royale	H42/29F	1997
31687	P592WSU	GS	Volvo Olympian OLY-56	Alexander Royale	H42/29F	1997
31688	P593WSU	GS	Volvo Olympian OLY-56	Alexander Royale	H42/29F	1997
31728	L551USU	BF	Leyland Olympian ON2R50C13V3	Alexander RL	H47/31F	1993
31731	L554USU	BF	Leyland Olympian ON2R50C13V3	Alexander RL	H47/31F	1993
31732	L156UNS	BF	Leyland Olympian ON2R50C13V3	Alexander RL	H47/31F	1993
31733	L157UNS	BF	Leyland Olympian ON2R50C13V3	Alexander RL	H47/31F	1993
31734	L158UNS	BF	Leyland Olympian ON2R50C13V3	Alexander RL	H47/31F	1993
31735	L159UNS	BK	Leyland Olympian ON2R50C13V3	Alexander RL	H47/29F	1993
31787	YN53EFE	SC	Volvo B7TL	Wright Eclipse Gemini	H45/29F	2003
31788	YN53EFF	SC	Volvo B7TL	Wright Eclipse Gemini	H45/29F	2003
31789	YN53EFG	C	Volvo B7TL	Wright Eclipse Gemini	H45/29F	2003
31790	YN53EFH	C GS	Volvo B7TL	Wright Eclipse Gemini	H45/29F	2003
31791	YN53EFJ	C GS	Volvo B7TL	Wright Eclipse Gemini	H45/29F	2003
31792	YN53EFK	C	Volvo B7TL	Wright Eclipse Gemini	H45/29F	2003
31793	YN53EFL	C	Volvo B7TL	Wright Eclipse Gemini	H45/29F	2003
31794	YN53EFM	C	Volvo B7TL	Wright Eclipse Gemini	H45/29F	2003
31795	YN53EFO	C	Volvo B7TL	Wright Eclipse Gemini	H45/29F	2003
31796	YN53EFP	C	Volvo B7TL	Wright Eclipse Gemini	H45/29F	2003
31797	YN53EFR	C	Volvo B7TL	Wright Eclipse Gemini	H45/29F	2003
31798	YN53EFT	SC	Volvo B7TL	Wright Eclipse Gemini	H45/29F	2003
31799	YN53EFU	C	Volvo B7TL	Wright Eclipse Gemini	H45/29F	2003
31800	YN53EFV	C	Volvo B7TL	Wright Eclipse Gemini	H45/29F	2003
31801	YN53EFW	C	Volvo B7TL	Wright Eclipse Gemini	H45/29F	2003
31802	YN53EFX	C	Volvo B7TL	Wright Eclipse Gemini	H45/29F	2003
31803	YN53EFZ	C	Volvo B7TL	Wright Eclipse Gemini	H45/29F	2003
31804	YN53EGC	C	Volvo B7TL	Wright Eclipse Gemini	H45/29F	2003
32221	LT52WUE	D	Volvo B7TL	Plaxton President	H42/23D	2002
32223	LT52WUH	D	Volvo B7TL	Plaxton President	H42/23D	2002

32226	LT52WUL	D	Volvo B7TL	Plaxton President	H42/23D	2002
32543	SF54OSD	SC	Volvo B7TL	Wright Eclipse Gemini	H45/29F	2004
32544	SF54OSE	SC	Volvo B7TL	Wright Eclipse Gemini	H45/29F	2004
32545	SF54OSG	SC	Volvo B7TL	Wright Eclipse Gemini	H45/29F	2004
32546	SF54OSJ	SC	Volvo B7TL	Wright Eclipse Gemini	H45/29F	2004
32547	SF54OSK	L	Volvo B7TL	Wright Eclipse Gemini	H45/29F	2004
32548	SF54OSL	SC	Volvo B7TL	Wright Eclipse Gemini	H45/29F	2004
32549	SF54OSM	SC	Volvo B7TL	Wright Eclipse Gemini	H45/29F	2004
32550	SF54OSN	SC	Volvo B7TL	Wright Eclipse Gemini	H45/29F	2004
32551	SF54OSO	SC	Volvo B7TL	Wright Eclipse Gemini	H45/29F	2004
32552	SF54OSP	SC	Volvo B7TL	Wright Eclipse Gemini	H45/29F	2004
32553	SF54OSR	SC	Volvo B7TL	Wright Eclipse Gemini	H45/29F	2004
32554	SF54OSU	SC	Volvo B7TL	Wright Eclipse Gemini	H45/29F	2004
32555	SF54OSV	SC	Volvo B7TL	Wright Eclipse Gemini	H45/29F	2004
32556	SF54OSW	SC	Volvo B7TL	Wright Eclipse Gemini	H45/29F	2004
32557	SF54OSX	SC	Volvo B7TL	Wright Eclipse Gemini	H45/29F	2004
32558	SF54OSY	SC	Volvo B7TL	Wright Eclipse Gemini	H45/29F	2004
32559	SF54OSZ	SC	Volvo B7TL	Wright Eclipse Gemini	H45/29F	2004
32560	SF54OTA	SC	Volvo B7TL	Wright Eclipse Gemini	H45/29F	2004
32561	SF54OTB	SC	Volvo B7TL	Wright Eclipse Gemini	H45/29F	2004
32562	SF54OTC	SC	Volvo B7TL	Wright Eclipse Gemini	H45/29F	2004
32563	SF54OTD	SC	Volvo B7TL	Wright Eclipse Gemini	H45/29F	2004
32564	SF54OTE	SC	Volvo B7TL	Wright Eclipse Gemini	H45/29F	2004
32565	SF54OTG	SC	Volvo B7TL	Wright Eclipse Gemini	H45/29F	2004
32566	SF54OTH	L	Volvo B7TL	Wright Eclipse Gemini	H45/29F	2004
32567	SF54OTJ	PH	Volvo B7TL	Wright Eclipse Gemini	H45/29F	2004
32568	SF54OTK	L	Volvo B7TL	Wright Eclipse Gemini	H45/29F	2004
32569	SF54OTL	SC	Volvo B7TL	Wright Eclipse Gemini	H45/29F	2004
32570	SF54OTM	SC	Volvo B7TL	Wright Eclipse Gemini	H45/29F	2004
32571	SF54OTN	SC	Volvo B7TL	Wright Eclipse Gemini	H45/29F	2004
32572	SF54OTP	SC	Volvo B7TL	Wright Eclipse Gemini	H45/29F	2004
32573	SF54OTR	SC	Volvo B7TL	Wright Eclipse Gemini	H45/29F	2004
32574	SF54OTT	SC	Volvo B7TL	Wright Eclipse Gemini	H45/29F	2004
32575	SF54OTU	SC	Volvo B7TL	Wright Eclipse Gemini	H45/29F	2005
32576	SF54OTV	SC	Volvo B7TL	Wright Eclipse Gemini	H45/29F	2004
32577	SF54OTW	SC	Volvo B7TL	Wright Eclipse Gemini	H45/29F	2004
32578	SF54OTX	SC	Volvo B7TL	Wright Eclipse Gemini	H45/29F	2004
32579	SF54OTY	SC	Volvo B7TL	Wright Eclipse Gemini	H45/29F	2005
32580	SF54OTZ	PH	Volvo B7TL	Wright Eclipse Gemini	H45/29F	2004
32581	SF54OUA	PH	Volvo B7TL	Wright Eclipse Gemini	H45/29F	2004
32582	SF54OUB	SC	Volvo B7TL	Wright Eclipse Gemini	H45/29F	2005
32583	SF54OUC	L	Volvo B7TL	Wright Eclipse Gemini	H45/29F	2004
32584	SF54OUD	L	Volvo B7TL	Wright Eclipse Gemini	H45/29F	2004
32585	SF54OUE	L	Volvo B7TL	Wright Eclipse Gemini	H45/29F	2004
32586	SF54OUG	SC	Volvo B7TL	Wright Eclipse Gemini	H45/29F	2004
32587	SF54OUH	L	Volvo B7TL	Wright Eclipse Gemini	H45/29F	2004
32588	SF54OUJ	L	Volvo B7TL	Wright Eclipse Gemini	H45/29F	2005
32589	SF54OUK	PH	Volvo B7TL	Wright Eclipse Gemini	H45/29F	2004
32590	SF54OUL	SC	Volvo B7TL	Wright Eclipse Gemini	H45/29F	2004
32591	SF54OUM	SC	Volvo B7TL	Wright Eclipse Gemini	H45/29F	2004
32592	SF54OUN	SC	Volvo B7TL	Wright Eclipse Gemini	H45/29F	2005
32593	SF54THV	SC	Volvo B7TL	Wright Eclipse Gemini	H45/29F	2005
32594	SF54THX	SC	Volvo B7TL	Wright Eclipse Gemini	H45/29F	2005
32595	SF54THZ	SC	Volvo B7TL	Wright Eclipse Gemini	H45/29F	2005
32596	SF54TJO	SC	Volvo B7TL	Wright Eclipse Gemini	H45/29F	2005
32597	SF54TJU	SC	Volvo B7TL	Wright Eclipse Gemini	H45/29F	2005
32598	SF54TJV	SC	Volvo B7TL	Wright Eclipse Gemini	H45/29F	2005
32599	SF54TJX	SC	Volvo B7TL	Wright Eclipse Gemini	H45/29F	2005
32600	SF54TJY	SC	Volvo B7TL	Wright Eclipse Gemini	H45/29F	2005
32601	SF54TJZ	SC	Volvo B7TL	Wright Eclipse Gemini	H45/29F	2005

32602	SF54TKA	SC	Volvo B7TL	Wright Eclipse Gemini	H45/29F	2005
32603	SF54TKC	SC	Volvo B7TL	Wright Eclipse Gemini	H45/29F	2005
32604	SF54TKD	SC	Volvo B7TL	Wright Eclipse Gemini	H45/29F	2005
32605	SF54TKE	SC	Volvo B7TL	Wright Eclipse Gemini	H45/29F	2005
32606	SF54TKJ	SC	Volvo B7TL	Wright Eclipse Gemini	H45/29F	2005
32607	SF54TKK	SC	Volvo B7TL	Wright Eclipse Gemini	H45/29F	2005
32608	SF54TKO	SC	Volvo B7TL	Wright Eclipse Gemini	H45/29F	2005
32609	SF54TKN	PH	Volvo B7TL	Wright Eclipse Gemini	H45/29F	2005
32610	SF54TKT	L	Volvo B7TL	Wright Eclipse Gemini	H45/29F	2005
32611	SF54TKU	PH	Volvo B7TL	Wright Eclipse Gemini	H45/29F	2005
32612	SF54TKV	PH	Volvo B7TL	Wright Eclipse Gemini	H45/29F	2005
32613	SF54TKX	PH	Volvo B7TL	Wright Eclipse Gemini	H45/29F	2005
32614	SF54TKY	SC	Volvo B7TL	Wright Eclipse Gemini	H45/29F	2005
32615	SF54TKZ	PH	Volvo B7TL	Wright Eclipse Gemini	H45/29F	2005
32616	SF54TLJ	PH	Volvo B7TL	Wright Eclipse Gemini	H45/29F	2005
32617	SF54TLK	PH	Volvo B7TL	Wright Eclipse Gemini	H45/29F	2005
32618	SF54TLN	PH	Volvo B7TL	Wright Eclipse Gemini	H45/29F	2005
32619	SF54TLO	C	Volvo B7TL	Wright Eclipse Gemini	H45/29F	2005
32620	SF54TLU	PH	Volvo B7TL	Wright Eclipse Gemini	H45/29F	2005
32621	SF54TLX	PH	Volvo B7TL	Wright Eclipse Gemini	H45/29F	2005
32622	SF54TLY	L	Volvo B7TL	Wright Eclipse Gemini	H45/29F	2005
32623	SF54TLZ	L	Volvo B7TL	Wright Eclipse Gemini	H45/29F	2005
32624	SF54TMO	L	Volvo B7TL	Wright Eclipse Gemini	H45/29F	2005
32625	SF54TMU	L	Volvo B7TL	Wright Eclipse Gemini	H45/29F	2005
32626	SF54TMV	L	Volvo B7TL	Wright Eclipse Gemini	H45/29F	2005
32669	SN55HDZ	LN	Volvo B7TL	Wright Eclipse Gemini	H45/29F	2005
32670	SN55HEJ	LN	Volvo B7TL	Wright Eclipse Gemini	H45/29F	2005
32671	SN55HEU	D	Volvo B7TL	Wright Eclipse Gemini	H45/29F	2005
32672	SN55HEV	D	Volvo B7TL	Wright Eclipse Gemini	H45/29F	2005
32673	SN55HFA	D	Volvo B7TL	Wright Eclipse Gemini	H45/29F	2005
32674	SN55HFB	D	Volvo B7TL	Wright Eclipse Gemini	H45/29F	2005
32675	SN55HFC	D	Volvo B7TL	Wright Eclipse Gemini	H45/29F	2005
32676	SN55HFD	D	Volvo B7TL	Wright Eclipse Gemini	H45/29F	2005
32677	SN55HFE	LN	Volvo B7TL	Wright Eclipse Gemini	H45/29F	2005
32678	SN55HFF	LN	Volvo B7TL	Wright Eclipse Gemini	H45/29F	2005
32679	SN55HFG	D	Volvo B7TL	Wright Eclipse Gemini	H45/29F	2005
32680	SN55HFH	LN	Volvo B7TL	Wright Eclipse Gemini	H45/29F	2005
32681	SN55HFJ	LN	Volvo B7TL	Wright Eclipse Gemini	H45/29F	2005
32682	SN55HFK	D	Volvo B7TL	Wright Eclipse Gemini	H45/29F	2005
32683	SN55HFL	LN	Volvo B7TL	Wright Eclipse Gemini	H45/29F	2005
32805	T805LLC	PH	Dennis Trident 9.9 SLF	Plaxton President	H39/23F	1999
32811	T811LLC	PH	Dennis Trident 9.9 SLF	Plaxton President	H39/23F	1999
32813	T813LLC	PH	Dennis Trident 9.9 SLF	Plaxton President	H39/20D	1999
32814	T814LLC	PH	Dennis Trident 9.9 SLF	Plaxton President	H39/20D	1999
32815	T815LLC	PH	Dennis Trident 9.9 SLF	Plaxton President	H39/20D	1999
32816	T816LLC	PH	Dennis Trident 9.9 SLF	Plaxton President	H39/21F	1999
32820	T820LLC	C	Dennis Trident 9.9 SLF	Plaxton President	H39/23F	1999
32821	T821LLC	C	Dennis Trident 9.9 SLF	Plaxton President	H39/20D	1999
32823	T823LLC	C	Dennis Trident 9.9 SLF	Plaxton President	H39/23F	1999
32824	T824LLC	C	Dennis Trident 9.9 SLF	Plaxton President	H39/23F	1999
32825	T825LLC	C	Dennis Trident 9.9 SLF	Plaxton President	H39/20D	1999
32826	T826LLC	C	Dennis Trident 9.9 SLF	Plaxton President	H39/20D	1999
32827	T827LLC	C	Dennis Trident 9.9 SLF	Plaxton President	H39/20D	1999
32828	T828LLC	C	Dennis Trident 9.9 SLF	Plaxton President	H39/23F	1999
32829	T829LLC	C	Dennis Trident 9.9 SLF	Plaxton President	H39/23F	1999
32830	T830LLC	C	Dennis Trident 9.9 SLF	Plaxton President	H39/23F	1999
32831	T831LLC	C	Dennis Trident 9.9 SLF	Plaxton President	H39/20D	1999
32832	T832LLC	C	Dennis Trident 9.9 SLF	Plaxton President	H39/23F	1999
32833	T833LLC	PH	Dennis Trident 9.9 SLF	Plaxton President	H39/23F	1999
32834	T834LLC	PH	Dennis Trident 9.9 SLF	Plaxton President	H39/23F	1999

32835	T835LLC	PH	Dennis Trident 9.9 SLF	Plaxton President	H39/23F	1999
32836	T836LLC	PH	Dennis Trident 9.9 SLF	Plaxton President	H39/23F	1999
32837	T837LLC	C	Dennis Trident 9.9 SLF	Plaxton President	H39/23F	1999
32838	T838LLC	PH	Dennis Trident 9.9 SLF	Plaxton President	H39/21F	1999
32839	T839LLC	PH	Dennis Trident 9.9 SLF	Plaxton President	H39/21F	1999
32840	T840LLC	PH	Dennis Trident 9.9 SLF	Plaxton President	H39/21F	1999
32841	T841LLC	PH	Dennis Trident 9.9 SLF	Plaxton President	H39/21F	1999
32842	T842LLC	PH	Dennis Trident 9.9 SLF	Plaxton President	H39/21F	1999
32843	T843LLC	PH	Dennis Trident 9.9 SLF	Plaxton President	H39/21F	1999
32844	T844LLC	PH	Dennis Trident 9.9 SLF	Plaxton President	H39/21F	1999
32845	T845LLC	PH	Dennis Trident 9.9 SLF	Plaxton President	H39/21F	1999
32848	T848LLC	PH	Dennis Trident 9.9 SLF	Plaxton President	H39/20F	1999
32865	T865KLF	PH	Dennis Trident 9.9 SLF	Plaxton President	H39/20D	1999
32866	T866KLF	PH	Dennis Trident 9.9 SLF	Plaxton President	H39/20D	1999
32867	V867HBY	PH	Dennis Trident 9.9 SLF	Plaxton President	H39/24F	1999
32868	T868KLF	PH	Dennis Trident 9.9 SLF	Plaxton President	H39/20D	1999
32869	V869HBY	PH	Dennis Trident 9.9 SLF	Plaxton President	H39/21F	1999
32870	T870KLF	PH	Dennis Trident 9.9 SLF	Plaxton President	H39/20D	1999
32871	T871KLF	PH	Dennis Trident 9.9 SLF	Plaxton President	H39/20D	1999
32888	V988HLH	PH	Dennis Trident 10.5 SLF	Plaxton President	H43/24D	2000
32889	V889HLH	PH	Dennis Trident 10.5 SLF	Plaxton President	H43/24D	2000
32890	V890HLH	PH	Dennis Trident 10.5 SLF	Plaxton President	H43/24D	2000
32891	V891HLH	PH	Dennis Trident 10.5 SLF	Plaxton President	H43/24D	2000
32892	V892HLH		Dennis Trident 10.5 SLF	Plaxton President	H43/24D	2000
32899	V899HLH	L	Dennis Trident 10.5 SLF	Plaxton President	H43/23D	2000
32904	W904VLN	PH	Dennis Trident 10.5 SLF	Plaxton President	H43/24D	2000
32906	W906VLN	L	Dennis Trident 10.5 SLF	Plaxton President	H43/21D	2000
32910	W895VLN	L	Dennis Trident 10.5 SLF	Plaxton President	H43/23D	2000
32911	W896VLN	L	Dennis Trident 10.5 SLF	Plaxton President	H43/26F	2000
32912	W912VLN	L	Dennis Trident 10.5 SLF	Plaxton President	H43/21D	2000
32913	W913VLN	L	Dennis Trident 10.5 SLF	Plaxton President	H43/23D	2000
32914	W914VLN	PH	Dennis Trident 10.5 SLF	Plaxton President	H43/23D	2000
32928	W928VLN	PH	Dennis Trident 10.5 SLF	Plaxton President	H43/24D	2000
32930	W899VLN		Dennis Trident 10.5 SLF	Plaxton President	H43/24D	2000
32931	W931ULL	PH	Dennis Trident 10.5 SLF	Alexander ALX400	H45/27F	2000
32934	W934ULL	PH	Dennis Trident 10.5 SLF	Alexander ALX400	H45/24D	2000
32935	W935ULL	PH	Dennis Trident 10.5 SLF	Alexander ALX400	H45/27F	2000
32936	W936ULL	PH	Dennis Trident 10.5 SLF	Alexander ALX400	H45/24D	2000
32937	W937ULL	PH	Dennis Trident 10.5 SLF	Alexander ALX400	H45/27F	2000
32939	W939ULL	PH	Dennis Trident 10.5 SLF	Alexander ALX400	H45/24D	2000
32940	W840VLO	PH	Dennis Trident 10.5 SLF	Alexander ALX400	H45/27F	2000
32941	W941ULL	PH	Dennis Trident 10.5 SLF	Alexander ALX400	H45/24D	2000
32942	W942ULL	PH	Dennis Trident 10.5 SLF	Alexander ALX400	H45/24D	2000
32946	W946ULL	PH	Dennis Trident 10.5 SLF	Alexander ALX400	H45/27F	2000
32947	W947ULL	PH	Dennis Trident 10.5 SLF	Alexander ALX400	H45/27F	2000
32948	W948ULL	PH	Dennis Trident 10.5 SLF	Alexander ALX400	H45/27F	2000
32949	W949ULL	PH	Dennis Trident 10.5 SLF	Alexander ALX400	H45/27F	2000
32950	W132VLO	PH	Dennis Trident 10.5 SLF	Alexander ALX400	H45/27F	2000
32951	W951ULL	PH	Dennis Trident 10.5 SLF	Alexander ALX400	H45/27F	2000
32952	W952ULL	PH	Dennis Trident 10.5 SLF	Alexander ALX400	H45/27F	2000
32958	X958HLT	PH	Dennis Trident 9.9 SLF	Plaxton President	H39/23D	2001
32959	X959HLT	PH	Dennis Trident 9.9 SLF	Plaxton President	H39/24F	2001
32960	X612HLT	PH	Dennis Trident 9.9 SLF	Plaxton President	H39/23D	2001
32961	X961HLT	PH	Dennis Trident 9.9 SLF	Plaxton President	H39/24F	2001
32962	X962HLT	PH	Dennis Trident 9.9 SLF	Plaxton President	H39/23D	2001
32964	X964HLT	L	Dennis Trident 9.9 SLF	Plaxton President	H39/24F	2001
32965	X965HLT	L	Dennis Trident 9.9 SLF	Plaxton President	H39/24F	2001
32966	X966HLT	PH	Dennis Trident 9.9 SLF	Plaxton President	H39/22D	2001
32969	X969HLT		Dennis Trident 9.9 SLF	Plaxton President	H39/20D	2001
32974	X974HLT		Dennis Trident 9.9 SLF	Plaxton President	H39/20D	2001

32980	X614HLT		Dennis Trident 9.9 SLF		Plaxton President	H39/20D	2001
32983	Y344NLF		Dennis Trident 9.9 SLF		Plaxton President	H39/20D	2001
33008	LK51UZF	L	Dennis Trident 10.5 SLF		Plaxton President	H42/23D	2001
33009	LK51UZG	L	Dennis Trident 10.5 SLF		Plaxton President	H42/23D	2001
33010	LK51UZH	L	Dennis Trident 10.5 SLF		Plaxton President	H42/23D	2001
33011	LK51UZJ	L	Dennis Trident 10.5 SLF		Plaxton President	H42/23D	2001
33012	LK51UZL	L	Dennis Trident 10.5 SLF		Plaxton President	H42/23D	2001
33013	LK51UZM	L	Dennis Trident 10.5 SLF		Plaxton President	H42/23D	2001
33014	LK51UZN	L	Dennis Trident 10.5 SLF		Plaxton President	H42/23D	2001
33015	LK51UYS	PH	Dennis Trident 10.5 SLF		Plaxton President	H42/23D	2001
33016	LK51UYT		Dennis Trident 10.5 SLF		Plaxton President	H42/23D	2001
33017	LK51UYU		Dennis Trident 10.5 SLF		Plaxton President	H42/23D	2001
33018	LK51UYV	L	Dennis Trident 10.5 SLF		Plaxton President	H42/23D	2001
33040	LN51DWE	PH	Dennis Trident 9.9 SLF		Plaxton President	H39/20D	2001
33089	LN51GMV	PH	Dennis Trident 10.5 SLF		Plaxton President	H42/23D	2002
33114	LT02NVW	PH	Dennis Trident 9.9 SLF		Plaxton President	H39/24F	2002
33115	LT02NVV	L	Dennis Trident 9.9 SLF		Plaxton President	H39/20D	2002
33116	LT02NVU	PH	Dennis Trident 9.9 SLF		Plaxton President	H39/24F	2002
33117	LT02NVZ	PH	Dennis Trident 9.9 SLF		Plaxton President	H39/24F	2002
33118	LT02NWA	PH	Dennis Trident 9.9 SLF		Plaxton President	H39/20D	2002
33119	LT02NWB	L	Dennis Trident 9.9 SLF		Plaxton President	H39/20D	2002
33120	LT02NWC	PH	Dennis Trident 9.9 SLF		Plaxton President	H39/20D	2002
33121	LT02NWD	L	Dennis Trident 9.9 SLF		Plaxton President	H39/20D	2002
33122	LT02NVL	PH	Dennis Trident 9.9 SLF		Plaxton President	H39/24F	2002
34006	N306JBV	C	Volvo Olympian YN2RV18Z4		Northern Counties Palatine II	H43/29F	1995
34007	N307JBV	L	Volvo Olympian YN2RV18Z4		Northern Counties Palatine II	H43/29F	1995
34008	N308JBV	L	Volvo Olympian YN2RV18Z4		Northern Counties Palatine II	H43/29F	1995
34009	N309JBV	C	Volvo Olympian YN2RV18Z4		Northern Counties Palatine II	H43/29F	1995
34015	P535EFL	BK	Volvo Olympian YN2RV18V3		Northern Counties Palatine I	H49/33F	1996
34042	P242UCW	L	Volvo Olympian OLY		Northern Counties Palatine II	H43/27F	1996
34047	P247UCW	GS	Volvo Olympian OLY		Northern Counties Palatine II	H43/27F	1996
34048	P248UCW	GS	Volvo Olympian OLY		Northern Counties Palatine II	H43/27F	1996
34066	P566EFL	BK	Volvo Olympian OLY-5639		Northern Counties Palatine I	H49/33F	1996
34067	P567EFL	BK	Volvo Olympian YN2RV18V3		Northern Counties Palatine I	H49/33F	1996
34073	P573EFL	BK	Volvo Olympian YN2RV18V3		Northern Counties Palatine I	H49/33F	1997
34075	P575EFL	BK	Volvo Olympian OLY-5639		Northern Counties Palatine I	H49/33F	1997
34076	P576EFL	BK	Volvo Olympian OLY-5639		Northern Counties Palatine I	H49/33F	1997
34083	P533EFL	BK	Volvo Olympian YN2RV18V3		Northern Counties Palatine I	H49/33F	1996
34136	L636SEU	BF	Volvo Olympian YN2RC16Z5		Northern Counties Palatine II	H47/29F	1993
34147	L647SEU	LT	Volvo Olympian YN2RC16Z5		Northern Counties Palatine II	H47/29F	1994
34148	L648SEU	LT	Volvo Olympian YN2RC16Z5		Northern Counties Palatine II	H47/29F	1994
34149	L649SEU	BF	Volvo Olympian YN2RC16Z5		Northern Counties Palatine II	H47/29F	1993
34151	L651SEU	BK	Volvo Olympian YN2RC16Z5		Northern Counties Palatine II	H47/29F	1993
34152	L652SEU	M	Volvo Olympian YN2RC16Z5		Northern Counties Palatine II	H47/29F	1993
34159	P659UFB	L	Volvo Olympian OLY-4953		Northern Counties Palatine II	H47/29F	1997
34160	P660UFB	L	Volvo Olympian OLY-4953		Northern Counties Palatine II	H47/29F	1997
34202	M922UYG	L	Volvo Olympian YN2RV18Z5		Alexander Royale	DPH45/27F	1995
34203	M923UYG	L	Volvo Olympian YN2RV18Z5		Alexander Royale	DPH45/27F	1995
34205	M925UYG	L	Volvo Olympian YN2RV18Z5		Alexander Royale	DPH45/27F	1995
34265	M86MYM	GS	Volvo Olympian YN2RV16Z4		Alexander Royale	H45/29F	1995
34329	H129FLX	r	Leyland Olympian ON2R50C13Z4		Northern Counties	H47/30F	1990
34339	H139FLX	r	Leyland Olympian ON2R50C13Z4		Northern Counties	H47/30F	1990
36007	SN05HWW	LN	Scania N94UD		East Lancs OmniDekka	H47/33F	2005
36008	SN05HWX	LN	Scania N94UD		East Lancs OmniDekka	H47/33F	2005
36009	SN05HWY	LN	Scania N94UD		East Lancs OmniDekka	H47/33F	2005
36010	SN05HWZ	LN	Scania N94UD		East Lancs OmniDekka	H47/33F	2005
36011	SN05HXA	LN	Scania N94UD		East Lancs OmniDekka	H47/33F	2005
36012	SN05HXB	LN	Scania N94UD		East Lancs OmniDekka	H47/33F	2005
36013	SN05HWL	BK	Scania N94UD		East Lancs OmniDekka	H47/33F	2005
36014	SN05HWK	LN	Scania N94UD		East Lancs OmniDekka	H47/33F	2005

36015	SN05HWO	LN	Scania N94UD	East Lancs OmniDekka	H47/33F	2005
36016	SN05HWM	LN	Scania N94UD	East Lancs OmniDekka	H47/33F	2005
36017	SN05HWJ	LN	Scania N94UD	East Lancs OmniDekka	H47/33F	2005
36018	SN05HWG	LN	Scania N94UD	East Lancs OmniDekka	H47/33F	2005
36019	SN05HWH	LN	Scania N94UD	East Lancs OmniDekka	H47/33F	2005
36020	SN05HWF	LN	Scania N94UD	East Lancs OmniDekka	H47/33F	2005
36021	SN05HWP	LN	Scania N94UD	East Lancs OmniDekka	H47/33F	2005
36022	SN05HWE	LN	Scania N94UD	East Lancs OmniDekka	H47/33F	2005
36023	SN05HWD	LN	Scania N94UD	East Lancs OmniDekka	H47/33F	2005
36024	SN05HWR	LN	Scania N94UD	East Lancs OmniDekka	H47/33F	2005
36025	SN05HWS	LN	Scania N94UD	East Lancs OmniDekka	H47/33F	2005
36026	SN05HWU	LN	Scania N94UD	East Lancs OmniDekka	H47/33F	2005
36027	SN05HWV	LN	Scania N94UD	East Lancs OmniDekka	H47/33F	2005
36028	SN05HWT	LN	Scania N94UD	East Lancs OmniDekka	H47/33F	2005
36029	SN55KKE	BK	Scania N94UD	East Lancs OmniDekka	H47/33F	2005
36030	SN55KKF	LN	Scania N94UD	East Lancs OmniDekka	H47/33F	2005
37133	SN57HDH	GS	Volvo B9TL	Wright Eclipse Gemini	H45/29F	2007
37134	SN57HDJ	GS	Volvo B9TL	Wright Eclipse Gemini	H45/29F	2007
37135	SN57HCP	LW	Volvo B9TL	Wright Eclipse Gemini	H45/29F	2007
37136	SN57HCU	LN	Volvo B9TL	Wright Eclipse Gemini	H45/29F	2007
37137	SN57HCV	LN	Volvo B9TL	Wright Eclipse Gemini	H45/29F	2007
37138	SN57HCX	LN	Volvo B9TL	Wright Eclipse Gemini	H45/29F	2007
37139	SN57HCY	LN	Volvo B9TL	Wright Eclipse Gemini	H45/29F	2007
37140	SN57HCZ	LN	Volvo B9TL	Wright Eclipse Gemini	H45/29F	2007
37141	SN57HDA	LN	Volvo B9TL	Wright Eclipse Gemini	H45/29F	2007
37142	SN57HDC	LN	Volvo B9TL	Wright Eclipse Gemini	H45/29F	2007
37143	SN57HDD	LN	Volvo B9TL	Wright Eclipse Gemini	H45/29F	2007
37144	SN57HDE	LN	Volvo B9TL	Wright Eclipse Gemini	H45/29F	2007
37145	SN57HDF	LN	Volvo B9TL	Wright Eclipse Gemini	H45/29F	2007
37147	YN06URA	C	Volvo B7TL	Wright Eclipse Gemini	H45/29F	2006
37148	YN06URB	C	Volvo B7TL	Wright Eclipse Gemini	H45/29F	2006
37149	YN06URC	C	Volvo B7TL	Wright Eclipse Gemini	H45/29F	2006
37150	YN06URD	C	Volvo B7TL	Wright Eclipse Gemini	H45/29F	2006
37151	YN06URE	C	Volvo B7TL	Wright Eclipse Gemini	H45/29F	2006
37152	YN06URF	C	Volvo B7TL	Wright Eclipse Gemini	H45/29F	2006
37153	YN06URG	C	Volvo B7TL	Wright Eclipse Gemini	H45/29F	2006
37154	YN06URH	C	Volvo B7TL	Wright Eclipse Gemini	H45/29F	2006
37155	YN06URJ	C	Volvo B7TL	Wright Eclipse Gemini	H45/29F	2006
37166	SF07FCP	L	Volvo B7TL	Wright Eclipse Gemini	H45/29F	2007
37167	SF07FCV	L	Volvo B7TL	Wright Eclipse Gemini	H45/29F	2007
37168	SF07FCX	L	Volvo B7TL	Wright Eclipse Gemini	H45/29F	2007
37169	SF07FCY	L	Volvo B7TL	Wright Eclipse Gemini	H45/29F	2007
37170	SF07FCZ	L	Volvo B7TL	Wright Eclipse Gemini	H45/29F	2007
37171	SF07FDA	L	Volvo B7TL	Wright Eclipse Gemini	H45/29F	2007
37172	SF07FDC	L	Volvo B7TL	Wright Eclipse Gemini	H45/29F	2007
37173	SF07FDD	L	Volvo B7TL	Wright Eclipse Gemini	H45/29F	2007
37174	SF07FDE	L	Volvo B7TL	Wright Eclipse Gemini	H45/29F	2007
37175	SF07FDG	L	Volvo B7TL	Wright Eclipse Gemini	H45/29F	2007
37176	SF07FDJ	L	Volvo B7TL	Wright Eclipse Gemini	H45/29F	2007
37177	SF07FDK	L	Volvo B7TL	Wright Eclipse Gemini	H45/29F	2007
37178	SF07FDL	L	Volvo B7TL	Wright Eclipse Gemini	H45/29F	2007
37179	SF07FDM	L	Volvo B7TL	Wright Eclipse Gemini	H45/29F	2007
37180	SF07FDN	L	Volvo B7TL	Wright Eclipse Gemini	H45/29F	2007
37181	SF07FDO	L	Volvo B7TL	Wright Eclipse Gemini	H45/29F	2007
37182	SF07FDP	L	Volvo B7TL	Wright Eclipse Gemini	H45/29F	2007
37183	SF07FDU	SC	Volvo B7TL	Wright Eclipse Gemini	H45/29F	2007
37184	SF07FDV	SC	Volvo B7TL	Wright Eclipse Gemini	H45/29F	2007
37185	SF07FDX	SC	Volvo B7TL	Wright Eclipse Gemini	H45/29F	2007
37186	SF07FDY	L	Volvo B9TL	Wright Eclipse Gemini	H45/29F	2007
37187	SF07FDZ	L	Volvo B9TL	Wright Eclipse Gemini	H45/29F	2007

37188	SF07FCC	L	Volvo B9TL	Wright Eclipse Gemini	H45/29F	2007
37189	SF07FCD	L	Volvo B9TL	Wright Eclipse Gemini	H45/29F	2007
37190	SF07FCE	L	Volvo B9TL	Wright Eclipse Gemini	H45/29F	2007
37191	SF07FCG	L	Volvo B9TL	Wright Eclipse Gemini	H45/29F	2007
37192	SF07FCJ	L	Volvo B9TL	Wright Eclipse Gemini	H45/29F	2007
37193	SF07FEG	L	Volvo B9TL	Wright Eclipse Gemini	H45/29F	2007
37194	SF07FEH	L	Volvo B9TL	Wright Eclipse Gemini	H45/29F	2007
37195	SF07FEJ	L	Volvo B9TL	Wright Eclipse Gemini	H45/29F	2007
37196	SF07FEK	L	Volvo B9TL	Wright Eclipse Gemini	H45/29F	2007
37197	SF07FEM	L	Volvo B9TL	Wright Eclipse Gemini	H45/29F	2007
37198	SF07FEO	L	Volvo B9TL	Wright Eclipse Gemini	H45/29F	2007
37199	SF07FCL	L	Volvo B9TL	Wright Eclipse Gemini	H45/29F	2007
37200	SF07FEP	L	Volvo B9TL	Wright Eclipse Gemini	H45/29F	2007
37201	SF07FCM	L	Volvo B9TL	Wright Eclipse Gemini	H45/29F	2007
37202	SF07FCO	L	Volvo B9TL	Wright Eclipse Gemini	H45/29F	2007
37203	SF07FET	L	Volvo B9TL	Wright Eclipse Gemini	H45/29F	2007
37204	SF07FEU	L	Volvo B9TL	Wright Eclipse Gemini	H45/29F	2007
37205	SF57MKA	L	Volvo B9TL	Wright Eclipse Gemini	H45/29F	2007
37206	SF57MKC	L	Volvo B9TL	Wright Eclipse Gemini	H45/29F	2007
37207	SF57MKD	L	Volvo B9TL	Wright Eclipse Gemini	H45/29F	2007
37208	SF57MKG	L	Volvo B9TL	Wright Eclipse Gemini	H45/29F	2007
37209	SF57MKJ	L	Volvo B9TL	Wright Eclipse Gemini	H45/29F	2007
37210	SF57MKK	L	Volvo B9TL	Wright Eclipse Gemini	H45/29F	2007
37211	SF57MKL	L	Volvo B9TL	Wright Eclipse Gemini	H45/29F	2007
37212	SF57MKM	L	Volvo B9TL	Wright Eclipse Gemini	H45/29F	2007
37213	SF57MKN	L	Volvo B9TL	Wright Eclipse Gemini	H45/29F	2007
37214	SF57MKO	L	Volvo B9TL	Wright Eclipse Gemini	H45/29F	2007
37215	SF57MKP	L	Volvo B9TL	Wright Eclipse Gemini	H45/29F	2007
37216	SF57MKU	L	Volvo B9TL	Wright Eclipse Gemini	H45/29F	2007
37217	SF57MKV	L	Volvo B9TL	Wright Eclipse Gemini	H45/29F	2007
37218	SF57MKX	L	Volvo B9TL	Wright Eclipse Gemini	H45/29F	2007
37219	SF57MKZ	L	Volvo B9TL	Wright Eclipse Gemini	H45/29F	2007
37220	SF57MLE	L	Volvo B9TL	Wright Eclipse Gemini	H45/29F	2007
37221	SF57MLJ	L	Volvo B9TL	Wright Eclipse Gemini	H45/29F	2007
37222	SF57MLK	L	Volvo B9TL	Wright Eclipse Gemini	H45/29F	2008
37223	SF57MLL	L	Volvo B9TL	Wright Eclipse Gemini	H45/29F	2008
37224	SF57MLN	L	Volvo B9TL	Wright Eclipse Gemini	H45/29F	2008
37225	SF57MLO	L	Volvo B9TL	Wright Eclipse Gemini	H45/29F	2008
37226	SF57MLU	L	Volvo B9TL	Wright Eclipse Gemini	H45/29F	2008
37227	SF57MLV	L	Volvo B9TL	Wright Eclipse Gemini	H45/29F	2008
37238	YN08LCT	BT	Volvo B9TL	Wright Eclipse Gemini	H45/29F	2008
37239	YN08LCU	L	Volvo B9TL	Wright Eclipse Gemini	H45/29F	2008
37240	YN08LCV	BT	Volvo B9TL	Wright Eclipse Gemini	H45/29F	2008
37241	YN08LCW	BT	Volvo B9TL	Wright Eclipse Gemini	H45/29F	2008
37242	YN08LCY	BT	Volvo B9TL	Wright Eclipse Gemini	H45/29F	2008
37243	YN08LCZ	BT	Volvo B9TL	Wright Eclipse Gemini	H45/29F	2008
37244	YN08LDA	BT	Volvo B9TL	Wright Eclipse Gemini	H45/29F	2008
37245	YN08LDC	BT	Volvo B9TL	Wright Eclipse Gemini	H45/29F	2008
37266	SN57HDG	LW	Volvo B9TL	Wright Eclipse Gemini	H45/29F	2007
37267	SN57JAO	LW	Volvo B9TL	Wright Eclipse Gemini	H45/29F	2008
37268	SN57JAU	LW	Volvo B9TL	Wright Eclipse Gemini	H45/29F	2008
37269	SN57JBE	LW	Volvo B9TL	Wright Eclipse Gemini	H45/29F	2008
37270	SN57JBO	LW	Volvo B9TL	Wright Eclipse Gemini	H45/29F	2008
37271	SN57JBU	LW	Volvo B9TL	Wright Eclipse Gemini	H45/29F	2008
37272	SN57JBV	LW	Volvo B9TL	Wright Eclipse Gemini	H45/29F	2008
37273	SN57JBX	LW	Volvo B9TL	Wright Eclipse Gemini	H45/29F	2008
37278	YN08LDD	BT	Volvo B9TL	Wright Eclipse Gemini	H45/29F	2008
37530	SF08SMU	L	Volvo B9TL	Wright Eclipse Gemini	H45/29F	2008
37531	SF08SMV	L	Volvo B9TL	Wright Eclipse Gemini	H45/29F	2008
37532	SF08SMX	L	Volvo B9TL	Wright Eclipse Gemini	H45/29F	2008

37533	SF08SNJ	L	Volvo B9TL	Wright Eclipse Gemini	H45/29F	2008
37534	SF08SNK	L	Volvo B9TL	Wright Eclipse Gemini	H45/29F	2008
37535	SF08SNN	L	Volvo B9TL	Wright Eclipse Gemini	H45/29F	2008
37536	SF08SNU	L	Volvo B9TL	Wright Eclipse Gemini	H45/29F	2008
37537	SF08SNV	L	Volvo B9TL	Wright Eclipse Gemini	H45/29F	2008
37538	SF08SNX	L	Volvo B9TL	Wright Eclipse Gemini	H45/29F	2008
37539	SF08SNY	L	Volvo B9TL	Wright Eclipse Gemini	H45/29F	2008
37540	SF08SNZ	L	Volvo B9TL	Wright Eclipse Gemini	H45/29F	2008
37541	SF58ATY	L	Volvo B9TL	Wright Eclipse Gemini	H45/29F	2008
37542	SF58ATZ	L	Volvo B9TL	Wright Eclipse Gemini	H45/29F	2008
37543	SF58AUA	L	Volvo B9TL	Wright Eclipse Gemini	H45/29F	2008
37544	SF58AUC	L	Volvo B9TL	Wright Eclipse Gemini	H45/29F	2008
37633	SV08FXP	AB	Volvo B9TL	Wright Eclipse Gemini	H45/29F	2008
37634	SV08FXR	AB	Volvo B9TL	Wright Eclipse Gemini	H45/29F	2008
37635	SV08FXS	AB	Volvo B9TL	Wright Eclipse Gemini	H45/29F	2008
37636	SV08FXT	AB	Volvo B9TL	Wright Eclipse Gemini	H45/29F	2008
37637	SV08FXV	AB	Volvo B9TL	Wright Eclipse Gemini	H45/29F	2008
37638	SV08FXW	AB	Volvo B9TL	Wright Eclipse Gemini	H45/29F	2008
37639	SV08FXX	AB	Volvo B9TL	Wright Eclipse Gemini	H45/29F	2008
37640	SV08FXY	AB	Volvo B9TL	Wright Eclipse Gemini	H45/29F	2008
37641	SV08FXZ	AB	Volvo B9TL	Wright Eclipse Gemini	H45/29F	2008
37642	SV08FYA	AB	Volvo B9TL	Wright Eclipse Gemini	H45/29F	2008
37643	SV08FYB	AB	Volvo B9TL	Wright Eclipse Gemini	H45/29F	2008
37644	SV08FYC	AB	Volvo B9TL	Wright Eclipse Gemini	H45/29F	2008
37736	SF09LDD	C	Volvo B9TL	Wright Eclipse Gemini	H45/29F	2009
37737	SF09LDE	C	Volvo B9TL	Wright Eclipse Gemini	H45/29F	2009
37738	SF09LDJ	C	Volvo B9TL	Wright Eclipse Gemini	H45/29F	2009
37739	SF09LDK	C	Volvo B9TL	Wright Eclipse Gemini	H45/29F	2009
37740	SF09LDL	C	Volvo B9TL	Wright Eclipse Gemini	H45/29F	2009
37741	SF09LDN	C	Volvo B9TL	Wright Eclipse Gemini	H45/29F	2009
37742	SF09LDO	C	Volvo B9TL	Wright Eclipse Gemini	H45/29F	2009
37743	SF09LDU	C	Volvo B9TL	Wright Eclipse Gemini	H45/29F	2009
37744	SF09LDV	C	Volvo B9TL	Wright Eclipse Gemini	H45/29F	2009
37745	SF09LDX	C	Volvo B9TL	Wright Eclipse Gemini	H45/29F	2009
37746	SF09LDY	C	Volvo B9TL	Wright Eclipse Gemini	H45/29F	2009
37747	SF09LDZ	C	Volvo B9TL	Wright Eclipse Gemini	H45/29F	2009
37748	SF09LEJ	C	Volvo B9TL	Wright Eclipse Gemini	H45/29F	2009
37749	SF09LEU	C	Volvo B9TL	Wright Eclipse Gemini	H45/29F	2009
37750	SF09LFA	C	Volvo B9TL	Wright Eclipse Gemini	H45/29F	2009
37751	SF09LFB	C	Volvo B9TL	Wright Eclipse Gemini	H45/29F	2009
38089	H289VRP	D-t	Volvo B10M-50	Alexander RV	DPH47/35F	1990
38091	H291VRP	GS	Volvo B10M-50	Alexander RV	DPH47/35F	1990
38092	H292VRP	GS	Volvo B10M-50	Alexander RV	DPH47/35F	1990
38096	J296GNV	GS	Volvo B10M-50	Alexander RV	DPH47/35F	1991
38201	SN09CAU	L	ADL Trident 12.1 SLF	ADL Enviro 500	H53/29F	2009
38202	SN09CAV	L	ADL Trident 12.1 SLF	ADL Enviro 500	H53/29F	2009
38203	SN09CAX	L	ADL Trident 12.1 SLF	ADL Enviro 500	H53/29F	2009
38204	SN09CBF	L	ADL Trident 12.1 SLF	ADL Enviro 500	H53/29F	2009
38205	SN09CBO	L	ADL Trident 12.1 SLF	ADL Enviro 500	H53/29F	2009
38206	SN09CBU	L	ADL Trident 12.1 SLF	ADL Enviro 500	H53/29F	2009
38207	SN09CBV	L	ADL Trident 12.1 SLF	ADL Enviro 500	H53/29F	2009
38208	SN09CBX	L	ADL Trident 12.1 SLF	ADL Enviro 500	H53/29F	2009
38209	SN09CBY	L	ADL Trident 12.1 SLF	ADL Enviro 500	H53/29F	2009
38210	SN09CCA	L	ADL Trident 12.1 SLF	ADL Enviro 500	H53/29F	2009
38211	SN09CCD	L	ADL Trident 12.1 SLF	ADL Enviro 500	H53/29F	2009
38212	SN09CCE	L	ADL Trident 12.1 SLF	ADL Enviro 500	H53/29F	2009
38213	SN09CCF	L	ADL Trident 12.1 SLF	ADL Enviro 500	H53/29F	2009
38214	SN09CCJ	L	ADL Trident 12.1 SLF	ADL Enviro 500	H53/29F	2009
38215	SN09CCK	L	ADL Trident 12.1 SLF	ADL Enviro 500	H53/29F	2009
38216	SN09CCO	L	ADL Trident 12.1 SLF	ADL Enviro 500	H53/29F	2009

38217	SN09CCU	L	ADL Trident 12.1 SLF	ADL Enviro 500	H53/29F	2009
38218	SN09CCV	L	ADL Trident 12.1 SLF	ADL Enviro 500	H53/29F	2009
38219	SN09CCX	L	ADL Trident 12.1 SLF	ADL Enviro 500	H53/29F	2009
38220	SN09CCY	L	ADL Trident 12.1 SLF	ADL Enviro 500	H53/29F	2009
38221	SN09CCZ	L	ADL Trident 12.1 SLF	ADL Enviro 500	H53/29F	2009
38222	SN09CDE	L	ADL Trident 12.1 SLF	ADL Enviro 500	H53/29F	2009
38223	SN09CDF	L	ADL Trident 12.1 SLF	ADL Enviro 500	H53/29F	2009
38224	SN09CDK	L	ADL Trident 12.1 SLF	ADL Enviro 500	H53/29F	2009
38225	SN09CDO	L	ADL Trident 12.1 SLF	ADL Enviro 500	H53/29F	2009
40558	T307VYG	BTLN	Volvo B6BLE	Wright Crusader 2	B36F	1999
40559	T308VYG	BT	Volvo B6BLE	Wright Crusader 2	B36F	1999
40560	T309VYG	BT	Volvo B6BLE	Wright Crusader 2	B36F	1999
40561	T310VYG	BT	Volvo B6BLE	Wright Crusader 2	B36F	1999
40562	T311VYG	BTLN	Volvo B6BLE	Wright Crusader 2	B36F	1999
40563	T312VYG	BTLN	Volvo B6BLE	Wright Crusader 2	B36F	1999
40697	P828YUM	D	Dennis Dart 10.7 SLF	Plaxton Pointer	B35F	1997
40698	P832YUM	D	Dennis Dart 10.7 SLF	Plaxton Pointer	B35F	1997
40701	P835YUM	D	Dennis Dart 10.7 SLF	Plaxton Pointer	B35F	1997
40703	R324HYG	GS	Dennis Dart 10.7 SLF	Plaxton Pointer 2	B37F	1998
40706	R342HYG	M	Dennis Dart 10.7 SLF	Plaxton Pointer 2	B37F	1998
40708	R343HYG	M	Dennis Dart 10.7 SLF	Plaxton Pointer 2	B37F	1998
40722	R308GHS	BT	Dennis Dart 10.7 SLF	Plaxton Pointer 2	B37F	1997
40724	P2UVG	L	Dennis Dart 10.7 SLF	UVG Urbanstar	B34F	1997
40739	P632WSU	w	Dennis Dart 10.7 SLF	Plaxton Pointer	B39F	1997
40740	P633WSU	BT	Dennis Dart 10.7 SLF	Plaxton Pointer	B39F	1997
40741	P634WSU	BT	Dennis Dart 10.7 SLF	Plaxton Pointer	B39F	1997
40742	P635WSU	BT	Dennis Dart 10.7 SLF	Plaxton Pointer	B39F	1997
40743	P748XUS	L	Dennis Dart 10.7 SLF	UVG Urbanstar	B39F	1997
40744	P749XUS	L	Dennis Dart 10.7 SLF	UVG Urbanstar	B39F	1997
40746	P751XUS	w	Dennis Dart 10.7 SLF	UVG Urbanstar	B39F	1997
40748	P753XUS	L	Dennis Dart 10.7 SLF	UVG Urbanstar	B39F	1997
40750	P756XUS	L	Dennis Dart 10.7 SLF	UVG Urbanstar	B39F	1997
40752	P758XUS	L	Dennis Dart 10.7 SLF	UVG Urbanstar	B39F	1997
40753	P759XUS	w	Dennis Dart 10.7 SLF	UVG Urbanstar	B39F	1997
40754	P760XUS	L	Dennis Dart 10.7 SLF	UVG Urbanstar	B39F	1997
40755	P761XUS	L	Dennis Dart 10.7 SLF	UVG Urbanstar	B39F	1997
40756	P762XUS	w	Dennis Dart 10.7 SLF	UVG Urbanstar	B39F	1997
40770	P822YUM	w	Dennis Dart 10.7 SLF	Plaxton Pointer	B35F	1997
40773	P825YUM	BT	Dennis Dart 10.7 SLF	Plaxton Pointer	B35F	1997
40774	P829YUM	BT	Dennis Dart 10.7 SLF	Plaxton Pointer	B35F	1997
40775	P830YUM	DU	Dennis Dart 10.7 SLF	Plaxton Pointer	B35F	1997
40776	P831YUM	w	Dennis Dart 10.7 SLF	Plaxton Pointer	B35F	1997
40782	P889TCV	O	Dennis Dart 10.7 SLF	Plaxton Pointer	B35F	1997
40783	P890TCV	BT	Dennis Dart 10.7 SLF	Plaxton Pointer	B35F	1997
40796	R301GHS	BT	Dennis Dart 10.7 SLF	Plaxton Pointer 2	B37F	1997
40797	R302GHS	BT	Dennis Dart 10.7 SLF	Plaxton Pointer 2	B37F	1997
40798	R303GHS	BT	Dennis Dart 10.7 SLF	Plaxton Pointer 2	B37F	1997
40799	R304GHS	w	Dennis Dart 10.7 SLF	Plaxton Pointer 2	B37F	1997
40800	R305GHS	O	Dennis Dart 10.7 SLF	Plaxton Pointer 2	B37F	1997
40801	R307GHS	O	Dennis Dart 10.7 SLF	Plaxton Pointer 2	B37F	1997
40802	R309GHS	BT	Dennis Dart 10.7 SLF	Plaxton Pointer 2	B37F	1997
40803	R310GHS	O	Dennis Dart 10.7 SLF	Plaxton Pointer 2	B37F	1997
40804	R311GHS	O	Dennis Dart 10.7 SLF	Plaxton Pointer 2	B37F	1997
40806	R313GHS	BT	Dennis Dart 10.7 SLF	Plaxton Pointer 2	B37F	1997
40807	R314GHS	O	Dennis Dart 10.7 SLF	Plaxton Pointer 2	B37F	1997
40808	R315GHS	O	Dennis Dart 10.7 SLF	Plaxton Pointer 2	B37F	1997
40809	R317GHS	O	Dennis Dart 10.7 SLF	Plaxton Pointer 2	B37F	1997
40810	R319GHS	O	Dennis Dart 10.7 SLF	Plaxton Pointer 2	B37F	1997
40811	R321GHS	O	Dennis Dart 10.7 SLF	Plaxton Pointer 2	B37F	1997
40812	R322GHS	O	Dennis Dart 10.7 SLF	Plaxton Pointer 2	B37F	1997

40813	R324GHS	w	Dennis Dart 10.7 SLF	Plaxton Pointer 2	B37F	1997
40814	R631DUS	O	Dennis Dart 10.7 SLF	Plaxton Pointer 2	B37F	1997
40815	R632DUS	O	Dennis Dart 10.7 SLF	Plaxton Pointer 2	B37F	1997
40816	R633DUS	O	Dennis Dart 10.7 SLF	Plaxton Pointer 2	B37F	1997
40817	R634DUS	O	Dennis Dart 10.7 SLF	Plaxton Pointer 2	B37F	1997
40818	R636DUS	O	Dennis Dart 10.7 SLF	Plaxton Pointer 2	B37F	1997
40819	R637DUS	BT	Dennis Dart 10.7 SLF	Plaxton Pointer 2	B37F	1997
40820	R638DUS	O	Dennis Dart 10.7 SLF	Plaxton Pointer 2	B37F	1997
40828	R664DUS	O	Dennis Dart 10.7 SLF	Plaxton Pointer 2	B37F	1997
40829	R665DUS	O	Dennis Dart 10.7 SLF	Plaxton Pointer 2	B37F	1997
40830	R667DUS	O	Dennis Dart 10.7 SLF	Plaxton Pointer 2	B37F	1997
40831	R668DUS	O	Dennis Dart 10.7 SLF	Plaxton Pointer 2	B37F	1997
40832	R669DUS	O	Dennis Dart 10.7 SLF	Plaxton Pointer 2	B37F	1997
40834	R671DUS	O	Dennis Dart 10.7 SLF	Plaxton Pointer 2	B37F	1997
40839	R676DUS	O	Dennis Dart 10.7 SLF	Plaxton Pointer 2	B37F	1997
40840	R677DUS	O	Dennis Dart 10.7 SLF	Plaxton Pointer 2	B37F	1998
40842	R757DYS	O	Dennis Dart 10.7 SLF	Plaxton Pointer 2	B37F	1997
40887	P201NSC	LN	Dennis Dart 10.1 SLF	Plaxton Pointer	B32F	1996
40888	P202NSC	LN	Dennis Dart 10.1 SLF	Plaxton Pointer	B32F	1996
40889	P214NSC	M	Dennis Dart 10.1 SLF	Plaxton Pointer	B38F	1997
40890	P218YSH	r	Dennis Dart 10.7 SLF	Plaxton Pointer	B39F	1997
40893 *	S240CSF	LW	Dennis Dart 10.7 SLF	Plaxton Pointer 2	B37F	1998
40894	S242CSF	LT	Dennis Dart 10.7 SLF	Plaxton Pointer 2	B37F	1998
40895	S243CSF	NB	Dennis Dart 10.7 SLF	Plaxton Pointer 2	B37F	1998
40896	S248CSF	LT	Dennis Dart 10.7 SLF	Plaxton Pointer 2	B37F	1999
40897	S249CSF	BK	Dennis Dart 10.7 SLF	Plaxton Pointer 2	B37F	1999
40898	S250CSF	BK	Dennis Dart 10.7 SLF	Plaxton Pointer 2	B37F	1999
40899	S251CSF	BK	Dennis Dart 10.7 SLF	Plaxton Pointer 2	B37F	1999
40900	R327HYG	LT	Dennis Dart 10.7 SLF	Plaxton Pointer 2	B37F	1998
40901	R232SBA	LN	Dennis Dart 10.7 SLF	Plaxton Pointer 2	B37F	1997
40910	N626XJM	GS	Dennis Dart 9.8 SFD	Plaxton Pointer	B37F	1996
40911	P632CGM	GS	Dennis Dart 9.8 SFD	Plaxton Pointer	B37F	1996
40912	P203NSC	M	Dennis Dart 10.1 SLF	Plaxton Pointer	B38F	1996
40913	P204NSC	GS	Dennis Dart 10.1 SLF	Plaxton Pointer	B38F	1996
40914	P205NSC	D	Dennis Dart 10.1 SLF	Plaxton Pointer	B38F	1996
40915	P206NSC	GS	Dennis Dart 10.1 SLF	Plaxton Pointer	B38F	1996
40916	P207NSC	M	Dennis Dart 10.1 SLF	Plaxton Pointer	B38F	1996
40917	P208NSC	GS	Dennis Dart 10.1 SLF	Plaxton Pointer	B38F	1997
40918	P209NSC	BKGS	Dennis Dart 10.1 SLF	Plaxton Pointer	B38F	1997
40919	P210NSC	GS	Dennis Dart 10.1 SLF	Plaxton Pointer	B38F	1997
40920	P211NSC	D	Dennis Dart 10.1 SLF	Plaxton Pointer	B38F	1997
40921	P212NSC	M	Dennis Dart 10.1 SLF	Plaxton Pointer	B38F	1997
40922	P213NSC	r	Dennis Dart 10.1 SLF	Plaxton Pointer	B38F	1997
40926	R219GFS	M	Dennis Dart 10.7 SLF	Plaxton Pointer 2	B37F	1997
40927	R220GFS	M	Dennis Dart 10.7 SLF	Plaxton Pointer 2	B37F	1997
40928	R221GFS	MLN	Dennis Dart 10.7 SLF	Plaxton Pointer 2	B37F	1997
40929	R223GFS	M	Dennis Dart 10.7 SLF	Plaxton Pointer 2	B37F	1997
40930	R225GFS	M	Dennis Dart 10.7 SLF	Plaxton Pointer 2	B37F	1997
40931	R226GFS	M	Dennis Dart 10.7 SLF	Plaxton Pointer 2	B37F	1997
40932	R227GFS	M	Dennis Dart 10.7 SLF	Plaxton Pointer 2	B37F	1997
40933	R228GFS	r	Dennis Dart 10.7 SLF	Plaxton Pointer 2	B37F	1997
40934	R229GFS	MN	Dennis Dart 10.7 SLF	Plaxton Pointer 2	B37F	1997
40937	R434PSH	M	Dennis Dart 10.7 SLF	Plaxton Pointer 2	B37F	1998
40938	S244CSF	LW	Dennis Dart 10.7 SLF	Plaxton Pointer 2	B37F	1999
40940	R226SBA	DLN	Dennis Dart 10.7 SLF	Plaxton Pointer 2	B37F	1997
40941	R227SBA	LN	Dennis Dart 10.7 SLF	Plaxton Pointer 2	B37F	1997
40942	R228SBA	w	Dennis Dart 10.7 SLF	Plaxton Pointer 2	B37F	1997
40943	R229SBA	D	Dennis Dart 10.7 SLF	Plaxton Pointer 2	B37F	1997
40944	R230SBA	D	Dennis Dart 10.7 SLF	Plaxton Pointer 2	B37F	1997
40945	R231SBA	D	Dennis Dart 10.7 SLF	Plaxton Pointer 2	B37F	1997

40946	R233SBA	LT	Dennis Dart 10.7 SLF	Plaxton Pointer 2	B37F	1997
40947	N611XJM	w	Dennis Dart 11.3 SLF	Plaxton Pointer	B37F	1996
40965	SJ03DNY	SC	Optare Solo M920	Optare	B30F	2003
40966	SJ03DOA	SC	Optare Solo M920	Optare	B30F	2003
41201	R201TLM	DU	Dennis Dart 9.3 SLF	Marshall Capital	B22D	1998
41202	R202TLM	DU	Dennis Dart 9.3 SLF	Marshall Capital	B22D	1998
41203	R203TLM	DU	Dennis Dart 9.3 SLF	Marshall Capital	B22D	1998
41204	R204TLM	DU	Dennis Dart 9.3 SLF	Marshall Capital	B22D	1998
41205	R205TLM	DU	Dennis Dart 9.3 SLF	Marshall Capital	B22D	1998
41206	R206TLM	DU	Dennis Dart 9.3 SLF	Marshall Capital	B22D	1998
41208	R208TLM	DU	Dennis Dart 9.3 SLF	Marshall Capital	B22D	1998
41209	R209TLM	DU	Dennis Dart 9.3 SLF	Marshall Capital	B22D	1998
41210	R210TLM	DU	Dennis Dart 9.3 SLF	Marshall Capital	B22D	1998
41211	R211TLM	BT	Dennis Dart 9.3 SLF	Marshall Capital	B22D	1998
41212	R212TLM	DU	Dennis Dart 9.3 SLF	Marshall Capital	B22D	1998
41213	R213TLM	BT	Dennis Dart 9.3 SLF	Marshall Capital	B22D	1998
41214	R214TLM	BT	Dennis Dart 9.3 SLF	Marshall Capital	B22D	1998
41215	R215TLM	L	Dennis Dart 9.3 SLF	Marshall Capital	B25F	1998
41216	R216TLM	O	Dennis Dart 9.3 SLF	Marshall Capital	B22D	1998
41217	R217TLM	DU	Dennis Dart 9.3 SLF	Marshall Capital	B22D	1998
41218	R218TLM	O	Dennis Dart 9.3 SLF	Marshall Capital	B22D	1998
41219	R219TLM	DU	Dennis Dart 9.3 SLF	Marshall Capital	B25F	1998
41221	R221TLM	SC	Dennis Dart 9.3 SLF	Marshall Capital	B25F	1998
41222	R322TLM	DU	Dennis Dart 9.3 SLF	Marshall Capital	B22D	1998
41224	R224TLM	BT	Dennis Dart 9.3 SLF	Marshall Capital	B22D	1998
41225	R225TLM	BT	Dennis Dart 9.3 SLF	Marshall Capital	B22D	1998
41226	R226TLM		Dennis Dart 9.3 SLF	Marshall Capital	B25F	1998
41227	R227TLM	SC	Dennis Dart 9.3 SLF	Marshall Capital	B22D	1998
41228	R228TLM	DU	Dennis Dart 9.3 SLF	Marshall Capital	B22D	1998
41236	S236KLM	DU	Dennis Dart 10.1 SLF	Marshall Capital	B29D	1998
41237	S237KLM	DU	Dennis Dart 10.1 SLF	Marshall Capital	B29D	1998
41242	S242KLM	L	Dennis Dart 10.1 SLF	Marshall Capital	B29D	1998
41243	S243KLM	SC	Dennis Dart 10.1 SLF	Marshall Capital	B33F	1998
41244	S244KLM	SC	Dennis Dart 10.1 SLF	Marshall Capital	B29D	1998
41245	S245KLM	DU	Dennis Dart 10.1 SLF	Marshall Capital	B33F	1998
41246	S246KLM	BT	Dennis Dart 10.1 SLF	Marshall Capital	B29D	1998
41278	T278JLD	L	Dennis Dart 9.3 SLF	Marshall Capital	B25F	1999
41279	T279JLD	L	Dennis Dart 9.3 SLF	Marshall Capital	B25F	1999
41288	T288JLD	DU	Dennis Dart 9.3 SLF	Marshall Capital	B22D	1999
41300	T430JLD	DU	Dennis Dart 9.3 SLF	Marshall Capital	B22D	1999
41301	T301JLD	DU	Dennis Dart 9.3 SLF	Marshall Capital	B22D	1999
41302	T302JLD	SC	Dennis Dart 9.3 SLF	Marshall Capital	B22D	1999
41303	T303JLD	DU	Dennis Dart 9.3 SLF	Marshall Capital	B22D	1999
41304	T304JLD	DU	Dennis Dart 9.3 SLF	Marshall Capital	B22D	1999
41305	T305JLD	DU	Dennis Dart 9.3 SLF	Marshall Capital	B22D	1999
41306	T306JLD	DU	Dennis Dart 9.3 SLF	Marshall Capital	B22D	1999
41307	V307GBY	SC	Dennis Dart 10.1 SLF	Marshall Capital	B28D	1999
41308	V308GBY	BT	Dennis Dart 10.1 SLF	Marshall Capital	B28D	1999
41309	V309GBY	BT	Dennis Dart 10.1 SLF	Marshall Capital	B28D	1999
41310	V310GBY	SC	Dennis Dart 10.1 SLF	Marshall Capital	B28D	1999
41311	V311GBY	BT	Dennis Dart 10.1 SLF	Marshall Capital	B28D	1999
41312	V312GBY	SC	Dennis Dart 10.1 SLF	Marshall Capital	B29F	1999
41313	V313GBY	BT	Dennis Dart 10.1 SLF	Marshall Capital	B28D	1999
41314	V314GBY	BT	Dennis Dart 10.1 SLF	Marshall Capital	B29F	1999
41337	T337ALR	BK	Dennis Dart 8.8 SLF	Marshall Capital	B25F	1999
41339	T339ALR	BK	Dennis Dart 8.8 SLF	Marshall Capital	B25F	1999
41342	T342ALR	BK	Dennis Dart 8.8 SLF	Marshall Capital	B25F	1999
41349	V349DLH	LN	Dennis Dart 8.8 SLF	Marshall Capital	B25F	1999
41357	V357DLH	r	Dennis Dart 8.8 SLF	Marshall Capital	B25F	1999
41359	V359DLH	r	Dennis Dart 8.8 SLF	Marshall Capital	B25F	1999

41681	W681ULL	SC	Dennis Dart 10.1 SLF	Marshall Capital	B27F	2000
41682	W682ULL	SC	Dennis Dart 10.1 SLF	Marshall Capital	B27F	2000
41683	W683ULL	BT	Dennis Dart 10.1 SLF	Marshall Capital	B27F	2000
41684	W684ULL	BT	Dennis Dart 10.1 SLF	Marshall Capital	B24D	2000
41685	W685ULL	SC	Dennis Dart 10.1 SLF	Marshall Capital	B25F	2000
42376	V676FPO	L	Dennis Dart 10.7 SLF	UVG Urbanstar	B38F	1999
42885	SF05KXJ	O	Dennis Dart 10.7 SLF	Alexander ALX200	B37F	2005
42886	SF05KXK	O	Dennis Dart 10.7 SLF	Alexander ALX200	B37F	2005
42887	SF05KXL	O	Dennis Dart 10.7 SLF	Alexander ALX200	B37F	2005
42888	SF05KXM	O	Dennis Dart 10.7 SLF	Alexander ALX200	B37F	2005
43843	SN04EFY	LW	TransBus Dart 8.8 SLF	TransBus Mini Pointer	B29F	2004
43844	SN04EFZ	LT	TransBus Dart 8.8 SLF	TransBus Mini Pointer	B29F	2004
48045	N345CJA	wa	Volvo B6-50	Alexander Dash	B16F	1996
50077	P420MEH	AB	Mercedes-Benz 709D	Plaxton Beaver	B22F	1996
50275	S306EWU	GS	Optare Solo M850	Optare	B27F	1998
50283	W314DWX	LT	Optare Solo M850	Optare	B27F	2000
50460	SJ03DOH	ABGS	Optare Solo M850	Optare	B27F	2003
50461	SJ03DPE	C	Optare Solo M850	Optare	B27F	2003
50462	SJ03DPF	C	Optare Solo M850	Optare	B20F	2003
50463	SJ03DPN	C	Optare Solo M850	Optare	B27F	2003
50464	SJ03DPU	SC	Optare Solo M850	Optare	B27F	2003
50465	SJ03DPV	C	Optare Solo M850	Optare	B27F	2003
50468	SJ03DPZ	ABGS	Optare Solo M850	Optare	B20F	2003
53201	YJ54BSV	SC	Optare Solo M950	Optare	B30F	2004
53202	SF05KUJ	C	Optare Solo M950	Optare	B30F	2005
53203	SF05KUK	C	Optare Solo M950	Optare	B30F	2005
56001	YN53VBT	AB-u	Mercedes-Benz Vario O.814D	Plaxton Cheetah	C29F	2003
56002	YN53VBU	AB-r	Mercedes-Benz Vario O.814D	Plaxton Cheetah	C29F	2003
56003	YN53VBV	r	Mercedes-Benz Vario O.814D	Plaxton Cheetah	C29F	2003
56004	EY54BPX	r	Mercedes-Benz Vario O.814D	Plaxton Cheetah	C29F	2004
56007	EY54BRV	AB	Mercedes-Benz Vario O.814D	Plaxton Cheetah	C29F	2004
56008	EY54BRX	AB	Mercedes-Benz Vario O.814D	Plaxton Cheetah	C29F	2004
56501	YX05AVV	AB	Mercedes-Benz Vario O.814D	Autobus Nouvelle	C26F	2005
60138	G612NWA	t	Volvo B10M-55	Alexander PS	B51F	1990
60163	S110TNB	BK	Scania L94UB	Wright Solar	B40F	1999
60165	S112TNB	BK	Scania L94UB	Wright Solar	B40F	1999
60166	S113TNB	LT	Scania L94UB	Wright Solar	B40F	1999
60167	S114TNB	LT	Scania L94UB	Wright Solar	B40F	1999
60168	S115TNB	BK	Scania L94UB	Wright Solar	B40F	1999
60178	V126DND	BK	Scania L94UB	Wright Solar	B42F	2000
60179	V127DND	LT	Scania L94UB	Wright Solar	B42F	2000
60180	V128DND	BK	Scania L94UB	Wright Solar	B42F	2000
60181	V129DND	BK	Scania L94UB	Wright Solar	B42F	2000
60182	V130DND	LT	Scania L94UB	Wright Solar	B40F	2000
60186	V134DND	BK	Scania L94UB	Wright Solar	B42F	2000
60187	V135DND	LT	Scania L94UB	Wright Solar	B42F	2000
60188	V136DND	BK	Scania L94UB	Wright Solar	B42F	2000
60191	V139DND	LT	Scania L94UB	Wright Solar	B42F	2000
60192	V140DND	LT	Scania L94UB	Wright Solar	B42F	2000
60195	Y343XBN	LT	Scania L94UB	Wright Solar	B43F	2001
60197	Y597KNE	BK	Scania L94UB	Wright Solar	B43F	2001
60198	Y344XBN	LT	Scania L94UB	Wright Solar	B43F	2001
60199	X256USH	LT	Scania L94UB	Wright Solar	B43F	2001
60203	Y632RTD	BK	Scania L94UB	Wright Solar	B43F	2001
60204	X272USH	LT	Scania L94UB	Wright Solar	B43F	2001
60220	T566BSS	LN	Scania L94UB	Wright Solar	B43F	1999
60221	T567BSS	BK	Scania L94UB	Wright Solar	B43F	1999
60464	G609NWA	l	Volvo B10M-55	Alexander PS	B51F	1990
60466	G613NWA	t	Volvo B10M-55	Alexander PS	B51F	1990
60483	G638NWA	L	Volvo B10M-55	Alexander PS	B51F	1990

60492	H648RKU	w	Volvo B10M-55	Alexander PS	B51F	1990
60520	H678THL	w	Volvo B10M-55	Alexander PS	B51F	1991
60578	N741CKY	LN	Volvo B10M-55	Alexander PS	DP49F	1996
60579	N742CKY	LN	Volvo B10M-55	Alexander PS	DP49F	1996
60580	N743CKY	BT	Volvo B10M-55	Alexander PS	DP49F	1996
60581	N744CKY	LW	Volvo B10M-55	Alexander PS	DP49F	1996
60582	N745CKY	BT	Volvo B10M-55	Alexander PS	DP49F	1996
60583	N746CKY	LN	Volvo B10M-55	Alexander PS	DP49F	1996
60584	N247CKY	w	Volvo B10M-55	Alexander PS	DP49F	1996
60585	N748CKY	LN	Volvo B10M-55	Alexander PS	DP49F	1996
60586	N749CKY	DU	Volvo B10M-55	Alexander PS	B49F	1996
60587	N750CKY	DU	Volvo B10M-55	Alexander PS	B49F	1996
60588	N751CKY	LN	Volvo B10M-55	Alexander PS	B49F	1996
60589	N752CKY	LT	Volvo B10M-55	Alexander PS	B49F	1996
60590	N753CKY	LN	Volvo B10M-55	Alexander PS	B49F	1996
60591	N754CKY	LN	Volvo B10M-55	Alexander PS	B49F	1996
60592	N755CKY	LN	Volvo B10M-55	Alexander PS	B49F	1996
60593	N756CKY	BT	Volvo B10M-55	Alexander PS	B49F	1996
60594	N757CKY	PH	Volvo B10M-55	Alexander PS	B49F	1996
60595	N758CKY	BT	Volvo B10M-55	Alexander PS	B49F	1996
60596	N759CKY	D	Volvo B10M-55	Alexander PS	B49F	1996
60601	N764CKY	w	Volvo B10M-55	Alexander PS	B49F	1996
61017	S116CSG	DU	Scania L94UB	Wright Solar	B43F	1999
61018	S117CSG	DU	Scania L94UB	Wright Solar	B43F	1999
61019	S118CSG	DU	Scania L94UB	Wright Solar	B43F	1999
61020	S119CSG	DU	Scania L94UB	Wright Solar	B43F	1999
61021	S220GKS	DU	Scania L94UB	Wright Solar	B43F	1999
61022	T421GUG	DU	Scania L94UB	Wright Solar	B43F	1999
61023	T422GUG	DU	Scania L94UB	Wright Solar	B43F	1999
61024	T423GUG	DU	Scania L94UB	Wright Solar	B43F	1999
61025	T424GUG	L	Scania L94UB	Wright Solar	B43F	1999
61026	T425GUG	L	Scania L94UB	Wright Solar	B43F	1999
61027	T426GUG	L	Scania L94UB	Wright Solar	B43F	1999
61028	T427GUG	L	Scania L94UB	Wright Solar	B43F	1999
61043	V142ESC	L	Scania L94UB	Wright Solar	B43F	1999
61044	V143ESC	L	Scania L94UB	Wright Solar	B43F	1999
61052	P432YSH	BK	Scania L113CRL	Wright Axcess-ultralow	B47F	1997
61053	P433YSH	BK	Scania L113CRL	Wright Axcess-ultralow	B47F	1997
61158	R175GSX	L	Scania L113CRL	Wright Axcess-ultralow	B40F	1998
61214	YM52UVK	D	Scania L94UB	Wright Solar	B43F	2003
61215	YM52UVL	NB	Scania L94UB	Wright Solar	B43F	2003
61216	YM52UVN	LTLN	Scania L94UB	Wright Solar	B43F	2003
61217	YM52UVO	NB	Scania L94UB	Wright Solar	B43F	2003
61218	YM52UVP	D	Scania L94UB	Wright Solar	B43F	2003
61219	YM52UVR	NB	Scania L94UB	Wright Solar	B43F	2003
61220	YM52UVS	D	Scania L94UB	Wright Solar	B43F	2003
61221	YM52UVT	D	Scania L94UB	Wright Solar	B43F	2003
61222	YM52UVU	LT	Scania L94UB	Wright Solar	B43F	2003
61223	YM52UVW	LT	Scania L94UB	Wright Solar	B43F	2003
61224	YM52UVZ	NB	Scania L94UB	Wright Solar	B43F	2003
61225	YM52UWA	GS	Scania L94UB	Wright Solar	B43F	2003
61226	YM52UWB	D	Scania L94UB	Wright Solar	B43F	2003
61227	YM52UWD	M	Scania L94UB	Wright Solar	B43F	2003
61228	YM52UWF	GS	Scania L94UB	Wright Solar	B43F	2003
61229	YM52UWG	M LN	Scania L94UB	Wright Solar	B43F	2003
61230	YM52UWH	D	Scania L94UB	Wright Solar	B43F	2003
61231	YM52UWJ	D	Scania L94UB	Wright Solar	B43F	2003
61232	YM52UWK	M	Scania L94UB	Wright Solar	B43F	2003
61233	YM52UWN	LT	Scania L94UB	Wright Solar	B43F	2003
61234	R174GSX	L	Scania L113CRL	Wright Axcess-ultralow	B40F	1998

Fleet	Reg		Type	Body	Seat	Year
61256	G601NWA	L	Volvo B10M-55	Alexander PS	B51F	1990
61259	G611NWA	L	Volvo B10M-55	Alexander PS	B51F	1990
61260	G614NWA	t	Volvo B10M-55	Alexander PS	B51F	1990
61261	G615NWA	L	Volvo B10M-55	Alexander PS	B51F	1990
61262	G616NWA	L	Volvo B10M-55	Alexander PS	B51F	1990
61266	G621NWA	t	Volvo B10M-55	Alexander PS	B51F	1990
61291	S106CSG	L	Scania L94UB	Wright Axcess-Floline	B43F	1998
61292	S107CSG	L	Scania L94UB	Wright Axcess-Floline	B43F	1998
61293	S108CSG	L	Scania L94UB	Wright Axcess-Floline	B43F	1998
61294	S109CSG	L	Scania L94UB	Wright Axcess-Floline	B43F	1998
61295	S110CSG	L	Scania L94UB	Wright Axcess-Floline	B43F	1998
61296	S211CSG	L	Scania L94UB	Wright Axcess-Floline	B43F	1998
61298	S113CSG	L	Scania L94UB	Wright Solar	B43F	1999
61299	S114CSG	L	Scania L94UB	Wright Solar	B43F	1999
61300	S115CSG	L	Scania L94UB	Wright Solar	B43F	1999
61306	SJ51DJZ	SC	Volvo B10BLE	Wright Renown	B41F	2001
61347	K711EDT	w	Volvo B10M-55	Alexander PS	B51F	1992
61371	M765PRS	w	Volvo B10M-55	Alexander PS	DP48F	1994
61372	M766PRS	w	Volvo B10M-55	Alexander PS	DP48F	1994
61373	M767PRS	w	Volvo B10M-55	Alexander PS	DP48F	1994
61374	M768PRS	w	Volvo B10M-55	Alexander PS	DP48F	1994
61375	M769PRS	w	Volvo B10M-55	Alexander PS	DP48F	1994
61376	M770PRS	w	Volvo B10M-55	Alexander PS	DP48F	1994
61377	M771PRS	w	Volvo B10M-55	Alexander PS	DP48F	1994
61378	M772PRS	O	Volvo B10M-55	Alexander PS	DP48F	1994
61379	M773PRS	w	Volvo B10M-55	Alexander PS	DP48F	1994
61380	M774PRS	w	Volvo B10M-55	Alexander PS	DP48F	1994
61381	M775PRS	w	Volvo B10M-55	Alexander PS	DP48F	1994
61382	M776PRS	w	Volvo B10M-55	Alexander PS	DP48F	1994
61384	M779PRS	w	Volvo B10M-55	Alexander PS	DP48F	1994
61387	M877PRS	BT	Volvo B10M-55	Alexander PS	DP48F	1994
61388	N120OGG	DU	Volvo B10M-55	Alexander PS	B49F	1996
61389	N121OGG	BT	Volvo B10M-55	Alexander PS	B49F	1996
61390	N122OGG	w	Volvo B10M-55	Alexander PS	B49F	1996
61391	N123OGG	BT	Volvo B10M-55	Alexander PS	B49F	1996
61392	N124OGG	BT	Volvo B10M-55	Alexander PS	B49F	1996
61393	N125OGG	BT	Volvo B10M-55	Alexander PS	B49F	1996
61394	N126OGG	SC	Volvo B10M-55	Alexander PS	B49F	1996
61395	N127OGG	DU	Volvo B10M-55	Alexander PS	B49F	1996
61396	N128OGG	w	Volvo B10M-55	Alexander PS	B49F	1996
61397	N129OGG	BT	Volvo B10M-55	Alexander PS	B49F	1996
61398	N130OGG	SC	Volvo B10M-55	Alexander PS	B49F	1996
61399	N131OGG	BT	Volvo B10M-55	Alexander PS	B49F	1996
61400	N132OGG	PH	Volvo B10M-55	Alexander PS	B49F	1996
61401	N133OGG	SC	Volvo B10M-55	Alexander PS	B49F	1996
61402	N134OGG	PH	Volvo B10M-55	Alexander PS	B49F	1996
61403	N135OGG	BT	Volvo B10M-55	Alexander PS	B49F	1996
61404	N136OGG	PH	Volvo B10M-55	Alexander PS	B49F	1996
61405	N137OGG	SC	Volvo B10M-55	Alexander PS	B49F	1996
61406	N138OGG	PH	Volvo B10M-55	Alexander PS	B49F	1996
61407	N190OGG	SC	Volvo B10M-55	Alexander PS	B49F	1996
61408	N199OGG	w	Volvo B10M-55	Alexander PS	B49F	1996
61409	N89OGG	DU	Volvo B10M-55	Alexander PS	B49F	1996
61410	N91OGG	C	Volvo B10M-55	Alexander PS	B49F	1996
61412	N92OGG	PH	Volvo B10M-55	Alexander PS	B49F	1996
61413	N930LSU	w	Volvo B10M-55	Alexander PS	B49F	1995
61414	N931LSU	PH	Volvo B10M-55	Alexander PS	B49F	1995
61415	N932LSU	PH	Volvo B10M-55	Alexander PS	B49F	1995
61416	N933LSU	w	Volvo B10M-55	Alexander PS	B49F	1995
61417	N934LSU	PH	Volvo B10M-55	Alexander PS	B49F	1995

61418	N935LSU	PH	Volvo B10M-55	Alexander PS	B49F	1995
61419	N936LSU	DU	Volvo B10M-55	Alexander PS	B49F	1995
61420	N937LSU	w	Volvo B10M-55	Alexander PS	B49F	1995
61421	N938LSU	w	Volvo B10M-55	Alexander PS	B49F	1995
61422	N939LSU	PH	Volvo B10M-55	Alexander PS	B49F	1995
61423	N93OGG	PH	Volvo B10M-55	Alexander PS	B49F	1996
61424	N940LSU	w	Volvo B10M-55	Alexander PS	B49F	1995
61425	N941LSU	w	Volvo B10M-55	Alexander PS	B49F	1995
61426	N942LSU	C	Volvo B10M-55	Alexander PS	B49F	1995
61427	N943LSU	DU	Volvo B10M-55	Alexander PS	B49F	1995
61428	N944LSU	DU	Volvo B10M-55	Alexander PS	B49F	1995
61430	N946LSU	SC	Volvo B10M-55	Alexander PS	B49F	1995
61431	N947LSU	PH	Volvo B10M-55	Alexander PS	B49F	1995
61432	N948LSU	SC	Volvo B10M-55	Alexander PS	B49F	1995
61433	N949LSU	PH	Volvo B10M-55	Alexander PS	B49F	1995
61434	N94OGG	SC	Volvo B10M-55	Alexander PS	B49F	1996
61435	N950LSU	w	Volvo B10M-55	Alexander PS	B49F	1995
61436	N951LSU	PH	Volvo B10M-55	Alexander PS	B49F	1995
61437	N952LSU	w	Volvo B10M-55	Alexander PS	B49F	1995
61438	N953LSU	PH	Volvo B10M-55	Alexander PS	B49F	1995
61439	N954LSU	SC	Volvo B10M-55	Alexander PS	B49F	1995
61440	N955LSU	PH	Volvo B10M-55	Alexander PS	B49F	1995
61441	N956LSU	DU	Volvo B10M-55	Alexander PS	B49F	1995
61442	N957LSU	w	Volvo B10M-55	Alexander PS	B49F	1995
61443	N958LSU	w	Volvo B10M-55	Alexander PS	B49F	1995
61444	N959LSU	w	Volvo B10M-55	Alexander PS	B49F	1995
61445	N95OGG	SC	Volvo B10M-55	Alexander PS	B49F	1996
61446	N960LSU	w	Volvo B10M-55	Alexander PS	B49F	1995
61447	N961LSU	PH	Volvo B10M-55	Alexander PS	B49F	1995
61448	N962LSU	PH	Volvo B10M-55	Alexander PS	B49F	1995
61449	N963LSU	PH	Volvo B10M-55	Alexander PS	B49F	1995
61450	N964LSU	L	Volvo B10M-55	Alexander PS	B49F	1995
61451	N965LSU	PH	Volvo B10M-55	Alexander PS	B49F	1995
61452	N966LSU	PH	Volvo B10M-55	Alexander PS	B49F	1995
61453	N967LSU	PH	Volvo B10M-55	Alexander PS	B49F	1995
61454	N968LSU	PH	Volvo B10M-55	Alexander PS	B49F	1995
61455	N969LSU	PH	Volvo B10M-55	Alexander PS	B49F	1995
61456	N96OGG	BT	Volvo B10M-55	Alexander PS	B49F	1996
61457	N970LSU	PH	Volvo B10M-55	Alexander PS	B49F	1995
61458	N971LSU	PH	Volvo B10M-55	Alexander PS	B49F	1995
61459	N972LSU	L	Volvo B10M-55	Alexander PS	B49F	1995
61460	N973LSU	SC	Volvo B10M-55	Alexander PS	B49F	1995
61461	N974LSU	DU	Volvo B10M-55	Alexander PS	B49F	1995
61462	N975LSU	PH	Volvo B10M-55	Alexander PS	B49F	1996
61463	N976LSU	PH	Volvo B10M-55	Alexander PS	B49F	1996
61464	N977LSU	DU	Volvo B10M-55	Alexander PS	B49F	1996
61465	N978LSU	w	Volvo B10M-55	Alexander PS	B49F	1996
61466	N979LSU	w	Volvo B10M-55	Alexander PS	B49F	1996
61467	N97OGG	BT	Volvo B10M-55	Alexander PS	B49F	1996
61468	N980LSU	w	Volvo B10M-55	Alexander PS	B49F	1996
61469	N981LSU	DU	Volvo B10M-55	Alexander PS	B49F	1996
61470	N982LSU	DU	Volvo B10M-55	Alexander PS	B49F	1996
61471	N983LSU	w	Volvo B10M-55	Alexander PS	B49F	1996
61472	N984LSU	DU	Volvo B10M-55	Alexander PS	B49F	1996
61473	N985LSU	BT	Volvo B10M-55	Alexander PS	B49F	1996
61474	N986LSU	SC	Volvo B10M-55	Alexander PS	B49F	1996
61475	N987LSU	PH	Volvo B10M-55	Alexander PS	B49F	1996
61476	N988LSU	DU	Volvo B10M-55	Alexander PS	B49F	1996
61477	N98OGG	PH	Volvo B10M-55	Alexander PS	B49F	1996
61478	P106MFS	L	Scania L113CRL	Wright Axcess-ultralow	B47F	1996

61479	P107MFS	L	Scania L113CRL	Wright Axcess-ultralow	B47F	1996
61480	P108MFS	L	Scania L113CRL	Wright Axcess-ultralow	B47F	1996
61481	P109MFS	L	Scania L113CRL	Wright Axcess-ultralow	B47F	1996
61482	P113YSH	L	Scania L113CRL	Wright Axcess-ultralow	B41F	1997
61489	P519TYS	DU	Volvo B10M-55	Alexander PS	B49F	1996
61490	P520TYS	BT	Volvo B10M-55	Alexander PS	B49F	1996
61491	P521TYS	DU	Volvo B10M-55	Alexander PS	B49F	1996
61492	P522TYS	BT	Volvo B10M-55	Alexander PS	B49F	1996
61493	P523TYS	BT	Volvo B10M-55	Alexander PS	B49F	1996
61494	P524TYS	BT	Volvo B10M-55	Alexander PS	B49F	1996
61495	P525TYS	DU	Volvo B10M-55	Alexander PS	B49F	1996
61496	P526TYS	DU	Volvo B10M-55	Alexander PS	B49F	1996
61497	P527TYS	BT	Volvo B10M-55	Alexander PS	B49F	1996
61498	P528TYS	BT	Volvo B10M-55	Alexander PS	B49F	1996
61499	P529TYS	DU	Volvo B10M-55	Alexander PS	B49F	1996
61500	P530TYS	DU	Volvo B10M-55	Alexander PS	B49F	1996
61501	P531TYS	DU	Volvo B10M-55	Alexander PS	B49F	1996
61502	P532TYS	SC	Volvo B10M-55	Alexander PS	B49F	1996
61503	P533TYS	C	Volvo B10M-55	Alexander PS	B49F	1996
61504	P534TYS	SC	Volvo B10M-55	Alexander PS	B49F	1997
61505	P535TYS	C	Volvo B10M-55	Alexander PS	B49F	1997
61506	P536TYS	C	Volvo B10M-55	Alexander PS	B49F	1997
61507	P537TYS	C	Volvo B10M-55	Alexander PS	B49F	1997
61508	P538TYS	C	Volvo B10M-55	Alexander PS	B49F	1997
61509	P539TYS	C	Volvo B10M-55	Alexander PS	B49F	1997
61510	P540TYS	C	Volvo B10M-55	Alexander PS	B49F	1997
61511	P541TYS	O	Volvo B10M-55	Alexander PS	B49F	1997
61512	P542TYS	O	Volvo B10M-55	Alexander PS	B49F	1997
61513	P543TYS	BT	Volvo B10M-55	Alexander PS	B49F	1997
61514	P544TYS	PH	Volvo B10M-55	Alexander PS	B49F	1997
61515	P545TYS	BT	Volvo B10M-55	Alexander PS	B49F	1997
61516	P546TYS	BT	Volvo B10M-55	Alexander PS	B49F	1997
61517	P547TYS	PH	Volvo B10M-55	Alexander PS	B49F	1997
61518	P548TYS	BT	Volvo B10M-55	Alexander PS	B49F	1997
61519	P549TYS	BT	Volvo B10M-55	Alexander PS	B49F	1997
61524	R110GSF	L	Scania L113CRL	Wright Axcess-ultralow	B40F	1997
61525	R112GSF	L	Scania L113CRL	Wright Axcess-ultralow	B40F	1997
61526	R114GSF	L	Scania L113CRL	Wright Axcess-ultralow	B40F	1997
61532	R120GSF	L	Scania L113CRL	Wright Axcess-ultralow	B40F	1997
61534	R122GSF	L	Scania L113CRL	Wright Axcess-ultralow	B40F	1997
61535	R123GSF	L	Scania L113CRL	Wright Axcess-ultralow	B40F	1997
61537	R128GSF	L	Scania L113CRL	Wright Axcess-ultralow	B40F	1997
61539	R130GSF	L	Scania L113CRL	Wright Axcess-ultralow	B40F	1997
61540	R131GSF	L	Scania L113CRL	Wright Axcess-ultralow	B40F	1997
61543	R158GSF	L	Scania L113CRL	Wright Axcess-ultralow	B40F	1998
61544	R159GSF	L	Scania L113CRL	Wright Axcess-ultralow	B40F	1998
61545	R160GSF	L	Scania L113CRL	Wright Axcess-ultralow	B40F	1998
61546	R161GSF	L	Scania L113CRL	Wright Axcess-ultralow	B40F	1998
61547	R162GSF	L	Scania L113CRL	Wright Axcess-ultralow	B40F	1998
61548	R163GSF	L	Scania L113CRL	Wright Axcess-ultralow	B40F	1998
61549	R164GSF	L	Scania L113CRL	Wright Axcess-ultralow	B40F	1998
61550	R165GSF	L	Scania L113CRL	Wright Axcess-ultralow	B40F	1998
61552	R167GSF	L	Scania L113CRL	Wright Axcess-ultralow	B40F	1998
61557	R172GSX	L	Scania L113CRL	Wright Axcess-ultralow	B40F	1998
61558	R195GSX	L	Scania L94UB	Wright Axcess-Floline	B43F	1998
61559	R211GSF	L	Scania L113CRL	Wright Axcess-ultralow	B40F	1997
61564	R344SUT	L	Scania L113CRL	Wright Axcess-ultralow	B40F	1998
61565	R345SUT	L	Scania L113CRL	Wright Axcess-ultralow	B40F	1998
61567	S550JSE	L	Scania L94UB	Wright Axcess-Floline	B40F	1998
61568	S551JSE	L	Scania L94UB	Wright Axcess-Floline	B40F	1998

61569	S552JSE	L	Scania L94UB	Wright Axcess-Floline	B40F	1998
61570	S553JSE	L	Scania L94UB	Wright Axcess-Floline	B40F	1998
61571	S554JSE	L	Scania L94UB	Wright Axcess-Floline	B40F	1998
61572*	S555JSE	L	Scania L94UB	Wright Axcess-Floline	B40F	1998
61573	S556JSE	L	Scania L94UB	Wright Axcess-Floline	B40F	1998
61574	S557JSE	L	Scania L94UB	Wright Axcess-Floline	B40F	1998
61575	S558JSE	L	Scania L94UB	Wright Axcess-Floline	B40F	1998
61576	S559JSE	L	Scania L94UB	Wright Axcess-Floline	B40F	1998
61577	S687BFS	L	Scania L113CRL	Wright Axcess-ultralow	B40F	1998
61579	S692BFS	L	Scania L94UB	Wright Axcess-Floline	B40F	1998
61580	S693BFS	L	Scania L94UB	Wright Axcess-Floline	B40F	1998
61581	S694BFS	SC	Scania L94UB	Wright Axcess-Floline	B40F	1998
61582	S696BFS	L	Scania L94UB	Wright Axcess-Floline	B43F	1998
61583	S697BFS	L	Scania L94UB	Wright Axcess-Floline	B43F	1998
61584	S698BFS	L	Scania L94UB	Wright Axcess-Floline	B43F	1998
61585	S699BFS	L	Scania L94UB	Wright Axcess-Floline	B43F	1998
61586	S701BFS	L	Scania L94UB	Wright Axcess-Floline	B43F	1998
61587	SA02BZD	PH	Volvo B7L	Wright Eclipse	B41F	2002
61588	SA02BZE	PH	Volvo B7L	Wright Eclipse	B41F	2002
61589	SA02BZF	PH	Volvo B7L	Wright Eclipse	B41F	2002
61590	SA02BZG	SC	Volvo B7L	Wright Eclipse	B41F	2002
61591	SA02BZH	SC	Volvo B7L	Wright Eclipse	B41F	2002
61592	SA02BZJ	SC	Volvo B7L	Wright Eclipse	B41F	2002
61593	SA02BZK	SC	Volvo B7L	Wright Eclipse	B41F	2002
61594	SA02BZL	SC	Volvo B7L	Wright Eclipse	B41F	2002
61595	SA02BZM	SC	Volvo B7L	Wright Eclipse	B41F	2002
61596	SA02BZN	SC	Volvo B7L	Wright Eclipse	B41F	2002
61597	SF51YAA	O	Volvo B10BLE	Wright Renown	B44F	2001
61598	SF51YAD	O	Volvo B10BLE	Wright Renown	B44F	2001
61599	SF51YAE	O	Volvo B10BLE	Wright Renown	B44F	2001
61600	SF51YAG	O	Volvo B10BLE	Wright Renown	B44F	2001
61601	SF51YAH	O	Volvo B10BLE	Wright Renown	B44F	2001
61602	SF51YAJ	O	Volvo B10BLE	Wright Renown	B44F	2001
61603	SF51YAK	O	Volvo B10BLE	Wright Renown	B44F	2001
61604	SF51YAO	O	Volvo B10BLE	Wright Renown	B44F	2001
61605	SF51YAU	O	Volvo B10BLE	Wright Renown	B44F	2001
61606	SF51YAV	O	Volvo B10BLE	Wright Renown	B44F	2001
61607	SF51YAW	O	Volvo B10BLE	Wright Renown	B44F	2001
61608	SF51YAX	O	Volvo B10BLE	Wright Renown	B44F	2001
61609	SF51YAY	O	Volvo B10BLE	Wright Renown	B44F	2001
61610	SF51YBA	O	Volvo B10BLE	Wright Renown	B44F	2001
61611	SF51YBB	O	Volvo B10BLE	Wright Renown	B44F	2001
61612	SF51YBC	O	Volvo B10BLE	Wright Renown	B44F	2001
61613	SF51YBD	O	Volvo B10BLE	Wright Renown	B44F	2001
61614	SF51YBE	O	Volvo B10BLE	Wright Renown	B44F	2001
61615	SF51YBG	SC	Volvo B7L	Wright Eclipse	B41F	2001
61616	SF51YBH	O	Volvo B10BLE	Wright Renown	B44F	2001
61617	SF51YBJ	O	Volvo B10BLE	Wright Renown	B44F	2001
61618	SF51YBK	O	Volvo B10BLE	Wright Renown	B44F	2001
61619	SF51YBL	O	Volvo B10BLE	Wright Renown	B44F	2001
61620	SF51YBM	O	Volvo B10BLE	Wright Renown	B44F	2001
61621	SF51YBN	O	Volvo B10BLE	Wright Renown	B44F	2001
61622	SF51YBO	O	Volvo B10BLE	Wright Renown	B44F	2001
61623	SF51YBP	O	Volvo B10BLE	Wright Renown	B44F	2001
61624	SF51YBR	z	Volvo B10BLE	Wright Renown	B44F	2001
61625	SF51YBS	BT	Volvo B10BLE	Wright Renown	B44F	2001
61626	SF51YBT	BT	Volvo B10BLE	Wright Renown	B44F	2001
61627	SH51MHY	SC	Volvo B7L	Wright Eclipse	B41F	2002
61628	SH51MHZ	SC	Volvo B7L	Wright Eclipse	B41F	2002
61629	SH51MJE	SC	Volvo B7L	Wright Eclipse	B41F	2002

61630	SH51MJF	SC	Volvo B7L	Wright Eclipse	B41F	2002
61632	SH51MKG	SC	Volvo B7L	Wright Eclipse	B41F	2002
61634	SH51MKK	SC	Volvo B7L	Wright Eclipse	B41F	2002
61635	SH51MKL	SC	Volvo B7L	Wright Eclipse	B41F	2002
61637	SJ51DHE	SC	Volvo B7L	Wright Eclipse	B41F	2002
61640	SJ51DHK	SC	Volvo B7L	Wright Eclipse	B41F	2002
61641	SJ51DHL	PH	Volvo B7L	Wright Eclipse	B41F	2002
61642	SJ51DHM	PH	Volvo B7L	Wright Eclipse	B41F	2001
61643	SJ51DHN	PH	Volvo B7L	Wright Eclipse	B41F	2001
61644	SJ51DHO	SC	Volvo B7L	Wright Eclipse	B41F	2001
61645	SJ51DHP	PH	Volvo B7L	Wright Eclipse	B41F	2001
61646	SJ51DHV	PH	Volvo B7L	Wright Eclipse	B41F	2001
61647	SJ51DHX	PH	Volvo B7L	Wright Eclipse	B41F	2001
61648	SJ51DHZ	SC	Volvo B7L	Wright Eclipse	B41F	2001
61649	SJ51DJD	PH	Volvo B7L	Wright Eclipse	B41F	2001
61650	SJ51DJE	SC	Volvo B7L	Wright Eclipse	B41F	2001
61651	SJ51DJF	PH	Volvo B7L	Wright Eclipse	B41F	2001
61652	SJ51DJK	BT	Volvo B10BLE	Wright Renown	B44F	2001
61653	SJ51DJO	BT	Volvo B10BLE	Wright Renown	B44F	2001
61654	SJ51DJU	BT	Volvo B10BLE	Wright Renown	B44F	2001
61656	SJ51DJX	SC	Volvo B7L	Wright Eclipse	B41F	2001
61657	SJ51DJY	SC	Volvo B7L	Wright Eclipse	B41F	2001
61658	SJ51DKA	SC	Volvo B7L	Wright Eclipse	B41F	2001
61659	SJ51DKD	SC	Volvo B7L	Wright Eclipse	B41F	2001
61660	SJ51DKE	PH	Volvo B7L	Wright Eclipse	B41F	2001
61661	SJ51DKF	SC	Volvo B7L	Wright Eclipse	B41F	2002
61663	SJ51DKL	SC	Volvo B7L	Wright Eclipse	B41F	2002
61664	SJ51DKN	PH	Volvo B7L	Wright Eclipse	B41F	2002
61667	V116FSF	L	Scania L94UB	Wright Solar	B43F	1999
61668	V117FSF	L	Scania L94UB	Wright Solar	B43F	1999
61669	V118FSF	L	Scania L94UB	Wright Solar	B43F	1999
61670	V119FSF	L	Scania L94UB	Wright Solar	B43F	1999
61671	V120FSF	L	Scania L94UB	Wright Solar	B43F	1999
61672	V122FSF	L	Scania L94UB	Wright Solar	B43F	1999
61673	V221GLS	L	Scania L94UB	Wright Solar	B43F	2000
61674	W723PSF	LN	Scania L94UB	Wright Solar	B43F	2000
61675	X424UMS	L	Scania L94UB	Wright Solar	B43F	2000
61676	X425UMS	L	Scania L94UB	Wright Solar	B43F	2000
61677	X426UMS	L	Scania L94UB	Wright Solar	B43F	2000
61678	X427UMS	L	Scania L94UB	Wright Solar	B43F	2000
61679	X429UMS	L	Scania L94UB	Wright Solar	B43F	2000
61680	X431UMS	L	Scania L94UB	Wright Solar	B43F	2000
61681	X432UMS	L	Scania L94UB	Wright Solar	B43F	2000
61682	X433UMS	L	Scania L94UB	Wright Solar	B43F	2000
61683	X434UMS	L	Scania L94UB	Wright Solar	B43F	2000
61684	X435UMS	L	Scania L94UB	Wright Solar	B43F	2000
61685	X436UMS	L	Scania L94UB	Wright Solar	B43F	2000
61686	X437UMS	L	Scania L94UB	Wright Solar	B43F	2000
61687	X438UMS	L	Scania L94UB	Wright Solar	B43F	2000
61688	X439UMS	L	Scania L94UB	Wright Solar	B43F	2000
61689	X441UMS	DU	Scania L94UB	Wright Solar	B43F	2000
61690	X442UMS	DU	Scania L94UB	Wright Solar	B43F	2000
61691	X443UMS	DU	Scania L94UB	Wright Solar	B43F	2000
61692	X445UMS	DU	Scania L94UB	Wright Solar	B43F	2000
61693	X446UMS	DU	Scania L94UB	Wright Solar	B43F	2000
61694	X447UMS	DU	Scania L94UB	Wright Solar	B43F	2000
61695	X448UMS	DU	Scania L94UB	Wright Solar	B43F	2000
61696	X449UMS	DU	Scania L94UB	Wright Solar	B43F	2000
61697	X451UMS	DU	Scania L94UB	Wright Solar	B43F	2000
61698	X452UMS	DU	Scania L94UB	Wright Solar	B43F	2000

61699	X453UMS	DU	Scania L94UB	Wright Solar	B43F	2000
61700	X454UMS	DU	Scania L94UB	Wright Solar	B43F	2000
61701	X457UMS	DU	Scania L94UB	Wright Solar	B43F	2000
61702	X458UMS	DU	Scania L94UB	Wright Solar	B43F	2000
61703	X459UMS	DU	Scania L94UB	Wright Solar	B43F	2000
61704	X461UMS	DU	Scania L94UB	Wright Solar	B43F	2000
61705	Y301RTD	BT	Volvo B10BLE	Wright Renown	B44F	2001
61706	Y302RTD	BT	Volvo B10BLE	Wright Renown	B44F	2001
61707	Y303RTD	BT	Volvo B10BLE	Wright Renown	B44F	2001
61708	Y304RTD	BT	Volvo B10BLE	Wright Renown	B44F	2001
61709	Y307RTD	BT	Volvo B10BLE	Wright Renown	B44F	2001
61710	Y949RTD	BT	Volvo B10BLE	Wright Renown	B44F	2001
62120	HSO61N	AB-p	Leyland Leopard PSU4C/4R	Alexander AY	C45F	1975
62121	RG1173	AB-p	Albion PMA28	Walker	B31R	1930
62122	X601NSS	AB	Volvo B10BLE	Wright Renown	B44F	2000
62123	X602NSS	AB	Volvo B10BLE	Wright Renown	B44F	2000
62124	X603NSS	AB	Volvo B10BLE	Wright Renown	B44F	2000
62125	X604NSS	AB	Volvo B10BLE	Wright Renown	B44F	2000
62126	X605NSS	AB	Volvo B10BLE	Wright Renown	B44F	2000
62127	X606NSS	AB	Volvo B10BLE	Wright Renown	B44F	2000
62128	X607NSS	w	Volvo B10BLE	Wright Renown	B44F	2000
62129	X608NSS	AB	Volvo B10BLE	Wright Renown	B44F	2000
62130	X609NSS	AB	Volvo B10BLE	Wright Renown	B44F	2000
62131	X69NSS	AB	Volvo B10BLE	Wright Renown	B44F	2000
62132	X611NSS	AB	Volvo B10BLE	Wright Renown	B44F	2000
62133	X612NSS	AB	Volvo B10BLE	Wright Renown	B44F	2000
62134	X613NSS	AB	Volvo B10BLE	Wright Renown	B44F	2000
62135	X614NSS	AB	Volvo B10BLE	Wright Renown	B44F	2000
62136	X615NSS	AB	Volvo B10BLE	Wright Renown	B44F	2000
62137	X616NSS	AB	Volvo B10BLE	Wright Renown	B44F	2000
62138	X617NSS	AB	Volvo B10BLE	Wright Renown	B44F	2000
62139	X618NSS	AB	Volvo B10BLE	Wright Renown	B44F	2000
62140	X619NSS	AB	Volvo B10BLE	Wright Renown	B44F	2000
62141	X944NSO	AB	Volvo B10BLE	Wright Renown	B44F	2000
62149	X621NSS	AB	Volvo B10BLE	Wright Renown	B44F	2001
62150	X622NSS	AB	Volvo B10BLE	Wright Renown	B44F	2001
62151	X623NSS	AB	Volvo B10BLE	Wright Renown	B44F	2001
62152	X624NSS	AB	Volvo B10BLE	Wright Renown	B44F	2001
62153	X477NSS	AB	Volvo B10BLE	Wright Renown	B44F	2001
62154	Y626RSA	AB	Volvo B10BLE	Wright Renown	B44F	2001
62155	Y627RSA	AB	Volvo B10BLE	Wright Renown	B44F	2001
62156	R330GHS	AB	Volvo B10BLE	Wright Renown	B41F	1997
62157	R331GHS	AB	Volvo B10BLE	Wright Renown	B41F	1997
62158	R332GHS	AB	Volvo B10BLE	Wright Renown	B41F	1998
62159	R334GHS	AB	Volvo B10BLE	Wright Renown	B41F	1998
62160	R335GHS	AB	Volvo B10BLE	Wright Renown	B41F	1998
62161	R336GHS	AB	Volvo B10BLE	Wright Renown	B41F	1998
62162	R337GHS	AB	Volvo B10BLE	Wright Renown	B41F	1998
62163	Y628RSA	AB	Volvo B10BLE	Wright Renown	B44F	2001
62164	Y629RSA	AB	Volvo B10BLE	Wright Renown	B44F	2001
62165	Y701RSA	AB	Volvo B10BLE	Wright Renown	B44F	2001
62166	Y631RSA	AB	Volvo B10BLE	Wright Renown	B44F	2001
62167	Y632RSA	AB	Volvo B10BLE	Wright Renown	B44F	2001
62168	Y633RSA	AB	Volvo B10BLE	Wright Renown	B44F	2001
62169	Y634RSA	AB	Volvo B10BLE	Wright Renown	B44F	2001
62170	W577RFS	AB	Volvo B10BLE	Alexander ALX300	B44F	2000
62171	W578RFS	AB	Volvo B10BLE	Alexander ALX300	B44F	2000
62172	W579RFS	AB	Volvo B10BLE	Alexander ALX300	B44F	2000
62173	W581RFS	AB	Volvo B10BLE	Alexander ALX300	B44F	2000
62174	W582RFS	AB	Volvo B10BLE	Alexander ALX300	B44F	2000

62175	W583RFS	AB	Volvo B10BLE	Alexander ALX300	B44F	2000
62176	W584RFS	AB	Volvo B10BLE	Alexander ALX300	B44F	2000
62177	Y635RSA	AB	Volvo B10BLE	Wright Renown	B44F	2001
62178	Y636RSA	AB	Volvo B10BLE	Wright Renown	B44F	2001
62179	Y637RSA	AB	Volvo B10BLE	Wright Renown	B44F	2001
62180	Y638RSA	AB	Volvo B10BLE	Wright Renown	B44F	2001
62181	Y639RSA	AB	Volvo B10BLE	Wright Renown	B44F	2001
62182	X683ADK	AB	Volvo B10BLE	Wright Renown	B43F	2000
62183	X684ADK	AB	Volvo B10BLE	Wright Renown	B43F	2000
62184	W585RFS	AB	Volvo B10BLE	Alexander ALX300	B44F	2000
62185	W586RFS	AB	Volvo B10BLE	Alexander ALX300	B44F	2000
62186	W587RFS	AB	Volvo B10BLE	Alexander ALX300	B44F	2000
62187	W588RFS	AB	Volvo B10BLE	Alexander ALX300	B44F	2000
62188	W589RFS	AB	Volvo B10BLE	Alexander ALX300	B44F	2000
62189	W591RFS	AB	Volvo B10BLE	Alexander ALX300	B44F	2000
62190	W592RFS	AB	Volvo B10BLE	Alexander ALX300	B44F	2000
62191	X685ADK	AB	Volvo B10BLE	Wright Renown	B43F	2000
62192	X686ADK	AB	Volvo B10BLE	Wright Renown	B43F	2000
62195	X689ADK	AB	Volvo B10BLE	Wright Renown	B43F	2000
62196	X691ADK	AB	Volvo B10BLE	Wright Renown	B43F	2000
62197	X692ADK	AB	Volvo B10BLE	Wright Renown	B43F	2000
62198	X693ADK	AB	Volvo B10BLE	Wright Renown	B43F	2000
62199	X694ADK	AB	Volvo B10BLE	Wright Renown	B43F	2000
62200	X695ADK	AB	Volvo B10BLE	Wright Renown	B43F	2000
62201	X696ADK	AB	Volvo B10BLE	Wright Renown	B43F	2000
62202	X697ADK	AB	Volvo B10BLE	Wright Renown	B43F	2000
62203	X698ADK	AB	Volvo B10BLE	Wright Renown	B43F	2000
62204	W681RNA	AB	Volvo B10BLE	Wright Renown	B43F	2000
62205	W593RFS	AB	Volvo B10BLE	Alexander ALX300	B44F	2000
62206	W594RFS	AB	Volvo B10BLE	Alexander ALX300	B44F	2000
62207	W595RFS	AB	Volvo B10BLE	Alexander ALX300	B44F	2000
62208	W596RFS	AB	Volvo B10BLE	Alexander ALX300	B44F	2000
62209	W597RFS	AB	Volvo B10BLE	Alexander ALX300	B44F	2000
62210	W598RFS	AB	Volvo B10BLE	Alexander ALX300	B44F	2000
62211	W599RFS	AB	Volvo B10BLE	Alexander ALX300	B44F	2000
62212	W682RNA	AB	Volvo B10BLE	Wright Renown	B43F	2000
62213	W683RNA	AB	Volvo B10BLE	Wright Renown	B43F	2000
62219	W601RFS	AB	Volvo B10BLE	Alexander ALX300	B44F	2000
62220	W602RFS	AB	Volvo B10BLE	Alexander ALX300	B44F	2000
62221	W603RFS	AB	Volvo B10BLE	Alexander ALX300	B44F	2000
62222	W604RFS	AB	Volvo B10BLE	Alexander ALX300	B44F	2000
62223	W605RFS	AB	Volvo B10BLE	Alexander ALX300	B44F	2000
62224 *	X606RFS	ABLT	Volvo B10BLE	Alexander ALX300	B44F	2000
62225	W607RFS	ABLT	Volvo B10BLE	Alexander ALX300	B44F	2000
62226	W608RFS	AB	Volvo B10BLE	Alexander ALX300	B44F	2000
62227	W609RFS	ABGS	Volvo B10BLE	Alexander ALX300	B44F	2000
62228	YS51JVD	w	Bluebird AARE	Bluebird	B60F	2002
62268 *	N500TCC	r	Volvo B10M-62	Plaxton Premiere 350	C48FT	1996
62282	N535VSA	w	Mercedes-Benz O.405	Optare Prisma	B47F	1996
62283	N536VSA	w	Mercedes-Benz O.405	Optare Prisma	B47F	1996
62286	N538VSA	w	Mercedes-Benz O.405	Optare Prisma	B47F	1996
62291	P503XSH	LT	Scania L113CRL	Wright Axcess-ultralow	DP47F	1996
62292	P504XSH	BKLT	Scania L113CRL	Wright Axcess-ultralow	DP47F	1996
62294	P506XSH	LT	Scania L113CRL	Wright Axcess-ultralow	DP47F	1996
62295	N407ENW	LT	Scania L113CRL	Wright Axcess-ultralow	B47F	1995
62296	N408ENW	LW	Scania L113CRL	Wright Axcess-ultralow	B45F	1995
62298	N411ENW	BF	Scania L113CRL	Wright Axcess-ultralow	B47F	1995
62299	N406ENW	BF	Scania L113CRL	Wright Axcess-ultralow	B47F	1995
62300	R443ALS	LT	Scania L113CRL	Wright Axcess-ultralow	B40F	1998
62301	R544ALS	BFBK	Scania L113CRL	Wright Axcess-ultralow	B40F	1998

62302	R445ALS	BF	Scania L113CRL	Wright Axcess-ultralow	B40F	1998
62303	R446ALS	BF	Scania L113CRL	Wright Axcess-ultralow	B40F	1998
62304	R447ALS	BF	Scania L113CRL	Wright Axcess-ultralow	B40F	1998
62305	R448ALS	BF	Scania L113CRL	Wright Axcess-ultralow	B40F	1998
62306	R519BMS	LT	Scania L113CRL	Wright Axcess-ultralow	B40F	1998
62308	R521BMS	LT	Scania L113CRL	Wright Axcess-ultralow	B40F	1998
62309	S523UMS	BK	Scania L113CRL	Wright Axcess-ultralow	B40F	1998
62310	R524BMS	BK	Scania L113CRL	Wright Axcess-ultralow	B40F	1998
62311	S525UMS	BK	Scania L113CRL	Wright Axcess-ultralow	B40F	1998
62312	S526UMS	BK	Scania L113CRL	Wright Axcess-ultralow	B40F	1998
62342	P575DMS	LT	Scania L113CRL	Wright Axcess-ultralow	DP47F	1996
62343	P576DMS	LT	Scania L113CRL	Wright Axcess-ultralow	DP47F	1996
62344	P577DMS	BF	Scania L113CRL	Wright Axcess-ultralow	DP47F	1996
62345	P578DMS	LT	Scania L113CRL	Wright Axcess-ultralow	DP47F	1996
62346	P579RSG	LW	Scania L113CRL	Wright Axcess-ultralow	B47F	1997
62348	P580RSG	LT	Scania L113CRL	Wright Axcess-ultralow	B47F	1997
62349	P581RSG	LT	Scania L113CRL	Wright Axcess-ultralow	B47F	1997
62350	R587BMS	LT	Scania L113CRL	Wright Axcess-ultralow	B40F	1998
62351	R588BMS	LT	Scania L113CRL	Wright Axcess-ultralow	B40F	1998
62352	R589BMS	LT	Scania L113CRL	Wright Axcess-ultralow	B40F	1998
62353	R590BMS	LT	Scania L113CRL	Wright Axcess-ultralow	B40F	1998
62354	R591BMS	LT	Scania L113CRL	Wright Axcess-ultralow	B40F	1998
62355	SN51MSV	GS	Scania L94UB	Wright Solar	B43F	2001
62356	SN51MSU	GS	Scania L94UB	Wright Solar	B43F	2001
62357	SN51MSY	GS	Scania L94UB	Wright Solar	B43F	2001
62358	SN51MSX	D	Scania L94UB	Wright Solar	B43F	2001
62359	R154GSF	BK	Scania L113CRL	Wright Axcess-ultralow	B40F	1998
62360	R156GSF	BK	Scania L113CRL	Wright Axcess-ultralow	B40F	1998
62361	R157GSF	BK	Scania L113CRL	Wright Axcess-ultralow	B40F	1998
62363	N62CSC	w	Mercedes-Benz O.405	Optare Prisma	B49F	1995
62366	N65CSC	LW	Mercedes-Benz O.405	Optare Prisma	B49F	1995
62367	N66CSC	w	Mercedes-Benz O.405	Optare Prisma	B49F	1995
62369	P171DMS	GS	Mercedes-Benz O.405	Optare Prisma	DP49F	1997
62370	P172DMS	w	Mercedes-Benz O.405	Optare Prisma	DP49F	1997
62371	P173DMS	w	Mercedes-Benz O.405	Optare Prisma	DP49F	1997
62373	P879YKS	BF	Mercedes-Benz O.405	Optare Prisma	B49F	1997
62381	N409ENW	w	Scania L113CRL	Wright Axcess-ultralow	B41F	1995
62382	N410ENW	M	Scania L113CRL	Wright Axcess-ultralow	B47F	1995
62383	S520UMS	M	Scania L113CRL	Wright Axcess-ultralow	B40F	1998
62384	R522BMS	w	Scania L113CRL	Wright Axcess-ultralow	B40F	1998
62385	V527ESH	LN	Scania L94UB	Wright Solar	B43F	1999
62386	V528ESH	LN	Scania L94UB	Wright Solar	B43F	1999
62387	V529ESH	LN	Scania L94UB	Wright Solar	B43F	1999
62388	V530ESH	LN	Scania L94UB	Wright Solar	B43F	1999
62389	V531ESH	LN	Scania L94UB	Wright Solar	B43F	1999
62390	V532ESH	LN	Scania L94UB	Wright Solar	B43F	1999
62391	V34ESC	LN	Scania L94UB	Wright Solar	B39F	1999
62392	V35ESC	LN	Scania L94UB	Wright Solar	B39F	1999
62393	R582YMS	NB	Scania L113CRL	Wright Axcess-ultralow	B40F	1998
62394	R583YMS	M	Scania L113CRL	Wright Axcess-ultralow	B40F	1998
62395	R584YMS	M	Scania L113CRL	Wright Axcess-ultralow	B40F	1998
62396	R585YMS	LN	Scania L113CRL	Wright Axcess-ultralow	B40F	1998
62398	R155GSF	NB	Scania L113CRL	Wright Axcess-ultralow	B40F	1998
62400	N68CSC	w	Mercedes-Benz O.405	Optare Prisma	B49F	1995
62401	N69CSC	D	Mercedes-Benz O.405	Optare Prisma	B49F	1995
62402	P875YKS	D	Mercedes-Benz O.405	Optare Prisma	B49F	1997
62403	P876YKS	w	Mercedes-Benz O.405	Optare Prisma	B49F	1997
62404	P877YKS	w	Mercedes-Benz O.405	Optare Prisma	B49F	1997
62405	P878YKS	w	Mercedes-Benz O.405	Optare Prisma	B49F	1997
62411	SN03WMJ	LT	TransBus Enviro 300 12.0 SLF	TransBus Enviro 300	B44F	2003

			First Scotland				
62412	SN03WMU	LT	TransBus Enviro 300 12.0 SLF	TransBus Enviro 300	B44F	2003
62935	T735JGB	BT	Optare Excel L1070	Optare	B39F	1999
62936	T736JGB	BT	Optare Excel L1070	Optare	B39F	1999
62949	W49WDS	BT	Optare Excel L1070	Optare	B39F	2000
62952	W52WDS	BT	Optare Excel L1070	Optare	B39F	2000
64811	M811PGM	L	Scania L113CRL	Northern Counties Paladin	B51F	1995
64812	M812PGM	L	Scania L113CRL	Northern Counties Paladin	B51F	1995
65530	R150GSF	L	Scania L113CRL	Wright Axcess-ultralow	B40F	1997
65533	R133GSF	L	Scania L113CRL	Wright Axcess-ultralow	B40F	1997
65535	R135GSF	L	Scania L113CRL	Wright Axcess-ultralow	B40F	1997
65536	R136GSF	L	Scania L113CRL	Wright Axcess-ultralow	B40F	1997
65591	W591SNG	L	Scania L94UB	Wright Solar	B43F	2000
65592	W592SNG	DU	Scania L94UB	Wright Solar	B43F	2000
65593	W593SNG	DU	Scania L94UB	Wright Solar	B43F	2000
65594	W594SNG	DLN	Scania L94UB	Wright Solar	B43F	2000
65595	W595SNG	LT	Scania L94UB	Wright Solar	B43F	2000
65596	W596SNG	L	Scania L94UB	Wright Solar	B43F	2000
65597	W597SNG	LT	Scania L94UB	Wright Solar	B43F	2000
65598	W598SNG	BK	Scania L94UB	Wright Solar	B43F	2000
65599	W599SNG	LT	Scania L94UB	Wright Solar	B43F	2000
65601	W601SNG	LT	Scania L94UB	Wright Solar	B43F	2000
65662	V362CNH	LT	Scania L94UB	Wright Solar	B43F	2000
65663	V363CNH	LT	Scania L94UB	Wright Solar	B43F	2000
65664	V364CNH	LT	Scania L94UB	Wright Solar	B43F	2000
65693	SN53KHH	GS	Scania L94UB	Wright Solar	B43F	2003
65694	SN53KHJ	BK	Scania L94UB	Wright Solar	B43F	2003
65695	SN53KHK	BK	Scania L94UB	Wright Solar	B43F	2003
65696	SN53KHL	GS	Scania L94UB	Wright Solar	B43F	2003
65697	SN53KHM	GS	Scania L94UB	Wright Solar	B43F	2003
65698	SN53KHO	LT	Scania L94UB	Wright Solar	B43F	2003
65699	SN53KHP	LT	Scania L94UB	Wright Solar	B43F	2003
65700	SN04CKY	LT	Scania L94UB	Wright Solar	B43F	2004
65701	SN04CKX	LT	Scania L94UB	Wright Solar	B43F	2004
65702	SN04CLF	LT	Scania L94UB	Wright Solar	B43F	2004
65703	SN04CNK	LN	Scania L94UB	Wright Solar	B43F	2004
65708	SN54KDF	BK	Scania L94UB	Wright Solar	B44F	2004
65709	SN54KDJ	BK	Scania L94UB	Wright Solar	B44F	2004
65710	SN54KDK	BK	Scania L94UB	Wright Solar	B44F	2004
65711	SN54KDO	BK	Scania L94UB	Wright Solar	B44F	2004
65712	SN54KDU	BK	Scania L94UB	Wright Solar	B44F	2004
65713	SN54KDV	BK	Scania L94UB	Wright Solar	B44F	2004
65714	SN54KDX	BK	Scania L94UB	Wright Solar	B44F	2004
65715	SN54KDZ	BK	Scania L94UB	Wright Solar	B44F	2004
65716	SN54KEJ	BK	Scania L94UB	Wright Solar	B44F	2005
65717	SN54KEK	BK	Scania L94UB	Wright Solar	B44F	2005
65718	SN54KEU	BK	Scania L94UB	Wright Solar	B44F	2005
65719	SN54KFA	BK	Scania L94UB	Wright Solar	B44F	2005
65720	SN54KFC	LW	Scania L94UB	Wright Solar	B44F	2005
65721	SN54KFD	BK	Scania L94UB	Wright Solar	B44F	2005
65722	SN54KFE	BK	Scania L94UB	Wright Solar	B44F	2005
65723	SN54KFF	BK	Scania L94UB	Wright Solar	B44F	2005
65742	SN55JVG	GS	Scania L94UB	Wright Solar	B43F	2005
65743	SN55JVH	GS	Scania L94UB	Wright Solar	B43F	2005
65744	SN55JVJ	GS	Scania L94UB	Wright Solar	B43F	2005
65745	SN55JVK	GS	Scania L94UB	Wright Solar	B43F	2005
65746	SN55JVL	GS	Scania L94UB	Wright Solar	B43F	2005
65747	SN55JVM	GS	Scania L94UB	Wright Solar	B43F	2005
65748	SN55JVO	GS	Scania L94UB	Wright Solar	B43F	2005
65749	SN55JVP	GS	Scania L94UB	Wright Solar	B43F	2005
65750	SN55JVA	GS	Scania L94UB	Wright Solar	B43F	2005

65751	SN55JVC	GS	Scania L94UB	Wright Solar	B43F	2005
65752	SN55JVD	LT	Scania L94UB	Wright Solar	B43F	2005
65753	SN55JVE	LT	Scania L94UB	Wright Solar	B43F	2005
65754	SN06AHK	D	Scania L94UB	Wright Solar	B43F	2006
65755	SK02ZYG	L	Scania L94UB	Wright Solar	B43F	2002
65756	SK02ZYH	L	Scania L94UB	Wright Solar	B43F	2002
65757	SN03CLX	L	Scania L94UB	Wright Solar	B43F	2003
65758	SN03CLY	L	Scania L94UB	Wright Solar	B43F	2003
66233	X303JGE	BT	Volvo B10BLE	Alexander ALX300	B44F	2000
66234	X304JGE	BT	Volvo B10BLE	Alexander ALX300	B44F	2000
66281	Y181BGB	BT	Volvo B10BLE	Wright Renown	B44F	2001
66282	Y182BGB	BT	Volvo B10BLE	Wright Renown	B44F	2001
66349	MV02VDZ	SC	Volvo B7L	Wright Eclipse	B41F	2002
66735	WX54XCW	O	Volvo B7RLE	Wright Eclipse Urban	B43F	2005
66736	WX54XCY	BT	Volvo B7RLE	Wright Eclipse Urban	B43F	2005
66737	WX54XCZ	BT	Volvo B7RLE	Wright Eclipse Urban	B43F	2005
66770	YJ05VVN	BT	Volvo B7RLE	Wright Eclipse Urban	B40F	2005
66771	YJ05VVO	BT	Volvo B7RLE	Wright Eclipse Urban	B40F	2005
66946	WX55TZH	BT	Volvo B7RLE	Wright Eclipse Urban	B43F	2005
66947	WX55TZJ	BT	Volvo B7RLE	Wright Eclipse Urban	B43F	2005
66948	WX55TZK	BT	Volvo B7RLE	Wright Eclipse Urban	B43F	2005
66949	WX55TZL	BT	Volvo B7RLE	Wright Eclipse Urban	B43F	2005
66951	WX55TZN	BT	Volvo B7RLE	Wright Eclipse Urban	B43F	2005
66952	WX55TZO	BT	Volvo B7RLE	Wright Eclipse Urban	B43F	2005
66954	WX55TZR	O	Volvo B7RLE	Wright Eclipse Urban	B43F	2005
66955	WX55TZS	O	Volvo B7RLE	Wright Eclipse Urban	B43F	2005
66988	SF56GYP	BT	Volvo B7RLE	Wright Eclipse Urban	B43F	2006
66989	SF56GYR	PH	Volvo B7RLE	Wright Eclipse Urban	B43F	2006
66990	SF56GYS	BT	Volvo B7RLE	Wright Eclipse Urban	B43F	2006
66991	SF56GYT	BT	Volvo B7RLE	Wright Eclipse Urban	B43F	2006
68089	SF06GYX	PH	Volvo B7RLE	Wright Eclipse Urban	B43F	2006
68518	SV54CFY	AB	BMC Falcon 1100FE	BMC	B60F	2004
68519	SV54CFV	AB	BMC Falcon 1100FE	BMC	B60F	2004
68566	SF55TXC	DU	BMC Falcon 1100FE	BMC	B55FL	2005
69014	SF55UAG	PH	Volvo B7RLE	Wright Eclipse Urban	B43F	2005
69015	SF55UAH	PH	Volvo B7RLE	Wright Eclipse Urban	B43F	2005
69016	SF55UAJ	PH	Volvo B7RLE	Wright Eclipse Urban	B43F	2005
69019	SF55UAM	PH	Volvo B7RLE	Wright Eclipse Urban	B43F	2005
69021	SF55UAO	PH	Volvo B7RLE	Wright Eclipse Urban	B43F	2005
69027	SF55UAV	PH	Volvo B7RLE	Wright Eclipse Urban	B43F	2005
69034	SF55UBU	PH	Volvo B7RLE	Wright Eclipse Urban	B43F	2006
69035	SF55UBV	PH	Volvo B7RLE	Wright Eclipse Urban	B43F	2006
69036	SF55UBW	PH	Volvo B7RLE	Wright Eclipse Urban	B43F	2006
69037	SF55UBX	BT	Volvo B7RLE	Wright Eclipse Urban	B43F	2006
69038	SF06GXJ	BT	Volvo B7RLE	Wright Eclipse Urban	B43F	2006
69039	SF06GXG	BT	Volvo B7RLE	Wright Eclipse Urban	B43F	2006
69040	SF06GXK	BT	Volvo B7RLE	Wright Eclipse Urban	B43F	2006
69041	SF06GXL	SC	Volvo B7RLE	Wright Eclipse Urban	B43F	2006
69042	SF55UBB		Volvo B7RLE	Wright Eclipse Urban	B43F	2005
69057	SF06GXM	SC	Volvo B7RLE	Wright Eclipse Urban	B43F	2006
69058	SF06GXN	SC	Volvo B7RLE	Wright Eclipse Urban	B43F	2006
69059	SF06GXH	SC	Volvo B7RLE	Wright Eclipse Urban	B43F	2006
69060	SF06GXO	SC	Volvo B7RLE	Wright Eclipse Urban	B43F	2006
69061	SF06GXP	SC	Volvo B7RLE	Wright Eclipse Urban	B43F	2006
69062	SF06GXR	SC	Volvo B7RLE	Wright Eclipse Urban	B43F	2006
69063	SF06GXS	SC	Volvo B7RLE	Wright Eclipse Urban	B43F	2006
69064	SF06GXT	SC	Volvo B7RLE	Wright Eclipse Urban	B43F	2006
69065	SF06GXU	SC	Volvo B7RLE	Wright Eclipse Urban	B43F	2006
69066	SF06GYB	SC	Volvo B7RLE	Wright Eclipse Urban	B43F	2006
69067	SF06GYC	SC	Volvo B7RLE	Wright Eclipse Urban	B43F	2006

69068	SF06GYD	SC	Volvo B7RLE	Wright Eclipse Urban	B43F	2006
69069	SF06GYE	SC	Volvo B7RLE	Wright Eclipse Urban	B43F	2006
69070	SF06GYG	SC	Volvo B7RLE	Wright Eclipse Urban	B43F	2006
69071	SF06GYH	SC	Volvo B7RLE	Wright Eclipse Urban	B43F	2006
69072	SF06GXV	SC	Volvo B7RLE	Wright Eclipse Urban	B43F	2006
69073	SF06GXW	SC	Volvo B7RLE	Wright Eclipse Urban	B43F	2006
69074	SF06GXX	SC	Volvo B7RLE	Wright Eclipse Urban	B43F	2006
69076	SF06GXZ	O	Volvo B7RLE	Wright Eclipse Urban	B43F	2006
69077	SF06GYA	O	Volvo B7RLE	Wright Eclipse Urban	B43F	2006
69078	SF06GYJ	O	Volvo B7RLE	Wright Eclipse Urban	B43F	2006
69079	SF06GYK	O	Volvo B7RLE	Wright Eclipse Urban	B43F	2006
69080	SF06GYN	BT	Volvo B7RLE	Wright Eclipse Urban	B43F	2006
69081	SF06GYO	PH	Volvo B7RLE	Wright Eclipse Urban	B43F	2006
69082	SF06GYP	PH	Volvo B7RLE	Wright Eclipse Urban	B43F	2006
69083	SF06GYR	PH	Volvo B7RLE	Wright Eclipse Urban	B43F	2006
69084	SF06GYS	PH	Volvo B7RLE	Wright Eclipse Urban	B43F	2006
69085	SF06GYT	PH	Volvo B7RLE	Wright Eclipse Urban	B43F	2006
69086	SF06GYU	PH	Volvo B7RLE	Wright Eclipse Urban	B43F	2006
69087	SF06GYV	PH	Volvo B7RLE	Wright Eclipse Urban	B43F	2006
69088	SF06GYW	PH	Volvo B7RLE	Wright Eclipse Urban	B43F	2006
69090	SF06GYY	PH	Volvo B7RLE	Wright Eclipse Urban	B43F	2006
69091	SF06GYZ	PH	Volvo B7RLE	Wright Eclipse Urban	B43F	2006
69092	SF06GZA	PH	Volvo B7RLE	Wright Eclipse Urban	B43F	2006
69093	SF06GZB	PH	Volvo B7RLE	Wright Eclipse Urban	B43F	2006
69094	SF06GZC	PH	Volvo B7RLE	Wright Eclipse Urban	B43F	2006
69095	SF06GZD	PH	Volvo B7RLE	Wright Eclipse Urban	B43F	2006
69096	SF06GZE	PH	Volvo B7RLE	Wright Eclipse Urban	B43F	2006
69097	SF06GZG	PH	Volvo B7RLE	Wright Eclipse Urban	B43F	2006
69098	SF06GZH	PH	Volvo B7RLE	Wright Eclipse Urban	B43F	2006
69099	SF06GZJ	PH	Volvo B7RLE	Wright Eclipse Urban	B43F	2006
69100	SF06GZK	PH	Volvo B7RLE	Wright Eclipse Urban	B43F	2006
69101	SF06GZL	PH	Volvo B7RLE	Wright Eclipse Urban	B43F	2006
69102	SF06GZM	PH	Volvo B7RLE	Wright Eclipse Urban	B43F	2006
69103	SF06GZN	SC	Volvo B7RLE	Wright Eclipse Urban	B43F	2006
69104	SF06GZO	SC	Volvo B7RLE	Wright Eclipse Urban	B43F	2006
69105	SF06GZP	SC	Volvo B7RLE	Wright Eclipse Urban	B43F	2006
69106	SF06GZR	SC	Volvo B7RLE	Wright Eclipse Urban	B43F	2006
69107	SF06GZS	SC	Volvo B7RLE	Wright Eclipse Urban	B43F	2006
69108	SF06GZT	SC	Volvo B7RLE	Wright Eclipse Urban	B43F	2006
69109	SF06GZV	SC	Volvo B7RLE	Wright Eclipse Urban	B43F	2006
69110	SV06GRF	AB	Volvo B7RLE	Wright Eclipse Urban	B43F	2006
69111	SF06GZX	PH	Volvo B7RLE	Wright Eclipse Urban	B43F	2006
69112	SF06GZY	PH	Volvo B7RLE	Wright Eclipse Urban	B43F	2006
69113	SF06GZZ	PH	Volvo B7RLE	Wright Eclipse Urban	B43F	2006
69114	SF06HAA	PH	Volvo B7RLE	Wright Eclipse Urban	B43F	2006
69115	SF06HAE	PH	Volvo B7RLE	Wright Eclipse Urban	B43F	2006
69116	SF06HAO	PH	Volvo B7RLE	Wright Eclipse Urban	B43F	2006
69117	SF06HAU	PH	Volvo B7RLE	Wright Eclipse Urban	B43F	2006
69118	SF06HAX	PH	Volvo B7RLE	Wright Eclipse Urban	B43F	2006
69119	SF06HBA	PH	Volvo B7RLE	Wright Eclipse Urban	B43F	2006
69120	SF06HBB	PH	Volvo B7RLE	Wright Eclipse Urban	B43F	2006
69121	SF06HBC	PH	Volvo B7RLE	Wright Eclipse Urban	B43F	2006
69122	SV06GRK	AB	Volvo B7RLE	Wright Eclipse Urban	B43F	2006
69123	SV06GRU	AB	Volvo B7RLE	Wright Eclipse Urban	B43F	2006
69124	SV06GRX	AB	Volvo B7RLE	Wright Eclipse Urban	B43F	2006
69125	SV07EHB	AB	Volvo B7RLE	Wright Eclipse Urban	B44F	2007
69126	SV07EHC	AB	Volvo B7RLE	Wright Eclipse Urban	B44F	2007
69127	SV07EHD	AB	Volvo B7RLE	Wright Eclipse Urban	B44F	2007
69128	SV07EHE	AB	Volvo B7RLE	Wright Eclipse Urban	B44F	2007
69129	SV07EHF	AB	Volvo B7RLE	Wright Eclipse Urban	B44F	2007

69130	SV07EHG	AB	Volvo B7RLE	Wright Eclipse Urban	B44F	2007
69131	SV07EHH	AB	Volvo B7RLE	Wright Eclipse Urban	B44F	2007
69132	SV07EHJ	AB	Volvo B7RLE	Wright Eclipse Urban	B44F	2007
69133	SV07EHK	AB	Volvo B7RLE	Wright Eclipse Urban	B44F	2007
69134	SV07EHL	AB	Volvo B7RLE	Wright Eclipse Urban	B44F	2007
69181	MX06YXN	BT	Volvo B7RLE	Wright Eclipse Urban	B43F	2006
69182	MX06YXO	BT	Volvo B7RLE	Wright Eclipse Urban	B43F	2006
69183	MX06YXP	BT	Volvo B7RLE	Wright Eclipse Urban	B43F	2006
69184	MX06YXR	BT	Volvo B7RLE	Wright Eclipse Urban	B43F	2006
69187	MX56ACZ	BT	Volvo B7RLE	Wright Eclipse Urban	B43F	2006
69188	MX56ADO	BT	Volvo B7RLE	Wright Eclipse Urban	B43F	2006
69189	MX56ADU	BT	Volvo B7RLE	Wright Eclipse Urban	B43F	2006
69190	MX56ADV	BT	Volvo B7RLE	Wright Eclipse Urban	B43F	2006
69191	MX56ADZ	BT	Volvo B7RLE	Wright Eclipse Urban	B43F	2006
69192	MX56AEA	BT	Volvo B7RLE	Wright Eclipse Urban	B43F	2006
69193	MX56AEB	BT	Volvo B7RLE	Wright Eclipse Urban	B43F	2006
69194	MX56AEC	BT	Volvo B7RLE	Wright Eclipse Urban	B43F	2006
69254	SK07JVN	LT	Volvo B7RLE	Wright Eclipse Urban	B43F	2007
69255	SK07JVO	LT	Volvo B7RLE	Wright Eclipse Urban	B43F	2007
69256	SK07JVP	LT	Volvo B7RLE	Wright Eclipse Urban	B43F	2007
69257	SK57ADO	GS	Volvo B7RLE	Wright Eclipse Urban	B43F	2007
69258	SK57ADU	GS	Volvo B7RLE	Wright Eclipse Urban	B43F	2007
69259	SK57ADV	GS	Volvo B7RLE	Wright Eclipse Urban	B44F	2007
69260	SK57ADX	GS	Volvo B7RLE	Wright Eclipse Urban	B44F	2007
69261	SK57ADZ	GS	Volvo B7RLE	Wright Eclipse Urban	B44F	2007
69262	SK57AEA	GS	Volvo B7RLE	Wright Eclipse Urban	B44F	2007
69263	SK57AEB	GS	Volvo B7RLE	Wright Eclipse Urban	B44F	2007
69264	SK57AEC	GS	Volvo B7RLE	Wright Eclipse Urban	B44F	2007
69265	SY57EYH	AB	Volvo B7RLE	Wright Eclipse Urban	B44F	2007
69266	SY57EYJ	AB	Volvo B7RLE	Wright Eclipse Urban	B44F	2007
69267	SY57EYK	AB	Volvo B7RLE	Wright Eclipse Urban	B44F	2007
69280	SN57MSU	LT	Volvo B7RLE	Wright Eclipse Urban	B44F	2008
69281	SN57JBZ	LT	Volvo B7RLE	Wright Eclipse Urban	B44F	2008
69282	SN57JCJ	LT	Volvo B7RLE	Wright Eclipse Urban	B44F	2008
69283	SN57JCO	LT	Volvo B7RLE	Wright Eclipse Urban	B44F	2008
69284	SN57JCU	LT	Volvo B7RLE	Wright Eclipse Urban	B44F	2008
69285	SN57JCV	LT	Volvo B7RLE	Wright Eclipse Urban	B44F	2008
69286	SN57JCX	LT	Volvo B7RLE	Wright Eclipse Urban	B44F	2008
69287	SN57JCY	LT	Volvo B7RLE	Wright Eclipse Urban	B44F	2008
69288	SN57JCZ	LT	Volvo B7RLE	Wright Eclipse Urban	B44F	2008
69289	SN57JDF	LT	Volvo B7RLE	Wright Eclipse Urban	B44F	2008
69290	SN57JDJ	LT	Volvo B7RLE	Wright Eclipse Urban	B44F	2008
69291	SN57JDK	LT	Volvo B7RLE	Wright Eclipse Urban	DP44F	2008
69292	SN57HZX	LT	Volvo B7RLE	Wright Eclipse Urban	DP44F	2008
69293	SN57HZY	LT	Volvo B7RLE	Wright Eclipse Urban	DP44F	2008
69294	SN57HZZ	LT	Volvo B7RLE	Wright Eclipse Urban	DP44F	2008
69295	SF04HXW	BT	Volvo B7RLE	Wright Eclipse Urban	B38F	2004
69296	SF04HXX	BT	Volvo B7RLE	Wright Eclipse Urban	B38F	2004
69297	SF04ZPE	BT	Volvo B7RLE	Wright Eclipse Urban	B38F	2004
69298	SF04ZPG	BT	Volvo B7RLE	Wright Eclipse Urban	B38F	2004
69351	SV08FHA	AB	Volvo B7RLE	Wright Eclipse Urban	B44F	2008
69352	SV08FHB	AB	Volvo B7RLE	Wright Eclipse Urban	B44F	2008
69353	SV08FHC	AB	Volvo B7RLE	Wright Eclipse Urban	B44F	2008
69354	SV08FHD	AB	Volvo B7RLE	Wright Eclipse Urban	B44F	2008
69355	SV08FHE	AB	Volvo B7RLE	Wright Eclipse Urban	B44F	2008
69356	SV08FHF	AB	Volvo B7RLE	Wright Eclipse Urban	B44F	2008
69357	SV08FHG	AB	Volvo B7RLE	Wright Eclipse Urban	B44F	2008
69402	SN09EZW	LT	Volvo B7RLE	Wright Eclipse Urban	B44F	2009
69403	SN09EZX	LT	Volvo B7RLE	Wright Eclipse Urban	B44F	2009
69404	SN09FAU	LT	Volvo B7RLE	Wright Eclipse Urban	B44F	2009

First Scotland

69405	SN09FBA	LT	Volvo B7RLE	Wright Eclipse Urban	B44F	2009
69406	SN09FBB	LT	Volvo B7RLE	Wright Eclipse Urban	B44F	2009
69407	SN09FBC	LT	Volvo B7RLE	Wright Eclipse Urban	B44F	2009
69408	SN09FBD	LT	Volvo B7RLE	Wright Eclipse Urban	B44F	2009
69409	SN09FBE	LT	Volvo B7RLE	Wright Eclipse Urban	B44F	2009
69410	SN09FBF	LT	Volvo B7RLE	Wright Eclipse Urban	B44F	2009
90146 *	PSU317	LT-a	Scania K113CRB	Plaxton Paramount 3500 IIIC	F	1990
90147 *	PSU315	D	Scania K113CRB	Plaxton Paramount 3500 IIIC	49FT	1990
DR2	YN04PNL	C	Volvo B12B	TransBus Panther	C53F	2004
DR3	YN04HHW	C	Volvo B12B	TransBus Panther	C53F	2004
	M867FSU		MAN 11.190	Optare Vecta	B42F	1995
	R27VSM		DAF DE33WSSB3000	Van Hool Alizée	C51FT	1998
	T732JGB		Volvo B10M-62	Berkhof Axial 50	C51FT	1999

Firth Coaches

Firth Coaches Ltd, 11 Dellingburn Street, Greenock PA15 4RN
Website
Depot   Unit 5, Earnhill Lane, Larkhill Industrial Estate, Greenock PA16 0EQ
Licence   PM1074359

	BX06OAJ	BMC Falcon 1100FE	BMC	B60F	2006
	BX54VTZ	BMC Falcon 1100FE	BMC	B60F	2004
	BX56XAS	BMC Falcon 1100FE	BMC	B55FL	2006
*	IIB457	Volvo B10M-62	Van Hool Alizée	C46FT	1999
*	J127MTY	Volvo B10M-60	Van Hool Alizée	C49FT	1992
	KX07HDF	Volvo B12B	Plaxton Panther	C53F	2007
—	KX09CHY	Volvo B12B	Plaxton Panther	C53F	2009
	SF07DLU	Volvo B12B	Caetano Levante	C53F	2007
	SF07DLV	Volvo B12B	Caetano Levante	C53F	2007
	SN06AZV	Volvo B12B	Van Hool Alizée	C49FT	2006
	YR52MBX	Mercedes-Benz Vario O.814D	Plaxton Cheetah	C25F	2002

Fishers Tours / Scottish Express

J & C Cosgrove, 16 West Port, Dundee DD1 5EP
Website   www.fisherstours.co.uk
Depot   Mid Craigie Trading Estate, Mid Craigie Road, Dundee DD4 7RH
Licence   PM0002937

*	4464RU	Volvo B10M-61	Van Hool Alizée	C49FT	1984
	A38DTV	Volvo B10M-61	Van Hool Alizée	C53F	1984
*	B10SBP	Volvo B10M-62	Van Hool Alizée	C52F	1994
	B494UNB	y	Leyland Tiger TRCTL11/3RZ	Plaxton Paramount 3500 II	C53F	1985
*	BHZ1255	Leyland Tiger TRCTL11/3RZ	Plaxton Derwent	B70F	1986
*	BHZ1256 —	Leyland Tiger TRCTL11/3RZ	Plaxton Derwent	B70F	1987
*	BHZ1257	Leyland Tiger TRCTL11/3RZ	Plaxton Derwent	B70F	1986
*	D53VSO	Leyland Tiger TRCLXC/2R	Plaxton Paramount 3200 IIExp.	C53F	1986
	FT03COS	Iveco EuroRider 391E.12.35	Plaxton Paragon	C49FT	2003
*	G21RHG	Dennis Javelin 8.5SDL	Duple 320	C39F	1989
	M61WER	Fiat Daily 59-12	Marshall C31	DP27F	1995
*	M251XWS	w	Dennis Javelin 12SDA	Wadham Stringer	C70F	1995
*	M778XHW	Dennis Javelin 12SDA	Wadham Stringer	C70F	1995
*	M780XHW	Dennis Javelin 12SDA	Wadham Stringer	C70F	1995
*	NUI1582	Mercedes-Benz Vario O.814D	Plaxton Cheetah	C32F	1998
*	PSU623	Leyland Tiger TRCLXC/2R	Plaxton Paramount 3200 II Exp	C53F	1986
	R909YBA	Volvo B10M-62	Van Hool Alizée	C48FT	1998
*	RJI2719	Leyland Tiger TRCLXC/2R	Plaxton Paramount 3200 II Exp	C49F	1986
*	RJI5715	Volvo B10M-60	Van Hool Alizée	C49FT	1990
	S151JUA	DAF DE33WSSB3000	Plaxton Premiere 320	C53F	1998

S152JUA	DAF DE33WSSB3000	Plaxton Premiere 320	C53F	1998
S617LRN	LDV Convoy	Jaycas	M16	1999
* SN04VUR	Mercedes-Benz Atego 1223L	Unvi Cimo	C37F	2004
T10HAY	Iveco EuroRider 391E.12.35	Beulas Stergo E	C51FT	1999
TDC854X	Leyland Tiger TRCTL11/2R	Duple Dominant IV Exp.	C53F	1982
* TIL4032	Volvo B10M-61	Van Hool Alizée	C53F	1988
* TIL4034	Volvo B10M-62	Van Hool Alizée	C53F	1989
X4HOF	Mercedes-Benz O.404	Hispano Carrocera	C49FT	2003
Y304KBN	Volvo B10M-62	Van Hool Alizée	C48FT	2001
Y309KBN	Volvo B10M-62	Van Hool Alizée	C46FT	2001
Y504BSF	Mercedes-Benz 614D	Onyx	C24F	2001

Fitzcharles

Fitzcharles Coaches Ltd, New Kerse Garage, 87 Newhouse Road, Grangemouth FK3 8NJ
Website www.fitzcharles.co.uk
Depot New Kerse Garage, 87 Newhouse Road, Grangemouth FK3 8NJ
Licence PM0000051

* FHZ2188	DAF DE40PSSB4000	Ayats	C49FT	2003
* FHZ3530	Volvo B10M-62	Caetano Algarve II	C49F	1995
* FHZ3531	Volvo B10M-60	Plaxton Premiere 350	C53F	1993
* FHZ4134	Volvo B10M-62	Plaxton Premiere 350	C48FT	2000
* FHZ4170	Volvo B10M-62	Caetano Algarve II	C53F	1995
* FHZ4171	Volvo B10M-62	Caetano Algarve II	C53F	1995
* FHZ4190	Volvo B10M-62	Plaxton Excalibur	C49FT	1996
* FHZ4191	Volvo B10M-62	Plaxton Premiere 320	C49FT	1996
* FHZ6882	DAF DE40PSSB4000	Ayats	C49FT	2003
* FHZ8395	Mercedes-Benz 711D	Plaxton Welfare Beaver 2	DP24FL	1997
* FHZ9593	Volvo B10M-60	Plaxton Premiere 350	C53F	1993
* FHZ9599	Volvo B10M-60	Plaxton Excalibur	C49F	1994
FJ06BPK	Volvo B12B	Sunsundegui Sideral	C53F	2006
FJ06BPO	Volvo B12B	Sunsundegui Sideral	C53F	2006
FJ08FYT	Volvo B9R	Sunsundegui Sideral	C53F	2008
FJ08FYU	Volvo B9R	Sunsundegui Sideral	C53F	2008

Frasers Coaches

R & E Fraser, The Garage, Littleburn, Munlochy IV8 8PE
Website www.fraserscoaches.com
Depot The Garage, Littleburn, Munlochy IV8 8PE
Licence PM0002547
PM0002075

* CEZ8152		Volvo B10M-62	Caetano Enigma	C49FT	1998
* CEZ8153		Volvo B10M-60	Van Hool Alizée	C49FT	1992
G454TST		Volvo B10M-60	Van Hool Alizée	C55F	1989
G818GSX		Leyland Olympian ON2R56C13Z4	Alexander RH	H51/33F	1990
* JIL5623		Leyland Tiger TRCTL11/3R	Plaxton Paramount 3200 I	C57F	1983
* JIL8256	w	Volvo B10M-61	Van Hool Alizée	C53F	1986
L4PHF	w	Mercedes-Benz 814D	Dormobile Routemaker	C33F	1983
* LIB8921		Volvo B10M-60	Van Hool Alizée	C49FT	1990
MK02GZU		Mercedes-Benz Sprinter 413CDI		M16	2002
P821GLS	x	Ford Transit	Ford	M8	1997
VNU328	w	Volvo B10M-61	Jonckheere Jubilee P50	C51FT	1985
YR02ZLX		Mercedes-Benz Vario O.814D	Plaxton Cheetah	C33F	2002

Fountain Executive
M Ewen, Goval Farm, Dyce AB21 7NX
Website
Depots   Goval Farm, Dyce AB21 7NX
             125 Victoria Street, Dyce AB21 7BY
Licence PM0001618

*	FXI194	Mercedes-Benz Atego 1223L	Unvi Cimo	C37F	2005
*	FXI249 —	Mercedes-Benz 616CDI	Unvi	C19F	2005
*	FXI253	Mercedes-Benz 616CDI	Unvi	C19F	2005
*	FXI457	Scania K114IB4	Irizar	C49FT	2004
*	FXI724	Scania K124IB4	Irizar	C49FT	1999
*	FXI782	Mercedes-Benz 412D	Concept	M13	1996
*	P532RGG	Mercedes-Benz 412D	Concept	M13	1996
	SN05JWZ	Scania K114IB4	Irizar	C49FT	2005
	SN05JXA	Scania K114IB4	Irizar	C49FT	2005

Galson-Stornoway Motor Services
Galson-Stornoway Motor Services Ltd, 1 Lower Barvas, Stornoway, Isle of Lewis HS2 0QS
Website
Depot   1 Lower Barvas, Stornoway, Isle of Lewis HS2 0QS
Licence PM0000610

GS57		SK02NYU	Mercedes-Benz Vario O.814D	Plaxton Beaver 2	C33F	2002
GS58		PCZ2674	Ford Transit	Ford	M15	2003
GS60	*	L345ERU	Volvo B10M-62	Plaxton Premiere 320	C49FT	1994
GS61	*	N224THO	Volvo B10M-62	Plaxton Premiere 320	C49FT	1996
GS62	*	M658ROS	Volvo B10M-62	Van Hool Alizée	C55F	1995
GS66		SC05ONS	Ford Transit	Ford	M16	2005
GS67	*	M534NCG	Volvo B10M-62	Plaxton Premiere 320	C53F	1995
GS68		V58KWO	Volvo B10M-62	Plaxton Premiere 320	C53F	2000
GS69	*	JSV486	Volvo B10M-62	Van Hool Alizée	C53F	1999
GS70	*	T782TSF	Mercedes-Benz Vario O.814D	Plaxton Beaver	DP31F	1999
GS71		SF04HXP	Mercedes-Benz Vario O.814D	TransBus Cheetah	C33F	2004
GS72		SG59XGS	Ford Transit	Ford	M16	2009
GS74		SH10PCV	Ford Transit	Ford	M16	2010

Garelochhead Minibuses & Coaches
Garelochhead Minibuses & Coaches Ltd, Woodlea Garage, Main Road, Garelochhead G84 0EG
Website www.garelochheadcoaches.co.uk
Depot   Woodlea Garage, Main Road, Garelochhead G84 0EG
Licence PM1004153

*	1528RU	Volvo B12B	Van Hool Alizée	C53F	2003
*	F106TML	Volvo B10M-50	Alexander RV	H47/32F	1989
	GN55XTD	Ford Transit	Ford	M16	2006
	L742NHE	Ford Transit	Advanced Vehicle Builders	M14	1994
	M634FJF	Mercedes-Benz 811D	Marshall C19	B31F	1994
	MX05ENC	Optare Solo M880	Optare	B28F	2005
	MX08DHP	Optare Solo M880	Optare	B27F	2008
	MX57UPV	Optare Solo M880SL	Optare	B27F	2008
	NU03VWA	Ford Transit	Ford	M16	2003
*	P782WOS	Dennis Javelin 12SFD	UVG Vanguard III	C47F	1997
	PK02WVV	Ford Transit	Jaycas	M14	2002
	SF59GZA	Bova FLD120.365	Bova Futura	C69F	2009
	VX54CKL	Mercedes-Benz Vario O.814D	Plaxton Beaver 2	DP33F	2004
	Y22APT	Volvo B10M-48	Van Hool Alizée	C28FT	2001
	Y25AMS	Volvo B10M-62	Van Hool Alizée	C49FT	2001
	YJ10MHF	Optare Solo M890SR	Optare	B27F	2010

G.E.M. Coaches
R Bonds, 10 Wellhall Road, Allanshaw Industrial Estate, Hamilton ML3 9BQ
Website
Depot   10 Wellhall Road, Allanshaw Industrial Estate, Hamilton ML3 9BQ
Licence   PM0002171

* A221XDS	Volvo B10M-61	Van Hool Alizée	C44FT	1984
C678KDS	Volvo B10M-61	Caetano Algarve	C53F	1986
C682KDS	Volvo B10M-61	Caetano Algarve	C53F	1986
E214WBG	Leyland Olympian ONCL10/1RZ	Northern Counties	H45/30F	1988
F212TAN	Bova FHD12-290	Bova Futura	C53F	1989
F850NJO	Mercedes-Benz 811D	Reeve Burgess Beaver	C33F	1989
* LOI1454	Volvo B10M-61	Ikarus Blue Danube VH	C49F	1990
M315VET	Scania K113CRB	Irlzar Century	C49FT	1995
M907XWA	Bova FHD12-340	Bova Futura	C49FT	1995
* SIB3933	Volvo B10M-62	Plaxton Excalibur	C53F	1994
* SXF615	Bova FHD12-340	Bova Futura	C51FT	1990
T373JWA	MAN 11.220	Irizar MidiCentury	C35F	1999

Gibson Direct
Gibson Direct Ltd, 6 Neil Street, Meadowside Industrial Estate, Renfrew PA4 8TA
Website   www.gibsondirectltd.co.uk
Depot   6 Neil Street, Meadowside Industrial Estate, Renfrew PA4 8TA
Licence   PM0002516

D393TAU		Leyland Lion LDTL11/1R	Northern Counties	H47/38D	1986
D394TAU		Leyland Lion LDTL11/1R	Northern Counties	H47/38D	1986
G505SFT		Leyland Olympian ONCL10/1RZ	Northern Counties	H47/30F	1989
* GIB6135		Leyland Lion LDTL11/1R	Northern Counties	H47/38D	1986
M876DDS		Ford Transit	Ford	B16F	1994
MC03LWX		Ford Transit	Ford	M16	2003
N992KUS	x	Ford Transit	Williams Deansgate	M8	1995
S374PGB		Mercedes-Benz Vario O.814D	Marshall Master	B31F	1999
S581PGB		Dennis Dart 8.8 SLF	Plaxton Mini Pointer	B29F	1998
SF04ZXC		TransBus Dart 8.8 SLF	TransBus Mini Pointer	B29F	2004
SF05FNV		Mercedes-Benz Vario O.814D	Plaxton Cheetah	C33F	2005
SF08FSU		Mercedes-Benz Vario O.816D	Plaxton Cheetah	C33F	2008
SF09GWM		Mercedes-Benz 515CDI	Onyx	M16	2009
SF54HWG		Optare Solo M850	Optare	B29F	2004
SF54HWH		Optare Solo M850	Optare	B29F	2004
SF54ORJ		Optare Solo M850	Optare	B29F	2004
SF54ORK		Optare Solo M850	Optare	B29F	2004
SF54ORN		Optare Solo M850	Optare	B20F	2004
SF54ORO		Optare Solo M850	Optare	B20F	2004
SF54OUU		Mercedes-Benz Vario O.814D	Plaxton Cheetah	C33F	2004
SF54RHX		Mercedes-Benz Vario O.814D	Mellor	C32F	2004
* SJ56BFL		Mercedes-Benz Vario O.814D	Plaxton Cheetah	C33F	2007
SN51FKG		LDV Convoy		M16	2001
W386WGE		Dennis Dart 10.7 SLF	Plaxton Pointer 2	B39F	2001
Y214BGB		Dennis Dart 10.7 SLF	Plaxton Pointer 2	B37F	2001
Y216BGB		Dennis Dart 10.7 SLF	Plaxton Pointer	B37F	2001
YE08EBA		Optare Solo M1020	Optare	B37F	2008
YE08EBC		Optare Solo M1020	Optare	B37F	2008
YE08EBD		Optare Solo M1020	Optare	B37F	2008
YE08EBF		Optare Solo M1020	Optare	B37F	2008
YE08EBG		Optare Solo M1020	Optare	B37F	2008
YE08EBJ		Optare Solo M1020	Optare	B37F	2008
YJ55BGY		Optare Solo M1020	Optare	B37F	2006
YJ55BGZ		Optare Solo M1020	Optare	B37F	2006
YJ55BHA		Optare Solo M1020	Optare	B37F	2006

		Gibson Direct			
YJ55BHD	Optare Solo M1020	Optare	B37F	2006	
YJ55BHE	Optare Solo M1020	Optare	B37F	2006	
YJ55BHK	Optare Solo M1020	Optare	B37F	2006	

(handwritten annotations: YR522?? Neoplan, G12 650, Vizar, ... in margins)

Gillens

Gillens Coaches Ltd, Dellingburn Street, Greenock PA15 4RN
Website www.gillenscoaches.co.uk
Depot Unit 3 Kingstone Business Park, Ardgowan Street, Port Glasgow PA14 5DG
Licence PM1055669

CU03CPX	Ford Transit	Ford	M16	2003	
* FCZ9700	Bova FHD12-290	Bova Futura	C51FT	1993	
GLZ5081	Ford Transit	Mayflower	M16	2000	
* NUI6046	Dennis Javelin 12SDA	Neoplan Transliner	C50FT	1996	
S581ACT	Mercedes-Benz Vario O.814D	Autobus Nouvelle	B33F	1999	
SF04ETE	Mercedes-Benz Vario O.814D	TransBus Beaver 2	DP33F	2004	
SL02LMO	Mercedes-Benz Vario O.814D	Plaxton Beaver 2	C33F	2002	
SN03UBJ	Mercedes-Benz Vario O.814D	Plaxton Cheetah	DP33F	2003	
SV06GUO	BMC Falcon 1100FE	BMC	B60F	2006	
SV06GUU	BMC Falcon 1100FE	BMC	B60F	2006	
T702BGB	LDV Convoy	LDV	M16	1999	
YR02YTD	Optare Alero L7200	Optare	B16F	2002	

Glasgow Citybus

Glasgow Citybus Ltd, 739 South Street, Glasgow G14 0BX
Website www.glasgowcitybus.co.uk
Depot 739 South Street, Glasgow G14 0BX
Licence PM1037373

J619KCU	Dennis Dart 9.8 SDL	Wright Handybus	B40F	1992	
MC02BLU	Dennis Dart 8.8 SLF	Plaxton Mini Pointer	B29F	2002	
* MX56YNU	Optare Solo M880	Optare	B28F	2006	
* MX56YOV	Optare Solo M880	Optare	B28F	2007	
N171WNF	Mercedes-Benz 709D	Alexander Sprint	B23F	1995	
N202WSB	Dennis Dart 9.8 SDL	Alexander Dash	B40F	1996	
P915XUG	Optare MetroRider MR17	Optare	B25F	1997	
R551UOT	Dennis Dart 10.7 SLF	UVG Urbanstar	B44F	1997	
R557UOT	Dennis Dart 10.7 SLF	UVG Urbanstar	B44F	1997	
SK07HMG	ADL Enviro Dart 8.9 SLF	ADL Enviro 200	B29F	2007	
SK07HMH	ADL Enviro Dart 8.9 SLF	ADL Enviro 200	B29F	2007	
SN51UCE	Dennis Dart 8.8 SLF	Plaxton Mini Pointer	B29F	2001	
SN57DXG	ADL Enviro Dart 8.9 SLF	ADL Enviro 200	B29F	2007	
T190AUA	Dennis Dart 8.8 SLF	Plaxton Mini Pointer	B29F	1999	
T191AUA	Dennis Dart 8.8 SLF	Plaxton Mini Pointer	B29F	1999	
V171EPS	Dennis Dart 11.3 SLF	Plaxton pointer 2	B42F	2000	
V175EPS	Dennis Dart 11.3 SLF	Plaxton Pointer 2	B42F	2000	
Y801WBT	DAF DE02CSSB120	Wright Cadet	B39F	2001	
Y802WBT	DAF DE02CSSB120	Wright Cadet	B39F	2001	
YJ03PGF	DAF DE12CSSB120	Wright Cadet	B39F	2003	
YJ04HUU	DAF DE12CSSB120	Wright Cadet	B39F	2004	
YJ06LDU	VDL DE12BSSB120	Plaxton Centro	B40F	2006	
YJ06LDV	VDL DE12BSSB120	Plaxton Centro	B40F	2006	
YJ06LDX	VDL DE12BSSB120	Plaxton Centro	B40F	2006	
YN07LHV	Scania N230UD	East Lancs	H45/23D	2007	
YX10EAJ	ADL Enviro Dart 10.7 SLF	ADL Enviro 200	B37F	2010	
YX10EAK	ADL Enviro Dart 10.7 SLF	ADL Enviro 200	B37F	2010	
YX10EAM	ADL Enviro Dart 10.7 SLF	ADL Enviro 200	B37F	2010	
YX10EAO	ADL Enviro Dart 10.7 SLF	ADL Enviro 200	B37F	2010	
YX10EAP	ADL Enviro Dart 10.7 SLF	ADL Enviro 200	B37F	2010	

Glasgow Corporation Transport
M Roulston, Robert James House, Willowyard Road, Beith KA15 1JG
Website
Depot   Robert James House, Willowyard Road, Beith KA15 1JG
Licence   PM1001381

BS94	B94PLU	Bedford VAS5	Plaxton Supreme IV	C25F	1985
LA1448	CUS302X	Leyland Atlantean AN68A/1R	Alexander AL	H45/33F	1981
LS355	HDB355V	Leyland Leopard PSU3F/5R	Plaxton Supreme IV	C57F	1980
	C233ENE	Leyland Olympian ONLXB/1R	Northern Counties	O43/30F	1986
	HRS265V	Leyland Atlantean AN68A/1R	Alexander AL	O45/29D	1980
	HRS271V	Leyland Atlantean AN68A/1R	Alexander AL	O45/29D	1980
	JJD365D	AEC Routemaster	Park Royal	H40/32R	1966
	JJD486D	AEC Routemaster	Park Royal	H40/32R	1966
	JJD553D	AEC Routemaster	Park Royal	H40/32R	1966
*	LIL9970	Leyland Tiger TRCTL11/3RZ	Plaxton Paramount 3200 III	C55F	1988
	MLL948 p	AEC Regal IV	Metro-Cammell	B39F	1952
*	SUX476X	Leyland Tiger TRCTL11/3R	Plaxton Supreme V	C49FT	1982
	URS321X	Leyland Atlantean AN68C/1R	Alexander AL	PO45/29F	1982
*	XJI5891	Leyland Tiger TRCTL11/3R	Plaxton Paramount 3500 I	C51F	1984

Glen Coaches
Glen Coaches Ltd, 11 Dellingburn Street, Greenock PA15 4RN
Website   www.glencoaches.co.uk
Depot   6 MacDougall Street, Greenock PA15 2TG
Licence   PM0002851

*	BAZ7912	Iveco EuroRider 391E.12.35	Beulas Stergo E	C49FT	1999
*	BAZ7918	Iveco EuroRider 391E.12.35	Beulas Stergo E	C49FT	1999
	FE51RFF	Iveco EuroRider 391E.12.35	Beulas Stergo E	C49FT	2001
	FN52GUF	Iveco EuroMidi CC80.E18	Indcar Maxim	C29F	2002
	MX59FYM	Volkswagen	Volkswagen	M16	2009
	N591GBW	Dennis Javelin 12SDA	Caetano Algarve II	C51FT	1996
	P647MSE	Dennis Javelin 12SDA	Plaxton Premiere 320	C57F	1996
*	RDZ4286	Volvo B10M-62	Jonckheere Deauville	C51FT	1994
	Y833NAY	Iveco EuroRider 391E.12.35	Beulas Stergo E	C49FT	2001

Golden Eagle Coaches
Golden Eagle Coaches Ltd, Muirhall Garage, 197 Main Street, Salsburgh ML7 4LS
Website   www.goldeneaglecoaches.com
Depot   197 Main Street, Salsburgh ML7 4LS
Licence   PM1039980

	A619BCN —	MCW MetroBus 2 DR102/43	MCW	H46/31F	1984
*	B12GEC	Volvo B12M	Jonckheere Mistral	C53F	2003
	F76TFU —	Dennis Dominator DDA	Alexander RH	H45/33F	1989
	F455BKF—	Leyland Olympian ONCL10/2RZ	Northern Counties	H51/34F	1989
	F459BKF—	Leyland Olympian ONCL10/2RZ	Northern Counties	H51/34F	1989
*	FSU371	Dennis Javelin 12SDA	Wadham Stringer	DP70F	1995
	G645EVV —	Leyland Olympian ONLXB/2RZ	Alexander RL	CH51/31F	1989
	G649EVV —	Leyland Olympian ONLXB/2RZ	Alexander RL	CH51/31F	1989
	G829GSX	Leyland Olympian ON2R56C13Z4	Alexander RH	H51/30D	1990
	GOG208W—w	MCW MetroBus 2 DR102/18	MCW	H43/30F	1981
	H665GPF	Volvo B10M-50	East Lancs	H45/34F	1991
	H679GPF	Volvo B10M-50	East Lancs	H45/34F	1991
*	J15GEC	Volvo B10M-62	Jonckheere Mistral	C53F	2001
*	J77GEC	Bova FHD12-370	Bova Futura	C49F	2000
*	JIL8560	Volvo B10M-60	Van Hool Alizée	C53F	1992
*	JIL8561 —	Volvo B10M-61	Van Hool Alizée	C53F	1986

Golden Eagle Coaches

* JIL8562	Volvo B10M-61	Van Hool Alizée	C53F	1988
K315MWV	Dennis Lance 11SDA	Wadham Stringer	B70F	1993
* M802ASL	Dennis Javelin 12SDA	Wadham Stringer	DP70F	1995
* WIL3629	Volvo B10M-60	Van Hool Alizée	C53F	1989
* YIL1206	Volvo B10M-62	Van Hool Alizée	C53F	1996
* YIL1207	Volvo B10M-62	Van Hool Alizée	C55F	1997
* YIL1208	Volvo B10M-60	Van Hool Alizée	C57F	1990
* YIL6691	Dennis Javelin 12SDA	Wadham Stringer Vanguard II	DP70F	1993

H Gordon

H Gordon, Bank Place Garage, Leslie KY6 3LD
Website
Depot Bank Place Garage, Leslie KY6 3LD
Licence PM0002426

* B8OVA	Bova FHD12.340	Bova Futura	C49FT	1996
HG08OVA	Bova FHD127.365	Bova Futura	C49FT	2008
* MBZ1758	Ford Transit	Ford	M14	1993
* MIL1085	Duple 425 SDA	Duple 425	C57F	1989
MX05CWL	Mercedes-Benz 413CDI	Onyx	M16	2005
N963ESD	Ford Transit	Ford	M14	1995
* P8OVA	Bova FHD12.340	Bova Futura	C49FT	1997
* R8OVA	Bova FHD12.340	Bova Futura	C49FT	2001
SG52VFJ	Mercedes-Benz Vario O.814D	Plaxton Cheetah	C33F	2002
SN06AZP	Mercedes-Benz O.815D	Sitcar Beluga	C33F	2006
SN56GTZ	Mercedes-Benz Atego 1523L	Unvi Cimo	C37F	2006
T8OVA	Bova FHD127.364	Bova Futura	C49FT	1999

Halls Coaches

W Hall, 163 Main Street, Overtown, Wishaw ML2 0JP
Website www.hallscoaches.co.uk
Depot Unit 2a, Pickerings Corner, off Castlehill Road, Wishaw ML2 0EQ
Licence PM0002660

B132CGG	Volvo B10M-61	Van Hool Alizée	C49F	1985
* F49MCA	Volvo B10M-60	Plaxton Paramount 3500 III	C53F	1989
L204JSX	Fiat Daily 49-10	Mellor	B15FL	1994
L205JSX	Fiat Daily 49-10	Mellor	B15FL	1994
M677TBF	Mercedes-Benz 711D	P.E.Van Technology	C24F	1994
N100SAS	Mercedes-Benz Vario O.814D	Autobus Classique	C33F	1996
* P17LJE	Bova FHD12-340	Bova Futura	C49FT	1997
* R137LNR	Mercedes-Benz Vario O.814D	Plaxton Beaver 2	B27F	1997
R888GSM	Mercedes-Benz 611D	Crystals	C24F	1997
S332CSF	Mercedes-Benz 614D	Onyx	C19F	1998
SA07VUG	Ford Transit	Ford	M16	2007
SF05AXW	Mercedes-Benz Sprinter 311CDI	Mercedes-Benz	M16	2005
SF57FXB	Mercedes-Benz Vario O.814D	Plaxton Cheetah	C33F	2007
* SIL8753	Volvo B10M-61	Macedonian Coach Industries	C55F	1983
* T99HAL	Volvo B10M-55	Van Hool Alizée	C49F	1999

Hardies Coaches
K Hardie, 38 Boglestone Avenue, Port Glasgow PA14 5TJ
Website
Depot   Unit 2 Kingston Business Park, Ardgowan Street, Port Glasgow PA14 5DG
Licence   PM1016886

BU53AXJ	Mercedes-Benz Touro	Mercedes-Benz	C49FT	2003
* H4KDY	Volvo B10M-62	Van Hool Alizée	C46FT	1997
* IIB379	Volvo B10M-62	Plaxton Premiere 350	C48FT	1995
MX06OOA	Mercedes-Benz Vario O.814D	Onyx	C24F	2006
MX07MPV	Mercedes-Benz 413CDI		M16	2007
PKZ5753	Mercedes-Benz 413CDI		M16	2007
* PVY569	Volvo B10M-60	Plaxton Premiere 350	C49F	1993
SF07KGE	Mercedes-Benz 515CDI	Onyx	M16L	2007
SF09GWL	Mercedes-Benz O816D	Plaxton Cheetah	C33F	2009
SF58FTX	Mercedes-Benz Vario O.814D	Plaxton Cheetah	C33F	2008

Harlequin Coaches (Dunblane)
Harlequin Coaches Limited, 8 Leewood Park, Dunblane FK15 0NX
Website   www.harlequincoaches-dunblane.co.uk
Depot   Bandeath Industrial Estate, Throsk, Stirling FK7 7NP
Licence   PM1043043

* A565WAV		DAF SB2300DHS585	Plaxton Paramount 3500 I	C53F	1984
* BJZ6602		Iveco Daily 59E12	Leicester Carriage Builders	C26FL	1998
D78HRU		Bedford YMP	Plaxton Paramount 3200 III	C33F	1987
FJ08FYW —		Volvo B7RLE	Wright Eclipse Urban	B44F	2008
L58YJF — r		Toyota Coaster HZB50R	Caetano Optimo	C18F	1993
* L717ERU		Toyota Coaster HZB50R	Caetano Optimo	C18F	1994
* MUI5346		Fiat Daily 49-10	Mellor	B15FL	1994
* MUI5348		Iveco Daily 40-10	Keillor	M15L	1996
MV02UGA		Iveco Daily 65C15	Mellor	B22FL	2002
* P994VOS —		Dennis Javelin 12SFD	Wadham Stringer	C47F	1997
* R182LBC		Toyota Coaster BB50R	Caetano Optimo	C16F	1997
R189LBC		Volvo B10M-62	Caetano Algarve II	C49F	1997
R354MPY		Iveco Daily 49-10	Mellor	M15L	1997
S663KSN r		Iveco Daily 59E12	Mellor	B16FL	1998
S987ERR		Mercedes-Benz 614D	Mellor	B24FL	1998
SL6069 — p		Bedford SB3	Plaxton Highway	C41F	1958
V388KVY		Optare Excel L1150	Optare	B45F	1999
* VJI9410		Mercedes-Benz Atego 1120L	Optare Solera	C35F	1999
YJ06FXO —		Optare Solo M1020	Optare	B37F	2006
YJ06FXZ		Optare Solo M1020	Optare	B37F	2006
YJ58CCV —		Optare Tempo X1260	Optare	B47F	2008

Harlequin Coaches (Livingston)
I Adam, West Clifton Farm, Muirieston, Livingston EH54 9BT
Website   www.harlequincoaches.co.uk
Depot   West Clifton Farm, Muirieston, Livingston EH54 9BT
Licence   PM0002444

* 536ATT	Neoplan N516/3	Neoplan Starliner	C44FT	2000
D169WRC	Bedford YMP	Plaxton Paramount 3200 III	C35F	1987
D224LWY	Volvo B10M-61	Plaxton Paramount 3500 III	C53F	1987
ENV827X	Volvo B10M-61	Jonckheere Jubilee P50	C49F	1982
* FNZ5671	Scania K113TRB	Irizar Century	C49FT	1996
* FNZ5672	Scania K113CRB	Irizar Century	C49FT	1995
G249GCC	Fiat Daily 49-10	Carlyle C4	DP25F	1989

Harlequin Coaches (Livingston)

* HMU118	Volvo B12M	Berkhof	C49FT	2005
* M623RCP	Van Hool EOS E180Z	EOS	C47FT	1995
* P678GNV	LDV Convoy	LDV	M16	1997
R853SDT	Scania K113CRB	Irizar Century	C51FT	1998
* RRS303X	DAF MB200DKTL600	Plaxton Supreme V	C51F	1982
* T594JLS	Volvo B10M-48	Jonckheere Mistral	C28FT	1999
* UCD528	Van Hool EOS E180Z	EOS	C51FT	1999
* USV981	Van Hool EOS E180Z	EOS	C48FT	1999

Harrolds Coaches
H Harrold, Northcote, Keiss, Wick KW1 4XG
Website
Depot   The Garage, Myreland, Lyth, Wick KW1 4UD
    Roadside, John O' Groats, Wick KW1 4YR
Licence   PM0002343

* 869SVX	Leyland Tiger TRCTL11/3R	Duple Laser	C57F	1983
AVK139V	Leyland Atlantean AN68A/2R	Alexander AL	H49/37F	1980
B417CVH	DAF SB2300DHTD585	Plaxton Paramount 3200 II	C57F	1985
B851KRY	Bedford YNT	Plaxton Paramount 3200 I	C53F	1984
D21EFS	Volvo B10M-61	Plaxton Paramount 3500 III	C53F	1987
D438TMB	Bedford YNV	Duple 320	C57F	1987
E235WMB	Mercedes-Benz 609D	PMT	C26F	1987
F990HGE	Volvo B10M-60	Plaxton Paramount 3500 III	C53F	1989
* G932TVO	Volvo B10M-60	Van Hool Alizée	C49FT	1990
* JIL2566	Volvo B10M-60	Plaxton Paramount 3500 II	C53F	1985
NOC598R	Leyland Fleetline FE30AGR	Park Royal	H43/33F	1978
* OIL2946	Volvo B10M-60	Plaxton Excalibur	C53F	2003
R967MGB	Mercedes-Benz Vario O.814D	Mellor	C33F	1998

Hebridean Coaches
D & A MacDonald, Howmore, Lochboisdale, Isle of South Uist HS8 5SH
Website   www.hebrideancoaches.co.uk
Depot   Howmore, Lochboisdale, Isle of South Uist HS8 5SH
Licence   PM0002538

AF02RZT	LDV Convoy	LDV	M16	2002
* AJZ9204	Dennis Javelin 11SDA	Plaxton Paramount 3200 III	C57F	1989
* C640UNV	Bedford YNV	Duple Laser II	C53F	1986
F878RFP	Dennis Javelin 12SDA	Duple 320	C57F	1989
G38SSR	Fiat Daily 49-10	Phoenix	B23F	1989
G278BEL	Dennis Javelin 11SDA	Duple 320	C53F	1989
* HIG2461	Dennis Javelin 12SDA	Plaxton Premiere 320	C57F	1997
* HIG2462	Mercedes-Benz Vario O.814D	Plaxton Cheetah	C33F	2003
NA04ZJU	Ford Transit	Ford	M16	2004
NJ07LRV	Ford Transit	Ford	M16	2007
* NUI2416	Mercedes-Benz 811D	Mellor	C31F	1994
* NUI2572	Dennis Javelin 12SDA	Plaxton Premiere 320	C53F	1994
* OUI3813	Mercedes-Benz Vario O.814D	Wadham Stringer	C28F	1995
UCZ3032	Ford Transit	Ford	M16	2003
VSB246T	Bedford SB5	Duple	C41F	1979
WDG230X	Ford R1114	Duple Dominant IV Exp.	C53F	1982
YX03LKY	LDV Convoy	LDV	M16	2003

Hebridean Transport

IA & C MacIver, Unit 4 & 5, Parkhead Industrial Estate, Stornoway HS2 0AN
Website
Depot   Unit 7, Parkhead Industrial Estate, Stornoway HS2 0AN
             3 Kendebig, Isle of Harris HS3 3DR
             11 Rodel, Isle of Harris HS5 3TW
             Ardhasaig, Isle of Harris HS3 3AJ
Licence PM0002728

* A10TBT	Leyland Leopard PSU3E/4R	Plaxton Premiere 320	C53F	1979
FNZ5833	Mercedes-Benz Vario O.814D	TransBus Cheetah	C33F	2004
FNZ5834	Mercedes-Benz Vario O.814D	TransBus Cheetah	C33F	2004
K944OPX	Dennis Javelin 10SDA	Wadham Stringer	B43FL	1993
ML02ONH	Mercedes-Benz Vario O.814D	Onyx	C24F	2002
N406SPC	Dennis Javelin 12SDA	Plaxton Premiere 320	C53F	1996
N407SPC	Dennis Javelin 12SDA	Plaxton Premiere 320	C53F	1996
N409SPC	Dennis Javelin 12SDA	Plaxton Premiere 320	C53F	1996
N479VPA	Dennis Javelin 12SFD	Plaxton Premiere 320	C53F	1996
P707DPA	Dennis Javelin 12SFD	Plaxton Premiere 320	C53F	1997
SD58LKP	Ford Transit	Ford	M16	2008
SG58EFC	Ford Transit	Ford	M16	2008
SH58VKP	Ford Transit	Ford	M16	2008
V828GGA	Mercedes-Benz Vario O.814D	Plaxton Beaver 2	C32F	1999
V956HEB	Mercedes-Benz 410D		M16L	2000
YN04HJX	Mercedes-Benz Vario O.814D	Plaxton Cheetah	C33F	2004

Henderson Travel

J & D Henderson, Unit 4, Whistleberry Industrial Estate, Hamilton ML3 0ED
Website   www.henderson-travel.co.uk
Depot   Unit 4, Whistleberry Industrial Estate, Hamilton ML3 0ED
Licence PM0001018

108	YJ08PKV	Optare Solo M780SE	Optare	B27F	2008
110	SN10CAU	ADL Enviro Dart 8.8 SLF	ADL Enviro 200	B29F	2010
154	YJ54UXB	Optare Solo M880	Optare	B20F	2004
156	YJ56WVH	Optare Solo M780SL	Optare	B24F	2007
157	SF57FZK	ADL Enviro Dart 8.9 SLF	ADL Enviro 200	B29F	2007
206	YJ06YSH	Optare Tempo X1060	Optare	B34F	2006
208	YJ08PKA	Optare Solo M780SE	Optare	B26F	2008
210	MX10DXO	ADL Enviro Dart 8.9 SLF	ADL Enviro 200	B29F	2010
256	WX56HLO	ADL Enviro 300 12.5 SLF	ADL Enviro 300	B62F	2006
257	YJ57XXC	Optare Solo M780SE	Optare	B25F	2008
306	YJ06YSE	Optare Solo M880	Optare	B20F	2006
307	SF07URJ	ADL Enviro Dart 8.9 SLF	ADL Enviro 200	B29F	2007
308	YJ08PHK	Optare Solo M780SE	Optare	B26F	2008
309	YJ09EVJ	Volkswagen Transporter	Bluebird Accessible	B11FL	2009
310	YJ10MGX	Optare Solo M950	Optare	B31F	2010
354	YJ54UXD	Optare Solo M880	Optare	B20F	2004
403	MX03YCW	Optare Solo M850	Optare	B29F	2003
406	YJ06YSF	Optare Solo M950	Optare	B33F	2006
407	SF07URL —	ADL Enviro Dart 8.9 SLF	ADL Enviro 200	B29F	2007
408	YJ08PGE	Optare Solo M780SE	Optare	B26F	2008
409	YJ09EVL	Volkswagen Transporter	Bluebird Accessible	B11FL	2009
410	SJ10AVR	Renault		B F	2010
503	MX03YCV	Optare Solo M850	Optare	B29F	2003
509	* YJ09HRC	Volkswagen Transporter	Volkswagen	B11FL	2009
510	SJ10AVT	Renault		B F	2010
554	YJ54UXE	Optare Solo M880	Optare	B20F	2004
607	YJ07VRK	Optare Solo M810SL	Optare	B24F	2007

		Henderson Travel				
609	YJ09HRD	Volkswagen Transporter	Volkswagen	B11FL	2009
610	SJ10NLJ	Renault		B F	2010
701	YJ07EHV	Optare Solo M780SE	Optare	B24F	2007
702	YJ07EHW	Optare Solo M780SE	Optare	B24F	2007
709	YJ09HRE	Volkswagen Transporter	Volkswagen	B11FL	2009
710	SJ10AVX	Renault		B F	2010
	AU53GWC	Mercedes-Benz Vario O.814D	Transbus Beaver	B33F	2003
*	HV02PAO	Dennis Dart 11.3 SLF	SCC Nimbus	DP41F	2002
	K875ODY w	Mercedes-Benz 709D	Alexander Sprint	B25F	1993
*	L252YOD w	Mercedes-Benz 709D	Plaxton Beaver	B25F	1993
	M367KVR	Mercedes-Benz 709D	Alexander Sprint	B27F	1995
	M609WFS	Mercedes-Benz 709D	Alexander Sprint	B29F	1995
	M662USX	Mercedes-Benz 709D	Alexander Sprint	B29F	1994
	P454MFS	Mercedes-Benz 711D	Alexander Sprint	B29F	1997
*	P683HND	Mercedes-Benz 709D	Alexander Sprint	B27F	1996
	S905DUB	Mercedes-Benz O.405	Optare Prisma	B49F	1998
	SF07VOB	ADL Enviro Dart 8.9 SLF	ADL Enviro 200	B29F	2007
	SF09LNZ	Renault		B F	2009
	SF09LOA	Renault		B F	2009
	W425CWX	Optare MetroRider MR17	Optare	B29F	2000
	YJ06YSG	Optare Solo M950	Optare	B33F	2006
	YJ58CBX	Optare Solo M780SE	Optare	B27F	2008
	YJ58CBY	Optare Solo M780SE	Optare	B27F	2008
	YJ58PKY	Optare Solo M780SE	Optare	B27F	2008
	YJ58PKZ	Optare Solo M780SE	Optare	B27F	2008
	YX07JPF	Optare Solo M780SL	Optare	B27F	2007

Highland Heritage

Highland Heritage Ltd, Dalmally Hotel, Dalmally PA33 1AY
Website www.highlandheritage.co.uk
Depots Dalmally Hotel, Dalmally PA33 1AY
Highland Hotel, Crianlarich FK20 8RW
Royal Hotel, Tyndrum, Crianlarich FK20 8RY
Ben Doran Hotel, Tyndrum FK20 8RZ
Licence PM0002817

2	SN06ACU	Volvo B12B(T)	Van Hool Alizée	C59F	2006
11	SN05DVW	Volvo B12B(T)	Van Hool Alizée	C59F	2005
12	SN05DVX	Volvo B12B(T)	Van Hool Alizée	C59F	2005
13	SN05DVY	Volvo B12B(T)	Van Hool Alizée	C59F	2005
14	SN05DVZ	Volvo B12B(T)	Van Hool Alizée	C59F	2005
15	SN05DWA	Volvo B12B(T)	Van Hool Alizée	C59F	2005
16	SN05DWC	Volvo B12B(T)	Van Hool Alizée	C59F	2005
17	SN05DWD	Volvo B12B(T)	Van Hool Alizée	C59F	2005
18	SN05DWE	Volvo B12B(T)	Van Hool Alizée	C59F	2005
19	SN05DWF	Volvo B12B(T)	Van Hool Alizée	C59F	2005
20	SN05DWG	Volvo B12B(T)	Van Hool Alizée	C59F	2005
21	SN05DWJ	Volvo B12B(T)	Van Hool Alizée	C59F	2005
22	SN05DWK	Volvo B12B(T)	Van Hool Alizée	C59F	2005
23	SN05DWL	Volvo B12B(T)	Van Hool Alizée	C59F	2005
24	SN54LRL	Volvo B12B(T)	Van Hool Alizée	C59F	2005
25	SN54LRO	Volvo B12B(T)	Van Hool Alizée	C59F	2005
	SN06ACO	Volvo B12B(T)	Van Hool Alizée	C59F	2006
	SN56FWT	Volvo B12B(T)	Van Hool Alizée	C59F	2006

E & M Horsburgh

E&M Horsburgh Ltd, 180 Uphall Station Road, Pumpherston EH53 0PD
Website www.horsburghcoaches.com
Depot 180 Uphall Station Road, Pumpherston EH53 0PD
Nasmyth Square, Houston Industrial Estate, Livingston EH54 5GG
Licence PM0003023

A736YFS	Leyland Olympian ONTL11/2R	Eastern Coach Works	H51/32D	1983
BU04ZYT	LDV Convoy	LDV	M16	2004
BV04CZJ	LDV Convoy	LDV	M16	2004
* C10EMH	Scania K113CRB	Van Hool Alizée	C53F	1996
* C16EMH	Mercedes-Benz O.816D	Plaxton Cheetah 2	C33F	2008
* C18EMH	Scania L94IB4	Irizar Century	C49F	1999
* C19EMH	Scania L94IB4	Irizar Century	C49F	1999
* C20EMH	Scania K113CRB	Van Hool Alizée	C53F	1996
C776SFS	Leyland Olympian ONTL11/2R	Eastern Coach Works	H51/32D	1985
C780SFS	Leyland Olympian ONTL11/2R	Eastern Coach Works	H51/32D	1985
C781SFS	Leyland Olympian ONTL11/2R	Eastern Coach Works	H51/32D	1985
C782SFS	Leyland Olympian ONTL11/2R	Eastern Coach Works	H51/32D	1985
DX05CZE	LDV Convoy	LDV	M16	2005
E316MSG	Leyland Olympian ONCL10/2RZ	Alexander RH	H51/30D	1988
E321MSG	Leyland Olympian ONCL10/2RZ	Alexander RH	H51/30D	1988
EH03EMH	Mercedes-Benz Vario O.813D	Plaxton Beaver 3	DP33FL	2003
* EIG1433	Leyland National 10351/1R	East Lancs Greenway (1994)	B41F	1975
* EIG1434	Leyland National 10351/2R	East Lancs Greenway (1993)	B41F	1975
EM04EMH	Optare Solo M9600SR	Optare	B F	2010
EM05EMH	Optare Solo M9600SR	Optare	B F	2010
EM06EMH	Optare Solo M9600SR	Optare	B F	2010
EM07EMH	Optare Solo M9600SR	Optare	B F	2010
EM08EMH	Optare Solo M9600SR	Optare	B F	2010
EM09EMH	Optare Solo M9600SR	Optare	B F	2010
FJ07AAZ	Volvo B7RLE	Wright Eclipse Urban	B45F	2007
G339CSG	Leyland Olympian ONCL10/2RZ	Alexander RH	H51/30D	1989
G340CSG	Leyland Olympian ONCL10/2RZ	Alexander RH	H51/30D	1989
G341CSG	Leyland Olympian ONCL10/2RZ	Alexander RH	H51/30D	1989
G342CSG	Leyland Olympian ONCL10/2RZ	Alexander RH	H51/30D	1989
G803GSX	Leyland Olympian ON2R56C13Z4	Alexander RH	H50/31D	1990
* G813GSX	Leyland Olympian ON2R56C13Z4	Alexander RH	H51/30D	1990
J848TSC	Leyland Olympian ON2R56C13Z4	Alexander RH	H51/30D	1991
K877CSF	Leyland Olympian ON2R56C13Z4	Alexander RH	H51/30D	1992
K879CSF	Leyland Olympian ON2R56C13Z4	Alexander RH	H51/30D	1992
L973MSC	Volvo Olympian YN2RC16Z4	Alexander RH	H51/30D	1994
L974MSC	Volvo Olympian YN2RC16Z4	Alexander RH	H51/30D	1994
M201VSX	Volvo Olympian YN2RC16Z4	Alexander RH	H51/30D	1995
M202VSX	Volvo Olympian YN2RC16Z4	Alexander RH	H51/30D	1995
* M203VSX	Volvo Olympian YN2RC16Z4	Alexander RH	H51/30D	1995
M204VSX	Volvo Olympian YN2RC16Z4	Alexander RH	H51/30D	1995
M454VCW	Volvo B10M-55	Alexander PS	DP48F	1995
M468ASW	Volvo B10M-55	Alexander PS	DP48F	1995
M471ASW	Volvo B10M-55	Alexander PS	DP48F	1995
M477ASW	Volvo B10M-55	Alexander PS	DP48F	1995
M480ASW	Volvo B10M-55	Alexander PS	DP48F	1995
M481FGG	Mercedes-Benz 609D	Devon Conversions	B18FL	1995
M593OSO	Volvo B10M-55	Alexander PS	DP48F	1994
M664UCT	Mercedes-Benz 711D	Autobus Classique	C24F	1995
MH03EMH	Mercedes-Benz Vario O.813D	Plaxton Beaver 3	DP33FL	2003
MX08MYK	Optare Solo M1020	Optare	B33F	2008
MX08MYL	Optare Solo M1020	Optare	B33F	2008
MX58AAF	Optare Solo M950	Optare	B33F	2008
MX58AAJ	Optare Solo M950	Optare	B33F	2008
MX58AAN	Optare Solo M950	Optare	B33F	2008

MX58AAO	Optare Solo M950	Optare	B33F	2008
N105WRC	Mercedes-Benz 811D	Plaxton Beaver	B30F	1995
N107WRC	Mercedes-Benz 811D	Plaxton Beaver	B30F	1995
P486TGA	Mercedes-Benz 711D	Mellor	C29F	1996
P671MSC	Mercedes-Benz 611D	Heggie	B15FL	1996
P894RSF	Mercedes-Benz Vario O.810D	Mellor	DP24FL	1997
R459VSD	Mercedes-Benz 614D	Adamson	C24F	1998
S456LGN	Dennis Dart 8.8 SLF	Plaxton Mini Pointer	B29F	1999
S457LGN	Dennis Dart 8.8 SLF	Plaxton Mini Pointer	B29F	1999
S458LGN	Dennis Dart 8.8 SLF	Plaxton Mini Pointer	B29F	1999
S463LGN	Dennis Dart 8.8 SLF	Plaxton Mini Pointer	B29F	1999
S940UAL	Dennis Dart 10.7 SLF	Plaxton Pointer 2	B36F	1998
S943UAL	Dennis Dart 10.7 SLF	Plaxton Pointer 2	B36F	1998
S944UAL	Dennis Dart 10.7 SLF		B36F	1998
SA02EDC	LDV Convoy	LDV	M16	2002
SA02UUH	LDV Convoy	LDV	M16	2002
SN06BRZ	ADL Enviro Dart 8.8 SLF	ADL Enviro 200	B29F	2006
SN06BSO	ADL Enviro Dart 8.8 SLF	ADL Enviro 200	B29F	2006
SN51UMC	LDV Convoy	LDV	M16	2001
SP02HMV	Ford Transit	Fisher	M14L	2002
SV52VXA	LDV Convoy	LDV	M16	2002
SV52VXB	LDV Convoy	LDV	M16	2002
T75JBA	Dennis Dart 8.8 SLF	Plaxton Mini Pointer	B29F	1999
T945BNN	Dennis Dart 10.7 SLF	Plaxton Pointer 2	B40F	1999
T947BNN	Dennis Dart 10.7 SLF	Plaxton Pointer 2	B40F	1999
T948BNN	Dennis Dart 10.7 SLF	Plaxton Pointer 2	B40F	1999
TJN505R	Leyland National 11351A/1R	East Lancs Greenway (1995)	B49F	1977
V154EFS	Dennis Dart 11.3 SLF	Plaxton Pointer 2	B42F	2000
V162EFS	Dennis Dart 11.3 SLF	Plaxton Pointer 2	B42F	2000
W594PFS	Mercedes-Benz Vario O.814D	Plaxton Beaver 2	DP31F	2000
W595PFS	Mercedes-Benz Vario O.814D	Plaxton Beaver 2	DP31F	2000
W596PFS	Mercedes-Benz Vario O.814D	Plaxton Beaver 2	DP31F	2000
W597PFS	Mercedes-Benz Vario O.814D	Plaxton Beaver 2	DP31F	2000
X89RGA	DAF FA45-150	Nu Trak	B25FL	2000
X221RGD	DAF FA45-150	Nu Trak	B25FL	2000
X235RGD	DAF FA45-150	Nu Trak	B25FL	2000
X415CSC	LDV Convoy	Aitken	M16L	2000
X416CSC	LDV Convoy	Aitken	M16L	2000
X534JGB	DAF FA45-150	Nu Trak	B25FL	2000
X555EMH	Volvo B9TL	Wright Eclipse Gemini	H70F	2007
X777EMH	Volvo B9TL	Wright Eclipse Gemini	H70F	2007
Y533RSD	LDV Convoy	LDV	M16L	2001
Y555EMH	Volvo B9TL	Wright Eclipse Gemini	H70F	2007
Y724TSJ	LDV Convoy	LDV	M16	2001
Y762TYS	LDV Convoy	LDV	M16	2001
Y777EMH	Volvo B9TL	Wright Eclipse Gemini	H70F	2007
YJ06HRN	LDV Convoy	LDV	M16L	2006
YJ06HRP	LDV Convoy	LDV	M16L	2006
YJ51XSH	Optare Solo M920	Optare	B31F	2001
YJ51XSK	Optare Solo M920	Optare	B31F	2001
YJ51XSL	Optare Solo M920	Optare	B31F	2001
YJ51XSM	Optare Solo M920	Optare	B31F	2001
YJ51XSN	Optare Solo M920	Optare	B31F	2001
YJ51XSO	Optare Solo M920	Optare	B31F	2001
YK05EMV	LDV Convoy	LDV	M16	2005
YK05EOY	LDV Convoy	LDV	M16	2005
YM52TOV	Optare Solo M920	Optare	B31F	2002
YN03NDY	Optare Solo M920	Optare	B31F	2003
YN03NDZ	Optare Solo M920	Optare	B31F	2003
YN52TOV	Optare Solo M920	Optare	B31F	2003

Houston

A & A Houston, 13 Stevenson Avenue, Lockerbie DG11 2PG
Website
Depot   Unit 5, 61-3 Bridge Street, Lockerbie DG11 2HS
Licence   PM1041723

BX10DHF	BMC Condor 225	BMC	B45F	2010
BX10DHG	BMC Condor 225	BMC	B45F	2010
BX10DHJ	BMC Hawk 900	BMC	B45F	2010
BX10DHK	BMC Hawk 900	BMC	B45F	2010
BX53SOC	Mercedes-Benz Sprinter 413CDI	Crest	M16	2003
G924TCU	Scania N113CRB	Alexander PS	B53F	1990
* G934TTV	Volvo B10M-62	Plaxton Paramount 3500 III	C53F	1990
* JCZ2065	Volvo B10M-60	Jonckheere	C53FT	1992
L644AFJ	DAF 400	G&M	M16	1993
MX09MKE	Optare Solo M880	Optare	B27F	2009
MX10DXP	Optare Solo M950	Optare	B32F	2010
MX10DXS	Optare Solo M950	Optare	B32F	2010
N409MWO	Iveco Daily 49-10	Bedwas	B17FL	1995
N835XRP	Iveco Daily 49-10	Premier	M16	1996
S579RGA	Mercedes-Benz Vario O.814D	Marshall Master	B33F	1999
S613HGD	Mercedes-Benz Vario O.814D	Mellor	B29F	1998
SF54ORA	Optare Solo M850	Optare	B20C	2004
SF54ORP	Optare Solo M850	Optare	B20C	2004
* TJI6264	Volvo B10M-61	Van Hool Alizée	C49FT	1992
W451PSG	Mercedes-Benz Vario O.814D	Plaxton Cheetah	C33F	2000
W918COJ	Mercedes-Benz 410D	Excel	M16	2000
WX05XWP	Mercedes-Benz 413CDI	UVM	B16FL	2005
YJ07EHB	Optare Solo M880	Optare	B28F	2007
YJ54ZXZ	Optare Solo M880	Optare	B26F	2005
YN09LLK	Mercedes-Benz Vario O.816D	Plaxton Cheetah	C33F	2009

Hunter's Coaches / William Hunter

W Hunter Ltd, Oakfield Garage, 21/23 The Loan, Loanhead EH20 9AE
Website   www.hunterscoaches.co.uk
Depot   Oakfield Garage, 21/23 The Loan, Loanhead EH20 9AE
Licence   PM1060979

* HIL2702	Volvo B10M-61	Van Hool Alizée	C53F	1988
* HIL2720	Toyota Coaster BB50R	Caetano Optimo	C22F	2001
* HIL3318	Toyota Coaster BB50R	Caetano Optimo	C22F	2000
* HIL4336	Volvo B10M-61	Van Hool Alizée	C53F	1988
* HIL5063	Volvo B10M-61	Van Hool Alizée	C53F	1984
* HIL5345	Volvo B10M-62	Van Hool Alizée	C49F	1999
* HIL5346	Volvo B10M-62	Van Hool Alizée	C51F	1998
* HIL5347	Volvo B10M-62	Van Hool Alizée	C49FT	1998
* HIL5348	Volvo B12M	Van Hool Alizée	C53F	2003
* HIL5349	Volvo B12M	Van Hool Alizée	C53F	2003
* HIL8617	Volvo B10M-61	Van Hool Alizée	C53F	1988
R650VNN	Dennis Javelin 12SFD	Marcopolo Explorer	C50FT	1998
* RRY342	Volvo B10M-62	Van Hool Alizée	C49F	1999
* SRU410	Volvo B10M-62	Van Hool Alizée	C49FT	2001
* UKZ7822	Volvo B10M-62	Van Hool Alizée	C70F	1996

Hunter's Executive / John Hunter
J Hunter, The Garage, Lochies Road, Clackmannan FK10 4EN
Website   www.huntersexecutivecoaches.co.uk
Depot   The Garage, Lochies Road, Clackmannan FK10 4EN
Licence   PM0002676

	Reg	Chassis	Body	Seating	Year
	FJ08BZL	Volvo B12B	Jonckheere Mistral	C49FT	2008
*	J3PUB	Volvo B10M-55	Van Hool Alizée	C49F	2001
*	MDM371	Dennis Javelin 12SDA	Marcopolo Explorer	C53F	1997
*	MNZ9303	Volvo B12B	Jonckheere Mistral	C49FT	2003
	MX05FPL	Mercedes-Benz 616CDI	Mellor	B18FL	2005
	N745LUS	Ford Transit	Williams Deansgate	M15	1995
*	OSU638	Volvo B10M-60	Jonckheere Deauville	C51F	1994
*	P301VWR	Volvo B10M-62	Van Hool Alizée	C46FT	1997
	PX07GXT	Volvo B12B	Jonckheere Mistral	C51FT	2007
	SF06NYG	Mercedes-Benz 614D	Onyx	C24F	2006
	SJ51NVY	Mercedes-Benz 413CDI	Onyx	M16	2001
*	SN03AXM	Mercedes-Benz 614D	Onyx	C24F	2003
	SN57DXJ	ADL Enviro Dart 8.9 SLF	ADL Enviro 200	B28FL	2007
	SN57EHX	Mercedes-Benz Vario O.814D	Unvi	C33F	2007
	SV53ELJ	Mercedes-Benz O.815D	Sitcar Beluga	C33F	2003
*	V1PHC	Scania K114EB6	Irizar Century	C57F	2007
*	XIL8788	Volvo B10M-62	Van Hool Alizée	C46FT	1997
	Y297SNB	LDV Convoy	LDV	M16	2001
	YN07NWD	Mercedes-Benz Vario O.814D	Killbeggan Vehicle Converters	C24F	2007
	YX06AXS	Mercedes-Benz Atego 1223L	Optare Solera	C39F	2006

Charlie Irons Coaches
Charlie Irons Coaches Ltd, 48 Hailes Gardens, Edinburgh EH13 0JH
Website   www.ironscoaches.co.uk
Depot   Units 6 & 7, Camps Industrial Estate, Kirknewton EH27 8DF
Licence   PM1007521

	Reg	Chassis	Body	Seating	Year
*	N200CHA	Volvo B10M-62	Van Hool Alizée	C51F	1999
*	N400CHA	MAN 18.310	Marcopolo Viaggio	C69F	2005
*	N500CHA	MAN 18.310	Marcopolo Viaggio	C70FL	2007
*	N600CHA	Mercedes-Benz Vario O.814D	Autobus Nouvelle	C33F	2004
*	N700CHA	Neoplan N516/2	Neoplan Starliner	C32FT	2000
*	N800CHA	Mercedes-Benz Sprinter 413CDI	Killbeggan Vehicle Converters	M16	2006
	PN57CVA	Irisbus EuroRider 397E.12.35	Marcopolo	C53L	2007

N300 CHA

Irvine Coaches / Law Bus & Coach
P Irvine, Lawmuir Road Garage, Law ML8 5JB
M Walker, 2 Muirhead Drive, Law, Carluke ML8 5FB
Website   www.irvinescoaches.co.uk
Depot   Lawmuir Road Garage, Law ML8 5JB
Licence   PM0002941 (Irvines Coaches)
          PM0003043 (Law Bus & Coach)

	Reg	Chassis	Body	Seating	Year
*	123TRL	Volvo B10M-62	Caetano Enigma	C49FT	2001
*	730UXG	Scania L94IB	Irizar	C49FT	1999
	AY53GHZ	DAF SB4000	Van Hool Alizée	C49FT	2003
	B301KVO	Volvo B10M-50	East Lancs	H51/35D	1985
	B302KVO	Volvo B10M-50	East Lancs	H51/35D	1985
	B303KVO	Volvo B10M-50	East Lancs	H51/35D	1985
	B304KVO	Volvo B10M-50	East Lancs	H51/35D	1985
	B305KVO	Volvo B10M-50	East Lancs	H51/35D	1985
	B307KVO	Volvo B10M-50	East Lancs	H51/35D	1985
	CHL772 p	Dennis CVD6SD	Willowbrook	B35F	1950

Irvine Coaches

Reg	Chassis	Body	Seating	Year
EU06KDJ —	ADL Enviro Dart 8.8 SLF	Caetano Compass	B28F	2006
FJ05HXX	Dennis Dart 8.8 SLF	Caetano Compass	B28F	2005
* GXI53 —	Volvo B10M-62	Plaxton Panther	C49FT	2000
* HSK857	Volvo B10M-62	Plaxton Panther	C48FT	2000
* HSU983	Volvo B10M-62	Jonckheere Mistral	C49FT	1997
* HUI8156	DAF SB300	Van Hool Alizée	C49FT	1996
L485NTO	Volvo Olympian YN2RV18Z5	East Lancs Pyoneer	H49/35F	1994
L486NTO	Volvo Olympian YV2RV18Z5	East Lancs Pyoneer	H49/35F	1994
L489NTO	Volvo Olympian YN2RV18Z5	East Lancs Pyoneer	H49/35F	1994
M553WTJ	Volvo B10M-58	Wright Endurance	B49F	1995
MX07BCU —	Optare Solo M880	Optare	B28F	2007
MX07NUA	Optare Solo M880SL	Optare	B29F	2007
MX08DJF	Optare Solo M880	Optare	B28FL	2008
MX54KXP	Optare Solo M880	Optare	B31F	2004
MX55BYH	Optare Solo M880SL	Optare	B25F	2005
MX56NMA	Enterprise Bus Plasma EB01	Plaxton Primo	B28F	2006
N754OAP	Scania N113DRB	East Lancs Cityzen	H47/31F	1996
* P11RVN —	Volvo B10M-66	Plaxton Premiere 350	C48FT	1996
* P66BUS —	Volvo B10M-62	Plaxton Premiere 320	C53F	1998
P258PS	Volvo Olympian-56	Alexander Royale	H57/35F	1997
P491CVO	Volvo Olympian YN2RV18Z5	East Lancs Pyoneer	H49/35F	1996
P492FRR	Volvo Olympian YN2RV18Z5	East Lancs Pyoneer	H49/35F	1996
P804BLJ	Volvo B10M-62	Plaxton Premiere 350	C49FT	1997
* P984JBC	Volvo B10M-62	Plaxton Premiere 350	C49FT	1997
* PP04BUS	Volvo B12B	Sunsundegui Sideral	C49F	2004
* PP06BUS	Bova FHD12.340	Bova Futura	C49FT	2006
S461ATV	Volvo Olympian	East Lancs	H49/35F	1999
SF03ACU	Volvo B7R	Plaxton Profile	C57F	2003
SF06HHN —	Bova FHD13-340	Bova Futura	C49FT	2006
SF54KHV	Dennis Dart 8.8 SLF	Caetano Compass	B28F	2005
SK07FOM	Bova HD120-340XF	Bova Magiq	C49F	2007
SN06AZB	Bova FHD12-340	Bova Futura	C49FT	2006
SN55DUU	Dennis Dart 8.8 SLF	Alexander ALX200	B29F	2005
SN56AWZ	ADL Enviro Dart 8.9 SLF	ADL Enviro 200	B29F	2006
* Y173CGC —	Volvo B7R	Plaxton Premiere 320	C53F	2001
YJ07VRX	Optare Solo M850	Optare	B28F	2007
YJ09OUV	Optare Solo M780SE	Optare	B21F	2009
YJ51EKO	DAF SB200	Ikarus Citibus	B44F	2001
YJ51EKP	DAF SB200	Ikarus Citibus	B44F	2001
YJ54UBY	Optare Solo M920	Optare	B31F	2004
YJ55WRA	VDL DE12BSSB120	Wright Cadet	B39F	2006
YJ55WRC	VDL DE12BSSB120	Wright Cadet	B39F	2006
YJ55YHC —	Optare Solo M950	Optare	B33F	2006
YJ60KBM —	Optare Solo M880	Optare	B28FL	2010
YN03WPZ	Scania K124IB	Irizar Century	C49FT	2003
YN05GZA	Scania K114EB4	Irizar Century	C49FT	2005
YN53YHJ	Optare Solo M850	Optare	B29F	2003

JD Travel

J Duggan, 104 Main Street, Calderbank, Airdrie ML6 9SU
Website   www.jdtravel.org.uk
Depot   102-104 Main Street, Calderbank, Airdrie ML6 9SU
Licence   PM0001520

* A20JPT	Volvo B10M-62	Plaxton Premiere 350	C53F	1995
AEF221Y	Leyland Olympian ONLXB/1R	Eastern Coach Works	H45/32F	1983
B964WRN	Leyland Olympian ONLXB/1R	Eastern Coach Works	H45/32F	1985
C402BUV	MCW MetroBus DR101/17	MCW	H43/28D	1985
K464PNR	Volvo B10M-60	Plaxton Premiere 350	C53F	1993
* L11JDT	Volvo B10M-62	Jonckheere Deauville	C53F	1994
* LAZ4470	Volvo B10M-61	Van Hool Alizée	C53F	1984
P11JDT	Mercedes-Benz 711D	Adamson	C24F	1996
R11JDT	Mercedes-Benz 614D	Adamson	C24F	1998
* RIB2901	Volvo B10M-62	Van Hool Alizée	C51FT	1995
* WJI6650	Volvo B10M-61	Plaxton Paramount 3500 III	C53F	1987
* WJI6730	Volvo B10M-46	Caetano Algarve	C41F	1986
* XAM124A	DAF SBR3000DKSB570	Plaxton Paramount 4000	CH55/17CT	1988

Jenkins Travel

J Davies & S Jenkins, Unit 1 Victoria Park, Newtongrange EH22 4QN
Website
Depot   Unit 1 Victoria Park, Newtongrange EH22 4QN
Licence   PM1017489

* C7OST	Dennis Javelin 12SDA	Plaxton Paramount 3200 III	C70F	1988
* FLZ6854	Volvo B10M-60	Plaxton Premiere 350	C53F	1988
* HIL2160	Leyland Tiger TRCTL11/3R	Plaxton Paramount 3200 II	C57F	1984
* J3EGT	Mercedes-Benz O.814D	Robin Hood	C18F	1996
* J5EGT	Ford Transit	Ford	M16	2002
* J7EGT	Volvo B10M-62	Van Hool Alizée	C46FT	1997
* K977XND	Mercedes-Benz 609D	Made to Measure	C26FL	1992
* LIW4290	Volvo B10M-61	Caetano	C49FT	1985
* MX04VBL	Mercedes-Benz 413CDI	Concept	M16	2004
* NCC745	Volvo B10M-62	Van Hool Alizée	C55F	1994
SF09LYZ	Volvo B7R	Plaxton Profile	C70F	2009
SF09LZW	Mercedes-Benz O.816D	Plaxton Cheetah	C33F	2009
* SIL8013	LDV Convoy	LDV	M16	1999
* X937MSP	Mercedes-Benz Vario O.814D	Plaxton Cheetah	C33F	2000

J J Travel / McNairns Coaches

J J Travel Ltd, 30 Northburn Road, Coatbridge ML5 2HY
J McNairn, 81 Burnbank Street, Coatbridge ML5 2AS
Website
Depot   30 Northburn Road, Coatbridge ML5 2HY
Licence   PM1026342 (J J Travel) / PM00000580 (McNairns Coaches)

AU04BZT	Mercedes-Benz Vario O.814D	Plaxton Beaver 2	B31F	2004
AU04BZV	Mercedes-Benz Vario O.814D	Plaxton Beaver 2	B31F	2004
B114SJA	Leyland Olympian ONLXB/1R	Northern Counties	H43/30F	1985
B269LPH	Leyland Olympian ONTL11/1R	Eastern Coach Works	H43/29F	1985
* BAZ7916	Volvo B10M-61	Van Hool Alizée	C48F	1982
C783SFS	Leyland Olympian ONTL11/2R	Eastern Coach Works	H51/32D	1986
C796USG	Volvo B10M-50	Alexander RV	H47/33F	1986
C805USG	Volvo B10M-50	Alexander RV	H47/33F	1986
CEF232Y	Leyland Olympian ONLXB/1R	Eastern Coach Works	H45/32F	1983
CU04AOL	Mercedes-Benz Vario O.814D		C24F	2004
* D131UGB	Dennis Dorchester SDA	Alexander TC	B69F	1987

DKS20X	Volvo B10M-56	Plaxton Supreme V Exp.	C53F	1982
E51UKL	Mercedes-Benz 609D	Reeve Burgess	B20F	1987
E359NEG	Volvo B10M-61	Plaxton Paramount 3200 III	C53DL	1988
F274JWL	Mercedes-Benz 811D	Reeve Burgess Beaver	C33F	1988
F348WSC	Leyland Olympian ONCL10/2RZ	Alexander RH	H51/30D	1989
G169LET	Volvo B10M-60	Plaxton Paramount 3500 III	C53F	1989
* G577XAE	Mercedes-Benz 811D	Reeve Burgess Beaver	C33F	1990
G816GSX	Leyland Olympian ON2R56C13Z4	Alexander RH	H51/30D	1990
H717LOL	Mercedes-Benz 811D	Carlyle C19	B33F	1990
H719LOL	Mercedes-Benz 811D	Carlyle C19	B33F	1990
J607KGB	Mercedes-Benz 709D	Dormobile Routemaker	B29F	1992
* J882UNA	Mercedes-Benz 709D	Plaxton Beaver	B25F	1991
JFR9W	Leyland Olympian ONLXB/1R	Eastern Coach Works	H45/32F	1981
K495OSU	Mercedes-Benz 709D	Leicester Carriage Builders	B24FL	1993
KSD103W	Volvo Ailsa B55-10	Alexander AV	H44/35F	1980
* L3OBS	Mercedes-Benz 811D	Autobus Classique	C33F	1994
L36ULA	Mercedes-Benz 709D	Mellor	B28FL	1993
L869LFS	Mercedes-Benz 711D	Plaxton Beaver	B25F	1994
* LAZ4120	Volvo B10M-46	Plaxton Paramount 3200 III	C38FT	1988
* LIL8050	Leyland Tiger TRCTL11/3R	Plaxton Paramount 3200 I Exp.	C55F	1983
* LUI1727	Mercedes-Benz 811D	TBP	C25F	2002
M568TJL	Mercedes-Benz 814D	Autobus Classique	B31F	1995
N200BUS	Volvo B10M-62	Van Hool Alizée	C53F	1996
OFS700Y	Leyland Olympian ONTL11/2R	Eastern Coach Works	H51/31D	1983
ORJ395W	Leyland Atlantean AN68A/1R	Northern Counties	H43/32F	1981
ORJ396W	Leyland Atlantean AN68A/1R	Northern Counties	H43/32F	1981
* PWV693	Mercedes-Benz Vario O.814D	Plaxton Cheetah	C33F	2002
RM03GSM	Volvo B7R	Plaxton Profile	C57F	2003
SA02OWW	Mercedes-Benz Vario O.814D	Essbee	C24F	2002
* UIL7828	Volvo B10M-60	Plaxton Paramount 3500 III	C53F	1989
V90CBC	Mercedes-Benz Vario O.814D	Mellor	C33F	2000
V451NGA	Mercedes-Benz Vario O.814D	Plaxton Beaver 2	B31F	1999
V490FSF	Mercedes-Benz Vario O.814D	Plaxton Beaver 2	B27F	2000
W854DHF	Ford Transit	Ford	M14	2000
* WAZ7316	Volvo B10M-60	Plaxton Premiere 350	C51FT	1995

JP Mini Coaches / Alba
JP Minicoaches Ltd, Unit 3, Orchardbank Industrial Estate, Forfar DD8 1TD
Website
Depot   Unit 3, Orchardbank Industrial Estate, Forfar DD8 1TD
Licence   PM1037871

* 679JPU		Mercedes-Benz Atego 1223L	Ferqui	C32FT	2004
* 825BGE		Mercedes-Benz 416CDI	Ferqui	C16F	2002
* CHZ1761		Dennis Javelin 12SDA	Duple 320	C70F	1989
CV02KFX		Mercedes-Benz O.814D	Cymric	B31F	2002
* F869TLJ		Dennis Javelin 11SDA	Duple 320	C53F	1988
* FSU335		Mercedes-Benz Atego 1120L	Optare Solera	C35F	1999
G809HRN	y	Mercedes-Benz 811D	Reeve Burgess Beaver	C33F	1989
GBZ7213		Mercedes-Benz 811D	Wright, Wishaw	B29F	1991
H551EVM		Ford Transit	Made to Measure	C16F	1991
J734MFY		Mercedes-Benz 709D	Wright NimBus	B29F	1992
* K579PHU		Dennis Javelin 10SDA	Wadham Stringer	C55F	1993
L945HTM		Mercedes-Benz 811D	Plaxton Beaver	B33F	1994
* LSK530		Dennis Javelin 8.5SDL	Plaxton Paramount 3200 III	C37F	1988
* LUI9240		Dennis Javelin 11SDL	Duple 320	C51F	1992
MX04DSZ		Mercedes-Benz 413CDi	Onyx	M16	2004
P206GSR		Optare MetroRider MR17	Optare	B29F	1996

JP Minicoaches

P238EJW	Mercedes-Benz 811D	Marshall C16	B27F	1997	
PX53ZLY	Ford Transit	Ford	M16	2003	
R74VVP	Volvo B10M-62	Plaxton Excalibur	C49FT	1998	
* R341KGG	mercedes-Benz Vario O.814D	Alexander Sprint	B27F	1998	
R688FYG	LDV Convoy	Concept	M16	1998	
* RUI2184	Mercedes-Benz 609D	Crystals	C26FL	1993	
* RUI2185	Mercedes-Benz 609D	Made to Measure	C24F	1990	
* RUI9469	Dennis Javelin 11SDA	Plaxton Paramount 3200 III	C55F	1992	
* RUI9470	Mercedes-Benz 412CD	Autobus Nouvelle	M16	1998	
S236EWU	Optare Solo M850	Optare	B29F	1998	
S276LGA	Mercedes-Benz Vario O.814D	Mellor	B31F	1998	
S279AOX	Optare Solo M850	Optare	B27F	1999	
S284AOX	Optare Solo M850	Optare	B27F	1999	
S285AOX	Optare Solo M850	Optare	B27F	1999	
S286AOX	Optare Solo M850	Optare	B27F	1998	
SP05CXY	Mercedes-Benz O.815D	Sitcar Beluga	C33F	2005	
* VIL6350	Mercedes-Benz 811D	Reeve Burgess Beaver	C25F	1988	
VX53AVC	Mercedes-Benz Vario O.814D	Mellor	C33F	2003	
W10CAT	Mercedes-Benz O.814D	Cymric	C33F	2000	
* XIL1540	Mercedes-Benz 709D	Alexander Sprint	DP25F	1994	
* XIL6465	Mercedes-Benz 711D	Mellor	C25F	1995	
* XIL6467	Mercedes-Benz 709D	Plaxton Beaver	B23F	1994	
* XIL6468	Mercedes-Benz 709D	Alexander Sprint	B25F	1995	
* XIL6471	Mercedes-Benz 410D	Ferguson	M15L	1997	
* XIL6472	Mercedes-Benz 814D	Autobus Classique	C33F	1994	
* XIL6473	Mercedes-Benz Vario O.814D	Plaxton Cheetah	C33F	2000	
* XIL6474	Mercedes-Benz 814D	Wright NimBus	DP33F	1991	
* YIL2180	Dennis Javelin 12SDA	Plaxton Premiere 320	C57F	1995	

KC Transport

KC Coaches Ltd, 68 Sandy Road, Carluke ML8 5DH
Website
Depot   68 Sandy Road, Carluke ML8 5DH
Licence   PM1065972

* B15KCT	Mercedes-Benz 609D	Autobus Classique	C23F	1994
* KC02BUS	Ford Transit	Ford	M16	2004
* KC51BUS	Ford Transit	Ford	M16	2003
* KCT50	Volvo B10M-62	Van Hool Alizee	C49FT	1997
* N7CTL	Volvo B10M-62	Van Hool Alizée	C53F	1996
R315FNS	Ford Transit	Ford	M14L	1997
R801KCU	Mercedes-Benz 614D	Adamson	C24F	1997
R940UWE	Ford Transit	Mayflower	M16	1998
* SE02TWJ	Ford Transit	Ford	M14	2003
SF58JFV	Mercedes-Benz Vario O.813D	Onyx	C24F	2008
ST05LMO	Ford Transit	Ford	M16	2005

Keenan of Ayr

J Keenan & Sons Ltd, Darwin Garage, Coalhall, Drongan KA6 6ND
Website   www.keenancoaches.co.uk
Depot   Darwin Garage, Coalhall, Drongan KA6 6ND
Licence   PM0000033

* 246AJF —	Volvo B10M-61	Van Hool Alizée	C53F	1986
* A1VOL —	Volvo B10M-61	Plaxton Paramount 3500 II	C49FT	1986
AVK155V — w	Leyland Atlantean AN68/2R	Alexander AL	H49/37F	1980
* B3VOL—	Volvo B10M-62	Van Hool Alizée	C53F	1994
* B4VOL —	Volvo B10M-62	Van Hool Alizée	C46FT	1995
* B5VOL	Volvo B10M-62	Van Hool Alizée	C46FT	1995
* B10VOL —	Volvo B10M-61	Van Hool Alizée	C57F	1988
B252CVX	DAF MB200DKFL600	Duple Laser	C57F	1985
BSJ931T —	Leyland Leopard PSU3E/4R	Alexander AY	B67F	1979
C802USG —	Volvo B10M-50	Alexander RV	H47/37F	1986
* GCS38V	Mercedes-Benz 709D	Alexander Sprint	B25F	1983
GCS48V —	Leyland Leopard PSU3E/4R	Alexander AY	B53F	1980
H113ABV —	Volvo B10M-50	Alexander AV	H47/37F	1991
HGD214T w	Leyland Atlantean AN68/1R	Alexander AL	H45/33F	1979
* LIL9814 —	Volvo B10M-60	Van Hool Alizée	C53F	1990
ORJ393W	Leyland Atlantean AN68A/1R	Northern Counties	H43/32F	1981
SF04ETK —	Mercedes-Benz Vario O.814D	TransBus Cheetah	C33F	2004
* STG476Y	Leyland Leopard PSU3/4R	Plaxton Paramount 3200 I	C53F	1967
* TIW9829 —	Volvo B10M-60	Van Hool Alizée	C53F	1991
* TJI1328	Volvo B10M-61	Plaxton Paramount 3500 II	C53F	1985
TMS407X —	Leyland Leopard PSU3G/4R	Alexander AY	DP49F	1982
TSJ71S	Leyland Leopard PSU3D/4R	Alexander AY	B53F	1977
* W77BUS	Volvo B10M-62	Van Hool Alizee	C46FT	2000
* WDS343V —	Leyland Leopard PSU3E/4R	Alexander AY	B53F	1980
WFS147W	Leyland Leopard PSU3F/4R	Alexander AYS	DP49F	1980
XMS423Y	Leyland Leopard PSU3G/4R	Alexander AYS	B53F	1982
XMS424Y	Leyland Leopard PSU3G/4R	Alexander AYS	B60F	1982
* YIJ3053	Leyland Tiger TRCTL11/3RZ	Plaxton Derwent	B70F	1986

Kelvin Valley Coaches

R MacKenzie, Richard Bruce House, Whitehill Farm, Denny FK6 5NA
Website
Depot   249 Greengairs Road, Greengairs, Airdrie ML6 7SZ
Glenhove Road, Luiggiebank, Glasgow G67 4AA
Whitehill Farm, Denny FK6 5NA
Licence   PM1077094

J442JBV	Volvo B10M-55	East Lancs	B51F	1991
* JJI3316	Leyland Tiger TRCTL11/3R	Plaxton Paramount 3200 I	C53F	1984
* M328TJA	Mercedes-Benz 709D	Marshall	B27F	1994
M879DDS	Mercedes-Benz 709D	Marshall C19	B27F	1995
P74HMC —	Mercedes-Benz 709D	Plaxton Beaver	DP24L	1996
R684MEW	Dennis Dart 10.1 SLF	Marshall Capital	B35F	1995

Key Coaches / Key Travel

S Forbes, 102 Dundonald Avenue, Johnstone PA5 0LT
Website
Depot   33B Braehead Industrial Estate, Old Govan Road, Renfrew PA4 8XJ
Licence   PM0002916 (Key Travel)
               PM0002491 (Key Coaches)

* DCZ7588 —	Mercedes-Benz 709D	Alexander Sprint	B25F	1994
* G194PAO	Mercedes-Benz 709D	Alexander Sprint	DP25F	1990
G926WGS	Mercedes-Benz 709D	Reeve Burgess Beaver	B23F	1990
J938WHJ	Mercedes-Benz 709D	Plaxton Beaver	B23F	1992
K96RGA	Mercedes-Benz 709D	Dormobile Routemaker	B29F	1993
K118XHG	Mercedes-Benz 709D	Alexander Sprint	B25F	1995
M649FYS	Mercedes-Benz 709D	Alexander Sprint	B25F	1995
M663FYS	Mercedes-Benz 709D	Alexander Sprint	B25F	1995
N622VSS	Mercedes-Benz 709D	Alexander Sprint	B25F	1995
P152LSC	Mercedes-Benz 709D	Alexander Sprint	B29F	1996
R733EGD	Mercedes-Benz 709D	Plaxton Beaver	B27F	1997
W754URD	Mercedes-Benz Sprinter 412CD	Frank Guy	B15F	2000

Kineil Coaches

Kineil Coaches Ltd, 7 Pitblae Place, Fraserburgh AB43 7BG
Website
Depot   Anderson Place, Westshore Industrial Estate, Fraserburgh AB43 9LG
               26 Permiter Road, Pinefield Industrial Estate, Elgin AB43 7BG
Licence   PM0003019

* 671YWC	Volvo B10M-61	Van Hool Alizée	C49DT	1984
* 953HBU	Volvo B10M-61	Van Hool Alizée	C51FT	1987
* A717ASJ	Volvo B10M-61	Van Hool Alizée	C50FT	1984
* GJI926	Volvo B10M-62	Van Hool Alizée	C70F	1994
* JSU384	Volvo B10M-60	Van Hool Alizée	C70F	1989
* JSV362	Volvo B10M-60	Van Hool Alizée	C70F	1994
K5SKY	Volvo B10M-60	Van Hool Alizée	C49FT	1993
L4LCC —	Volvo B10M-60	Van Hool Alizée	C55F	1994
M12BUS	Volvo B10M-62	Van Hool Alizee	C53F	1995
M760GGE	Volvo B10M-62	Van Hool Alizée	C70F	1995
* M831HNS	Volvo B10M-62	Van Hool Alizée	C70F	1995
PDX782	DAF MB200DKFL600	Van Hool Alizée	C50F	1983
* PSU755	Volvo B10M-62	Van Hool Alizée	C53F	1996
* R402EOS	Volvo B10M-62	Van Hool Alizée	C49FT	1998
* RIB7742	Volvo B10M-60	Van Hool Alizée	C53F	1989
SF10AZT	Mercedes-Benz O.816D	Sitcar Beluga	C29F	2010
SM02GSM	Scania K124IB4	Van Hool Alizée	C49FT	2002
SN04GFE	Mercedes-Benz Vario O.814D	Plaxton Cheetah	C33F	2004
SN53DYA	Mercedes-Benz 614D	Onyx	C24F	2003
SV03JZK —	Mercedes-Benz Vario O.815D	Sitcar Beluga	C33F	2003
T9TAP	Mercedes-Benz 614D	Onyx	C24F	1999
* TIW7700	Volvo B10M-61	Van Hool Alizée	C50FT	1984
V326XDO	Mercedes-Benz 412CD	Autobus Nouvelle	M16	1999
V540DYA	Volvo B10M-62	Van Hool Alizée	C49FT	2000
* VIA488	Volvo B10M-62	Van Hool Alizée	C49FT	1998
* VIA508	Volvo B10M-60	Van Hool Alizee	C70F	1995
* VIA963	Volvo B10M-62	Van Hool Alizée	C57F	1996
W623NWG	Volvo B7R	Plaxton Premiere 320	C55F	2000
WA51JYE	Volvo B10M-62	Van Hool Alizée	C49FT	2002
X974NRS	Mercedes-Benz 614D	Onyx	C24F	2000
Y226NYA	Volvo B10M-62	Van Hool Alizée	C49FT	2001
YJ10OAA	Optare Solo M880SL	Optare	B27F	2010

		Kineil Coaches			
YJ10OAB	Optare Solo M880SL		Optare	B27F	2010
YJ10OAC	Optare Solo M880SL		Optare	B27F	2010
YJ10OAD	Optare Solo M880SL		Optare	B27F	2010
YJ10OAE	Optare Solo M880SL		Optare	B27F	2010
YN54WVX	Mercedes-Benz Vario O.814D		Plaxton Cheetah	C33F	2004
YN57MEU	Mercedes-Benz O816D		Plaxton Cheetah	C33F	2007
YN57MFK	Mercedes-Benz Vario O.814D		Plaxton Cheetah	C33F	2007

James King

James T King, 36 Main Street, Kirkcowan DG8 0HG
Website www.kingscoachhire.com
Depot 36 Main Street, Kirkcowan DG8 0HG
Station Street, Station Yard, Stranraer DG9 7HL
Licence PM0000387

F550TMH	w	Volvo B10M-60	Van Hool Alizée	C53F	1989
* FE02FBK		Volvo B10M-62	Plaxton Panther	C49FT	2002
G864RNC		Volvo B10M-60	Van Hool Alizée	C53F	1989
GX02AHN		Toyota Coaster BB50R	Caetano Optimo	C22F	2002
H195DVM		Volvo B10M-60	Van Hool Alizée	C53F	1991
H660UWE		Mercedes-Benz 609D	Whittaker	C21F	1991
H757DTM		Volvo B10M-60	Plaxton Paramount 3500 III	C53F	1990
* J864XFS		Dennis Javelin 8.5SDA	Plaxton Paramount 3200 III	C53F	1992
K917RGE		Volvo B10M-60	Jonckheere Deauville	C53F	1993
* KIW1102		Volvo B10M-61	Plaxton Paramount 3500 III	C49FT	1988
L931NWW		Volvo B10M-60	Plaxton Excalibur	C50F	1994
* LCZ3677		Volvo B10M-61	Van Hool Alizée	C53F	1988
* M438ECS		Volvo B10M-62	Van Hool Alizée	C53F	1994
M464YAS		Bova FHD12-330	Bova Futura	C43FT	1995
M482CSD		Volvo B10M-62	Van Hool Alizée	C55F	1995
M527UGS		Mercedes-Benz OH1416	Wright Urbanranger	B47F	1995
N103CSN		Volvo B10M-62	Jonckheere Deauville	C53F	1995
N276HSD		Volvo B10M-62	Van Hool Alizée	C53FT	1996
N348EHJ		Ford Transit	Ford	M14	1996
* RJI6395		Volvo B10M-61	Van Hool Alizée	C49FT	1989
SF05FNS		Mercedes-Benz Vario O.814D	Plaxton Beaver 2	B31F	2005
SF05FNT		Mercedes-Benz Vario O.814D	Plaxton Beaver 2	DP33F	2005
* T50TPB		Bova FHD12.340	Bova Futura	C70F	1999
V143FOS		Mercedes-Benz 614D	Autobus Nouvelle	C24F	1999
V401SVV		Mercedes-Benz Vario O.814D	Plaxton Beaver 2	DP31F	1999
W836PPD		Mercedes-Benz Vario O.814D	Autobus Nouvelle	C33F	2000
W837PPD		Mercedes-Benz Vario O.814D	Autobus Nouvelle	C33F	2000
X178BNH		Mercedes-Benz Vario O.814D	Plaxton Beaver 2	B33F	2000
* XLM923		Volvo B10M-62	Van Hool Alizée	C57F	1996
YJ05JXT		Optare Solo M920	Optare	B25F	2005
YJ07VRL		Optare Solo M780SE	Optare	B23F	2007
YJ07VRM		Optare Solo M880	Optare	B25F	2007
YJ07VRO		Optare Solo M880	Optare	B25F	2007
YN08OWX		Volvo B12M	Plaxton Paragon	C57F	2008

L A Travel

L McChrystal, 25 Briar Road, Kirkintilloch G66 9SA
Website www.latravel.co.uk
Depot Pit Road, Kirkintilloch, Glasgow G66 3SA
Licence PM0002747

*	DCZ7109	Iveco EuroRider 391E.12.35	Beulas Stergo E	C51F	1998
*	ECZ9120	Bova FHD12-340	Bova Futura	C51FT	1994
*	ECZ9122	Bova FLD12-270	Bova Futura	C53F	1994
*	G5LAT —	Mercedes-Benz Atego 1223L	Optare Solera	C30FT	2001
*	J642CWJ	Mercedes-Benz 811D	Optare StarRider	C29F	1992
*	LAZ7403	Scania K92CRB	Van Hool Alizée	C53F	1988
	SN06ASU	Mercedes-Benz Vario O.814D	Killbeggan Vehicle Converters	C24F	2006
	W18RED	Scania L94IB4	Van Hool Alizée	C49FT	2000

John Leask & Son

EP & J Leask, Esplanade, Lerwick, Mainland, Shetland ZE1 0LL
Websites www.leaskstravel.co.uk
Depot Gremista Depot, Gremista, Lerwick ZE1 0PX
Licence PM0000714

*	K600JLS	DAF MB230LT615	Van Hool Alizée	C51FT	1993
*	L388YNV	Dennis Javelin 12SDA	Plaxton Premiere 320	C70F	1994
	M20JLS	DAF MB230LT615	Van Hool Alizée	C57F	1995
	N20JLS	DAF DE33WSSB3000	Ikarus Blue Danube 350	C55F	1996
	R20JLS	DAF DE33WSSB3000	Ikarus Blue Danube 350	C53F	1998
	S20JLS	Mercedes-Benz Vario O.814D	Plaxton Cheetah	C33F	2007
*	T20JLS	DAF DE12BSSB120	Wright Cadet	B39F	2003
	T30JLS	Volvo B7RLE	Plaxton Centro	B42F	2007
	T40JLS	Volvo B7RLE	Plaxton Centro	B42F	2007
	T50JLS	DAF DE02GSSB220	Ikarus Citibus 481	B43F	1999
	T70JLS	VDL DE02CSSB120	Wright Cadet	B39F	2005
	V40JLS	ADL Enviro 300 12.0 SLF	ADL Enviro 300	B43F	2005
*	V90JLS	Temsa Safari	Temsa	C57F	2007
	V258DPS	Volvo B10BLE	Wright Renown	B47F	1999
*	W20JLS	Mercedes-Benz 614D	Excel	C16F	2005
	W30JLS	Volkswagen LT46	VDL-Kusters	M16L	2007
	W60JLS	Optare Solo M950	Optare	B31F	2008
	W90JLS	Temsa Safari	Temsa	C57F	2008
	X228RCS	Mercedes-Benz Vario O.815D	Sitcar Beluga	C27F	2000
	YD02RDY	DAF DE02CSSB200	Wright Commander	B44F	2002

Liddell

James Liddell, 1 Mauchline Road, Auchinleck KA18 2BJ
Website
Depot 11 Market Place, Auchinleck KA18 2BH
Licence PM0000060

*	151EWU		Volvo B10M-61	Wright Contour	C49FT	1988
*	479DKH		Volvo B10M-50	East Lancs	CH45/33F	1985
	A102RGE	w	Dennis Dorchester SDA	Alexander TS	B65F	1983
	A709UOE		MCW MetroBus 2 DR102/27	MCW	H43/30F	1983
*	B899RSH		Volvo B10M-50	Alexander RV	H47/44F	1985
	BV04AFA		Mercedes-Benz Vario O.814D	Frank Guy	C22FL	2004
	BX06UMU		Setra S415GT-HD	Setra TopClass	C49FT	2006
	BX55XGV		LDV Convoy	LDV	M16	2005
*	CNZ2263		Volvo B10M-61	Duple 320	C57F	1989
	D517DSX		Leyland Tiger TRCTL11/3RH	Alexander	B61F	1987
	DWU37T		Bedford VAS5	Plaxton Supreme	C29F	1978

	E107DJR	Volvo B10M-61	Duple 300	B55F	1987
*	F107TML	Volvo B10M-50	Alexander RV	H47/32F	1989
	F108TML	Volvo B10M-50	Alexander RV	H47/32F	1989
*	F109TML	Volvo B10M-50	Alexander RV	H47/32F	1989
	F110TML	Volvo B10M-50	Alexander RV	H47/32F	1989
	F119PHM	Volvo B10M-50	Alexander RV	H46/36F	1988
	F771JYS	Volvo B10M-56	Duple 300	B69F	1989
	F772JYS	Volvo B10M-56	Duple 300	B69F	1989
*	F956HWB	Volvo B10M-60	Duple	C57F	1989
*	FJZ9714	Dennis Javelin 12SDA	Duple 320	C72F	1989
	G373RTO	Scania N113DRB	Alexander RH	H47/33F	1990
	G926TCU	Scania N113CRB	Alexander PS	B51F	1990
	H219LOM	Scania N113DRB	MCW	H47/33F	1990
	H433EFT	Scania N113CRB	Alexander PS	B51F	1991
	H678GPF	Volvo B10M-50	East Lancs	H45/42F	1990
*	HIL8129	DAF MB230DKFL615	Duple 340	C53FT	1986
*	HIL9155	DAF MB230DKFL615	Duple 340	C51FT	1986
*	JIL8206	Volvo B10M-61	Van Hool Alizée	C53DLT	1987
*	L18TVL	Mercedes-Benz Vario O.814D	Autobus Nouvelle	C29F	1998
	LF51EKX	LDV Convoy	LDV	M16	2001
*	LJ04JFZ	LDV Convoy	LDV	M16	2004
	M6BUS	Volvo B10M-62	Van Hool Alizée	C53F	1994
	M7BUS	Volvo B10M-62	Van Hool Alizée	C53F	1994
	N205LTN	Volvo B10M-55	Alexander PS	B49F	1995
	N206LTN	Volvo B10M-55	Alexander PS	B60F	1995
	N215LTN	Volvo B10M-55	Alexander PS	B49F	1995
	N217LTN	Volvo B10M-55	Alexander PS	B49F	1995
	N716UVR	Volvo B10M-62	Van Hool Alizée	C46FT	1996
*	NBZ1357	Volvo B10M-61	Van Hool Alizée	C49FT	1988
	NXI4616	Leyland Tiger TRBTLX/2RP	Alexander (Belfast)	B42F	1988
*	OJI7161	Volvo B10M-61	Macedonian Coach Industries	C55F	1982
	P73MRE	LDV Convoy	LDV	M16	1996
	P478FKJ	Mercedes-Benz Vario O.814D	Cacciamali	C25F	1986
	P682DRS	Volvo B10M-62	Caetano Algarve II	C49F	1997
	P721RWU	DAF DE33WSSB3000	Van Hool Alizée	C49FT	1996
*	PJI5631	Volvo B10M-61	East Lancs Flyte (1998)	CH45/35F	1983
*	PJY534	Mercedes-Benz 811D	Reeve Burgess Beaver	C33F	1988
	POG568Y	MCW MetroBus 2 DR102/27	MCW	H43/30F	1982
	PSD281H	p	Bedford VAS5	Plaxton Panorama	C29F	1970
*	PV55GNX	Ford Transit	Ford	M16	2005
	PX56NNC	Ford Transit	Ford	M16	2006
*	RIB8036	Volvo B10M-61	Van Hool Alizée	C49FT	1985
	S955TGB	Mercedes-Benz Vario O.814D	Plaxton Cheetah	C32F	1999
	SA02CCN	LDV Convoy	LDV	M16	2002
	SA02ECW	LDV Convoy	LDV	M16	2002
	SA02EDF	LDV Convoy	LDV	M16	2002
	SA02EDO	LDV Convoy	LDV	M16	2002
	SC02HHA	Mercedes-Benz Vario O.814D	Plaxton Cheetah	C29F	2002
	SC02VCD	Ford Transit	Ford	M16	2002
	SD02RZK	Ford Transit	Ford	M14	2002
	SD55WXK	Ford Transit	Ford	M16	2005
	SJ51MXY	LDV Convoy	LDV	M16	2001
	T35CNN	Scania L94IB4	Irizar InterCentury	C57F	1999
*	T721KFJ	Dennis Javelin 12SFD	Caetano Enigma	C49FT	1999
	T872MKL	LDV Convoy	LDV	M16	1999
*	TIB2865	Dennis Javelin 12SDA	Plaxton Paramount 3200 III	C57F	1990
*	UJI4521	w	Volvo B10M-61	Duple 340	C53F	1986
	W252KDO	Mercedes-Benz Atego 1120L	Optare Solera	C35F	2000
	W556BOV	LDV Convoy	LDV	M9	2000

			Liddell			
W762DCS		Mercedes-Benz Vario O.814D	Plaxton Beaver 2	DP33F	2000
* XWA907	w	Volvo B10M-61	Ikarus Blue Danube VL	C53F	1989
YX05HHA		LDV Convoy	LDV	M16	2005

Lippen
C Graham, 53 Scotts Road, Paisley PA2 7AN
Website
Depot   53 Scotts Road, Paisley PA2 7AN
Licence PM0000947

* GBZ8812	Mercedes-Benz Vario O.810D	Plaxton Beaver 2	C31F	1998
GBZ9059	Mercedes-Benz 709D	Wright NimBus	B29F	1992
K579MGT	Dennis Dart 9 SDL	Plaxton Pointer	B32F	1993
K590MGT	Dennis Dart 9 SDL	Plaxton Pointer	B32F	1993
* L1PPN	Mercedes-Benz Vario O.814D	Marshall Master	B31F	1999
L2PPN	Mercedes-Benz Vario O.814D	Plaxton Beaver 2	B31F	2000
* L4PPN	Mercedes-Benz Vario O.814D	Plaxton Beaver 2	B31F	1998
L5PPN	Optare Solo M920	Optare	B30F	2004
* L8PPN	LDV Convoy	LDV	M16	2000
L9PPN	Mercedes-Benz Sprinter 411CDI	Frank Guy	M15	2003
* L11PPN	Mercedes-Benz 412CD	Concept	M16	1996
L12PPN	Enterprise Bus Plasma EB01	Plaxton Primo	B28F	2006
L15PPN	Optare Solo M880	Optare	B21F	2006
* L776AUS	Mercedes-Benz 609D	North West Coach Sales	B17F	1993
P408RGG	Mercedes-Benz 609D	Adamson	C24F	1996
R776MGB	Ford Transit	Ford	M16	1998

Lochs & Glens Holidays
M F Wells (Hotels) Ltd, Gartocharn, School Road, Alexandria G83 8RW
Website   www.lochsandglens.com
Depot   Loch Long Hotel, Arrochar G83 7AA
         Loch Tummel Hotel, Tummel Bridge, Pitlochry PH16 5SB
         Achray Hotel, Trossachs, Callander FK17 8HZ
         Highland Hotel, Union Road, Fort William PH33 6QY
         Inversnaid Hotel, Loch Awe, Dalmally, PA33 1AQ
Licence PM0002220

FJ06BSX	Volvo B12B	Jonckheere Mistral	C57FT	2006
FJ07AED	Volvo B12B	Jonckheere Mistral	C57FT	2007
FJ07AEE	Volvo B12B	Jonckheere Mistral	C57FT	2007
FJ07AEF	Volvo B12B	Jonckheere Mistral	C57FT	2007
FJ08BZA	Volvo B12B	Jonckheere Mistral	C57FT	2008
FJ08BZB	Volvo B12B	Jonckheere Mistral	C57FT	2008
FJ08BZC	Volvo B12B	Jonckheere Mistral	C57FT	2008
FJ08BZD	Volvo B12BT	Jonckheere Mistral	C57FT	2008
FJ08BZE	Volvo B12BT	Jonckheere Mistral	C57FT	2008
FJ08BZF	Volvo B12BT	Jonckheere Mistral	C57FT	2008
FJ08BZG	Volvo B12BT	Jonckheere Mistral	C57FT	2008
SN09AZP	Volvo B12B(T)	Van Hool Alizée	C57FT	2009
SN09AZR	Volvo B12B(T)	Van Hool Alizée	C57FT	2009
SN09AZT	Volvo B12B(T)	Van Hool Alizée	C57FT	2009
SN09AZU	Volvo B12B(T)	Van Hool Alizée	C57FT	2009
SN09AZV	Volvo B12B(T)	Van Hool Alizée	C57FT	2009

Lothian Buses
City Sightseeing; Edinburgh Tours; Mac Tours; Majestic Tours

Lothian Buses plc, Schedules Office, 55 Annandale Street, Edinburgh, EH7 4AZ

Website	www.lothianbuses.co.uk
Depots	As per list
Licence	PM0000002 (Lothian Buses)
	PM0002884 (Lothian Buses)
	PM0002883 (The Overground Ltd)
	PM1050765 (Edinburgh Buses / Edinburgh Shuttle)
	PM1004999 (Mac Tours)
	PM1064277 (Majestic Tours)
	PM1007722 (Edinburgh Tours)

1	* JSJ749	res	AEC Routemaster	Park Royal	O44/32R	1959
2	VLT163	S	AEC Routemaster	Park Royal	O43/32RD	1959
3	VLT235	S	AEC Routemaster	Park Royal	O43/32RD	1960
4	* JSJ746	res	AEC Routemaster	Park Royal	O43/32RD	1959
5	* JSJ747	res	AEC Routemaster	Park Royal	O43/32RD	1959
6	* JSJ748	res	AEC Routemaster	Park Royal	O43/32RD	1959
7	VLT143	S	AEC Routemaster	Park Royal	O43/32RD	1959
8	VLT237	S	AEC Routemaster	Park Royal	O43/32RD	1960
9	VLT242	S	AEC Routemaster	Park Royal	PO43/32RD	1960
10	VLT281	S	AEC Routemaster	Park Royal	PO43/32RD	1960
11	CUV241C	S	AEC Routemaster	Park Royal	PO35/29RD	1965
12	CUV248C	S	AEC Routemaster	Park Royal	PO35/29RD	1965
18	CUV203C	res	AEC Routemaster	Park Royal	PO31/28RD	1965
20	NMY634E	S	AEC Routemaster	Park Royal	H32/24F	1967
31	W631PSX	S	Dennis Trident 10.5 SLF	Plaxton President	O51/26F	2000
32	W632PSX	S	Dennis Trident 10.5 SLF	Plaxton President	O51/26F	2000
33	W633PSX	S	Dennis Trident 10.5 SLF	Plaxton President	O51/26F	2000
34	W634PSX	S	Dennis Trident 10.5 SLF	Plaxton President	O51/26F	2000
35	SN08BYW	M	Optare Solo M960	Optare	B31F	2008
36	SN08BYY	M	Optare Solo M960	Optare	B31F	2008
37	SN08BYZ	r	Optare Solo M960	Optare	B31F	2008
38	SN08BZA	r	Optare Solo M960	Optare	B31F	2008
39	SN08BZB	M	Optare Solo M960	Optare	B31F	2008
40	SN08BZC	M	Optare Solo M960	Optare	B31F	2008
54	SK52OHX	C	Dennis Dart 11.3 SLF	Plaxton Pointer 2	B42F	2002
55	SK52OHY	C	Dennis Dart 11.3 SLF	Plaxton Pointer 2	B42F	2002
56	SK52OHZ	C	Dennis Dart 11.3 SLF	Plaxton Pointer 2	B42F	2002
57	SK52OJA	C	Dennis Dart 11.3 SLF	Plaxton Pointer 2	B42F	2002
58	SK52OJB	C	Dennis Dart 11.3 SLF	Plaxton Pointer 2	B42F	2002
59	SK52OJC	C	Dennis Dart 11.3 SLF	Plaxton Pointer 2	B42F	2002
60	SK52OJD	C	Dennis Dart 11.3 SLF	Plaxton Pointer 2	B42F	2002
61	SK52OJE	C	Dennis Dart 11.3 SLF	Plaxton Pointer 2	B42F	2002
62	SK52OJF	C	Dennis Dart 11.3 SLF	Plaxton Pointer 2	B42F	2002
63	SK52OJG	C	Dennis Dart 11.3 SLF	Plaxton Pointer 2	B42F	2002
64	SK52OJH	C	Dennis Dart 11.3 SLF	Plaxton Pointer 2	B42F	2002
65	SK52OJJ	M	Dennis Dart 11.3 SLF	Plaxton Pointer 2	B42F	2002
66	SK52OJL	M	Dennis Dart 11.3 SLF	Plaxton Pointer 2	B42F	2002
67	SK52OJM	M	Dennis Dart 11.3 SLF	Plaxton Pointer 2	B42F	2002
68	SK52OJN	M	Dennis Dart 11.3 SLF	Plaxton Pointer 2	B42F	2002
69	SK52OJO	r	Dennis Dart 11.3 SLF	Plaxton Pointer 2	B42F	2002
70	SK52OJP	M	Dennis Dart 11.3 SLF	Plaxton Pointer 2	B42F	2002
71	SK52OJR	M	Dennis Dart 11.3 SLF	Plaxton Pointer 2	B42F	2002
72	SK52OJS	M	Dennis Dart 11.3 SLF	Plaxton Pointer 2	B42F	2002
73	SK52OJT	M	Dennis Dart 11.3 SLF	Plaxton Pointer 2	B42F	2002
74	SK52OJU	M	Dennis Dart 11.3 SLF	Plaxton Pointer 2	B42F	2002
75	SN53JNO	M	Dennis Dart 11.3 SLF	Plaxton Pointer 2	B42F	2002
76	SK52OJW	M	Dennis Dart 11.3 SLF	Plaxton Pointer 2	B42F	2002

\multicolumn{7}{c}{Lothian Buses}						

77	SK52OJX	M	Dennis Dart 11.3 SLF	Plaxton Pointer 2	B42F	2002
78	SK52OJY	M	Dennis Dart 11.3 SLF	Plaxton Pointer 2	B42F	2002
79	SK52OJZ	M	Dennis Dart 11.3 SLF	Plaxton Pointer 2	B42F	2002
80	SK52OKA	M	Dennis Dart 11.3 SLF	Plaxton Pointer 2	B42F	2002
81	SK52OKB	M	Dennis Dart 11.3 SLF	Plaxton Pointer 2	B42F	2002
82	SK52OKC	M	Dennis Dart 11.3 SLF	Plaxton Pointer 2	B42F	2003
83	SK52OKD	M	Dennis Dart 11.3 SLF	Plaxton Pointer 2	B42F	2003
84	SK52OKE	M	Dennis Dart 11.3 SLF	Plaxton Pointer 2	B42F	2003
85	SK52OKF	M	Dennis Dart 11.3 SLF	Plaxton Pointer 2	B42F	2003
86	SN53AUW	M	Dennis Dart 11.3 SLF	TransBus Pointer 2	B42F	2003
87	SN53AUX	M	Dennis Dart 11.3 SLF	TransBus Pointer 2	B42F	2003
88	SN53AUY	L	Dennis Dart 11.3 SLF	TransBus Pointer 2	B42F	2003
89	SN53AVC	L	Dennis Dart 11.3 SLF	TransBus Pointer 2	B42F	2003
90	SN53AVD	L	Dennis Dart 11.3 SLF	TransBus Pointer 2	B42F	2003
91	SN53AVE	L	Dennis Dart 11.3 SLF	TransBus Pointer 2	B42F	2003
92	SN53AVF	L	Dennis Dart 11.3 SLF	TransBus Pointer 2	B42F	2003
93	SN53AVG	L	Dennis Dart 11.3 SLF	TransBus Pointer 2	B42F	2003
94	SN53AVK	L	Dennis Dart 11.3 SLF	TransBus Pointer 2	B42F	2003
95	SN53AVL	L	Dennis Dart 11.3 SLF	TransBus Pointer 2	B42F	2003
96	SN53AVM	L	Dennis Dart 11.3 SLF	TransBus Pointer 2	B42F	2003
97	SN53AVO	L	Dennis Dart 11.3 SLF	TransBus Pointer 2	B42F	2003
98	SN53AVP	L	Dennis Dart 11.3 SLF	TransBus Pointer 2	B42F	2003
99	SN53AVR	L	Dennis Dart 11.3 SLF	TransBus Pointer 2	B42F	2003
100	SN53AVT	L	Dennis Dart 11.3 SLF	TransBus Pointer 2	B42F	2003
101	SN04NFZ	L	Volvo B7RLE	Wright Eclipse Urban	B42F	2004
102	SN04NGE	L	Volvo B7RLE	Wright Eclipse Urban	B42F	2004
103	SN04NGF	L	Volvo B7RLE	Wright Eclipse Urban	B42F	2004
104	SN04NGG	L	Volvo B7RLE	Wright Eclipse Urban	B42F	2004
105	SN04NGJ	L	Volvo B7RLE	Wright Eclipse Urban	B42F	2004
106	SN04NGU	L	Volvo B7RLE	Wright Eclipse Urban	B42F	2004
107	SN04NGX	L	Volvo B7RLE	Wright Eclipse Urban	B42F	2004
108	SN04NGY	L	Volvo B7RLE	Wright Eclipse Urban	B42F	2004
109	SN04NGZ	L	Volvo B7RLE	Wright Eclipse Urban	B42F	2004
110	SN04NHA	L	Volvo B7RLE	Wright Eclipse Urban	B42F	2004
111	SN04NHB	L	Volvo B7RLE	Wright Eclipse Urban	B42F	2004
112	SN04NHC	L	Volvo B7RLE	Wright Eclipse Urban	B42F	2004
113	SN04NHD	L	Volvo B7RLE	Wright Eclipse Urban	B42F	2004
114	SN04NHE	L	Volvo B7RLE	Wright Eclipse Urban	B42F	2004
115	SN04NHF	L	Volvo B7RLE	Wright Eclipse Urban	B42F	2004
116	SN04NHG	L	Volvo B7RLE	Wright Eclipse Urban	B42F	2004
117	SN04NHH	L	Volvo B7RLE	Wright Eclipse Urban	B42F	2004
118	SN04NHJ	L	Volvo B7RLE	Wright Eclipse Urban	B42F	2004
119	SN04NHK	L	Volvo B7RLE	Wright Eclipse Urban	B42F	2004
120	SN04NHL	L	Volvo B7RLE	Wright Eclipse Urban	B42F	2004
121	SN04NHM	L	Volvo B7RLE	Wright Eclipse Urban	B42F	2004
122	SN04NHP	L	Volvo B7RLE	Wright Eclipse Urban	B42F	2004
123	SN04NHT	L	Volvo B7RLE	Wright Eclipse Urban	B42F	2004
124	SN04NHU	L	Volvo B7RLE	Wright Eclipse Urban	B42F	2004
125	SN04NHV	L	Volvo B7RLE	Wright Eclipse Urban	B42F	2004
126	SN04NHX	C	Volvo B7RLE	Wright Eclipse Urban	B42F	2004
127	SN04NHY	C	Volvo B7RLE	Wright Eclipse Urban	B42F	2004
128	SN04NHZ	C	Volvo B7RLE	Wright Eclipse Urban	B42F	2004
129	SN04NJE	C	Volvo B7RLE	Wright Eclipse Urban	B42F	2004
130	SN04NJF	C	Volvo B7RLE	Wright Eclipse Urban	B42F	2004
131	SN55BJJ	C	Volvo B7RLE	Wright Eclipse Urban	B40F	2005
132	SN55BJK	C	Volvo B7RLE	Wright Eclipse Urban	B40F	2005
133	SN55BJO	C	Volvo B7RLE	Wright Eclipse Urban	B40F	2005
134	SN55BJU	C	Volvo B7RLE	Wright Eclipse Urban	B40F	2005
135	SN55BJV	C	Volvo B7RLE	Wright Eclipse Urban	B40F	2005
136	SK07CGO	C	Volvo B7RLE	Wright Eclipse Urban	B38F	2007

137	SK07CGU	C	Volvo B7RLE	Wright Eclipse Urban	B38F	2007
138	SK07CGV	C	Volvo B7RLE	Wright Eclipse Urban	B38F	2007
139	SK07CGX	C	Volvo B7RLE	Wright Eclipse Urban	B38F	2007
140	SK07CGY	C	Volvo B7RLE	Wright Eclipse Urban	B38F	2007
141	SK07CFO	C	Volvo B7RLE	Wright Eclipse Urban	B38F	2007
142	SK07CFP	C	Volvo B7RLE	Wright Eclipse Urban	B38F	2007
143	SK07CFU	C	Volvo B7RLE	Wright Eclipse Urban	B38F	2007
144	SK07CFV	C	Volvo B7RLE	Wright Eclipse Urban	B38F	2007
145	SK07CFX	C	Volvo B7RLE	Wright Eclipse Urban	B38F	2007
146	SK07CFY	C	Volvo B7RLE	Wright Eclipse Urban	B38F	2007
147	SK07CFZ	C	Volvo B7RLE	Wright Eclipse Urban	B38F	2007
148	SK07CGE	C	Volvo B7RLE	Wright Eclipse Urban	B38F	2007
149	SK07CGF	C	Volvo B7RLE	Wright Eclipse Urban	B38F	2007
150	SK07CGG	C	Volvo B7RLE	Wright Eclipse Urban	B38F	2007
151	SN57DCF	C	Volvo B7RLE	Wright Eclipse Urban	B38F	2007
152	SN57DCO	C	Volvo B7RLE	Wright Eclipse Urban	B38F	2007
153	SN57DCU	C	Volvo B7RLE	Wright Eclipse Urban	B38F	2007
154	SN57DCV	C	Volvo B7RLE	Wright Eclipse Urban	B38F	2007
155	SN57DCX	C	Volvo B7RLE	Wright Eclipse Urban	B38F	2007
156	SN57DCY	C	Volvo B7RLE	Wright Eclipse Urban	B38F	2007
157	SN57DCZ	C	Volvo B7RLE	Wright Eclipse Urban	B38F	2007
158	SN57DDA	C	Volvo B7RLE	Wright Eclipse Urban	B38F	2007
159	SN57DDE	C	Volvo B7RLE	Wright Eclipse Urban	B38F	2007
160	SN57DDF	C	Volvo B7RLE	Wright Eclipse Urban	B38F	2007
161	SN58BYM	M	Volvo B7RLE	Wright Eclipse Urban	B38F	2008
162	SN58BYO	M	Volvo B7RLE	Wright Eclipse Urban	B38F	2008
163	SN58BYP	M	Volvo B7RLE	Wright Eclipse Urban	B38F	2008
164	SN58BYR	M	Volvo B7RLE	Wright Eclipse Urban	B38F	2008
165	SN58BYS	M	Volvo B7RLE	Wright Eclipse Urban	B38F	2008
166	SN58BYT	M	Volvo B7RLE	Wright Eclipse Urban	B38F	2008
167	SN58BYU	M	Volvo B7RLE	Wright Eclipse Urban	B38F	2009
168	SN58BYV	M	Volvo B7RLE	Wright Eclipse Urban	B38F	2009
169	SN58BYW	M	Volvo B7RLE	Wright Eclipse Urban	B38F	2009
170	SN58BYX	L	Volvo B7RLE	Wright Eclipse Urban	B38F	2008
176	Y176CFS	L	Dennis Dart 11.3 SLF	Plaxton Pointer 2	B42F	2001
177	Y177CFS	r	Dennis Dart 11.3 SLF	Plaxton Pointer 2	B42F	2001
178	Y178CFS	r	Dennis Dart 11.3 SLF	Plaxton Pointer 2	B42F	2001
179	Y179CFS	r	Dennis Dart 11.3 SLF	Plaxton Pointer 2	B42F	2001
181	Y181CFS	r	Dennis Dart 11.3 SLF	Plaxton Pointer 2	B42F	2001
182	Y182CFS	C	Dennis Dart 11.3 SLF	Plaxton Pointer 2	B42F	2001
183	Y183CFS	C	Dennis Dart 11.3 SLF	Plaxton Pointer 2	B42F	2001
184	Y184CFS	C	Dennis Dart 11.3 SLF	Plaxton Pointer 2	B42F	2001
185	Y185CFS	C	Dennis Dart 11.3 SLF	Plaxton Pointer 2	B42F	2001
186	Y186CFS	C	Dennis Dart 11.3 SLF	Plaxton Pointer 2	B42F	2001
187	Y187CFS	M	Dennis Dart 11.3 SLF	Plaxton Pointer 2	B42F	2001
188	Y188CFS	C	Dennis Dart 11.3 SLF	Plaxton Pointer 2	B42F	2001
189	Y189CFS	M	Dennis Dart 11.3 SLF	Plaxton Pointer 2	B42F	2001
191	Y191CFS	M	Dennis Dart 11.3 SLF	Plaxton Pointer 2	B42F	2001
192	SN51FZB	M	Dennis Dart 11.3 SLF	Plaxton Pointer 2	B42F	2001
264	P264PSX	r	Volvo Olympian OLY-56	Alexander Royale	H51/30D	1997
285	P285PSX	S	Volvo Olympian OLY-56	Alexander Royale	H51/30D	1997
291	W291PFS	M	Volvo B7TL	Plaxton President	H45/30F	2000
292	W292PFS	M	Volvo B7TL	Plaxton President	H45/30F	2000
293	W293PFS	M	Volvo B7TL	Plaxton President	H45/30F	2000
294	* W294PFS	M	Volvo B7TL	Plaxton President	H45/30F	2000
295	W295PFS	M	Volvo B7TL	Plaxton President	H45/30F	2000
296	W296PFS	M	Volvo B7TL	Plaxton President	H45/30F	2000
297	* WDF297	M	Volvo B7TL	Plaxton President	H45/29F	2000
301	SN09CTK	M	Volvo B9TL	Wright Eclipse Gemini	H48/32F	2009
302	SN09CTO	M	Volvo B9TL	Wright Eclipse Gemini	H48/32F	2009

303	SN09CTU	M	Volvo B9TL	Wright Eclipse Gemini	H48/32F	2009
304	SN09CTV	M	Volvo B9TL	Wright Eclipse Gemini	H48/32F	2009
305	SN09CTX	M	Volvo B9TL	Wright Eclipse Gemini	H48/32F	2009
306	SN09CTY	M	Volvo B9TL	Wright Eclipse Gemini	H48/32F	2009
307	SN09CTZ	M	Volvo B9TL	Wright Eclipse Gemini	H48/32F	2009
308	SN09CUA	M	Volvo B9TL	Wright Eclipse Gemini	H48/32F	2009
309	SN09CUC	M	Volvo B9TL	Wright Eclipse Gemini	H48/32F	2009
310	SN09CUG	M	Volvo B9TL	Wright Eclipse Gemini	H48/32F	2009
311	SN09CUH	M	Volvo B9TL	Wright Eclipse Gemini	H48/32F	2009
312	SN09CUJ	M	Volvo B9TL	Wright Eclipse Gemini	H48/32F	2009
313	SN09CUK	M	Volvo B9TL	Wright Eclipse Gemini	H48/32F	2009
314	SN09CUO	M	Volvo B9TL	Wright Eclipse Gemini	H48/32F	2009
315	SN09CUU	M	Volvo B9TL	Wright Eclipse Gemini	H48/32F	2009
316	SN09CUV	M	Volvo B9TL	Wright Eclipse Gemini	H48/32F	2009
317	SN09CUW	M	Volvo B9TL	Wright Eclipse Gemini	H48/32F	2009
318	SN09CUX	M	Volvo B9TL	Wright Eclipse Gemini	H48/32F	2009
319	SN09CUY	M	Volvo B9TL	Wright Eclipse Gemini	H48/32F	2009
320	SN09CVA	M	Volvo B9TL	Wright Eclipse Gemini	H48/32F	2009
321	SN09CVB	M	Volvo B9TL	Wright Eclipse Gemini	H48/32F	2009
322	SN09CVC	M	Volvo B9TL	Wright Eclipse Gemini	H48/32F	2009
323	SN09CVD	M	Volvo B9TL	Wright Eclipse Gemini	H48/32F	2009
324	SN09CVE	M	Volvo B9TL	Wright Eclipse Gemini	H48/32F	2009
325	SN09CVF	M	Volvo B9TL	Wright Eclipse Gemini	H48/32F	2009
326	SN09CVG	L	Volvo B9TL	Wright Eclipse Gemini	H48/30F	2009
327	SN09CVH	L	Volvo B9TL	Wright Eclipse Gemini	H48/30F	2009
328	SN09CVJ	L	Volvo B9TL	Wright Eclipse Gemini	H48/30F	2009
329	SN09CVK	L	Volvo B9TL	Wright Eclipse Gemini	H48/30F	2009
330	SN59BFL	L	Volvo B9TL	Wright Eclipse Gemini	H48/32F	2009
331	SN59BFM	L	Volvo B9TL	Wright Eclipse Gemini	H48/32F	2009
332	SN59BFO	L	Volvo B9TL	Wright Eclipse Gemini	H48/32F	2009
333	SN59BFP	L	Volvo B9TL	Wright Eclipse Gemini	H48/32F	2009
334	SN59BFU	L	Volvo B9TL	Wright Eclipse Gemini	H48/32F	2009
335	SN59BFV	L	Volvo B9TL	Wright Eclipse Gemini	H48/32F	2009
336	SN59BFX	L	Volvo B9TL	Wright Eclipse Gemini	H48/32F	2009
337	SN59BFY	L	Volvo B9TL	Wright Eclipse Gemini	H48/32F	2009
338	SN59BFZ	L	Volvo B9TL	Wright Eclipse Gemini	H48/32F	2009
339	SN59BGE	L	Volvo B9TL	Wright Eclipse Gemini	H48/32F	2009
340	SN59BGF	L	Volvo B9TL	Wright Eclipse Gemini	H48/32F	2009
341	SN59BGK	L	Volvo B9TL	Wright Eclipse Gemini	H48/30F	2009
342	SN59BGO	L	Volvo B9TL	Wright Eclipse Gemini	H48/30F	2009
343	SN59BGV	L	Volvo B9TL	Wright Eclipse Gemini	H48/30F	2009
344	SN59BGX	L	Volvo B9TL	Wright Eclipse Gemini	H48/30F	2009
345	SN59BGY	L	Volvo B9TL	Wright Eclipse Gemini	H48/30F	2009
346	SN59BGZ	L	Volvo B9TL	Wright Eclipse Gemini	H48/30F	2009
347	SN59BHA	L	Volvo B9TL	Wright Eclipse Gemini	H48/30F	2009
348	SN59BHD	L	Volvo B9TL	Wright Eclipse Gemini	H48/30F	2009
349	SN59BHE	L	Volvo B9TL	Wright Eclipse Gemini	H48/30F	2009
350	SN59BHF	L	Volvo B9TL	Wright Eclipse Gemini	H48/30F	2009
357	F357WSC	y	Leyland Olympian ONCL10/2RZ	Alexander RH	PO46/30F	1989
358	F358WSC	y	Leyland Olympian ONCL10/2RZ	Alexander RH	PO46/30F	1989
371	F371WSC	y	Leyland Olympian ONCL10/2RZ	Alexander RH	CH47/31F	1989
433	P433KSX	r	Volvo Olympian YN2RV18Z4	Alexander Royale	H51/33F	1996
501	T501SSG	res	Dennis Trident 10.5 SLF	Alexander ALX400	O51/24F	1999
502	T502SSG	res	Dennis Trident 10.5 SLF	Alexander ALX400	O51/24F	1999
503	T503SSG	res	Dennis Trident 10.5 SLF	Alexander ALX400	O51/23F	1999
504	T504SSG	res	Dennis Trident 10.5 SLF	Alexander ALX400	PO47/24F	1999
505	T505SSG	C	Dennis Trident 10.5 SLF	Alexander ALX400	PO47/24F	1999
506	T506SSG	S	Dennis Trident 10.5 SLF	Plaxton President	PO45/25F	1999
507	T507SSG	S	Dennis Trident 10.5 SLF	Plaxton President	PO45/25F	1999
508	T508SSG	S	Dennis Trident 10.5 SLF	Plaxton President	PO45/25F	1999

509	T509SSG	S	Dennis Trident 10.5 SLF	Plaxton President	PO45/26F	1999
510	T510SSG	S	Dennis Trident 10.5 SLF	Plaxton President	PO45/26F	1999
511	V511ESC	S	Dennis Trident 10.5 SLF	Plaxton President	PO45/26F	1999
512	V512ESC	S	Dennis Trident 10.5 SLF	Plaxton President	PO45/26F	1999
513	V513ESC	res	Dennis Trident 10.5 SLF	Plaxton President	PO45/26F	1999
514	V514ESC	res	Dennis Trident 10.5 SLF	Plaxton President	O45/26F	1999
515	V515ESC	res	Dennis Trident 10.5 SLF	Plaxton President	O45/26F	1999
516	V516ESC	res	Dennis Trident 10.5 SLF	Plaxton President	O45/26F	1999
517	V517ESC	S	Dennis Trident 10.5 SLF	Plaxton President	O45/30D	1999
518	V518ESC	S	Dennis Trident 10.5 SLF	Plaxton President	O45/30F	1999
519	V519ESC	S	Dennis Trident 10.5 SLF	Plaxton President	O45/26F	1999
520	V520ESC	S	Dennis Trident 10.5 SLF	Plaxton President	O45/26F	1999
521	V521ESC	Maj	Dennis Trident 10.5 SLF	Plaxton President	H45/30F	1999
522	V522ESC	Maj	Dennis Trident 10.5 SLF	Plaxton President	H45/30F	1999
523	V523ESC	Maj	Dennis Trident 10.5 SLF	Plaxton President	H45/30F	1999
524	V524ESC	Maj	Dennis Trident 10.5 SLF	Plaxton President	H45/30F	1999
525	V525ESC	S	Dennis Trident 10.5 SLF	Plaxton President	PO45/26F	1999
526	V526ESC	S	Dennis Trident 10.5 SLF	Plaxton President	PO45/26F	1999
527	V527ESC	S	Dennis Trident 10.5 SLF	Plaxton President	PO45/26F	1999
528	V528ESC	S	Dennis Trident 10.5 SLF	Plaxton President	PO45/26F	1999
529	V529ESC	L	Dennis Trident 10.5 SLF	Plaxton President	H45/30F	1999
530	V530ESC	L	Dennis Trident 10.5 SLF	Plaxton President	H45/30F	1999
531	V531ESC	r	Dennis Trident 10.5 SLF	Plaxton President	H45/30F	1999
532	V532ESC	M	Dennis Trident 10.5 SLF	Plaxton President	H45/26D	1999
533	V533ESC	M	Dennis Trident 10.5 SLF	Plaxton President	H45/30F	1999
534	V534ESC	L	Dennis Trident 10.5 SLF	Plaxton President	H45/30F	1999
535	V535ESC	M	Dennis Trident 10.5 SLF	Plaxton President	H45/30F	1999
536	V536ESC	M	Dennis Trident 10.5 SLF	Plaxton President	H45/30F	1999
537	V537ESC	M	Dennis Trident 10.5 SLF	Plaxton President	H45/30F	1999
538	V538ESC	M	Dennis Trident 10.5 SLF	Plaxton President	H45/30F	1999
539	V539ESC	M	Dennis Trident 10.5 SLF	Plaxton President	H45/29F	1999
540	V540ESC	M	Dennis Trident 10.5 SLF	Plaxton President	H45/29F	1999
541	V541ESC	M	Dennis Trident 10.5 SLF	Plaxton President	H45/29F	1999
542	V542ESC	M	Dennis Trident 10.5 SLF	Plaxton President	H45/29F	1999
543	V543ESC	M	Dennis Trident 10.5 SLF	Plaxton President	H45/29F	1999
544	V544ESC	r	Dennis Trident 10.5 SLF	Plaxton President	H45/29F	1999
545	V545ESC	M	Dennis Trident 10.5 SLF	Plaxton President	H45/29F	1999
546	W546RSG	M	Dennis Trident 10.5 SLF	Plaxton President	H45/29F	2000
547	W547RSG	M	Dennis Trident 10.5 SLF	Plaxton President	H45/29F	2000
548	* W548RSG	M	Dennis Trident 10.5 SLF	Plaxton President	H45/29F	2000
549	W549RSG	M	Dennis Trident 10.5 SLF	Plaxton President	H45/29F	2000
551	W551RSG	L	Dennis Trident 10.5 SLF	Plaxton President	H47/28F	2000
552	W552RSG	L	Dennis Trident 10.5 SLF	Plaxton President	H47/24D	2000
553	W553RSG	L	Dennis Trident 10.5 SLF	Plaxton President	H47/28F	2000
554	W554RSG	L	Dennis Trident 10.5 SLF	Plaxton President	H47/24D	2000
556	W556RSG	r	Dennis Trident 10.5 SLF	Plaxton President	H47/24D	2000
557	W557RSG	L	Dennis Trident 10.5 SLF	Plaxton President	H47/28F	2000
558	W558RSG	L	Dennis Trident 10.5 SLF	Plaxton President	H47/28F	2000
559	W559RSG	L	Dennis Trident 10.5 SLF	Plaxton President	H47/28F	2000
561	W561RSG	L	Dennis Trident 10.5 SLF	Plaxton President	H47/28F	2000
562	W562RSG	r	Dennis Trident 10.5 SLF	Plaxton President	H47/24D	2000
563	W563RSG	L	Dennis Trident 10.5 SLF	Plaxton President	H47/28F	2000
564	W564RSG	L	Dennis Trident 10.5 SLF	Plaxton President	H47/24F	2000
566	W566RSG	L	Dennis Trident 10.5 SLF	Plaxton President	H47/24D	2000
567	W567RSG	C	Dennis Trident 10.5 SLF	Plaxton President	H47/24D	2000
568	W568RSG	L	Dennis Trident 10.5 SLF	Plaxton President	H47/28F	2000
569	W569RSG	L	Dennis Trident 10.5 SLF	Plaxton President	H47/28F	2000
571	W571RSG	L	Dennis Trident 10.5 SLF	Plaxton President	H47/28F	2000
572	W572RSG	C	Dennis Trident 10.5 SLF	Plaxton President	H47/24D	2000
573	W573RSG	L	Dennis Trident 10.5 SLF	Plaxton President	H47/24D	2000

574	W574RSG	L	Dennis Trident 10.5 SLF	Plaxton President	H47/28F	2000
575	W575RSG	M	Dennis Trident 10.5 SLF	Plaxton President	H47/28F	2000
576	W576RSG	M	Dennis Trident 10.5 SLF	Plaxton President	H47/28F	2000
577	W577RSG	L	Dennis Trident 10.5 SLF	Plaxton President	H47/24D	2000
578	X578USC	M	Dennis Trident 10.5 SLF	Plaxton President	H47/28F	2000
579	X579USC	M	Dennis Trident 10.5 SLF	Plaxton President	H47/28F	2000
581	X581USC	r	Dennis Trident 10.5 SLF	Plaxton President	H47/24D	2000
582	X582USC	M	Dennis Trident 10.5 SLF	Plaxton President	H47/28F	2000
583	X583USC	M	Dennis Trident 10.5 SLF	Plaxton President	H47/28F	2000
584	X584USC	r	Dennis Trident 10.5 SLF	Plaxton President	H47/24D	2000
585	X585USC	r	Dennis Trident 10.5 SLF	Plaxton President	H47/24D	2000
586	X586USC	r	Dennis Trident 10.5 SLF	Plaxton President	H47/24D	2000
587	X587USC	M	Dennis Trident 10.5 SLF	Plaxton President	H47/28F	2000
588	X588USC	M	Dennis Trident 10.5 SLF	Plaxton President	H47/28F	2000
589	X589USC	M	Dennis Trident 10.5 SLF	Plaxton President	H47/28F	2000
591	X591USC	r	Dennis Trident 10.5 SLF	Plaxton President	H47/24D	2000
592	X592USC	r	Dennis Trident 10.5 SLF	Plaxton President	H47/24D	2000
593	X593USC	M	Dennis Trident 10.5 SLF	Plaxton President	H47/28F	2000
594	X594USC	M	Dennis Trident 10.5 SLF	Plaxton President	H47/28F	2000
595	X595USC	M	Dennis Trident 10.5 SLF	Plaxton President	H47/28F	2000
596	X596USC	M	Dennis Trident 10.5 SLF	Plaxton President	H47/28F	2000
597	X597UKS	M	Dennis Trident 10.5 SLF	Plaxton President	H47/28F	2000
598	X598USC	M	Dennis Trident 10.5 SLF	Plaxton President	H47/28F	2000
599	SN51AYO	M	Dennis Trident 10.5 SLF	Plaxton President	H47/25D	2001
600	SN51AYP	M	Dennis Trident 10.5 SLF	Plaxton President	H47/25D	2001
601	SN51AXF	M	Dennis Trident 10.5 SLF	Plaxton President	H45/29F	2001
602	SN51AXG	M	Dennis Trident 10.5 SLF	Plaxton President	H45/29F	2001
603	SN51AXH	M	Dennis Trident 10.5 SLF	Plaxton President	H45/29F	2001
604	SN51AXJ	M	Dennis Trident 10.5 SLF	Plaxton President	H45/29F	2001
605	SN51AXK	M	Dennis Trident 10.5 SLF	Plaxton President	H45/29F	2001
606	SN51AXO	M	Dennis Trident 10.5 SLF	Plaxton President	H47/25D	2001
607	SN51AXP	M	Dennis Trident 10.5 SLF	Plaxton President	H47/25D	2001
608	SN51AXR	C	Dennis Trident 10.5 SLF	Plaxton President	H47/25D	2001
609	SN51AXS	C	Dennis Trident 10.5 SLF	Plaxton President	H47/25D	2001
610	SN51AXT	C	Dennis Trident 10.5 SLF	Plaxton President	H47/25D	2001
611	SN51AXU	C	Dennis Trident 10.5 SLF	Plaxton President	H47/25D	2001
612	SN51AXV	C	Dennis Trident 10.5 SLF	Plaxton President	H47/25D	2001
613	SN51AXW	m	Dennis Trident 10.5 SLF	Plaxton President	H47/25D	2001
614	SN51AXX	M	Dennis Trident 10.5 SLF	Plaxton President	H47/25D	2001
615	SN51AXY	M	Dennis Trident 10.5 SLF	Plaxton President	H47/25D	2001
616	SN51AXZ	M	Dennis Trident 10.5 SLF	Plaxton President	H47/25D	2001
617	SN51AYA	M	Dennis Trident 10.5 SLF	Plaxton President	H47/25F	2001
618	SN51AYB	M	Dennis Trident 10.5 SLF	Plaxton President	H47/25D	2001
620	SN51AYD	M	Dennis Trident 10.5 SLF	Plaxton President	H47/25D	2001
621	SN51AYE	M	Dennis Trident 10.5 SLF	Plaxton President	H47/25D	2001
622	SN51AYF	M	Dennis Trident 10.5 SLF	Plaxton President	H47/25D	2001
623	SN51AYG	M	Dennis Trident 10.5 SLF	Plaxton President	H47/25D	2001
624	SN51AYH	M	Dennis Trident 10.5 SLF	Plaxton President	H47/25D	2001
625	SN51AYJ	M	Dennis Trident 10.5 SLF	Plaxton President	H47/25D	2001
626	SN51AYK	M	Dennis Trident 10.5 SLF	Plaxton President	H47/25D	2001
627	SN51AYL	M	Dennis Trident 10.5 SLF	Plaxton President	H47/25D	2001
628	SN51AYM	M	Dennis Trident 10.5 SLF	Plaxton President	H47/25D	2001
629	SN53AVU	L	Dennis Trident 11.4 SLF	Plaxton President	H51/27F	2003
630	SN53AVV	L	Dennis Trident 11.4 SLF	Plaxton President	H51/27F	2003
631	SN53AVW	L	Dennis Trident 11.4 SLF	Plaxton President	H51/27F	2003
632	SN53AVX	L	Dennis Trident 11.4 SLF	Plaxton President	H51/27F	2003
633	SN53AVZ	L	Dennis Trident 11.4 SLF	Plaxton President	H51/27F	2003
634	SK52OHT	L	Dennis Trident 11.4 SLF	Plaxton President	H49/32F	2002
635	SK52OGT	L	Dennis Trident 11.4 SLF	Plaxton President	H51/32F	2002
636	SK52OGU	L	Dennis Trident 11.4 SLF	Plaxton President	H51/32F	2002

637	SK52OGV	L	Dennis Trident 11.4 SLF	Plaxton President	H51/32F	2002
638	SK52OGW	L	Dennis Trident 11.4 SLF	Plaxton President	H51/32F	2002
639	SK52OGX	L	Dennis Trident 11.4 SLF	Plaxton President	H51/32F	2002
640	SK52OGY	L	Dennis Trident 11.4 SLF	Plaxton President	H51/32F	2002
641	SK52OGZ	L	Dennis Trident 11.4 SLF	Plaxton President	H51/32F	2002
642	SK52OHA	L	Dennis Trident 11.4 SLF	Plaxton President	H51/32F	2002
643	SK52OHB	L	Dennis Trident 11.4 SLF	Plaxton President	H51/32F	2002
644	SK52OHC	L	Dennis Trident 11.4 SLF	Plaxton President	H51/32F	2002
645	SK52OHD	L	Dennis Trident 11.4 SLF	Plaxton President	H51/32F	2002
646	SK52OHE	L	Dennis Trident 11.4 SLF	Plaxton President	H51/32F	2002
647	SK52OHG	M	Dennis Trident 11.4 SLF	Plaxton President	H51/32F	2002
648	SK52OHH	M	Dennis Trident 11.4 SLF	Plaxton President	H51/32F	2002
649	SK52OHJ	M	Dennis Trident 11.4 SLF	Plaxton President	H51/32F	2002
650	SK52OHL	M	Dennis Trident 11.4 SLF	Plaxton President	H51/32F	2002
651	SK52OHN	M	Dennis Trident 11.4 SLF	Plaxton President	H51/32F	2002
652	SK52OHO	M	Dennis Trident 11.4 SLF	Plaxton President	H49/32F	2002
653	SK52OHP	M	Dennis Trident 11.4 SLF	Plaxton President	H49/32F	2002
654	SK52OHR	M	Dennis Trident 11.4 SLF	Plaxton President	H49/32F	2002
655	SK52OHS	M	Dennis Trident 11.4 SLF	Plaxton President	H49/32F	2002
656	SN04AEV	M	TransBus Trident 11.4 SLF	TransBus President	H51/32F	2004
657	SN04AEW	M	TransBus Trident 11.4 SLF	TransBus President	H51/32F	2004
658	SN04AEX	M	TransBus Trident 11.4 SLF	TransBus President	H51/32F	2004
659	SN04AEY	M	TransBus Trident 11.4 SLF	TransBus President	H51/32F	2004
660	SN04AEZ	L	TransBus Trident 11.4 SLF	TransBus President	H51/30F	2004
661	SN04AFA	L	TransBus Trident 11.4 SLF	TransBus President	H51/30F	2004
662	SN04AAE	L	TransBus Trident 11.4 SLF	TransBus President	H53/27F	2004
663	SN04AAF	L-r	TransBus Trident 11.4 SLF	TransBus President	H51/27F	2004
664	SN04AAJ	L-r	TransBus Trident 11.4 SLF	TransBus President	H51/27F	2004
665	SN04AAK	L	TransBus Trident 11.4 SLF	TransBus President	H53/27F	2004
666	SN04AAU	L	TransBus Trident 11.4 SLF	TransBus President	H53/27F	2004
667	SN04AAV	M	TransBus Trident 11.4 SLF	TransBus President	H51/32F	2004
668	SN04AAX	M	TransBus Trident 11.4 SLF	TransBus President	H51/32F	2004
669	SN04AAY	M	TransBus Trident 11.4 SLF	TransBus President	H51/32F	2004
670	SN04AAZ	M	TransBus Trident 11.4 SLF	TransBus President	H51/32F	2004
671	SN04ABF	M	TransBus Trident 11.4 SLF	TransBus President	H51/32F	2004
672	SN04ABK	M	TransBus Trident 11.4 SLF	TransBus President	H51/32F	2004
673	SN04ABU	M	TransBus Trident 11.4 SLF	TransBus President	H51/32F	2004
674	SN04ABV	M	TransBus Trident 11.4 SLF	TransBus President	H51/32F	2004
675	SN04ABX	M	TransBus Trident 11.4 SLF	TransBus President	H51/32F	2004
676	SN04ABZ	M	TransBus Trident 11.4 SLF	TransBus President	H51/32F	2004
677	SN04ACJ	M	TransBus Trident 11.4 SLF	TransBus President	H51/32F	2004
678	SN04ACU	M	TransBus Trident 11.4 SLF	TransBus President	H51/32F	2004
679	SN04ACV	r	TransBus Trident 11.4 SLF	TransBus President	H51/32F	2004
680	SN04ACX	M	TransBus Trident 11.4 SLF	TransBus President	H51/32F	2004
681	SN04ACY	M	TransBus Trident 11.4 SLF	TransBus President	H51/32F	2004
682	SN04ACZ	M	TransBus Trident 11.4 SLF	TransBus President	H51/32F	2004
683	SN04ADU	M	TransBus Trident 11.4 SLF	TransBus President	H51/32F	2004
684	SN04ADV	M	TransBus Trident 11.4 SLF	TransBus President	H51/32F	2004
685	SN04ADX	r	TransBus Trident 11.4 SLF	TransBus President	H51/32F	2004
686	SN04ADZ	M	TransBus Trident 11.4 SLF	TransBus President	H51/32F	2004
687	SN04AEA	M	TransBus Trident 11.4 SLF	TransBus President	H51/32F	2004
688	SN04AEB	M	TransBus Trident 11.4 SLF	TransBus President	H51/32F	2004
689	SN04AEC	M	TransBus Trident 11.4 SLF	TransBus President	H51/32F	2004
690	SN04AED	M	TransBus Trident 11.4 SLF	TransBus President	H51/32F	2004
691	SN04AEE	M	TransBus Trident 11.4 SLF	TransBus President	H51/32F	2004
692	SN04AEF	M	TransBus Trident 11.4 SLF	TransBus President	H51/32F	2004
693	SN04AEG	M	TransBus Trident 11.4 SLF	TransBus President	H51/32F	2004
694	SN04AEJ	M	TransBus Trident 11.4 SLF	TransBus President	H51/32F	2004
695	SN04AEK	M	TransBus Trident 11.4 SLF	TransBus President	H51/32F	2004
696	SN04AEL	M	TransBus Trident 11.4 SLF	TransBus President	H51/32F	2004

697	SN04AEM	M	TransBus Trident 11.4 SLF	TransBus President	H51/32F	2004
698	SN04AEP	M	TransBus Trident 11.4 SLF	TransBus President	H51/32F	2004
699	SN04AET	M	TransBus Trident 11.4 SLF	TransBus President	H51/32F	2004
700	SN04AEU	M	TransBus Trident 11.4 SLF	TransBus President	H51/32F	2004
701	SN55BJX	L	Volvo B7TL	Wright Eclipse Gemini	H49/31F	2005
702	SN55BJY	L	Volvo B7TL	Wright Eclipse Gemini	H49/31F	2005
703	SN55BJZ	L	Volvo B7TL	Wright Eclipse Gemini	H49/31F	2005
704	SN55BKA	L	Volvo B7TL	Wright Eclipse Gemini	H49/31F	2005
705	SN55BKD	L	Volvo B7TL	Wright Eclipse Gemini	H45/29F	2005
706	SN55BKE	L	Volvo B7TL	Wright Eclipse Gemini	H45/29F	2005
707	SN55BKF	L	Volvo B7TL	Wright Eclipse Gemini	H45/29F	2005
708	SN55BKG	L	Volvo B7TL	Wright Eclipse Gemini	H45/29F	2005
709	SN55BKJ	L	Volvo B7TL	Wright Eclipse Gemini	H45/29F	2005
710	SN55BKK	L	Volvo B7TL	Wright Eclipse Gemini	H45/29F	2005
711	SN55BKL	L	Volvo B7TL	Wright Eclipse Gemini	H45/29F	2005
712	SN55BKU	L	Volvo B7TL	Wright Eclipse Gemini	H45/29F	2005
713	SN55BKV	L	Volvo B7TL	Wright Eclipse Gemini	H45/29F	2005
714	SN55BKX	L	Volvo B7TL	Wright Eclipse Gemini	H45/29F	2005
715	SN55BKY	L	Volvo B7TL	Wright Eclipse Gemini	H45/29F	2005
716	SN55BKZ	L	Volvo B7TL	Wright Eclipse Gemini	H45/29F	2005
717	SN55BLF	L	Volvo B7TL	Wright Eclipse Gemini	H45/29F	2005
718	SN55BLJ	L	Volvo B7TL	Wright Eclipse Gemini	H45/29F	2005
719	SN55BLK	L	Volvo B7TL	Wright Eclipse Gemini	H45/29F	2005
720	SN55BLV	L	Volvo B7TL	Wright Eclipse Gemini	H49/31F	2005
721	SN55BLX	L	Volvo B7TL	Wright Eclipse Gemini	H45/29F	2005
722	SN55BLZ	L	Volvo B7TL	Wright Eclipse Gemini	H45/29F	2005
723	SN55BMO	L	Volvo B7TL	Wright Eclipse Gemini	H45/29F	2005
724	SN55BMU	L	Volvo B7TL	Wright Eclipse Gemini	H45/29F	2005
725	SN55BMV	L	Volvo B7TL	Wright Eclipse Gemini	H45/29F	2005
726	SN55BMY	L	Volvo B7TL	Wright Eclipse Gemini	H45/29F	2005
727	SN55BMZ	L	Volvo B7TL	Wright Eclipse Gemini	H45/29F	2005
728	SN55BNA	L	Volvo B7TL	Wright Eclipse Gemini	H45/29F	2005
729	SN55BNB	L	Volvo B7TL	Wright Eclipse Gemini	H45/29F	2005
730	SN55BND	L	Volvo B7TL	Wright Eclipse Gemini	H45/29F	2005
731	SN55BNE	L	Volvo B7TL	Wright Eclipse Gemini	H45/29F	2005
732	SN55BNF	L	Volvo B7TL	Wright Eclipse Gemini	H45/29F	2005
733	SN55BNJ	L	Volvo B7TL	Wright Eclipse Gemini	H45/29F	2005
734	SN55BNK	L	Volvo B7TL	Wright Eclipse Gemini	H45/29F	2005
735	SN55BNL	L	Volvo B7TL	Wright Eclipse Gemini	H45/29F	2005
736	SN55BNO	L	Volvo B7TL	Wright Eclipse Gemini	H45/29F	2005
737	SN55BNU	L	Volvo B7TL	Wright Eclipse Gemini	H45/29F	2005
738	SN55BNV	L	Volvo B7TL	Wright Eclipse Gemini	H45/29F	2005
739	SN55BNX	L	Volvo B7TL	Wright Eclipse Gemini	H45/29F	2005
740	SN55BNY	L	Volvo B7TL	Wright Eclipse Gemini	H45/29F	2005
741	SN55BNZ	L	Volvo B7TL	Wright Eclipse Gemini	H45/29F	2005
742	SN55BOF	L	Volvo B7TL	Wright Eclipse Gemini	H45/29F	2005
743	SN55BOH	L	Volvo B7TL	Wright Eclipse Gemini	H45/29F	2005
744	SN55BOJ	L	Volvo B7TL	Wright Eclipse Gemini	H45/29F	2005
745	SN55BOU	L	Volvo B7TL	Wright Eclipse Gemini	H45/29F	2005
746	SN55BOV	L	Volvo B7TL	Wright Eclipse Gemini	H45/29F	2005
747	SN55BPE	L	Volvo B7TL	Wright Eclipse Gemini	H45/29F	2005
748	SN55BPF	L	Volvo B7TL	Wright Eclipse Gemini	H45/29F	2005
749	SN55BPK	L	Volvo B7TL	Wright Eclipse Gemini	H45/29F	2005
750	SN55BPO	L	Volvo B7TL	Wright Eclipse Gemini	H45/29F	2005
751	SN56AAE	C	Volvo B7TL	Wright Eclipse Gemini	H48/33F	2006
752	SN56AAF	C	Volvo B7TL	Wright Eclipse Gemini	H48/33F	2006
753	SN56AAJ	C	Volvo B7TL	Wright Eclipse Gemini	H48/33F	2006
754	SN56AAK	C	Volvo B7TL	Wright Eclipse Gemini	H48/33F	2006
755	SN56AAO	C	Volvo B7TL	Wright Eclipse Gemini	H48/33F	2006
756	SN56AAU	C	Volvo B7TL	Wright Eclipse Gemini	H48/33F	2006

Lothian Buses

757	SN56AAV	C	Volvo B7TL	Wright Eclipse Gemini	H48/33F	2006
758	SN56AAX	C	Volvo B7TL	Wright Eclipse Gemini	H48/33F	2006
759	SN56AAY	C	Volvo B7TL	Wright Eclipse Gemini	H48/33F	2006
760	SN56AAZ	C	Volvo B7TL	Wright Eclipse Gemini	H48/33F	2006
761	SN56ABF	C	Volvo B7TL	Wright Eclipse Gemini	H48/33F	2006
762	SN56ABK	C	Volvo B7TL	Wright Eclipse Gemini	H48/33F	2006
763	SN56ABO	C	Volvo B7TL	Wright Eclipse Gemini	H48/33F	2006
764	SN56ABU	C	Volvo B7TL	Wright Eclipse Gemini	H48/33F	2006
765	SN56ABV	C	Volvo B7TL	Wright Eclipse Gemini	H48/33F	2006
766	SN56ABX	C	Volvo B7TL	Wright Eclipse Gemini	H48/33F	2006
767	SN56ABZ	C	Volvo B7TL	Wright Eclipse Gemini	H48/33F	2006
768	SN56ACF	C	Volvo B7TL	Wright Eclipse Gemini	H48/33F	2006
769	SN56ACJ	C	Volvo B7TL	Wright Eclipse Gemini	H48/33F	2006
770	SN56ACO	C	Volvo B7TL	Wright Eclipse Gemini	H48/33F	2006
771	SN56ACU	C	Volvo B7TL	Wright Eclipse Gemini	H48/33F	2006
772	SN56ACV	C	Volvo B7TL	Wright Eclipse Gemini	H48/33F	2006
773	SN56ACX	C	Volvo B7TL	Wright Eclipse Gemini	H48/33F	2006
774	SN56ACZ	C	Volvo B7TL	Wright Eclipse Gemini	H48/33F	2006
775	SN56ADO	C	Volvo B7TL	Wright Eclipse Gemini	H48/33F	2006
776	SN56ADU	C	Volvo B7TL	Wright Eclipse Gemini	H48/33F	2006
777	SN56ADV	C	Volvo B7TL	Wright Eclipse Gemini	H48/33F	2006
778	SN56ADX	C	Volvo B7TL	Wright Eclipse Gemini	H48/33F	2006
779	SN56ADZ	C	Volvo B7TL	Wright Eclipse Gemini	H48/33F	2006
780	SN56AEA	C	Volvo B7TL	Wright Eclipse Gemini	H48/33F	2006
781	SN56AEB	C	Volvo B7TL	Wright Eclipse Gemini	H48/33F	2006
782	SN56AEC	C	Volvo B7TL	Wright Eclipse Gemini	H48/33F	2006
783	SN56AED	C	Volvo B7TL	Wright Eclipse Gemini	H48/33F	2006
784	SN56AEE	C	Volvo B7TL	Wright Eclipse Gemini	H48/33F	2006
785	SN56AEF	C	Volvo B7TL	Wright Eclipse Gemini	H48/33F	2006
786	SN56AEG	C	Volvo B7TL	Wright Eclipse Gemini	H48/33F	2006
787	SN56AEJ	C	Volvo B7TL	Wright Eclipse Gemini	H48/33F	2006
788	SN56AEK	C	Volvo B7TL	Wright Eclipse Gemini	H48/33F	2006
789	SN56AEL	C	Volvo B7TL	Wright Eclipse Gemini	H48/33F	2006
790	SN56AEM	C	Volvo B7TL	Wright Eclipse Gemini	H48/33F	2006
791	SN56AEO	C	Volvo B7TL	Wright Eclipse Gemini	H48/33F	2006
792	SN56AEP	C	Volvo B7TL	Wright Eclipse Gemini	H48/33F	2006
793	SN56AET	C	Volvo B7TL	Wright Eclipse Gemini	H48/33F	2006
794	SN56AEU	C	Volvo B7TL	Wright Eclipse Gemini	H48/33F	2006
795	SN56AEV	C	Volvo B7TL	Wright Eclipse Gemini	H48/33F	2006
796	SN56AEW	C	Volvo B7TL	Wright Eclipse Gemini	H48/33F	2006
797	SN56AEX	C	Volvo B7TL	Wright Eclipse Gemini	H48/33F	2006
798	SN56AEY	C	Volvo B7TL	Wright Eclipse Gemini	H48/33F	2006
799	SN56AEZ	C	Volvo B7TL	Wright Eclipse Gemini	H48/33F	2006
800	SN56AFA	C	Volvo B7TL	Wright Eclipse Gemini	H48/33F	2006
801	SN56AFE	C	Volvo B7TL	Wright Eclipse Gemini	H48/33F	2006
802	SN56AFF	C	Volvo B7TL	Wright Eclipse Gemini	H48/33F	2006
803	SN56AFJ	C	Volvo B7TL	Wright Eclipse Gemini	H48/33F	2006
804	SN56AFK	C	Volvo B7TL	Wright Eclipse Gemini	H48/33F	2006
805	SN56AFO	C	Volvo B7TL	Wright Eclipse Gemini	H48/33F	2006
806	SN56AFU	C	Volvo B7TL	Wright Eclipse Gemini	H48/33F	2006
807	SN56AFV	C	Volvo B7TL	Wright Eclipse Gemini	H48/33F	2006
808	SN56AFX	C	Volvo B7TL	Wright Eclipse Gemini	H48/33F	2006
809	SN56AFY	C	Volvo B7TL	Wright Eclipse Gemini	H48/33F	2006
810	SN56AFZ	C	Volvo B7TL	Wright Eclipse Gemini	H48/33F	2006
811	SN56AGO	C	Volvo B7TL	Wright Eclipse Gemini	H48/33F	2006
812	SN56AGU	C	Volvo B7TL	Wright Eclipse Gemini	H48/33F	2006
814	SN56AGX	C	Volvo B7TL	Wright Eclipse Gemini	H48/33F	2006
815	SN56AGY	C	Volvo B7TL	Wright Eclipse Gemini	H48/33F	2006
816	SN56AGZ	C	Volvo B7TL	Wright Eclipse Gemini	H48/33F	2006
817	SN56AHA	C	Volvo B7TL	Wright Eclipse Gemini	H48/33F	2006

818	SN56AHC	C	Volvo B7TL	Wright Eclipse Gemini	H48/33F	2006
819	SN56AHD	C	Volvo B7TL	Wright Eclipse Gemini	H48/33F	2006
820	SN56AHE	C	Volvo B7TL	Wright Eclipse Gemini	H48/33F	2006
821	SN56AHF	C	Volvo B7TL	Wright Eclipse Gemini	H48/33F	2006
822	SN56AHG	C	Volvo B7TL	Wright Eclipse Gemini	H48/33F	2007
823	SN56AHJ	C	Volvo B7TL	Wright Eclipse Gemini	H48/33F	2007
824	SN56AHK	C	Volvo B7TL	Wright Eclipse Gemini	H48/33F	2007
825	SN56AHL	C	Volvo B7TL	Wright Eclipse Gemini	H48/33F	2007
826	SK07CAA	C	Volvo B9TL	Wright Eclipse Gemini	H48/33F	2007
827	SK07CAE	C	Volvo B9TL	Wright Eclipse Gemini	H48/33F	2007
828	SK07CAO	C	Volvo B9TL	Wright Eclipse Gemini	H48/33F	2007
829	SK07CAU	C	Volvo B9TL	Wright Eclipse Gemini	H48/33F	2007
830	SK07CAV	C	Volvo B9TL	Wright Eclipse Gemini	H48/33F	2007
831	SK07CAX	C	Volvo B9TL	Wright Eclipse Gemini	H48/33F	2007
832	SK07CBF	C	Volvo B9TL	Wright Eclipse Gemini	H48/33F	2007
833	SK07CBO	C	Volvo B9TL	Wright Eclipse Gemini	H48/33F	2007
834	SK07CBU	C	Volvo B9TL	Wright Eclipse Gemini	H48/33F	2007
835	SK07CBV	C	Volvo B9TL	Wright Eclipse Gemini	H48/33F	2007
836	SK07CBX	C	Volvo B9TL	Wright Eclipse Gemini	H48/33F	2007
837	SK07CBY	C	Volvo B9TL	Wright Eclipse Gemini	H48/33F	2007
838	SK07CCA	C	Volvo B9TL	Wright Eclipse Gemini	H48/33F	2007
839	SK07CCD	C	Volvo B9TL	Wright Eclipse Gemini	H48/33F	2007
840	SN57DDJ	C	Volvo B9TL	Wright Eclipse Gemini	H48/33F	2007
841	SN57DDK	C	Volvo B9TL	Wright Eclipse Gemini	H48/33F	2007
842	SN57DDL	C	Volvo B9TL	Wright Eclipse Gemini	H48/33F	2007
843	SN57DDO	C	Volvo B9TL	Wright Eclipse Gemini	H48/33F	2007
844	SN57DDU	C	Volvo B9TL	Wright Eclipse Gemini	H48/33F	2007
845	SN57DDV	C	Volvo B9TL	Wright Eclipse Gemini	H48/33F	2007
846	SN57DDX	C	Volvo B9TL	Wright Eclipse Gemini	H48/33F	2007
847	SN57DDY	C	Volvo B9TL	Wright Eclipse Gemini	H48/33F	2007
848	SN57DDZ	C	Volvo B9TL	Wright Eclipse Gemini	H48/33F	2007
849	SN57DEU	C	Volvo B9TL	Wright Eclipse Gemini	H48/33F	2007
850	SN57DFA	C	Volvo B9TL	Wright Eclipse Gemini	H48/33F	2007
851	SN57DFC	C	Volvo B9TL	Wright Eclipse Gemini	H48/33F	2007
852	SN57DFD	C	Volvo B9TL	Wright Eclipse Gemini	H48/33F	2007
853	SN57DFE	C	Volvo B9TL	Wright Eclipse Gemini	H48/33F	2007
854	SN57DFF	C	Volvo B9TL	Wright Eclipse Gemini	H48/33F	2007
855	SN57DFG	C	Volvo B9TL	Wright Eclipse Gemini	H48/33F	2007
856	SN57DFJ	C	Volvo B9TL	Wright Eclipse Gemini	H48/33F	2007
857	SN57DFK	C	Volvo B9TL	Wright Eclipse Gemini	H48/33F	2007
858	SN57DFL	C	Volvo B9TL	Wright Eclipse Gemini	H48/33F	2007
859	SN57DFO	C	Volvo B9TL	Wright Eclipse Gemini	H48/33F	2007
860	SN57DFP	C	Volvo B9TL	Wright Eclipse Gemini	H48/33F	2007
861	SN57DFU	C	Volvo B9TL	Wright Eclipse Gemini	H48/33F	2007
862	SN57DFV	C	Volvo B9TL	Wright Eclipse Gemini	H48/33F	2007
863	SN57DFX	C	Volvo B9TL	Wright Eclipse Gemini	H48/33F	2007
864	SN57DFY	C	Volvo B9TL	Wright Eclipse Gemini	H48/33F	2007
865	SN57GMO	C	Volvo B9TL	Wright Eclipse Gemini	H48/33F	2007
866	SN57GMU	C	Volvo B9TL	Wright Eclipse Gemini	H48/33F	2007
867	SN57GMV	C	Volvo B9TL	Wright Eclipse Gemini	H48/33F	2007
868	SN57GMX	C	Volvo B9TL	Wright Eclipse Gemini	H48/33F	2007
869	SN57GMY	C	Volvo B9TL	Wright Eclipse Gemini	H48/33F	2007
870	SN57GMZ	C	Volvo B9TL	Wright Eclipse Gemini	H48/33F	2007
871	SN57GNF	C	Volvo B9TL	Wright Eclipse Gemini	H48/33F	2007
872	SN57GNJ	C	Volvo B9TL	Wright Eclipse Gemini	H48/33F	2007
873	SN57GNK	C	Volvo B9TL	Wright Eclipse Gemini	H48/33F	2007
874	SN57GNO	C	Volvo B9TL	Wright Eclipse Gemini	H48/33F	2007
875	SN57GNP	C	Volvo B9TL	Wright Eclipse Gemini	H48/33F	2007
876	SN08BWJ	C	Volvo B9TL	Wright Eclipse Gemini	H48/32F	2008
877	SN08BWK	C	Volvo B9TL	Wright Eclipse Gemini	H48/32F	2008

878	SN08BWL	C	Volvo B9TL	Wright Eclipse Gemini	H48/32F	2008
879	SN08BWM	C	Volvo B9TL	Wright Eclipse Gemini	H48/32F	2008
880	SN08BWO	C	Volvo B9TL	Wright Eclipse Gemini	H48/32F	2008
881	SN08BWP	C	Volvo B9TL	Wright Eclipse Gemini	H48/32F	2008
882	SN08BWU	C	Volvo B9TL	Wright Eclipse Gemini	H48/32F	2008
883	SN08BWV	C	Volvo B9TL	Wright Eclipse Gemini	H48/32F	2008
884	SN08BWW	C	Volvo B9TL	Wright Eclipse Gemini	H48/32F	2008
885	SN08BWX	C	Volvo B9TL	Wright Eclipse Gemini	H48/32F	2008
886	SN08BWY	C	Volvo B9TL	Wright Eclipse Gemini	H48/32F	2008
887	SN08BWZ	C	Volvo B9TL	Wright Eclipse Gemini	H48/32F	2008
888	SN08BXA	C	Volvo B9TL	Wright Eclipse Gemini	H48/32F	2008
889	SN08BXB	B	Volvo B9TL	Wright Eclipse Gemini	H48/32F	2008
890	SN08BXC	C	Volvo B9TL	Wright Eclipse Gemini	H48/32F	2008
891	SN08BXD	C	Volvo B9TL	Wright Eclipse Gemini	H48/32F	2008
892	SN08BXE	C	Volvo B9TL	Wright Eclipse Gemini	H48/32F	2008
893	SN08BXF	C	Volvo B9TL	Wright Eclipse Gemini	H48/32F	2008
894	SN08BXG	C	Volvo B9TL	Wright Eclipse Gemini	H48/32F	2008
895	SN08BXH	C	Volvo B9TL	Wright Eclipse Gemini	H48/32F	2008
896	SN08BXJ	L	Volvo B9TL	Wright Eclipse Gemini	H48/32F	2008
897	SN08BXK	L	Volvo B9TL	Wright Eclipse Gemini	H48/32F	2008
898	SN08BXL	L	Volvo B9TL	Wright Eclipse Gemini	H48/32F	2008
899	SN08BXM	L	Volvo B9TL	Wright Eclipse Gemini	H48/32F	2008
900	SN08BXO	L	Volvo B9TL	Wright Eclipse Gemini	H48/32F	2008
901	SN08BXP	L	Volvo B9TL	Wright Eclipse Gemini	H48/32F	2008
902	* SN08BXR	L	Volvo B9TL	Wright Eclipse Gemini	H48/32F	2008
903	* SN08BXS	L	Volvo B9TL	Wright Eclipse Gemini	H48/32F	2008
904	SN08BXU	L	Volvo B9TL	Wright Eclipse Gemini	H48/32F	2008
905	SN08BXV	L	Volvo B9TL	Wright Eclipse Gemini	H48/32F	2008
906	SN08BXW	L	Volvo B9TL	Wright Eclipse Gemini	H48/32F	2008
907	SN08BXX	L	Volvo B9TL	Wright Eclipse Gemini	H48/32F	2008
908	SN08BXY	L	Volvo B9TL	Wright Eclipse Gemini	H48/32F	2008
909	SN08BXZ	L	Vclvo B9TL	Wright Eclipse Gemini	H48/32F	2008
910	SN08BYA	L	Volvo B9TL	Wright Eclipse Gemini	H48/32F	2008
911	SN08BYB	L	Volvo B9TL	Wright Eclipse Gemini	H48/32F	2008
912	SN08BYC	L	Volvo B9TL	Wright Eclipse Gemini	H48/32F	2008
913	SN08BYD	L	Volvo B9TL	Wright Eclipse Gemini	H48/32F	2008
914	SN08BYF	L	Volvo B9TL	Wright Eclipse Gemini	H48/32F	2008
915	SN08BYG	L	Volvo B9TL	Wright Eclipse Gemini	H48/32F	2008
916	SN08BYH	L	Volvo B9TL	Wright Eclipse Gemini	H48/32F	2008
917	SN08BYK	L	Volvo B9TL	Wright Eclipse Gemini	H48/32F	2008
918	SN08BYL	L	Volvo B9TL	Wright Eclipse Gemini	H48/32F	2008
919	SN08BYM	L	Volvo B9TL	Wright Eclipse Gemini	H48/32F	2008
920	SN08BYO	L	Volvo B9TL	Wright Eclipse Gemini	H48/32F	2008
921	SN08BYP	L	Volvo B9TL	Wright Eclipse Gemini	H48/32F	2008
922	SN08BYR	L	Volvo B9TL	Wright Eclipse Gemini	H48/32F	2008
923	SN08BYT	L	Volvo B9TL	Wright Eclipse Gemini	H48/32F	2008
924	SN08BYU	L	Volvo B9TL	Wright Eclipse Gemini	H48/32F	2008
925	SN08BYV	L	Volvo B9TL	Wright Eclipse Gemini	H48/32F	2008
926	SN09CVL	L	Volvo B9TL	Wright Eclipse Gemini	H48/32F	2009
927	SN09CVM	L	Volvo B9TL	Wright Eclipse Gemini	H48/32F	2009
928	SN09CVO	L	Volvo B9TL	Wright Eclipse Gemini	H48/32F	2009
929	SN09CVP	L	Volvo B9TL	Wright Eclipse Gemini	H48/32F	2009
930	SN09CVR	L	Volvo B9TL	Wright Eclipse Gemini	H48/32F	2009
931	SN09CVS	L	Volvo B9TL	Wright Eclipse Gemini	H48/32F	2009
932	SN09CVT	L	Volvo B9TL	Wright Eclipse Gemini	H48/32F	2009
933	SN09CVU	L	Volvo B9TL	Wright Eclipse Gemini	H48/32F	2009
934	* SN09CVV	L	Volvo B9TL	Wright Eclipse Gemini	H48/32F	2009
935	SN09CVW	L	Volvo B9TL	Wright Eclipse Gemini	H48/32F	2009
936	SN09CVX	L	Volvo B9TL	Wright Eclipse Gemini	H48/32F	2009
937	SN10DKE	C	Volvo B9TL	Wright Eclipse Gemini	H43/32F	2010

938	SN10DKF	C	Volvo B9TL	Wright Eclipse Gemini	H43/23F	2010
939	SN10DKJ	C	Volvo B9TL	Wright Eclipse Gemini	H43/23F	2010
940	SN10DKK	C	Volvo B9TL	Wright Eclipse Gemini	H43/23F	2010
941	SN10DKL	C	Volvo B9TL	Wright Eclipse Gemini	H43/23F	2010
942	SN10DKO	C	Volvo B9TL	Wright Eclipse Gemini	H42/23F	2010
943	SN10DKU	C	Volvo B9TL	Wright Eclipse Gemini	H43/23F	2010
944	SN10DKV	C	Volvo B9TL	Wright Eclipse Gemini	H43/23F	2010
945	SN10DKX	C	Volvo B9TL	Wright Eclipse Gemini	H43/23F	2010
946	SN10DKY	C	Volvo B9TL	Wright Eclipse Gemini	H43/23F	2010
947	SN10DLD	C	Volvo B9TL	Wright Eclipse Gemini	H43/23F	2010
948	SN10DLE	C	Volvo B9TL	Wright Eclipse Gemini	H43/23F	2010
949	SN10DLF	C	Volvo B9TL	Wright Eclipse Gemini	H43/23F	2010
950	* LB10BUS	C	Volvo B9TL	Wright Eclipse Gemini	H43/23F	2010
985	SN57DAA	r	Scania N94UD	Scania OmniCity	H45/23F	2007
986	SN57DAO	r	Scania N94UD	Scania OmniCity	H45/23F	2007
987	SN57DAU	r	Scania N94UD	Scania OmniCity	H45/23F	2007
988	SN57DBO	r	Scania N94UD	Scania OmniCity	H45/23F	2007
989	SN57DBU	r	Scania N94UD	Scania OmniCity	H45/23F	2007
990	SN57DBV	r	Scania N94UD	Scania OmniCity	H45/23F	2007
991	SN57DBX	r	Scania N94UD	Scania OmniCity	H45/23F	2007
992	SN57DBY	r	Scania N94UD	Scania OmniCity	H45/23F	2007
993	SN57DBZ	r	Scania N94UD	Scania OmniCity	H45/23F	2007
994	SN57DCE	r	Scania N94UD	Scania OmniCity	H45/23F	2007
995	SK06AHF	r	Scania N94UD	Scania OmniCity	H45/23F	2006
996	SK06AHG	r	Scania N94UD	Scania OmniCity	H45/23F	2006
997	SK06AHJ	r	Scania N94UD	Scania OmniCity	H45/23F	2006
998	SK06AHL	r	Scania N94UD	Scania OmniCity	H45/23F	2006
999	SK06AHN	r	Scania N94UD	Scania OmniCity	H45/23F	2006
TB318	E318MSG	L(t)	Leyland Olympian ONCL10/2RZ	Alexander RH	H27/22D	1988
TB319	E319MSG	L (t)	Leyland Olympian ONCL10/2RZ	Alexander RH	H27/22D	1988
TB320	E320MSG	t	Leyland Olympian ONCL10/2RZ	Alexander RH	H27/22D	1988
TB322	E322MSG	L(t)	Leyland Olympian ONCL10/2RZ	Alexander RH	H51/30D	1988
TB51	SK52OHU	t	Dennis Dart 11.3 SLF	Plaxton Pointer 2	B42F	2002
TB52	SK52OHV	t	Dennis Dart 11.3 SLF	Plaxton Pointer 2	B42F	2002
TB53	SK52OHW	t	Dennis Dart 11.3 SLF	Plaxton Pointer 2	B42F	2002
	K873CSF	r	Leyland Olympian ON2R56C13Z4	Alexander RH	H51/30D	1992
	K875CSF	S	Leyland Olympian ON2R56C13Z4	Alexander RH	PO47/30F	1992
	K876CSF	r	Leyland Olympian ON2R56C13Z4	Alexander RH	H51/30D	1992
	K881CSF	r	Leyland Olympian ON2R56C13Z4	Alexander RH	H51/30D	1993

M & C Coaches

M&C McClure, 7 Wallace Avenue, Elderslie PA5 9LN
Website www.m-c-coaches.co.uk
Depot Unit 6A Shanks Industrial Park, Blackbyres Road, Barrhead, Glasgow G78 1TG
Russell Street, Johnstone PA5 8BZ
Licence PM0001623

F351FGA	DAF SB2305DHS585	Duple 320	C55F	1988
G774DSK	Volvo B10M-60	Duple 340	C53FT	1990
G954WNR	Dennis Javelin 8.5SDA	Duple 320	C39F	1990
H178EJF	Toyota Coaster HDB30R	Caetano Optimo	C18F	1991
* M685MRP *	Volvo B10M-62	Plaxton Premiere 350	C53F	1994
N108AVN	Volvo B10M-62	Plaxton Premiere 350	C53F	1996
* P157XNW *	Boba FLD12-270	Bova Futura	C70F	1997
P766JBU	Mercedes-Benz 709D	Leicester Carriage Builders	C29F	1996
R206VJF	Iveco EuroRider 391E.12.35	Beulas Stergo E	C49FT	1998
R453FCE	Volvo B10M-62	Plaxton Premiere 350	C70F	1997
R626ULX	Mercedes-Benz Vario O.814D	Autobus Nouvelle	C33F	1997
* R685WRN	Bova FHD12.340	Bova Futura	C76F	1997

M & C Coaches				
S887KRG	Mercedes-Benz 512D	Adamson	C20FL	1998
T881JBC	MAN 13.220	Marcopolo Viaggio	C35FT	1999

Macbackpackers
MacBackpackers Ltd, 23a Blair Street, Edinburgh EH1 8BH
Website
Depot 173 Duddingston Park Road South, Ed1nburgh EH15 3EG
Licence PM1010756

R220RRG	Mercedes-Benz 614D	Crest	C24F	1997
SN10AJO	Mercedes-Benz O.813D	Unvi	C29F	2010
SN10ENH	Mercedes-Benz O.813D	Carrocerias Modernas	C29F	2010
SN10WNT	Mercedes-Benz O.813D	Unvi	C29F	2010
SN10ENU	Mercedes-Benz O.813D	Unvi	C29F	2010
SP56VHY	Ford Transit	Ford	M16	2006
V103DBB	Mercedes-Benz 614D	Crest	C24F	1999
VX08HZU	Mercedes-Benz O.816D	Mellor	C29F	2008
* XCZ 7782	Mercedes-Benz O.303	Mercedes-Benz	C49FT	1988
YN06CYG	Mercedes-Benz Vario O.814D	Plaxton Cheetah	C29F	2006
YN06CYH	Mercedes-Benz Vario O.814D	Plaxton Cheetah	C29F	2006
YN06CYJ	Mercedes-Benz Vario O.814D	Plaxton Cheetah	C29F	2006

MacDonalds Coaches
R MacDonald, West Myvot Farm, Cumbernauld G67 4HD
Website www.macdonaldcoaches.co.uk
Depot West Myvot Farm, Cumbernauld G67 4HD
Licence PM1044260

C404LRP	Volvo B10M-46	Jonckheere Piccolo	C31FT	1986
* D825YCH	Volvo B10M-61	Van Hool Alizée	C53F	1987
* E100LBC	Volvo B10M-61	Duple 320	C55F	1988
* FIL8613	Volvo B10M-61	Van Hool Astrobel	CH49/9FT	1983
G197PAO	Mercedes-Benz 709D	Alexander Sprint	DP25F	1990
* J880RHA	Volvo B10M-60	Van Hool Alizée	C49FT	1992
L930UGA	Mercedes-Benz 609D	Made to Measure	C26F	1993
N470PYS	Volvo B10M-62	Van Hool Alizée	C53F	1996
* NXI9004	Volvo B10M-61	Van Hool Alizée	C51FT	1989
* OIL5265	Volvo B10M-61	Caetano Algarve	C51FT	1985
* P279VUS	Volvo B10M-62	Van Hool Alizée	C53FT	1997
* PIL2167	Volvo B10M-61	Plaxton Paramount 3500 I	C28FT	1984
R549MSS	Volvo B10M-62	Caetano Algarve II	C49FT	1998
* VIL9331	Volvo B10M-46	Plaxton Paramount 3200 III	C38FT	1990

MacEwan's Coach Services

J MacEwan, Johnfield, Amisfield, Dumfries DG1 3LS
Website
Depots Johnfield, Amisfield, Dumfries DG1 3LS
Unit 4 Catherinefield Road Industrial Estate, Heathhall, Dumfries DG1 3PJ
Licence PM0000890

Reg		Chassis	Body	Layout	Year
571BWT	p	AEC Reliance	Duple Dominant	C41F	1962
A375BDL		Bedford YNT	Duple Laser	C53F	1983
A768WVP		MCW MetroBus 2 DR102/27	MCW	H43/30F	1984
B100XTW	–	Leyland Tiger TRCTL11/3RP	Duple	C57F	1984
B500MPY	–	Leyland DAB Tiger Cub	DAB/Eastern Coach Works	B46F	1985
B885DOM		MCW MetroBus 2 DR102/27	MCW	H43/30F	1985
CN53GWO		BMC Falcon 1100	BMC	B35F	2004
CN53GWP		BMC Falcon 1100	BMC	B35F	2004
* CNZ3830	–	Scania L94IB4	Van Hool Alizée	C49FT	1999
D285XCX		DAF SB2300	Plaxton Paramount 3500 II	C53F	1987
F201HSO	–	Leyland Tiger TRCTL11/3ARZM	Plaxton Paramount 3200 III	C53F	1988
GFM882	– p	Bristol L6A	Eastern Coach Works	B35F	1948
K477SSM	–	Mercedes-Benz 709D	Dormobile Routemaker	B29F	1993
K478SSM	–	Mercedes-Benz 709D	Dormobile Routemaker	B29F	1993
K766DAO	–	Volvo B10M-55	Alexander PS	B49F	1993
K788DAO	– z	Volvo B10M-55	Alexander PS	DP49F	1993
K851RBB	–	Optare MetroRider MR07	Optare	DP28F	1992
K852RBB	–	Optare MetroRider MR07	Optare	DP28F	1992
KU02YUL	–	Mercedes-Benz Vario O.814D	Plaxton Beaver 2	B31F	2002
KU02YUN		Mercedes-Benz Vario O.814D	Plaxton Beaver 2	B31F	2002
* LIL8970		Volvo B10M-60	Plaxton Paramount 3500 III	C53F	1989
M291OUR	–	Fiat 480.10.21	Wadham Stringer	B47F	1994
M578BSM	–	Mercedes-Benz 709D	Alexander Sprint	B29F	1995
N114DWE	–	Mercedes-Benz 709D	Plaxton Welfare Beaver 2	DP24FL	1996
N117FSM	–	Scania K113CRB	Van Hool Alizée	C49FT	1996
N317DAG		LDV 400	Jubilee	M16	1995
N321DAG	x	LDV 400	Jubilee	M16	1995
NDL869	p	AEC Reliance	Duple	C41F	1957
P630FTV		Volvo B10M-62	Jonckheere Mistral	C53FT	1997
PGD216F	p	Bedford SB5	Plaxton	C F	1968
PGD220F	p	Bedford SB5	Plaxton	C F	1968
PX09APO		MAN 12.240	Plaxton Centro	B38F	2009
PX09APU		MAN 12.240	Plaxton Centro	B38F	2009
R102HUA		Optare MetroRider MR11	Optare	B28F	1997
RAR777W	z	Ford R1114	Plaxton Supreme	C53F	1980
ROX638Y	z	MCW MetroBus 2 DR102/27	MCW	H43/30F	1983
ROX641Y		MCW MetroBus 2 DR102/27	MCW	H43/30F	1983
RSJ812Y		Volvo B10M-61	Duple Goldliner	C53F	1982
SA03YDB	–	Mercedes-Benz Vario O.814D	Plaxton Beaver 2	DP33F	2003
SJ04MFV	–	Mercedes-Benz Vario O.814D	TransBus Beaver 2	DP33F	2004
SJ09GDV		MAN NL273	Wright Meridian	B44F	2009
SJ60GBF		Optare 9600SR	Optare	B30F	2010
SN56GBZ	–	Mercedes-Benz Vario O.814D	Plaxton Beaver 2	DP33F	2006
SYJ961X		Bedford YMQ	Plaxton Supreme V	C45F	1982
T136ARE	z	Mercedes-Benz 614D	Minibus Options	DP14L	1999
T716TCS		LDV Convoy	LDV	M16	1999
V829GGA	–	Mercedes-Benz Vario O.814D	Plaxton Beaver 2	B31F	2000
W137OSM	–	Mercedes-Benz Vario O.814D	Plaxton Beaver 2	B31F	2000
* W158WTA	–	Scania L94IB4	Irizar InterCentury	C53F	2000
W494PLS		LDV Convoy	LDV	M16	2000
WVH868V		Leyland Leopard PSU3E/4R	Duple Dominant II Exp.	C53F	1979
YP02AAY	–	Scania L94UB	Wright Solar	B43F	2002
YP02AAZ	–	Scania L94UB	Wright Solar	B43F	2002

SA03 ZVA —

Mackies Coaches
J Mackie, 32 Glasshouse Loan, Alloa FK10 1PE
Website   www.mackiescoaches.com
Depot   32 Glasshouse Loan, Alloa FK10 1PE
Licence   PM0001736

*	B496MFS	Leyland Tiger TRCTL11/3R	Plaxton Paramount 3500 I	C53F	1985
*	DLS520Y u	Ward Dalesman	Plaxton Paramount 3200 I	C51F	1983
	F774JYS	Volvo B10M-55	Duple 300	B53F	1989
	FJ04ETY	Volvo B7RLE	Wright Eclipse Urban	B43F	2004
	KW56LZU	Mercedes-Benz 311CDI	Concept	M8	2006
	LS04OSL	Volvo B7RLE	Wright Eclipse Urban	B43F	2004
*	M141TMS	Volvo B10M-62	Jonckheere Deauville	C53F	1995
	M174XTC	Bova FHD12.340	Bova Futura	C49FT	1995
*	PFG362	Volvo B10M-60	Van Hool Alizée	C53F	1992
	R476GFM	Mercedes-Benz Vario O.814D	Plaxton Beaver	B31F	1998
	S266JUG	Mercedes-Benz 614D	UVG	B14L	1998
	SL04OLS	Volvo B7RLE	Wright Eclipse Urban	B43F	2004
	SL54OSL	Volvo B7RLE	Wright Eclipse Urban	B43F	2005
	SL9483 p	Bedford SB5	Duple	C41F	1964
	SN05EOV	Bova FHD13-340	Bova Futura	C57F	2005
	SN05EOW	Bova FHD13-340	Bova Futura	C57F	2005
	SN06GGJ	Bova XHD122.D340	Bova Magiq	C49FT	2006
	SN06GGK	Volvo B7RLE	Wright Eclipse Urban	B43F	2006
	SP04EVB	Bova FHD12-340	Bova Futura	C49FT	2004
*	T11OUR	Mercedes-Benz 614D	Phail	C8F	2001
*	TSV956	Bova FHD12.340	Bova Futura	C49FT	1996
	XSV270	Bova FHD120-365	Bova Futura	C49FT	2008
*	YBL526	Volvo B10M-60	Van Hool Alizée	C53F	1992
*	YFS438	Volvo B10M-62	Van Hool Alizée	C53F	1994

MacLennan
A MacLennan, 24 Inaclete Road, Stornoway HS1 2RN
Website
Depot   24 Inaclete Road, Stornoway HS1 2RN
Licence   PM0001491

BV57XLJ	LDV Convoy	Onyx	M16	2007
GX51CFF	Volvo B10M-62	Plaxton Paragon	C49FT	2001
M259OKN	Dennis Javelin 12SDA	Plaxton Premiere 320	C53F	1994
T3APT	Volvo B10M-61	Van Hool Alizée	C48FT	1999
T504EUB	Volvo B10M-62	Plaxton Premiere 350	C46FT	1999
T527EUB	Volvo B10M-62	Plaxton Premiere 350	C49F	1999
T599BRG	Volvo B10M-62	Plaxton Premiere 350	C57F	1999
YN09HDX	Mercedes-Benz 515CDI	Kilbeggan Vehicle Converters	C16F	2009
YN53VBP	Mercedes-Benz Vario O.814D	TransBus Beaver 2	C33F	2004

MacLeod's Coaches
J MacLeod, Tigh An Alt, Acheilidh, Rogart IV28 3UD
Website   www.macleodscoaches.co.uk
Depot   Tigh An Alt, Acheilidh, Rogart IV28 3UD
Licence   PM0002183

*	DEZ4258	Volvo B10M-62	Van Hool Alizée	C55F	1997
	DK04LWN	Mercedes-Benz 413CDI		M16	2004
	J168CTO	Mercedes-Benz 709D	Plaxton Beaver	B25F	1991
*	NUI4223	DAF DE33WSSB3000	Van Hool Alizée	C51FT	1996
*	RO06ART	Temsa Opalin	Temsa	C35F	2007
	SY05DRX	Mercedes-Benz Vario O.814D	Plaxton Welfare Beaver 2	DP29FL	2005
*	T333BUS	Volvo B10M-55	Van Hool Alizée	C49FT	1999

	Macleod's			
* XIW1182	Volvo B10M-60	Van Hool Alizée	C49FT	1992

MacPherson Luxury Travel
A MacPherson, 6 Academy Park, Airdrie ML6 9BT
Website
Depot 221 Burnbank Street, Coatbridge ML5 2AZ
Licence PM0002366

* C11MMM	Volvo B10M-61	Plaxton Paramount 3500 II	C51F	1986
* E11MMM	Volvo B10M-60	Plaxton Paramount 3200 III	C70F	1988
* F1MMM	Volvo B10M-62	Van Hool Alizée	C49FT	1993
* F11MMM	Volvo B10M-62	Jonckheere Deauville	C57F	1993
* S273LGA	Mercedes-Benz Vario O.814D	Mellor	C33F	1998
* V133ESF	Mercedes-Benz Vario O.814D	Plaxton Cheetah	C33F	1999
* W153RYB	Bova FHD12.370	Bova Futura	C75F	2000

MacPhails Coaches
MacPhails Coaches Ltd, 40 Main Street, Salsburgh ML7 4LW
Website
Depot 40 Main Street, Salsburgh ML7 4LW
Licence PM1040390

* ATV24Y	Volvo B10M-62	Van Hool Alizée	C49FT	2000
* DEZ9611	Volvo B10M-61	Van Hool Alizée	C53F	1985
* GFA955	Volvo B12B(T)	Van Hool Alizée	C53FT	2007
* KSK933	Bova FHD12-340	Bova Futura	C49FT	2002
* KSK934	Volvo B12B	Van Hool Alizée	C49FT	2005
SF07ODH	Volvo B12B	Van Hool Alizée	C49FT	2007
SF08MKV	Bova FHD127-365	Bova Futura	C53F	2008
SN10AVG	Bova FHD127-365	Bova Futura	C53F	2010
* UAX891	Volvo B10M-62	Van Hool Alizée	C55F	1998
* WSV713	Bova FHD12-340	Bova Futura	C49FT	2002

Marbill Travel
Marbill Coach Services Ltd, Highmains Garage, Mains Road, Beith KA15 2AP
Website www.marbillcoaches.com
Depot Yard No 2, Mains Road, Beith KA15 1DA
Licence PM0000434

* 2154K	Volvo B12M	Van Hool Alizée	C55F	2002
A715YFS	Leyland Olympian ONTL11/2R	Eastern Coach Works	H51/35F	1983
A716YFS	Leyland Olympian ONTL11/2R	Eastern Coach Works	H51/35F	1983
A718YFS – r	Leyland Olympian ONTL11/2R	Eastern Coach Works	H51/36F	1983
A722YFS r	Leyland Olympian ONTL11/2R	Eastern Coach Works	H50/36F	1983
A723YFS r	Leyland Olympian ONTL11/2R	Eastern Coach Works	H51/35F	1983
A724YFS	Leyland Olympian ONTL11/2R	Eastern Coach Works	H51/35F	1983
A732YFS	Leyland Olympian ONTL11/2R	Eastern Coach Works	H51/35F	1983
B762GSC –	Leyland Olympian ONTL11/2R	Eastern Coach Works	H51/32D	1984
* BJI6863	Volvo B12M	Van Hool Alizée	C57F	2002
C775SFS	Leyland Olympian ONTL11/2R	Eastern Coach Works	H51/35F	1985
E916NAC	Leyland Tiger TRBTL11/2RP	Plaxton Verde	B69F	1988
E917NAC	Leyland Tiger TRBTL11/2RP	Plaxton Verde	B69F	1988
E918NAC	Leyland Tiger TRBTL11/2RP	Plaxton Verde	B69F	1988
F337RWK	Leyland Tiger TRBTL11/2RP	Plaxton Verde	B69F	1988
* GJI627	Volvo B10M-48	Van Hool Alizée	C40FT	1995
H149SKU –	Volvo B10M-55	Plaxton Derwent II	B69F	1990
H150SKU	Volvo B10M-55	Plaxton Derwent II	B69F	1990
H151SKU	Volvo B10M-55	Plaxton Derwent II	B69F	1990

H152SKU	Volvo B10M-55	Plaxton Derwent II	B69F	1990
H153SKU	Volvo B10M-55	Plaxton Derwent II	B69F	1990
H154SKU	Volvo B10M-55	Plaxton Derwent II	B69F	1990
H155SKU	Volvo B10M-55	Plaxton Derwent II	B69F	1990
H156SKU	Volvo B10M-55	Plaxton Derwent II	B69F	1990
H157SKU	Volvo B10M-55	Plaxton Derwent II	B69F	1990
H158SKU	Volvo B10M-55	Plaxton Derwent II	B69F	1990
H159SKU	Volvo B10M-55	Plaxton Derwent II	B69F	1990
* HJI565	Volvo B12B	Van Hool Alizee	C49F	2003
* LJI978	Bova FHD12-340	Bova Futura	C49FT	2003
M210VSX	Volvo Olympian YV2RC16Z4	Alexander RH	H51/30D	1995
M217VSX	Volvo Olympian YV2RC16Z4	Alexander RH	H51/30D	1995
M218VSX	Volvo Olympian YV2RC16Z	Alexander RH	H51/30D	1995
M219VSX	Volvo Olympian YV2RC16Z	Alexander RH	H51/30D	1995
M220VSX	Volvo Olympian YV2RC16Z	Alexander RH	H51/30D	1995
M224VSX	Volvo Olympian YV2RC16Z4	Alexander RH	H51/30D	1995
M226VSX	Volvo Olympian YV2RC16Z4	Alexander RH	H51/30D	1995
M229VSX	Volvo Olympian YV2RC16Z	Alexander RH	H51/30D	1995
M230VSX	Volvo Olympian YV2RC16Z	Alexander RH	H51/30D	1995
M232VSX	Volvo Olympian YV2RC16Z4	Alexander RH	H51/30D	1995
OFS686Y	Leyland Olympian ONTL11/2R	Eastern Coach Works	H50/36F	1982
OFS687Y	Leyland Olympian ONTL11/2R	Eastern Coach Works	H50/36F	1983
SF04WMX	Bova FHD12.340	Bova Futura	C55F	2004
SF05KWM	Volvo B7R	Plaxton Profile	C70F	2005
SF05KWO	Volvo B7R	Plaxton Profile	C70F	2005
SF06LKD	Mercedes-Benz Vario O.815D	Sitcar Beluga	C33F	2006
SF06LKE	Mercedes-Benz Vario O.815D	Sitcar Beluga	C33F	2006
SF07NLU	Bova FLD120.365	Bova Futura	C70F	2007
SF07NLV	Bova FLD120.365	Bova Futura	C70F	2007
SF07NLX	Bova FLD120.365	Bova Futura	C70F	2007
SF07NLY	Bova FLD120.365	Bova Futura	C70F	2007
SF07NLZ	Bova FLD120.365	Bova Futura	C70F	2007
SF08OKK	Bova FLD120.365	Bova Futura	C57F	2008
SJ06CBX	Volvo B12B(T)	Van Hool Alizée	C49FT	2006
SN10AZP	Bova FHD127.365	Bova Futura	C70F	2010
SN10AZR	Bova FHD127-365	Bova Futura	C70F	2010
* SXI2887	Bova FHD12-370	Bova Futura	C49FT	2000
* TIW5725	Volvo B12B	Van Hool Alizée	C49FT	2003
* XRY278	Volvo B7R	Plaxton Profile	C70F	2005

Marshall of Baillieston

Marshall of Baillieston Ltd, 23 Gillies Lane, Baillieston, Glasgow G69 7HJ
Website www.marshallofbaillieston.co.uk
Depot 23 Gillies Lane, Baillieston, Glasgow G69 7HJ
Licence PM1022415

* 731AFD	Volvo B10M-62	Berkhof Axial 50	C51FT	2001
* 7617SM	Volvo B10M-62	Van Hool Alizée	C46FT	1995
H668GPF	Volvo B10M-50	East Lancs	H45/34F	1991
* HIL6570	Volvo B10M-61	Van Hool Alizée	C53F	1988
* RIJ774	Volvo B10M-62	Van Hool Alizée	C50FT	1996
* VIW7191	Volvo B10M-50	East Lancs	H47/36F	1983
* WNR536	Volvo B10M-62	Van Hool Alizée	C53F	1995

A&A Mason Coach Hire

A Mason, The Factory, East Kerse Mains, Grangemouth Road, Bo'ness EH51 0PY
Website
Depot   The Factory, East Kerse Mains, Grangemouth Road, Bo'ness EH51 0PY
Licence   PM0001534

	ANA184Y	MCW MetroBus 2 DR102/23	MCW	H43/30F	1983
	CN58EBM	Renault Master	Tawe	M16	2008
*	F651GNT —	Volvo B10M-60	Van Hool Alizée	C49F	1989
	F703COA	Volvo B10M-53	Plaxton Paramount 4000	CH53/12CT	1989
*	HIG7814	Volvo B10M-62	Plaxton Premiere 350	C48FT	1997
*	HJZ3949	DAF MB230LT615	Van Hool Alizee	C51F	1992
	J120AHH	Volvo B10M-60	Plaxton Paramount 3500 III	C46FT	1991
*	JAZ4886	Leyland Tiger TRTCL11/3RZ	Van Hool Alizée	C53F	1986
*	K918RGE	Volvo B10M-60	Jonckheere	C53F	1993
	MRJ40W	MCW MetroBus 2 DR102/21	MCW	H43/30F	1981
	MRJ55W	MCW MetroBus 2 DR102/21	MCW	H43/30F	1981
*	NIW8920	Volvo B10M-61	Van Hool Alizée	C53F	1985
*	PNR723	Volvo B10M-62	Van Hool Alizée	C53F	1996
*	R100DJD	Dennis Javelin 10.5SFD	Berkhof Excellence 1000 Midi	C35F	1998
*	RJI5716	Volvo B10M-53	Van Hool Astrobel	CH51/29CT	1985
*	S33AAM x	Fiat Ducato	Mason, Bo'ness	M8	2007
	SA56VMT	Volkswagen Transporter	Mason, Bo'ness	M8	2006
	SF59FVA	Ford Transit	Ford	M16	2009
	SIB8045	Volvo B10M-60	Van Hool Alizée	C53F	1993
	YN55KWJ	Mercedes-Benz Atego 1018L	Unvi Cimo	C33F	2005

Maynes Coaches

Maynes Coaches Ltd, Cluny Garage, 4 March Road West, Buckie AB56 4BU
Website   www.maynes.co.uk
Depots   Cluny Garage, 4 March Road West, Buckie AB56 4BU
              Linkwood Industrial Estate, Elgin IV30 1XS
Licence   PM1033727

1	EM10GSM	MAN R33	Plaxton Panther	C51FTL	2010
2	GM10GSM	Neoplan 440X SHD	Neoplan Tourliner	C49FT	2010
3	KM57GSM	Volvo B12B	Van Hool Alizée	C49FT	2007
4	GM57GSM	Volvo B12B	Van Hool Alizée	C49FT	2007
5	MM06GSM —	Volvo B12B	Van Hool Alizée	C49F	2006
7	KM07GSM —	Volvo B12B	Van Hool Alizée	C49FT	2007
8	SV09DNN—	Neoplan N216SHD	Neoplan Euroliner	C49FT	2009
9	* SV09DNJ	Neoplan N216SHD	Neoplan Euroliner	C49FT	2009
10	SM07GSM	Volvo B12B	Van Hool Alizée	C49FT	2007
11	EM59GSM	Volvo B12B	Van Hool Alizée	C51FT	2009
12	SV09AOT	Volvo B12B	Van Hool Alizée	C49FT	2009
14	SV09AOU	Volvo B12B	Van Hool Alizée	C49FT	2009
16	SM06GSM	MAN 18.350	Marcopolo Viaggio	C70F	2006
17	CM05GSM	MAN 18.310	Marcopolo Viaggio	C70F	2005
18	SV09AOA	MAN 18.350	Marcopolo	C57F	2009
19	YSU990	Mercedes-Benz Vario O.814D	Plaxton Cheetah	C29F	2008
20	YSU989 O	Mercedes-Benz Vario O.814D	Plaxton Cheetah	C33F	2008
22	* MM54GSM	Mercedes-Benz 614D	Onyx	C24F	2005
23	MX57CDN	Optare Solo M950	Optare	B29F	2007
24	7MCB	Mercedes-Benz O.816D	Plaxton Cheetah	C25F	2010
26	SV09AEZ	Mercedes-Benz O.813D	Plaxton Beaver	DP33FL	2009
28	SV09AOB O	MAN 18.350	Marcopolo	C57F	2009
31	CE59ZLK	Renault Master	Tawe	M16	2009
	CM10GSM	Neoplan N400X SHD	Neoplan Tourliner	C49FT	2010
	DM10GSM —	Neoplan N400X SHD	Neoplan Tourliner	C49FT	2010

Maynes Coaches

FJ06URK	Volvo B12M	Caetano Optimo	C49FT	2006
K827HUM	Volvo B10M-60	Jonckheere	C50F	1993
KKN752 p	Bedford OB	Duple	C29F	1948
KM10GSM	Neoplan N2216SHD	Neoplan Euroliner	C49FT	2010
PUF249M p	Ford R1114	Duple Dominant	C49F	1974
SM10GSM	Neoplan N400X SHD	Neoplan Tourliner	C49FT	2010
* Y7NES	Renault Master	Mellor	M16	2001
Y752NAY	Volvo B10M-62	Caetano Optimo	C49FT	2001

McCall's Coaches
McCall's Coaches Ltd, 4 Lammonbie Cottage, Lockerbie, Lockerbie DG11 2RN
Website
Depot 4 Lammonbie Cottage, Lockerbie, Lockerbie DG11 2RN
Brownrigg Business Park, Brownrigg Loaning, Dumfries DG1 3JT
Site 16, Hallmuir Camp, Dalton Road, Lockerbie DG11 1BL
Licence PM1057000

* C408HVH	Scania K112CRS	Van Hool	C49FT	1985
D526BBV	Duple 425 SDA	Duple 425	C53FT	1987
* D780FVT	Volvo B10M-61	Plaxton Paramount 3200 III	C53F	1987
* FIL4166	Leyland Tiger TRCTL11/3R	Van Hool	C57F	1984
G799RNC	Leyland Tiger TRCTL11/3RZ	Duple 320	C70F	1989
* GEZ1277	Leyland Leopard PSU3E/4R	Alexander (Belfast)	B63F	1980
* KAO238V	Volvo B58-61	Plaxton Supreme	C57F	1980
L33NMS	Bova FHD12-340	Bova Futura	C49F	1993
N996XNT	Scania K113TRB	Irizar Century	C49FT	1996
* OAZ1372	Volvo B10M-62	Jonckheere	C51F	1986
* OIL5079	Volvo B10M-60	Jonckheere	C51FT	1989
VAZ4859	Volvo B10M-60	Van Hool Alizée	C49FT	1990
* YJI1309	Leyland Tiger TRCTL11/3R	Plaxton Paramount 3500 I	C49FT	1983

McColl's Coaches
W McColl, Block 4, Vale of Leven Industrial Estate, Dumbarton G82 3PD
McColls Commercial Repairs Ltd, Block 4, Vale of Leven Industrial Estate, Dumbarton G82 3PD
W McColl, Blairusk Farm, Alexandria G83 8NB
Loch Lomond Bus Services Ltd, Block 4, Vale of Leven Industrial Estate, Dumbarton G82 3PD
Website www.mccolls.org.uk
Depot Block 4, Vale of Leven Industrial Estate, Dumbarton G82 3PD
Unit 1, Tontine Park, Renton, Dumbarton G82 4LP
Unit 1 Dalquham Industrial Estate, Renton, Alexandria G83 8LY
Ballagan Garage, Stirling Road, Balloch, Alexandria G83 8EP
Auld Street, Dalmuir, Clydebank G81 4HB
Loch Lomond Bus Services Ltd, Block 4, Vale of Leven Ind Estate, Dumbarton G82 3PD
Licence PM0002928 (McColl's Coaches)
PM0002409 (McColl's Commercial Repairs Ltd)
PM0000938 (McColl's Coaches)
PM1036390 (Loch Lomond Bus Services)

1001	L404BBC	Mercedes-Benz 811D	Wadham Stringer	B31F	1994
1002	L407BBC	Mercedes-Benz 811D	Wadham Stringer	B31F	1994
1006	R272XDA	Mercedes-Benz Vario O.814D	Alexander Sprint	B27F	1998
1009	* YX04DLY	Mercedes-Benz Vario O>814D	Autobus Nouvelle	C29F	2004
1010	S287NRB	Optare Solo M920	Optare	B33F	1998
1011	S288NRB	Optare Solo M920	Optare	B33F	1998
2002	J25MCW	Volvo B10M-50	East Lancs	B45F	1992
2004	M722BCS	Volvo B6-50	Alexander Dash	DP40F	1994
2005	M772BCS	Volvo B6-50	Alexander Dash	DP40F	1994

2008	K574LTS	Volvo B10M-55	Alexander PS	B49F	1993
2009	K718DAO	Volvo B10M-55	Alexander PS	B52F	1992
2010	K578LTS	Volvo B10M-55	Alexander PS	B49F	1993
2011	K715DAO	Volvo B10M-55	Alexander PS	B52F	1992
2014	* R984SSA	Volvo B10L	Alexander (Dublin) Ultra	B39D	1997
2015	* R993SSA	Volvo B10L	Alexander (Dublin) Ultra	B39D	1997
2016	* R985SSA	Volvo B10L	Alexander (Dublin) Ultra	B39D	1997
2017	* R986SSA	Volvo B10L	Alexander (Dublin) Ultra	B39D	1997
2018	* V167MYS	Volvo B6BLE	Wright Crusader	B35F	1999
2019	* V170MYS	Volvo B6BLE	Wright Crusader	B35F	1999
2020	* V168MYS	Volvo B6BLE	Wright Crusader	B52F	1999
2021	* V169MYS	Volvo B6BLE	Wright Crusader	B35F	1999
2022	R985EWU	Optare Excel L1000	Optare	B33F	1998
2023	P227AAP	Volvo B6LE	Wright Crusader	B28F	1997
2025	P242AAP	Volvo B6BLE-53	Wright Crusader	B28F	1997
2027	P245AAP	Volvo B6BLE-53	Wright Crusader	B28F	1997
2028	P246AAP	Volvo B6BLE-53	Wright Crusader	B28F	1997
2029	P248AAP	Volvo B6BLE-53	Wright Crusader	B28F	1997
2030	P249AAP	Volvo B6BLE-53	Wright Crusader	B28F	1997
2032	T504TOL	Volvo B6BLE-53	Wright Crusader	B31F	1999
2033	P241AAP	Volvo B6LE-53	Wright Crusader	B28F	1997
2034	P231AAP	Volvo B6LE	Wright Crusader	B28F	1997
2035	P238AAP	Volvo B6LE	Wright Crusader	B28F	1997
2036	P239AAP	Volvo B6IE	Wright Crusader	B28F	1997
2038	R514KNJ	Volvo B6LE-53	Wright Crusader 2	B28F	1998
2040	P373DSA	Volvo B6BLE-53	Alexander ALX200	DP36F	1997
2041	P366DSA	Volvo B6BLE-53	Alexander ALX200	DP36F	1997
2042	P367DSA	Volvo B6BLE-53	Alexander ALX200	DP36F	1997
2043	P368DSA	Volvo B6BLE-53	Alexander ALX200	DP36F	1997
2044	P369DSA	Volvo B6BLE-53	Alexander ALX200	DP36F	1997
2045	P371DSA	Volvo B6BLE-53	Alexander ALX200	DP36F	1997
2046	P372DSA	Volvo B6BLE-53	Alexander ALX200	DP36F	1997
2047	P374DSA	Volvo B6BLE-53	Alexander ALX200	DP36F	1997
2048	P375DSA	Volvo B6BLE-53	Alexander ALX200	DP36F	1997
2049	P378DSA	Volvo B6BLE-53	Alexander ALX200	DP36F	1997
2050	P380DSA	Volvo B6BLE-53	Alexander ALX200	DP36F	1997
2051	P382DSA	Volvo B6BLE-53	Alexander ALX200	DP36F	1997
2052	P384DSA	Volvo B6BLE-53	Alexander ALX200	DP36F	1997
3001	A703UOE w	MCW MetroBus 2 DR102/27	MCW	H43/30F	1983
3004	B806AOP	MCW MetroBus 2 DR102/27	MCW	H43/30F	1984
3006	C612LFT	Leyland Olympian ONLXB/1R	Alexander RV	H45/31F	1986
3010	D954NDA w	MCW MetroBus 2 DR102/59	MCW	H43/30F	1986
3011	E326BVO	Volvo B10M-50	East Lancs	H47/38D	1988
3013	* M271JGB	Volvo Olympian YN2RC16Z4	Alexander RH	H47/27D	1995
3014	* M274JGB	Volvo Olympian YN2RC16Z4	Alexander RH	H47/31F	1995
3015	* M275JGB	Volvo Olympian YN2RC16Z4	Alexander RH	H47/31F	1995
3016	* M277JGB	Volvo Olynpian YN2RC16Z4	Alexander RH	H47/27D	1985
3017	* M345JGB	Volvo Olympian YN2RC16Z4	Alexander RH	H47/27D	1995
3018	* M346JGB	Volvo Olympian YN2RC16Z4	Alexander RH	H47/28D	1995
3019	* N731RGD	Volvo Olympian YN2RC16Z4	Alexander RH	H47/27D	1995
3021	* N732RGD	Volvo Olympian YN2RC16Z4	Alexander RH	H47/27D	1996
3023	* NUI1247	Leyland Olympian ONTL11/2R	Eastern Coach Works	H51/35F	1984
3024	POG477Y w	MCW MetroBus 2 DR102/27	MCW	H43/30F	1982
3025	C462SSO	Leyland Olympian ONLXB/1RV	Alexander RL	CH43/27F	1989
3026	C650LFT	Leyland Olympian OLXB/1R	Alexander RH	H45/31F	1989
3027	B858AOP	MCW MetroBus 2 DR102/27	MCW	H43/30F	1985
3028	* M381JGB	Volvo Olympian YN2RC16Z4	Alexander RH	H47/27D	1996
3029	* M258JGB	Volvo Olympian YN2RC16Z4	Alexander RH	H47/27D	1996
3030	* N920RGD	Volvo Olympian YN2RC16Z4	Alexander RH	H47/27D	1996

McColls Coaches

Fleet	Reg		Chassis	Body	Layout	Year
3031	* N931RGD		Volvo Olympian YN2RC16Z4	Alexander RH	H47/27D	1996
3033	F46XOF		MCW MetroBus DR102/64	MCW	H43/30F	1989
3035	* M302JGB		Volvo Olympion YN2RV16V3	Alexander R	H42/27D	1995
3036	C647LFT		Leyland Olympian ONLXB/1R	Alexander RH	H45/31F	1986
3038	B183FFS	w	Volvo B10M-50	Alexander RV	H47/37F	1988
3039	G337KKW		Leyland Olympian ONLXB/2RZ	Alexander RL	CH51/31F	1989
3040 —	* T874TGD		Volvo Olympian	Alexander	H47/27D	1999
4001	* TXI4242		Volvo B12(T)	Jonckheere Deauville P599	C49FT	1997
4002	* MUD490		Volvo B10M-62	Jonckheere Mistral	C53F	1997
4003	* VAZ4918		Volvo B10M-62	Plaxton Premiere 350	C49F	1994
4004	* NIL8646		Volvo B10M-60	Plaxton Excalibur	C49FT	1992
4006	* L421ORS		Volvo B10M-62	Plaxton Premiere 320	C53F	1994
4007	* N905AAS		Volvo B10M-62	Plaxton Premiere 350	C48FT	1996
	98-D-20408	z	Volvo Olympian	Alexander	H47/27D	1998
	99-D-504	z	Volvo Olympian	Alexander	H47/28D	1999
	99-D-519	z	Volvo Olympian	Alexander	H47/28D	1999
	99-D-544	z	Volvo Olympian	Alexander	H47/28D	1999
	99-D-60017		Volvo 6BLE	Wright Crusader 2	B35F	1999
	A114WVP		MCW MetroBus 2 DR133/1	MCW	H43/30F	1984
	B184FFS		Volvo B10M-50	Alexander RV	H47/37F	1985
	B185FFS		Volvo B10M-50	Alexander RV	H47/37F	1985
	B774AOC		MCW MetroBus 2 DR102/27	MCW	H43/30F	1984
	B777AOC		MCW MetroBus 2 DR102/27	MCW	H43/30F	1984
	B848AOP		MCW MetroBus 2 DR102/27	MCW	H43/30F	1985
	* B852OSB	w	Dennis Dorchester SDA	Plaxton Paramount 3500 II	C55F	1985
	B853AOP	w	MCW MetroBus 2 DR102/27	MCW	H43/30F	1985
	B867DOM	w	MCW MetroBus 2 DR102/27	MCW	H43/30F	1985
	B884DOM	w	MCW MetroBus 2 DR102/27	MCW	H43/30F	1985
	C463SSO		Leyland Olympian ONLXB/1RV	Alexander RL	CH43/27F	1986
	C785SFS		Leyland Olympian ONTL11/2R	Eastern Coach Works	H51/32D	1986
	C786SFS		Leyland Olympian ONTL11/2R	Eastern Coach Works	H51/32D	1986
	D947NDA	w	MCW MetroBus 2 DR102/59	MCW	H43/30F	1986
	E987VUK		MCW MetroBus 2 DR102/64	MCW	H43/30F	1988
	G118KUB		Mercedes-Benz 811D	Optare StarRider	B26F	1989
	G285TSL		Mercedes-Benz 709D	Alexander Sprint	B25F	1990
	J24MCW		Volvo B10M-50	East Lancs	B45F	1992
	L405BBC	y	Mercedes-Benz 811D	Wadham Stringer	B31FL	1994
	* M396JGB		Volvo Olympian YN2RC16Z4	Alexander RH	H47/27D	1995
	* M937JGB		Volvo Olympian YN2RC16Z4	Alexander RH	H47/27D	1995
	P230AAP		Volvo B6LE	Wright Crusader	B28F	1997
	P243AAP		Volvo B6LE	Wright Crusader	B28F	1997
	P250AAP		Volvo B6LE	Wright Crusader	B28F	1997
	PO56PCZ		MAN 18.360	Marcopolo	C56FT	2007
	POG601Y	w	MCW MetroBus 2 DR102/27	MCW	H43/30F	1983
	R262XDA		Mercedes-Benz Vario O.814D	Alexander Sprint	B27F	1997
	R267XDA		Mercedes-Benz Vario O.814D	Alexander Sprint	B27F	1997
	R270XDA		Mercedes-Benz Vario O.814D	Alexander Sprint	B27F	1998
	* SIW9154		Volvo B6-45	Caetano	C34F	1993
	T505TOL		Volvo B6BLE-55	Wright Crusader 2	B31F	1999
	* TXI2251		Mercedes-Benz 811D	PMT	DP33F	1992

McCreadie Coaches
L McCreadie, 53 Motherwell Street, Airdrie ML6 7HU
Website
Depot   The Garage, Crowwood Road, Calderbank Road, Airdrie ML6 7HU
Licence PM1072020

FN02VBG —	Iveco EuroMidi CC80.E18	Indcar Maxim	C29F	2002
* JAZ3285	Volvo B10M-61	Plaxton Paramount 3500 III	C53F	1987
* KDZ6277	Volvo B10M-61	Van Hool Alizée	C53F	1988
* L637AYS	Volvo B10M-60	Van Hool Alizée	C53F	1994
* LCN36	Bova FHD12-340	Bova Futura	C49FT	1986
M629WBV	Optare MetroRider MR17	Optare	B29F	1995
* NIL3792 —	Volvo B10M-62	Van Hool Alizée	C55F	1996
R481GLG	Volvo B10M-62	Plaxton Excalibur	C49FT	1998
S369PGB	Mercedes-Benz Vario O.810D	Marshall Master	B27F	1998
* VAZ2534	Volvo B10M-60	Jonckheere	C49FT	1991
* W785BCF	Volvo B10M-62	Berkhof Axial 50	C49FT	2000
YN04LXS	Optare Solo M880	Optare	B29F	2004

McDades Coaches
McDade Travel Ltd, John Henry Road, Bothwell Park Industrial Estate, Uddingston G71 7EJ
Website
Depot   John Henry Road, Bothwell Park Industrial Estate, Uddingston G71 7EJ
Licence PM0002620

* 2396FH —	Volvo B10M-62	Van Hool Alizée	C44DTL	1997
A104OUG	Leyland Olympian ONLXB/1R	Northern Counties	H43/28F	1984
AEF228Y	Leyland Olympian ONLXB/1R	Eastern Coach Works	H45/32F	1983
BU51AYL	Mercedes-Benz 614D	Crest	C24FL	2001
CWR505Y	Leyland Olympian ONLXB/1R	Eastern Coach Works	H45/32F	1982
* EKS69X	Leyland Olympian ONLXB/1R	Eastern Coach Works	H45/32F	1982
F366WSC	Leyland Olympian ONCL10/2RZ	Alexander RH	H51/30D	1989
G345CSG	Leyland Olympian ONCL10/2RZ	Alexander RH	H51/30D	1989
G814GSX	Leyland Olympian ON2R56C13Z4	Alexander RH	H51/30D	1990
G826GSX	Leyland Olympian ON2R56C13Z4	Alexander RH	H51/30D	1990
G827GSX	Leyland Olympian ON2R56C13Z4	Alexander RH	H51/30D	1990
G833GSX	Leyland Olympian ON2R56C13Z4	Alexander RH	H51/30D	1990
G834GSX	Leyland Olympian ON2R56C13Z4	Alexander RH	H51/30D	1990
G835GSX	Leyland Olympian ON2R56C13Z4	Alexander RH	H51/30D	1990
J862TSC	Leyland Olympian ON2R56C13Z4	Alexander RH	H51/30D	1991
J869TSC	Leyland Olympian ON2R56C13Z4	Alexander RH	H51/30D	1991
J870TSC	Leyland Olympian ON2R56C13Z4	Alexander RH	H51/30D	1991
* JBZ4910	Leyland Tiger TRCTL11/3LZ	Wadham Stringer	B68F	1985
MX54PJU	Mercedes-Benz Sprinter 616CDI	Mellor	B22FL	2004
N78LGD	Mercedes-Benz 709D	Wadham Stringer	B16FL	1995
N79LGD	Mercedes-Benz 709D	Wadham Stringer	B16FL	1995
N81LGD	Mercedes-Benz 709D	Wadham Stringer	B16FL	1995
* N474PYS	Volvo B10M-62	Van Hool Alizée	C49FT	1995
N639LGG	Mercedes-Benz 709D	Wadham Stringer	B16FL	1995
N640LGG	Mercedes-Benz 709D	Wadham Stringer	B16FL	1995
N838LGA	Mercedes-Benz 709D	Wadham Stringer	B16FL	1995
N839LGA	Mercedes-Benz 709D	Wadham Stringer	B16FL	1995
N840LGA	Mercedes-Benz 709D	Wadham Stringer	B16FL	1995
N841LGA	Mercedes-Benz 709D	Wadham Stringer	B16FL	1995
N843LGA	Mercedes-Benz 709D	Wadham Stringer	B16FL	1995
N965LHS	Mercedes-Benz 709D	Wadham Stringer	B16FL	1995
OSN857Y	Volvo Ailsa B55-10	Northern Counties	H48/36F	1983
* P840HRM	Volvo B12BT	Jonckheere Deauville	C53FT	1996
SF55BKA	Mercedes-Benz Vario O.814D	Plaxton Welfare Beaver 2	DP29FL	2005
* SIL1075	Volvo B10M-62	Jonckheere Deauville	C46FT	1995
* SIL1598	Volvo B10M-62	Van Hool Alizée	C48FLT	1995

		McDade Coaches			
* SIL6715		Volvo B10M-61	Van Hool Alizée	C57F	1989
* SIL7566		Volvo B10M-62	Van Hool Alizée	C53F	1994
* T949BAK		Bova FLC 12.340	Bova Futura	C70F	1999
VEF151Y		Leyland Fleetline FE30AGR	Northern Counties	H43/31F	1982
VU06KEJ		Mercedes-Benz Vario O.814D	Plaxton Cheetah	C33F	2006
VU06KFG		Mercedes-Benz Vario O.814D	Plaxton Cheetah	C33F	2006
VX55FWN		Mercedes-Benz Vario O.814D	Plaxton Cheetah	B29FL	2005
VX57GYU		Mercedes-Benz Vario O.814D	Plaxton Cheetah	C33F	2007
YAJ154Y		Leyland Fleetline FE30AGR	Northern Counties	H43/31F	1982
YK04KWJ		Optare Solo M850	Optare	B17F	2004
YN09LMK		Mercedes-Benz O.813D	Plaxton Beaver	DP31FL	2009

McGills

Greenock & District, 20 Burns Drive, Highcliffe, Wemyss Bay PA18 6BY
McGills Bus Services Ltd, 99 Earnhill Road, Larkfield Industrial Estate, Greenock PA16 0EQ
Website
Depot   Bus Depot, 1 Muriel Street, Barrhead, Glasgow G78 1QB
    99 Earnhill Road, Larkfield Industrial Estate, Greenock PA16 0EQ
Licences PM1006849 (Greenock & District)
    PM0000015 (McGills Bus Service Ltd)

100	P526UGA		Mercedes-Benz 711D	Marshall C19	B29F	1996
101	N752LUS	w	Mercedes-Benz 709D	UVG CityStar	B29F	1996
102	N228MUS		Mercedes-Benz 709D	Marshall C19	B29F	1996
104	N256PGD		Mercedes-Benz 709D	Marshall C19	B29F	1996
105	N258PGD		Mercedes-Benz 709D	Marshall C19	B29F	1996
107	K491FFS		Mercedes-Benz 709D	Alexander (Belfast)	B29F	1993
109	L970VGE	w	Mercedes-Benz 709D	Alexander (Belfast)	B29F	1994
111	N990FNK	w	Mercedes-Benz 709D	Marshall C19	B27F	1995
112	N34GSX	w	Mercedes-Benz 709D	Alexander (Belfast)	B29F	1996
114	N991FNK		Mercedes-Benz 709D	Marshall C19	B27F	1995
116	X476XVG		Mercedes-Benz Vario O.814D	Plaxton Beaver 2	B31F	2001
117	X477XVG		Mercedes-Benz Vario O.814D	Plaxton Beaver 2	B31F	2001
118	V500CBC		Mercedes-Benz Vario O.814D	Plaxton Beaver 2	B31F	1999
119	V10CBC		Mercedes-Benz Vario O.814D	Plaxton Beaver 2	B31F	1999
120	N802PDS	w	Mercedes-Benz 709D	Marshall C19	B29F	1996
121	P527UGA	w	Mercedes-Benz 711D	Marshall C19	B29F	1996
122	* K85DTM	w	Mercedes-Benz 811D	Wright Nimbus	B33F	1993
124	N943MGG	w	Mercedes-Benz 709D	Marshall C19	B29F	1995
125	L641DNA	w	Mercedes-Benz 709D	Plaxton Beaver	B27F	1994
127	N779PDS	w	Mercedes-Benz 709D	Marshall C19	B29F	1996
128	M7JPT	w	Mercedes-Benz 709D	Marshall C19	B27F	1996
129	K580YOJ	w	Mercedes-Benz 811D	Wright Nimbus	B33F	1993
200	V110ESF		Mercedes-Benz Vario O.814d	Plaxton Beaver 2	B31F	1999
201	OA02RKA		Optare Solo M850	Optare	B26F	2002
210	YR52VEX		Scania L94UB	Wright Solar	B43F	2002
211	SK52HYP		Scania L94UB	Wright Solar	B43F	2002
220	RX06WPP		Volvo B7RLE	Wright Eclipse Urban	B55F	2006
221	RX06WPR		Volvo B7RLE	Wright Eclipse Urban	B55F	2006
223	DX03XEA		Volvo B7RLE	Wright Eclipse Urban	B44F	2003
224	DX03XEB		Volvo B7RLE	Wright Eclipse Urban	B44F	2003
225	DX03XEC		Volvo B7RLE	Wright Eclipse Urban	B44F	2003
226	SA02CCV		Volvo B7L	Wright Eclipse	B41F	2002
227	SA02CDF		Volvo B7L	Wright Eclipse	B41F	2002
228 —	BX03OVA		Volvo B7L	Wright Eclipse *tigmano*	B41F	2003
300 —	BX06UNP		Mercedes-Benz Citaro O.530	Mercedes-Benz	B42F	2006
301 —	BX06UNR		Mercedes-Benz Citaro O.530	Mercedes-Benz	B42F	2006
302	BX56VTK		Mercedes-Benz Citaro O.530	Mercedes-Benz	B42F	2006
303 —	BX56VTL		Mercedes-Benz Citaro O.530	Mercedes-Benz	B42F	2006

McGills

304	BV57JYG	Mercedes-Benz Citaro O.530	Mercedes-Benz	B42F	2007
305	BV57JYH	Mercedes-Benz Citaro O.530	Mercedes-Benz	B42F	2007
306	BV08ZWC	Mercedes-Benz Citaro O.530	Mercedes-Benz	B42F	2008
307	BV08ZWG	Mercedes-Benz Citaro O.530	Mercedes-Benz	B42F	2008
308	BV08ZWP	Mercedes-Benz Citaro O.530	Mercedes-Benz	B42F	2008
310	BU06HSV	Mercedes-Benz Citaro O.530	Mercedes-Benz	B42F	2006
400	SA52EXD	Dennis Dart 10.7 SLF	Plaxton Pointer 2	B37F	2002
401	SG52XMO	Dennis Dart 10.7 SLF	Plaxton Pointer 2	B37F	2002
402	SG52XMP	Dennis Dart 10.7 SLF	Plaxton Pointer 2	B37F	2002
403	SG52XMR	Dennis Dart 10.7 SLF	Plaxton Pointer 2	B37F	2002
404	SG52XMK	Dennis Dart 10.7 SLF	Plaxton Pointer 2	B37F	2002
405	SG52XML	Dennis Dart 10.7 SLF	Plaxton Pointer 2	B37F	2002
407	SN05HCX	Dennis Dart 10.7 SLF	Alexander ALX200	B37F	2005
408	SN05HCY	Dennis Dart 10.7 SLF	Alexander ALX200	B37F	2005
409	SN05HCZ	Dennis Dart 10.7 SLF	Alexander ALX200	B37F	2005
410	SN05HDA	Dennis Dart 10.7 SLF	Alexander ALX200	B37F	2005
411	T52JBA	Dennis Dart 10.7 SLF	Plaxton Pointer 2	B36F	1999
412	T53JBA	Dennis Dart 10.7 SLF	Plaxton Pointer 2	B36F	1999
413	* N501KCD	Dennis Dart 9.8 SDL	Marshall Dartline	B40F	1993
414	N502KCD	Dennis Dart 9.8 SDL	Marshall Dartline	B40F	1993
415	* N503KCD	Dennis Dart 9.8 SDL	Marshall Dartline	B40F	1993
417	N506KCD	Dennis Dart 9.8 SDL	Marshall Dartline	B40F	1993
418	N511KCD	Dennis Dart 9.8 SDL	Marshall Dartline	B40F	1993
419	N513KCD	Dennis Dart 9.8 SDL	Marshall Dartline	B40F	1993
420	N516KCD	Dennis Dart 9.8 SDL	Marshall Dartline	B40F	1993
422	N518KCD	Dennis Dart 9.8 SDL	Marshall Dartline	B40F	1993
423	N519KCD	Dennis Dart 9.8 SDL	Marshall Dartline	B40F	1993
424	M813GFT	Dennis Dart 9.8 SDL	Marshall Dartline	B40F	1994
425	N123WBR	Dennis Dart 9.8 SDL	Marshall Dartline	B40F	1996
426	M805GFT	Dennis Dart 9.8 SDL	Marshall Dartline	B40F	1994
427	M815GFT	Dennis Dart 9.8 SDL	Marshall Dartline	B40F	1994
428	M806GFT	Dennis Dart 9.8 SDL	Marshall Dartline	B40F	1994
429	M807GFT	Dennis Dart 9.8 SDL	Marshall Dartline	B40F	1994
430	M818GFT	Dennis Dart 9.8 SDL	Marshall Dartline	B40F	1994
431	M812GFT	Dennis Dart 9.8 SDL	Marshall Dartline	B40F	1994
432	N119WBR	Dennis Dart 9.8 SDL	Marshall Dartline	B40F	1996
433	N122WBR	Dennis Dart 9.8 SDL	Marshall Dartline	B40F	1996
434	L910JRN	Dennis Dart 9.5SDL	East Lancs EL2000	B34F	1994
435	W814UAG	Dennis Dart 8.8 SLF	Plaxton Mini Pointer	B29F	2000
436	W815UAG	Dennis Dart 8.8 SLF	Plaxton Mini Pointer	B29F	2000
437	W816UAG	Dennis Dart 10.7 SLF	Plaxton Pointer 2	B39F	2000
438	W991XDM	Dennis Dart 8.8 SLF	Plaxton Mini Pointer	B29F	2000
439	Y489PTU	Dennis Dart 8.8 SLF	Plaxton Mini Pointer	B39F	2001
440	AA0BUS	TransBus Dart 8.8 SLF	TransBus Mini Pointer	B25F	2002
441	AA52BUS	TransBus Dart 8.8 SLF	TransBus Mini Pointer	B25F	2003
442	SF53KUK	TransBus Dart 10.7 SLF	TransBus Pointer 2	B37F	2003
443	SF53KUN	TransBus Dart 10.7 SLF	TransBus Pointer 2	B37F	2003
444	SN57DXL	ADL Enviro Dart 10.7 SLF	ADL Enviro 200	B37F	2007
445	SN57DXM	ADL Enviro Dart 10.7 SLF	ADL Enviro 200	B37F	2007
446	SF04RHK	TransBus Dart 10.7 SLF	TransBus Pointer 2	B37F	2004
447	SN51SXD	Dennis Dart 8.8 SLF	Alexander ALX200	B29F	2001
450	SN51SXP	Dennis Dart 8.8 SLF	Alexander ALX200	B29F	2001
451	SN51SXR	Dennis Dart 8.8 SLF	Alexander ALX200	B29F	2001
452	SN51SXS	Dennis Dart 8.8 SLF	Alexander ALX200	B29F	2001
453	SN51SXT	Dennis Dart 8.8 SLF	Alexander ALX200	B29F	2001
454	SN51SXW	Dennis Dart 8.8 SLF	Alexander ALX200	B29F	2001
455	SN09CGY	ADL Enviro 300 12 SLF	ADL Enviro 300	B45F	2009
456	SN09CGZ	ADL Enviro 300 12 SLF	ADL Enviro 300	B45F	2009
457	* X23SPT	Dennis Dart 10.7 SLF	Caetano Nimbus	B26D	2001

McGills					

458	* X23OUR	Dennis Dart 10.7 SLF	Caetano Nimbus	B26D	2001
459	* X23SLF	Dennis Dart 10.7 SLF	Caetano Nimbus	B26D	2001
460 —	* X23BUS	Dennis Dart 10.7 SLF	Caetano Nimbus	B26D	2001
461 —	* X22BUS	Dennis Dart 10.7 SLF	Caetano Nimbus	B26D	2001
462	* X23MCG	Dennis Dart 10.7 SLF	Caetano Nimbus	B26D	2001
463	* X23TOP	Dennis Dart 10.7 SLF	Caetano Nimbus	B26D	2001
464	* X23MGL	Dennis Dart 10.7 SLF	Caetano Nimbus	B26D	2001
466	SF05LFU	Dennis Dart 10.1 SLF	Alexander ALX200	B34F	2005
467	SF05LFV	Dennis Dart 10.1 SLF	Alexander ALX200	B34F	2005
468	SF05LFW	Dennis Dart 10.1 SLF	Alexander ALX200	B34F	2005
500	SF53KGE	DAF DE12BSSB120	Wright Cadet	B39F	2003
501 —	SF53KGG	DAF DE12BSSB120	Wright Cadet	B39F	2003
502 —	SF53KGJ	DAF DE12BSSB120	Wright Cadet	B39F	2003
503 —	SF53KGK	DAF DE12BSSB120	Wright Cadet	B39F	2005
504 —	SF53JXJ	DAF DE12BSSB120	Wright Cadet	B39F	2003
505 —	SF53JXK	DAF DE12BSSB120	Wright Cadet	B39F	2003
506 —	SF53JXL	DAF DE12BSSB120	Wright Cadet	B39F	2003
507 —	SF53JXM	DAF DE12BSSB120	Wright Cadet	B39F	2003
508	GX04LWR	DAF DE12BSSB120	Wright Cadet	B39F	2004
509	GX04LWS	DAF DE12BSSB120	Wright Cadet	B39F	2004
510	GX04LWT	DAF DE12BSSB120	Wright Cadet	B39F	2004
511	GX04LWU	DAF DE12BSSB120	Wright Cadet	B39F	2004
512	GX04LWV	DAF DE12BSSB120	Wright Cadet	B39F	2004
513	GX04LWW	DAF DE12BSSB120	Wright Cadet	B39F	2004
600 —	T517EUB	Volvo B10M-62	Plaxton Premiere 350	C46FT	1999
601	T520EUB	Volvo B10M-62	Plaxton Premiere 350	C46FT	1999
602	* T401JSL	Volvo B10M-62	Van Hool Alizée	C53F	1999
603	W600SOU	Volvo B10M-62	Van Hool Alizée	C51FT	2000
604 —	T534EUB	Volvo B10M-62	Plaxton Premiere 350	C48FT	1999
605	* TIW4227	Volvo B10M-62	Jonckheere Mistral	C49FT	2001
701	GM04GSM	Bova FHD12-340	Bova Futura	B39F	2004
702 —	* SM04GSM	Bova FHD12-340	Bova Futura	B39F	2004
900	* X7DCR	Volvo B7TL	Plaxton President	H43/24D	2001
901 —	* X7DKR	Volvo B7TL	Plaxton President	H43/24D	2001
	BU06CTE	Mercedes-Benz O.530D	Mercedes-Benz	B42F	2006
	* RX06WPT	Volvo B7RLE	Wright Eclipse Urban	B55F	2006
	SF03AUC	Bova FHD12-340	Bova Futura	C49FT	2003
	SF05HPJ	Dennis Dart 10.7 SLF	Alexander ALX200	B37F	2005
	SF05LFT	Dennis Dart 10.1 SLF	Alexander ALX200	B34F	2005
	SN51SXC	Dennis Dart 8.8 SLF	Alexander ALX200	B29F	2001
	SN59BAA	ADL Enviro 300 12 SLF	ADL Enviro 300	B45F	2009
	SN59BBE	ADL Enviro 300 12 SLF	ADL Enviro 300	B45F	2009

McKendry Coaches

A McKendry, 100 Straiton Road, Straiton, Loanhead EH20 9NP
Website www.mckendrycoaches.co.uk
Depot Ramsay Colliery, Engine Road, Loanhead EH20 9RF
Licence PM1032735

*	A4JYT	Volvo B10M-62	Plaxton Excalibur	C49FT	1998
	C3BCP	Volvo B7R	Plaxton Premiere 320	C53F	2002
	F489GGG	Ford Transit	Williams Deansgate	M15	1988
*	G973KTX	Volvo B10M-60	Plaxton Paramount 3500 III	C48FT	1990
*	HIL8441 —	Volvo B10M-61	Jonckheere Jubilee P599	C51FT	1988
	K544RJX	DAF SB3000DKVF601	Van Hool Alizée	C53F	1993
*	LCZ1890	r Scania K93CRB	Van Hool Alizée	C53F	1990
	M358LFX	Scania K113CRB	Van Hool Alizée	C49FT	1995
	N121RJF —	Volvo B10M-62 —	Plaxton Premiere 350	C53F	1996
	N554SJF —	Volvo B10M-62 —	Jonckheere Mistral	C53F	1996

		McKendry Coaches		

N800SAS	Mercedes-Benz 814D	Autobus Classique	C28F	1996
OFV21X	Leyland Olympian ONLXB/1R	Eastern Coach Works	H45/32F	1981
R598EAB	Scania K113CRB	Van Hool Alizée	C57F	1998
SW52FCF	Ford Transit	Ford	M16	2003
TJT196X r	Leyland Olympian ONLXB/1R	Leyland Olympian	H47/31F	1982
W272MKY	Scania L94IB4	Irizar InterCentury	C49FT	2000
Y737KSC	Mercedes-Benz Vario O.814D		C24F	2001
* YEZ2366	Volvo B10M-62	Plaxton Premiere 350	C46FT	1999
* YEZ2427	Volvo B10M-62	Plaxton Premiere 350	C53F	1996
* YEZ2486	Volvo B10M-62	Caetano Algarve II	C48FT	1997
* YEZ2505	Volvo B10M-62	Jonckheere Mistral	C53F	1996
* YEZ3754 *	Volvo B10M-60	Caetano Algarve II	C49FT	1993
* YEZ5539	Dennis Javelin 12SDA	Marcopolo Explorer	C69F	1996

McKechnie of Bathgate
McKechnie of Bathgate Ltd, 2 Easton Road, Bathgate EH48 2QG
Website
Depot 2 Easton Road, Bathgate EH48 2QG
Licence PM0002290

K505WNR	Volvo B10M-60	Plaxton Premiere 350	C51FT	1992
L21LSG	Mercedes-Benz 410D	Onyx	M16	1993
N102XNU	LDV 400	LDV	M16L	1995
* NIL3296	Volvo B10M-62	Plaxton Premiere 350	C50F	1994
* RIB8847	Mercedes-Benz 711D	Devon Conversions	C24F	1991
* RIB8848	Leyland Tiger TRCTL11/3R	Duple	C55F	1988
S679ASX	Mercedes-Benz Vario O.814D	Plaxton Cheetah	C F	1998
SJ03AVG	Mercedes-Benz 413CDI	Essbee	M16	2003
* T469BCN	Optare Solo M850	Optare	B28F	1999
* VIA230	Volvo B10M-61	Plaxton Paramount 3500 I	C53F	1983
* VJI5885	Volvo B10M-61	Jonckheere	C51FT	1987

MCT
MCT Group Travel Ltd, Nethan Street Depot, Nethan Street, Motherwell ML1 3TF
Website www.mctgrouptravel.com
Depot Nethan Street Depot, Nethan Street, Motherwell ML1 3TF
Licence PM0001645

DH55MCT	Mercedes-Benz Atego 1223L	Unvi Cimo	C39FL	2005
J17BUS	Volvo B10M-55	Duple 300	B53F	1992
* M1MCT	Volvo B12M	Jonckheere Mistral	C53F	2002
* M10MCT	Volvo B12M	Plaxton Paragon	C49FT	2002
M868FSU	MAN 11.190	Optare Vecta	B42F	1995
N608OGE	MAN 11.190	Optare Vecta	B42F	1996
* P1MCT	Volvo B12M	Jonckheere Mistral	C53F	2004
* P9MCT	Volvo B12M	Jonckheere Mistral	C49FT	2004
* P10MCT	Volvo B12M	Plaxton Paragon	C49FT	2002
P995RHS	MAN 11.190	Optare Vecta	B42F	1996
* S10MCT	Toyota Coaster BB50R	Caetano Optimo	C21F	2008
* SIA637	Renault Master		M8L	2000
* T10MCT	Iveco Daily 65C15	Unvi	C FL	2009
T20MCT	Toyota Coaster BB50R	Caetano Optimo	C16FL	1999
T347AGR	Toyota Coaster BB50R	Caetano Optimo	C24FL	1999
T710SUT	Toyota Coaster BB50R	Caetano Optimo	C24FL	1999

Mearns Exclusive Travel
Mearns Exclusive Travel Ltd, Unit 23 Coalvilles Park, East Kilbride, Glasgow G75 0GZ
Website   www.mearnsexclusivetravel.co.uk
Depot   Unit 23 Coalvilles Park, East Kilbride, Glasgow G75 0GZ
Licence   PM1084800

MX10DEU	Neoplan N2213	Neoplan Tourliner	C62F	2010
MX59BLV	MAN 18.360	Noge	C53F	2009
SF08HHC	Bova HD122-340XF	Bova Magiq	C49FT	2008
SF09JWE	Bova FHD127-365	Bova Futura	C53FT	2009
SN08HUH	Mercedes-Benz Atego 1022L	Unvi Cimo	C35F	2008
SN08HUV	Mercedes-Benz 515CDI	Killbeggan Vehicle Converters	M16	2008
SN10CXH	Scania K340EB4	Irizar Century	C F	2010
SN59CZR	Scania K340EB4	Irizar Century	C FT	2009
YN05GYZ	Scania K114EB4	Irizar Century	C49FT	2005

Millers Coaches
Millers Coaches Scotland Ltd, Faskine Brae, Sykeside Road, Airdrie ML6 9RQ
Website
Depot   Faskine Brae, Sykeside Road, Airdrie ML9 HR
Licence   PM1033473

*	837XHW	Volvo B10M-61	Van Hool Alizée	C53F	1987
	B238ANK	Volvo B10M-61	Van Hool Alizée	C57F	1985
	F725USF	Mercedes-Benz 811D	Alexander AM	C33F	1989
	G94VFP	Volvo B10M-60	Van Hool Alizée	C53F	1989
*	G999SJR	Volvo B10M-60	Van Hool Alizée	C53F	1989
*	HIL6462	Volvo B10M-61	Van Hool Alizée	C48FT	1984
	J235NNC	Volvo B10M-61	Van Hool Alizée	C49FT	1992
*	LUI5800	Mercedes-Benz 811D	Autobus Classique	C33F	1992
	M363KVR	Mercedes-Benz 709D	Alexander Sprint	B27F	1995
*	MIL5016	Volvo B10M-60	Van Hool Alizée	C51FT	1989
	P612RGB	Mercedes-Benz 609D	Adamson	C24F	1996
	P756HHF	Mercedes-Benz 711d	Onyx	C24F	1996
	T331BNL	Mercedes-Benz 614D	Crest	C24F	1999
*	XIL9007	Mercedes-Benz 811D	Wright NimBus	B33F	1992

Milligan's Coach Holidays
Milligan Coach Travel Ltd, Loan Garage, Mauchline KA5 6AN
Website   www.milliganscoachtravel.co.uk
Depot   Loan Garage, Mauchline KA5 6AN
Licence   PM1019379

	BM10WSM	Van Hool T915	Van Hool Astron	C51F	2010
	CU04EOW	Ford Transit	Ford	M16	2004
*	F935ENV	Bova FHD12.290	Bova Futura	C70F	1989
*	L586JSA	Volvo B10M-60	Plaxton Premiere 320	C53F	1993
*	MAZ6509	Duple 425SDA	Duple 300	C53FT	1987
*	MIL1846	Volvo B10M-61	Van Hool Alizée	c70f	1988
*	MIL1920	Volvo B10M-60	Plaxton Paramount 3500 III	C70F	1991
*	MIL2410	Scania K113CRB	Van Hool Alizée	C49FT	1995
*	MIL2515	Volvo B10M-60	Plaxton Paramount 3500 III	C70F	1991
*	MIL 2979	Volvo B10M-62	Van Hool Alizée	C53F	1994
*	MIL3218	Scania K124IB4	Irizar Century	C49FT	1999
*	MIL3606	Volvo B10M-60	Caetano Optimo	C53F	1995
*	MIL4314	Volvo B10M-60	Plaxton Paramount 3500 II	C53F	1991
*	MIL5830	Bova FHD12-340	Bova Futura	C49F	2003
*	MIL7795	Volvo B10M-60	Plaxton Paramount 3200 III	C53F	1993
*	MIL8028	Bova FHD12-340	Bova Futura	C49F	2004
*	MIL9145	Leyland Tiger TRCTL11/3RZ	Plaxton Paramount 3200 II	C70F	1986

Milligans Coach Holidays				
MX10DDK	Neoplan N400X SHD	Neoplan Tourliner	C49FT	2010
SN09FFD	Scania K340EB4	Lahden	C51FT	2009
SN09FFE	Scania K340EB4	Lahden	C51FT	2009
YM08MPU	Scania K340EB4	Irizar	C49FT	2008

M-Line International Coaches
M-Line International Coaches Ltd, The Coach House, Kelliebank, Alloa FK10 1NT
Website www.m-line.co.uk
Depot The Coach House, Kelliebank, Alloa FK10 1NT
Licence PM1036322

	AC03HGF	LDV Convoy	LDV	M16	2003
	AM02PXO	LDV Convoy	LDV	M16	2002
	BU04UTF	Mercedes-Benz Touro 1836RL	Mercedes-Benz	C49FT	2004
	BU52LAS	Iveco Euro Rider 391E 12.35	Beulas Stergo E	C51FT	2003
	E225WBG	Leyland Olympian ONCL10/1RZ	Alexander RH	H45/30F	1988
*	F854LTU	Volvo B10M-60	Plaxton Premiere 350	C53F	1989
	G879TVS	Scania N113DRB	Alexander RH	H47/33F	1990
	G970KTX	Volvo B10M-62	Plaxton Paramount 3500 III	C53F	1990
*	GIL6540	Volvo B10M-60	Plaxton Excalibur	C49FT	1994
*	IJI336	Neoplan N122/3	Neoplan Skyliner	CH57/20CT	1988
	J818HMC	Scania N113DRB	Alexander RH	H47/31F	1991
*	K987SUS	Dennis Javelin 12SDA	Wadham Stringer Vanguard II	C70F	1992
	L975MSC	Volvo Olympian YN2R16Z4	Alexander RH	H51/30D	1994
	L976MSC	Volvo Olympian YN2R16Z4	Alexander RH	H51/30D	1994
	L977MSC	Volvo Olympian YN2R16Z4	Alexander RH	H51/30D	1994
	L978MSC	Volvo Olympian YN2R16Z4	Alexander RH	H51/30D	1994
*	MIL5575	Volvo B10M-61	Plaxton Paramount 3500 III	C53F	1987
	MTU118Y	Leyland Olympian ONLXB/1R	Eastern Coach Works	H45/32F	1983
*	NIL3416	Volvo B10M-61	Van Hool Alizée	C51F	1985
	OFS676Y	Leyland Olympian ONTL11/2R	Eastern Coach Works	H50/31D	1982
	S7CED	Setra S250	Setra Special	C49FT	1998
*	S55ECH	Iveco Euro Rider 391E 12.35	Beulas Stergo E	C49FT	1998
	SH03XBE x	Ford Transit	Ford	M14	2003
*	SJI8112	Scania K112CRB	Jonckheere Jubilee P50	C47FT	1988
	T34JBA	Mercedes-Benz Vario O.814D	Plaxton Beaver 2	B31F	1999

Moffat & Williamson
Moffat & Williamson Ltd, Old Railway Yard, St Fort, Wormit, Newport-on-Tay DD6 8RG
Website www.moffat-williamson.co.uk
Depot Old Railway Yard, St Fort, Wormit, Newport-on-Tay DD6 8RG
Boston Road, Glenrothes KY6 2RE
Licence PM0001027

*	121ASV	Volvo B10M-62	Plaxton Panther	C53F	2000
	AB04MTB	Dennis R	Plaxton Paragon	C70F	2004
*	BSK790	Volvo B10M-46	Plaxton Paramount 3200 III	C43F	1992
	EB54MTB	Dennis R	Plaxton Paragon	C70F	2004
*	FSU375	Dennis Javelin 12SFD	Plaxton Premiere 320	C70F	1999
*	FSU394	Mercedes-Benz 412CD	Onyx	M16	1998
	MK02VFM	Volvo B7R	Plaxton Premiere 320	C70F	2002
	MW08DCW	Volvo B12B	Plaxton Panther	C52FT	2008
	MW08JPW	Volvo B12B	Plaxton Panther	C49FTL	2008
	MW08LEW	Volvo B12B	Plaxton Panther	C53F	2008
	MW10JFR	Volvo B9R	Plaxton Elite	C49FT	2010
	MW58HGW	Volvo B7R	Plaxton President	C70F	2008
	MW59JAV	ADL Dennis Javelin 12SFD	Plaxton Profile	C70F	2009
	MX06ACZ	Optare Solo M880	Optare	B25F	2006
	MX06ADO	Optare Solo M880	Optare	B25F	2006

MX54KYG	Optare Solo M920	Optare	B31F	2004
MX55XKK	ADL Enviro Dart 8.8 SLF	ADL Enviro 200	B29F	2005
MX58KZN	Optare Versa V1100	Optare	B38F	2008
* N86FHL	Dennis Javelin 10SDA	Wadham Stringer	C49F	1996
* P451LSR	Dennis Javelin 12SFD	Wadham Stringer	C57F	1997
* P459LSR	Dennis Javelin 12SFD	Wadham Stringer	C57F	1996
* P492LSR	Dennis Javelin 12SFD	Wadham Stringer	C57F	1996
PK02PUO	Dennis R	Plaxton Paragon	C70F	2002
* PNB800W	Ford R1114	Plaxton Supreme	C53F	1981
* PR06PET	Volvo B7R	Plaxton Excalibur	C70FL	2006
* PY52PHN	Volvo B7R	Plaxton Profile	C70F	2003
* R687TTS	Dennis Javelin 12SFD	Plaxton Premiere 320	C69F	1998
R958FYS	Mercedes-Benz Vario O.810D	Plaxton Beaver 2	B31F	1998
S2HMC	Volvo B7R	Plaxton Premiere 320	C70F	1998
* S4DPC	Dennis Javelin 12SFD	Plaxton Premiere 320	C53F	1998
* SF06WDZ	Volvo B12M	Plaxton Panther	C53F	2006
SJ03FPW	Volvo B7R	Plaxton Profile	C70F	2003
SP54AHX	Mercedes-Benz Vario O.814D	Plaxton Beaver 2	B33F	2004
SP54FML	Volvo B7R	Plaxton Profile	C70F	2005
SP54FMM	Volvo B7R	Plaxton Profile	C70F	2005
SP55EEF	Mercedes-Benz Vario O.814D	Plaxton Cheetah	C33F	2005
SP59BSX	Optare Versa V1100	Optare	B38F	2009
SP59DCE	Optare Solo M950	Optare	B32F	2009
ST52GZN	Volvo B10M-62	Plaxton Panther	C53F	2003
T110JBC	Volvo B7R	Plaxton Premiere 320	C70F	1999
T206OWG	Dennis Javelin 12SFD	Plaxton Premiere 320	C70F	1999
X366GWH	Dennis Dart 10.7 SLF	East Lancs Spryte	B37F	2000
YK05CDE	Optare Solo M920	Optare	B31F	2005
YK05CDF	Optare Solo M920	Optare	B31F	2005
YN04HHR	Mercedes-Benz Vario O814D	Plaxton Cheetah	DP33F	2004
YN04WTG	Volvo B7R	TransBus Profile	C70F	2004
YN04WTT	Volvo B12M	Plaxton Paragon	C49FT	2004
YN04WTV	Volvo B12B	Plaxton Panther	C49FT	2004
YN05HVT	Volvo B12M	Plaxton Paragon	C53F	2005
* YN06MXR	Volvo B7R	Plaxton Profile	C57F	2006
YN06OPK	Volvo B12B	Plaxton Panther	C53FT	2006
YN06PDX	Volvo B12B	Plaxton Panther	C53FT	2006
YN07OPF	Volvo B12M	Plaxton Panther	C50FT	2007
YN07OPG	Volvo B12M	Plaxton Panther	C50FT	2007
YN10ABX	ADL Dennis Javelin 12SFD	Plaxton Profile	C57F	2010
YN10ABZ	ADL Dennis Javelin 12SFD	Plaxton Profile	C57F	2010
YN53VCD	Volvo B7R	TransBus Profile	C70F	2004
YN54WCM	Volvo B7R	Plaxton Profile	C57F	2004
YN56OSM	Volvo B7R	Plaxton Excalibur	C57F	2006
YN59GOX	Mercedes-Benz O.816D	Plaxton Cheetah	C33F	2009
* YO06TXF	VDL DE12BSSB120	Plaxton Centro	B39F	2006

John Morrow Coaches

J Morrow, Block 5, Unit 18, Albion Industrial Estate, Halley Street, Glasgow G13 4DJ
Website www.morrow-coaches.demon.co.uk
Depot Block 5, Unit 18, Albion Industrial Estate, Halley Street, Glasgow G13 4DL
Licence PM0000448

M756LAX	Volvo B10M-55	Alexander	DP48F	1995
MP51BUZ	Optare Solo M850	Optare	B27F	2001
P564PNE	Mercedes-Benz Vario O.814D	Plaxton Beaver 2	B27F	1997
R132LNR	Mercedes-Benz Vario O.814D	Plaxton Beaver 2	B27F	1997
R185OCW	Mercedes-Benz Vario O.814D	Plaxton Beaver 2	B27F	1998
R585HDS	Mercedes-Benz Vario O.810D	Plaxton Beaver 2	B29F	1998

John Morrow				
R716TRV —	Mercedes-Benz Vario O.814D	UVG CityStar	B31F	1997
S975CSG —	Mercedes-Benz Vario O.810D	Plaxton Beaver 2	B27F	1999
SF04LHU —	Optare Solo M850	Optare	B29F	2004
SJ54GDA —	Optare Solo M880	Optare	B28F	2004
SJ54GDE —	Optare Solo M880	Optare	B28F	2004
T341LGB	Mercedes-Benz Vario O.810D	Plaxton Beaver 2	B27F	1999
YC51HAO	Optare Solo M920	Optare	B34F	2001
YPJ207Y	Leyland Tiger TRCTL11/3R	East Lancs	B59F	1983

Munro's of Jedburgh

Munro's of Jedburgh Ltd, Oakvale Garage, Bongate, Jedburgh TD8 6DU
Website www.munrosofjedburgh.co.uk
Depot Oakvale Garage, Bongate, Jedburgh TD8 6DU
Licence PM1023941

46 —	N46FWU	Van Hool EOS E180Z	EOS	C53FT	1996
85 —	N85FWU	Van Hool EOS E180Z	EOS	C51FT	1996
101 —	AE06HBP	MAN 14.220	MCV Evolution	B43F	2006
102 —	AE06VPO	MAN 14.220	MCV Evolution	B43F	2006
103 —	AE06VPP	MAN 14.220	MCV Evolution	B43F	2006
104	AE06VPR	MAN 14.220	MCV Evolution	B43F	2006
105	AE06VPT	MAN 14.220	MCV Evolution	B43F	2006
106 —	AE06VPU	MAN 14.220	MCV Evolution	B43F	2006
107 —	AE06VPV	MAN 14.220	MCV Evolution	B43F	2006
163 —	R163GNW	DAF SB3000	Ikarus Blue Danube	C70F	1998
213	P213RWR	Van Hool EOS E180Z	EOS	C49FT	1997
403	SN57EWJ	Enterprise Bus Plasma EB03	Plaxton Primo	B28F	2007
404 —	SN57EXE	Enterprise Bus Plasma EB03	Plaxton Primo	B28F	2007
431 —	SF06ODS	Mercedes-Benz Vario O.814D	Plaxton Welfare Beaver 2	DP28FL	2006
432 —	T432EBD	Mercedes-Benz Vario O.814D	Plaxton Beaver 2	B29F	1999
435 —	T435EBD	Mercedes-Benz Vario O.814D	Plaxton Beaver 2	B29F	1999
469 —	SK51AYD	Dennis Dart 8.8 SLF	Plaxton Mini Pointer	B29F	2002
471	W562JVV	Dennis Dart 8.8 SLF	Plaxton Mini Pointer	B29F	2000
472 —	V246BNV	Dennis Dart 8.8 SLF	Plaxton Mini Pointer	B29F	2000
473 —	W362ABD	Dennis Dart 8.8 SLF	Plaxton Mini Pointer	B29F	2000
501 —	* YR03UMR	Optare Excel L1180	Optare	B41F	2004
502 —	YN53WZJ	Optare Excel L1180	Optare	B41F	2004
503 —	YO53OVA	Optare Excel L1180	Optare	B41F	2004
504 —	YO53OVB	Optare Excel L1180	Optare	B41F	2004
561 —	SN56AXW	ADL Enviro 300 12.5 SLF	ADL Enviro 300	B60F	2007
562 —	SN56AXX	ADL Enviro 300 12.5 SLF	ADL Enviro 300	B60F	2007
631	M631RCP	DAF SB3000WS601	Van Hool Alizée	C51FT	1995
662	N662KCW	Van Hool EOS E180Z	EOS	C49FT	1996
794	* T794TWX	DAF DE02GSSB220	Ikarus Citibus 481	B43F	1999
955 —	* K101UJR	Dennis Javelin 10SDA	Wadham Stringer Vanguard II	DP46F	1992
C5 —	MX03OCB	Mercedes-Benz Vario O.814D	Crest	DP20F	2003
D3	MX56FWE	Locomotors H0C12	Olympus	M16	2006
	CU03BHP	Mercedes-Benz Vario O.814D	Plaxton Beaver	B31F	2003
	* YIL5456	Van Hool EOS E180Z	EOS	C48FT	1999

NCP

National Car Parks Ltd, MSCP 1 Glasgow Airport, Abbotsinch, Paisley PA3 2ST
Website   www.ncp.co.uk
Depot   Aberdeen Airport, Dyce, Aberdeen AB21 7DU
              Scotparks, Eastfield Road, Edinburgh EH28 8NB
              Longstay Car Park, Gogar Burn Turnhouse Road, Edinburgh Airport EH12 9DN
              MSCP 1 Glasgow Airport, Abbotsinch, Paisley PA3 2ST
Licence   PM0002485

1022	BW05LGW	Mercedes-Benz O.530D	Mercedes-Benz	B33F	2005
1027	KX57OVC	Enterprise Bus Plasma EB03	Plaxton Primo	B25F	2007
1030	KX57OVA	Enterprise Bus Plasma EB03	Plaxton Primo	B25F	2007
1031	KX57OVB —	Enterprise Bus Plasma EB03	Plaxton Primo	B25F	2007
	AE06HBZ	MAN 14.220	MCV Evolution	B28D	2006
	AE06HCL	MAN 14.220	MCV Evolution	B28D	2006
	AE08KUH	MAN A66	MCV Evolution	B28F	2008
	AE56OUV	MAN 14.220	MCV Evolution	B28D	2007
	MX55WDT	Enterprise Bus Plasma EB03	Plaxton Primo	B28F	2006
	SF08UZJ	MAN 14.220	MCV Evolution	B28D	2008

M W Nicoll

M Nicoll Hirers(Laurencekirk) Ltd, Laurencekirk Business Park, Aberdeen Road, Laurencekirk AB30 1EY
Website   www.nicoll-coaches.co.uk
Depot   Laurencekirk Business Park, Aberdeen Road, Laurencekirk AB30 1EY
Licence   PM0000765
              PM1087582

	A4MWN	Mercedes-Benz Sprinter 413CDI	Killbeggan Vehicle Converters	M16	2004
*	A5MWN	Volvo B10M-61	Van Hool Alizée	C53F	1986
*	A12MWN	Volvo B10M-61	Van Hool Alizée	C53F	1986
*	A15MWN	Volvo B10M-61	Van Hool Alizée	C53F	1987
*	A19MWN —	Volvo B10M-60	Van Hool Alizée	C53F	1989
*	A20MWN	Volvo B10M-60	Van Hool Alizée	C53F	1991
	B220WEU	Leyland Tiger TRCTL1/3RH	Duple Laser	C51F	1988
*	E173FRA	Volvo B10M-61	Van Hool Alizée	C53F	1988
*	E996FRA	Volvo B10M-61	Van Hool Alizée	C53F	1988
	L65ORB	Mercedes-Benz 711D	Marshall	C29F	1994
*	M2CLL	Bova FHD12-340	Bova Futura	C49FT	1995
	M275TSB	Volvo B10M-62	Van Hool Alizée	C53F	1998
*	N2CLL	Bova FHD12-340	Bova Futura	C55F	1996
*	N3CLL	Volvo B10M-62	Van Hool Alizée	C53F	1998
	N10CLL	Mercedes-Benz 312D	Whitacres	M13	1998
*	N22CLL	Mercedes-Benz Sprinter 413CDI	Killbeggan Vehicle Converters	M16	2004
*	N33CLL	Mercedes-Benz Sprinter 413CDI	Killbeggan Vehicle Converters	M16	2004
*	P127FRS —	Toyota Coaster HZB50R	Caetano Optimo	C21F	1997
	RKZ8284	Mercedes-Benz O.815D	Unvi	C29F	2006
	S137JSO —	Mercedes-Benz Vario O.810D	Plaxton Beaver 2	C25F	1998
	SF04EMW	Mercedes-Benz Vario O.810D	TransBus Beaver 2	DP33F	2004
	SK02VCG	Mercedes-Benz Vario O.810D	Killbeggan Vehicle Converters	C24FL	2002
	SK02VCL	Mercedes-Benz Vario O.810D	Killbeggan Vehicle Converters	C24FL	2002
	SK52OCO	Mercedes-Benz Vario O.810D	Plaxton Beaver 2	C33F	2002
	SL52AFC	Mercedes-Benz Sprinter 413CDI	Killbeggan Vehicle Converters	M16	2002
	SL52AKN	Mercedes-Benz Sprinter 413CDI	Killbeggan Vehicle Converters	M16	2002
	SN51WYC	Mercedes-Benz 614D	Onyx	C24F	2002
	V501FSF	Mercedes-Benz 614D	Onyx	C24F	2000
	V502FSF	Mercedes-Benz 614D	Onyx	C24F	2000
	W343GSS	Ford Transit	Ford	M14	2000
	W462RSX	Mercedes-Benz Sprinter 413CDI	Onyx	M16	2000
	W463RSX	Mercedes-Benz Vario O.810D	Plaxton Beaver 2	DP33F	2000
	W464RSX	Mercedes-Benz 614D	Onyx	C24F	2000

A17MWN — Mercedes-Benz   Unvi   C29F

W959GSS	Ford Transit	Ford	M14	2000
W961GSS	Ford Transit	Ford	M8	2000
W962GSS	Ford Transit	Ford	M14	2000
X675USX	Mercedes-Benz Vario O.814D	Plaxton Cheetah	C33F	2000
YJ05WCT	Optare Solo M850	Optare	B34F	2005
YL02FKZ	Optare Solo M920	Optare	B29F	2002

Oban & District Buses

Oban & District Buses Ltd, Unit 2, GlengallanRoad, GlenshellachIndustrial Estate, Oban PA34 4HH
Website
Depot   Unit 2, GlengallanRoad, GlenshellachIndustrial Estate, Oban PA34 4HH
Licence   PM0001581

*	J10WCM	Dennis Dart 9.8 SFD	Plaxton Pointer	B43F	1997
*	J20WCM	Dennis Dart 9.8 SFD	Plaxton Pointer	B43F	1997
*	J30WCM	Dennis Dart 9.8 SFD	Plaxton Pointer	B43F	1997
*	J40WCM	Dennis Dart 9.8 SFD	Plaxton Pointer	B43F	1997
*	J50WCM	Dennis Dart 9.8 SFD	Plaxton Pointer	B43F	1997
*	J60WCM	Dennis Dart 9.8 SFD	Plaxton Pointer	B43F	1997
	J306BRM	Dennis Dart 9.8 SDL	Alexander Dash	B40F	1992
*	L300WCM	DAF DE33WSSB3000	Van Hool Alizée	C53F	1998
	M200WCM	DAF SB3000WS601	Van Hool Alizée	C53F	1995
	N400WCM	Mercedes-Benz Vario O.814D	Plaxton Beaver Coach	B33F	1996
	P204RUM	DAF DE2GSSB3000	Ikarus Citibus 480	B49F	1997
	R24GNW	DAF DE02GSSB220	Ikarus Citibus 480	B49F	1998
	R74GNW	DAF DE02GSSB220	Ikarus Citibus 480	B51F	1998
	R400WCM	Mercedes-Benz Vario O.814D	Plaxton Beaver Coach 2	C33F	1998
	S373PGB	LDV Convoy	Onyx	M16	1998
*	SA02CJO	Mercedes-Benz Vito 108CDI	Mercedes-Benz	M8	2002
	SN54FCF	Dennis Dart 10.1 SLF	Alexander ALX200	B39F	2004
*	SSU727	Mercedes-Benz Vario O.814D	Plaxton Cheetah	C33F	2004
*	W173CDN	Mercedes-Benz Vario O.814D	Alexander	B27F	2000
	W689XSB	Dennis Dart 10.7 SLF	Plaxton Pointer 2	B39F	2000
	YJ05PYT	VDL SB12BSSB120	Wright Cadet	B39F	2005
	YJ56JYC	VDL SB12BSSB120	Plaxton Centro	B40F	2007
	YJ56JYD	VDL SB12BSSB120	Plaxton Centro	B40F	2007
	YN08NXP	Enterprise Bus Plasma EB03	Plaxton Primo	B28F	2008

Order of Malta

Order of Malta Dial-a-Journey Ltd, 3 Cunningham Road, Springkerse Ind Estate, Stirling FK7 7SW
Website   www.dial-a-journey.org
Depot   3 Cunningham Road, Springkerse Ind Estate, Stirling FK7 7SW
Licence   PM0002570

	CE52TZW	Mercedes-Benz 413CDI	UVG	B16FL	2002
	FP53ESO	Iveco 65-10	Frank Guy	B24FL	2003
	GK53EBP	Volkswagen LT46	Stanford	M16L	2003
	GK53EBU	Volkswagen LT46	Stanford	M16L	2003
	KX10DVF	ADL Enviro 300 12.0 SLF	ADL Enviro 300	B45F	2010
	KX10DVG	ADL Enviro 300 12.0 SLF	ADL Enviro 300	B45F	2010
	KX10DVH	ADL Enviro 300 12.0 SLF	ADL Enviro 300	B45F	2010
	KX10DVJ	ADL Enviro 300 12.0 SLF	ADL Enviro 300	B45F	2010
	KX10DVM	ADL Enviro Dart 8.9 SLF	ADL Enviro 200	B29F	2010
	KX10DVN	ADL Enviro Dart 8.9 SLF	ADL Enviro 200	B29F	2010
	NJ08BHW	Mercedes-Benz 411CDI		M12L	2008
	NL58ZZK	Mercedes-Benz 411CDI	Bluebird	M12L	2008
	PE57KFU	Mercedes-Benz 313CDI		M12L	2007
*	R16DAB	Mercedes-Benz 511CDI		M16	2009

Order of Malta				
SN08EHE	Volkswagen Crafter		M14L	2008
W174MWF	Mercedes-Benz Vario O.814D	Mellor	B24FL	2000
WX05WXO	Mercedes-Benz 413CDI	UMV	B16FL	2005
Y329PNW	Mercedes-Benz 413CDI	UVG	DP16FL	2001

Park's of Hamilton

Park's of Hamilton, 14 Bothwell Road, Hamilton ML3 0AY

Website www.parksofhamilton.co.uk
Depots 14 Bothwell Road, Hamilton ML3 0AY
Forrest Street, Blantyre G72 0JP
Walkham Business Park, Burrington Way, Plymouth PL5 3LS
Licence PM0000133 (Parks of Hamilton Coach Hirers)
PM0000460 (Parks of Hamilton Townhead Garage)
PH1089775 (Parks of Hamilton Coach Hirers)

1RWM	Volvo B9R	Plaxton Elite	C53F	2010
2HAN	Volvo B9R	Plaxton Elite	C53F	2010
2HW	Volvo B12M	Jonckheere Mistral	C53F	2009
2RWM	Volvo B9R	Plaxton Elite	C53F	2010
2WR	Volvo B9R	Plaxton Elite	C53F	2010
3HWS	Volvo B9R	Plaxton Elite	C53F	2010
3RWM	Volvo B9R	Plaxton Elite	C53F	2010
12HM	Volvo B12M	Jonckheere Mistral	C57FTF	2010
15RWM	Volvo B12M	Jonckheere Mistral	C53F	2009
HSK641	Volvo B12B	Plaxton Panther	C54FT	2010
HSK642	Volvo B12M	Jonckheere Mistral	C53F	2008
HSK644	Volvo B12M	Jonckheere Mistral	C53F	2008
HSK645	Volvo B12M	Jonckheere Mistral	C53F	2008
HSK646	Volvo B12M	Jonckheere Mistral	C53F	2008
HSK647	Volvo B12B	Plaxton Panther	C54FLT	2010
HSK648	Volvo B12B	Plaxton Panther	C54FLT	2010
HSK649	Volvo B12B	Plaxton Panther	C54FLT	2010
HSK650	Volvo B12B	Plaxton Panther	C54FLT	2010
HSK651	Volvo B12M	Plaxton Panther	C49FTL	2008
HSK655	Volvo B12B	Plaxton Panther	C49FTL	2008
HSK656	Volvo B12B	Plaxton Panther	C49FTL	2008
KSK976	Volvo B12B(T)	Plaxton Panther	C65FTL	2008
KSK977	Volvo B12B(T)	Plaxton Panther	C65FTL	2008
KSK978	Volvo B12B(T)	Plaxton Panther	C65FTL	2008
* KSK979	Volvo B12B(T)	Plaxton Panther	C65FTL	2007
* KSK980	Volvo B12B(T)	Plaxton Panther	C65FTL	2007
* KSK985	Volvo B12B(T)	Berkhof Axial 100	CH65/18CT	2007
LSK444	Volvo B12M	Jonckheere Mistral	C57FT	2010
LSK483	Volvo B12M	Jonckheere Mistral	C53F	2010
* LSK495	Volvo B12M	Jonckheere Mistral	C49F	2008
* LSK496	Volvo B12M	Jonckheere Mistral	C49FT	2008
LSK498	Volvo B12M	Jonckheere Mistral	C53F	2009
LSK499	Volvo B12M	Jonckheere Mistral	C53F	2009
LSK500	Volvo B12M	Jonckheere Mistral	C53F	2009
LSK501	Volvo B12M	Jonckheere Mistral	C53F	2009
LSK502	Volvo B12M	Jonckheere Mistral	C53F	2009
LSK503	Volvo B12M	Jonckheere Mistral	C53F	2009
LSK505	Volvo B12M	Jonckheere Mistral	C53F	2009
* LSK507	Volvo B12B(T)	Plaxton Panther	C65FTL	2008
LSK510	Volvo B12M	Plaxton Panther	C65FLT	2009
LSK512	Volvo B12B(T)	Plaxton Panther	C65FTL	2008
LSK513	Volvo B12M	Plaxton Panther	C65FLT	2009
LSK555	Volvo B12M	Jonckheere Mistral	C57FT	2010
LSK614	Volvo B12M	Jonckheere Mistral	C53F	2010

LSK813	Volvo B12M	Jonckheere Mistral	C53F	2010
LSK820	Volvo B12M	Jonckheere Mistral	C53F	2010
LSK824	Volvo B12M	Jonckheere Mistral	C53F	2010
LSK844	Volvo B12M	Jonckheere Mistral	C53F	2010
LSK871	Volvo B12B(T)	Plaxton Panther	C65FTL	2007
LSK875	Volvo B12B(T)	Plaxton Panther	C65FTL	2007
LSK876	Volvo B12B(T)	Plaxton Panther	C65FTL	2007
LSK878	Volvo B12B(T)	Plaxton Panther	C65FTL	2007
LSK879	Volvo B12B(T)	Plaxton Panther	C65FTL	2007
LSK821	Volvo B12M	Jonckheere Mistral	C53F	2010
* SV08VUW	Volvo B12M	Jonckheere Mistral	C53F	2008
* SV08VVE	Volvo B12M	Jonckheere Mistral	C53F	2008
* SV08VVG	Volvo B12M	Jonckheere Mistral	C53F	2008
* SV08VVH	Volvo B12M	Jonckheere Mistral	C53F	2008

Passenger Travel Ltd
Passenger Travel Ltd, 1 Briar Gardens, Whitburn, Bathgate EH47 9LT
Website
Depot   5 Inchcross, Bathgate EH48 2HT
Licence   PM1060877

2	S618HGD	Mercedes-Benz Vario O.814D	Mellor	B29F	1998
4	P126HCH	Mercedes-Benz Vario O.814D	Alexander Sprint	B24F	1997
5	SA01BZP	Optare Solo M920	Optare	B30F	2002
7	L154YVK	Dennis Dart 9 SDL	Northern Counties Paladin	B35F	1994
9	R730EGD	Mercedes-benz O.810D	Plaxton Beaver	B27F	1997
11	VU52UEH	Dennis Dart 8.8 SLF	Plaxton Mini Pointer	B29F	2002
13	R110VLX	Marshall Minibus	Marshall Minibus	B26F	1998
16	R104VLX	Marshall Minibus	Marshall Minibus	B29F	1998
20	SH51MHV	Optare Solo M920	Optare	B30F	2002
	L132YVK	Dennis Dart 9 SDL	Northern Counties	B35F	1994
	P125HCH	Mercedes-Benz Vario O.814D	Alexander Sprint	B24F	1997
	R101VLX	Marshall Minibus	Marshall Minibus	B29F	1997
	R112VLX	Marshall Minibus	Marshall Minibus	B26F	1998
	S282NRB	Optare Solo M920	Optare	B33F	1998
	T37JBA	Mercedes-Benz Vario O.814D	Plaxton Beaver 2	B31F	1999
	T299BNN	Optare Solo M920	Optare	B33F	1999
	V277DRC	Optare Solo M920	Optare	B33F	1999
	VU52UEG	Dennis Dart 8.8 SLF	Plaxton Mini Pointer	B29F	2002

Peace
J D Peace & Co (Aberdeen) Ltd, Echt Garage, Echt, Westhill AB32 7AL
Website   www.peacescoaches.co.uk
Depot   Farepark, Echt, Westhill AB32 7AL
Licence   PM0001586

FJ04PXX	Bova FHD12.340	Bova Futura	C40FLT	2004
* LKU618	Volvo B10M-61	Van Hool Alizée	C50DTL	1987
* R27HNS	Bova FHD12-340	Bova Futura	C70F	1998
SF06NBY	Bova HD122-340XF	Bova Magiq	C49FT	2006
SF08JDO	Bova FHD127-365	Bova Futura	C55F	2008
SF52EBD	Ford Transit	Ford	M14	2002
SK06BZN	Mercedes-Benz Sprinter 413CDI	Killbeggan Vehicle Converters	M16	2006
SK52AUK	Mercedes-Benz Vario O.814D	Killbeggan Vehicle Converters	C24F	2002
SN06AVT	Mercedes-Benz Vario O.814D	Killbeggan Vehicle Converters	C24F	2006
WA04EWS	Bova FHD10-340	Bova Futura	C36FT	2004
Y768TSJ	Bova FHD12-370	Bova Futura	C49FT	2001
YN09HEJ	Mercedes-Benz O.816D	Unvi	C33F	2009

Photoflash
J & K Purdie, 16 James Street, Carluke ML8 4DE
Website www.photoflashcoaches.co.uk
Depot 16 James Street, Carluke ML8 4DE
Licence PM1009532

*	5287ENJ	Mercedes-Benz Vario O.814D	Plaxton Cheetah	C25F	2000
*	5692FM	Volvo B10M-60	Van Hool Alizée	C49F	1990
*	A17PHO	Ford Transit	Ford	M16	2005
*	EIG6554	Mercedes-Benz Sprinter 310CDI	Corporate Vehicle Conversions	M16	2000
*	LEZ3945	Ford Transit	Ford	M16	2004
*	LIL4398	Volvo B10M-61	Van Hool Alizée	C46FT	1982
	M31KAX	Mercedes-Benz 711D	Autobus Classique	C25F	1994
	ND53YFV	Ford Transit	Ford	M16	2004
*	P17PHO	Volvo B12M	Plaxton Paragon	C51FT	2003
	P484GEF	Mercedes-Benz Vario O.814D	Autobus Nouvelle	C29F	1997
*	RJI2162	Volvo B10M-61	Plaxton Paramount 3200 II	C57F	1985
*	RJI8711	Volvo B10M-62	Van Hool Alizée	C51FT	1995
	SK51VVW	Vauxhall Movano	Warner	M11	2001
*	SN53KYO	Mercedes-Benz Atego 1223L	Unvi Cimo	C37F	2004
*	SR02NRN	Volvo B10M-62	Van Hool Alizée	C49FT	2002
	TIL5416	Mercedes-Benz 814D	Autobus Classique	C29F	1993
*	VIL6685	Mercedes-Benz 609D	Made to Measure	C26F	1990
*	VIL6686	Volvo B10M-61	Van Hool Alizée	C53F	1986
	WBZ3465	Mercedes-Benz Vario O.814D	Onyx	C24F	1999
	YJ54EXH	Mercedes-Benz O.815D	Sitcar Beluga	C33F	2004

Prentice Coaches / Don Prentice
D R Prentice, 2D Hospital Road, Haddington EH41 3BH
R Prentice, Station Garage, 2D Hospital Road, Haddington EH41 3BH
Prentice Coaches Ltd, 2D Hospital Road, Haddington EH41 3BH
Website www.prenticeofhaddington.info
Depot 2D Hospital Road, Haddington EH41 3BH
Licence PM1089522 (Prentice Coaches)
PM1049377 (Don Prentice Coaches)
PM0003051 (Prentice Coaches)

*	B14PCH	TransBus Javelin 12.0 SFD	Transbus Profile	C57F	2003
	JSU550	Mercedes-Benz Vario O.814D	Plaxton Cheetah	C33F	2000
	MFS444P p	Bedford YRQ	Plaxton Supreme	C45F	1975
*	PH54PCH	Mercedes-Benz Vario O.814D	Killbeggan Vehicle Converters	C29F	2004
	SC02DPC	Mercedes-Benz Vario O.814D	Plaxton Cheetah	C33F	2002
	SC56DPC	Volvo B12M	Plaxton Paragon	C59FL	2006
	SC57DPC	Irisbus EuroRider 397E.12.31	Plaxton Paragon	C57F	2007
	SF55FVR	Mercedes-Benz Vario O.814D	Plaxton Cheetah	C33F	2006
	SH60PCH	Volvo B12B	Plaxton	C57F	2010
	SS06PCH	Mercedes-Benz Vario O.814D	Plaxton Cheetah	C33F	2006
	SS08PCH	Dennis Javelin 12SFD	Plaxton Profile	C70F	2008
	SS10PCH	Mercedes-Benz O.816D	Plaxton Cheetah	C33F	2010
	SS57PCH	Mercedes-Benz O.816D	Plaxton Cheetah	C33F	2007
*	WSU982	Dennis Javelin 12SFD	Plaxton Premiere 320	C70F	1999
*	Y10DPC	Mercedes-Benz Vario O.814D	Plaxton Beaver 2	DP33F	2001
*	YCX320	Mercedes-Benz Vario O.814D	Olympus	C24F	2002
	YN57OTV	Mercedes-Benz Vario O.813D	Plaxton Cheetah	DP31FL	2008
	YX08HGC	Mercedes-Benz Vario O.814D	Tawe	C24F	2008

Prentice Westwood

Prentice Westwood Ltd, Westwood, West Calder EH55 8PW
R J Prentice, Prentice Coaches, Westwood, West Calder EH55 8PW
Website www.prenticewestwoodcoaches.co.uk
Depot Westwood, West Calder EH55 8PW
Licence PM0002466 (Prentice Westwood)
PM0001825 (Westwood Coach & Commercials)

*	81CBK		Volvo B12BT	Jonckheere Monaco	CH57/14CT	2000
*	138ASV		Volvo B10M-60	Van Hool Alizée	C57F	1989
*	367NHA		DAF DE33WSSB3000	Van Hool Alizée	C48FT	1995
*	755ABL		Volvo B10M-62	Plaxton Premiere 350	C53FT	2000
*	828EWB		Volvo B10M-60	Caetano Algarve II	C49FT	1993
*	835BUS		Volvo B10M-62	Berkhof	C51FT	2001
	B758GSC	y	Leyland Olympian ONTL11/2R	Eastern Coach Works	H51/32D	1984
	B759GSC		Leyland Olympian ONTL11/2R	Eastern Coach Works	H51/32D	1984
	C772SFS	y	Leyland Olympian ONTL11/2R	Eastern Coach Works	H51/32D	1985
	C773SFS		Leyland Olympian ONTL11/2R	Eastern Coach Works	H51/32D	1985
	C774SFS		Leyland Olympian ONTL11/2R	Eastern Coach Works	H51/32D	1985
	C788SFS		Leyland Olympian ONTL11/2R	Eastern Coach Works	H51/32D	1985
*	DSU355		Mercedes-Benz Vario O.815D	Sitcar Beluga	C27F	2001
*	E775NVT	y	Volvo B10M-61	Plaxton Paramount 3200 III	C53F	1988
	F364WSC		Leyland Olympian ONCL10/2RZ	Alexander RH	H51/30D	1989
*	F523UVW		Volvo B10M-60	Plaxton Paramount 3200 III	C57F	1989
*	G326PEW		Volvo B10M-61	Plaxton Paramount 3500 III	C70F	1990
*	GHZ8752		Volvo B10M-62	Plaxton Premiere 350	C53F	1990
	H202LOM		Scania N113DRB	Alexander RH	H47/33F	1990
	H676GPF		Volvo B10M-50	East Lancs	H45/34F	1990
*	IUI2129		Neoplan N122/3	Neoplan Skyliner	CH57/22CT	1992
	J857TSC		Leyland Olympian ON2R56C13Z4	Alexander RH	H51/30D	1991
*	JBZ3675		Volvo B10M-60	Jonckheere Deauville	C51FT	1989
*	JHZ4804		Volvo B10m-62	Plaxton Excalibur	C49FT	1996
*	JSV440		Volvo B12B	Berkhof Axial 50	C49FT	2005
	KX09CGU		Volvo B12B	Plaxton Panther	C53F	2009
*	LSU689		Volvo B10M-62	Caetano Algarve II	C51FT	1995
	N504LUA		DAF SB3000	Ikarus Blue Danube 350	C53F	1996
*	NCH868		Bova FHD12.34	Bova Futura	C49FT	1999
*	NGH456		Volvo B10M-62	Jonckheere Mistral	C51FT	1996
*	NIL2266		Neoplan N122/3	Neoplan Skyliner	CH59/18CT	1987
*	OJU106		Volvo B10M-62	Plaxton Premiere 350	C49FT	1995
*	ONR314		Volvo B10M-62	Jonckheere Mistral	C49F	1998
*	OUJ969		MAN 24.350	Jonckheere Monaco	CH53/15FT	1999
*	OUR610		Mercedes-Benz Atego 1324L	Beulas	C39F	2008
	S268NRB		Optare Solo M920	Optare	B33F	1998
	SJ53CUU		Volvo B7R	TransBus Profile	C70F	2004
	SJ53CUV		Volvo B7R	TransBus Profile	C70F	2004
	SN06AEF		Volvo B12B	Berkhof Axial 50	C53F	2006
	SN06OWV		Mercedes-Benz O.815D	Unvi	C29F	2006
	SN08NWH		Bova FHD120.365	Bova Futura	C49FT	2008
	SN08NWJ		Bova FHD120.365	Bova Futura	C49FT	2008
	SN57EGV		Optare Solo M950SL	Optare	B33F	2007
	SN58JAU		Volvo B12B	Plaxton Panther	C53F	2008
	SN60AEB		Bova FHD127-365	Bova Futura	C53F	2010
*	TDZ1960		Volvo B10M-62	Plaxton Premiere 350	C53F	1994
*	USY858		Bova FHD12-340	Bova Futura	C57F	2005
*	VSV632		Volvo B10M-62	Plaxton Premiere 350	C53FT	2000
*	WNB604		Volvo B12BT	Van Hool Astrobel	CH57/14CT	1996
	YJ06YRG		Optare Solo M880	Optare	B28F	2006
	YJ56WTW		Optare Solo M880	Optare	B28F	2007
	YN07EAJ		MAN 18.360	Noge	C53F	2007

YN07EAY	MAN 18.360	Plaxton Panther	C53F	2007
YRR436	MAN 24.350	Jonckheere Monaco	CH53/15FT	1999
YSU572	Volvo B12B	Jonckheere	C51FT	2003
YSV125	Bova FHD12-340	Bova Futura	C49FT	2005
YSV607	Bova FHD12-340	Bova Futura	C49FT	2003
YSV608	Bova FHD12-340	Bova Futura	C49FT	2005
YSV618	Bova FHD12-340	Bova Futura	C55F	2004

Pride of the Clyde

Pride of the Clyde Coaches Ltd, 11 Dellingburn Street, Greenock PA15 4RN
Website www.prideoftheclyde.net
Depot 11 Dellingburn Street, Greenock PA15 4RN
Licence PM0000467

BU04EZZ	Mercedes-Benz Touro 1836RL	Mercedes-Benz	C49FT	2004
C3POC	Volvo B10M-62	Caetano Enigma	C51FT	2001
C8POC	Volvo B10M-62	Plaxton Premiere 350	C49F	1998
C9POC	Volvo B10M-62	Plaxton Premiere 350	C49FT	1995
C10POC	Volvo B10M-62	Van Hool Alizée	C53F	1996
C12POC	Volvo B10M-62	Van Hool Alizée	C50FT	2001
C14POC	Volvo B10M-62	Plaxton Premiere 350	C49FT	1998
KX07HDE	Volvo B12B	Plaxton Panther	C49FT	2007
M1PCV	Ayats A3E/BR1	Ayats Bravo	CH57/16DT	2001
MIL1053	DAF MB230LB615	Van Hool Alizée	C51FT	1988
R339RRA	Volvo B10M-50	East Lancs Pyoneer	CH47/35F	1997
R886YOM	LDV Convoy	LDV	M16	1998
SF06OKJ	Bova FHD12-340	Bova Futura	C49FT	2006
SF06PHK	Bova FHD13-340	Bova Futura	C49FT	2006
SF06PHN	Bova FHD13-340	Bova Futura	C49FT	2006
SF07DMO	Volvo B12B	Caetano Levante	C49FT	2007
SF07DMV	Volvo B12B	Caetano Levante	C49FT	2007
YR02ZKY	Dennis R	Plaxton Panther	C70F	2002
YX07EED	LDV Convoy	Olympus	M16	2007

Puma Coaches

A Morrin, 29 Don Drive, Paisley PA2 0AF
Website
Depot Bay 3, Block F, Westway Development, Porterfield Road, Renfrew PA4 8DJ
Licence PM0001915

G49TGW	Dennis Dart 8.5 SDL	Carlyle Dartline	B28F	1990
H71MOB	Dennis Dart 8.5 SDL	Carlyle Dartline	B28F	1990
K103OMW	Dennis Dart 8.5 SDL	Plaxton Pointer	B33F	1993
K122SRH	Dennis Dart 9 SDL	Plaxton Pointer	B34F	1993
KX08HMK	MAN 12.240	Plaxton Centro	B38F	2008
KX08HMO	MAN 12.240	Plaxton Centro	B38F	2008
L138VRH	Dennis Dart 9 SDL	Plaxton Pointer	B34F	1993
L304PSC	Volvo B10M-55	Alexander	B49F	1994
M134PKS	Volvo B10M-55	Alexander	B49F	1995
M804GFT	Dennis Dart 9.8 SDL	Marshall Dartline	B40F	1994
M809GFT	Dennis Dart 9.8 SDL	Marshall Dartline	B40F	1994
M811HCU	Dennis Dart 9.8 SDL	Plaxton Pointer	B40F	1994
M819GFT	Dennis Dart 9.8 SDL	Marshall Dartline	B40F	1994
N97ALS	Mercedes-Benz 709D	Alexander	DP25F	1996
N208GCS	Mercedes-Benz 709D	Wadham Stringer	B28FL	1995
N343KKH	Mercedes-Benz 709D	Alexander (Belfast)	B23F	1996
N468RVK	Mercedes-Benz 709D	Alexander Sprint	B23F	1996
N799FSD	Mercedes-Benz 709D	Wadham Stringer	B28FL	1995

		Puma Coaches			
N801FSD	Mercedes-Benz 709D	Wadham Stringer	B24FL	1995
NDZ3146	Dennis Dart 8.5 SDL	Wright Handybus	B29F	1993
* P349ASO	Mercedes-Benz 709D	Alexander	DP25F	1996
P612CMS	Mercedes-Benz 709D	Alexander (Belfast)	B23F	1996
T705TCS	LDV Convoy	LDV	M16	1999
T712TCS	LDV Convoy	LDV	M16	1999

Rabbies Trail Burners

Rabbies Trail Burners Ltd, 207 High Street, Edinburgh EH1 1PE

Website www.rabbies.com
Depot 207 High Street, Edinburgh EH1 1PE
21A Graham Street, Edinburgh EH1 1PE
Bangor Road, Edinburgh EH6 5JU
Licence PM0002523

5	SN07FVO	Mercedes-Benz 515CDi	Killbeggan Vehicle Converters	M16	2007
10	SN05LFD	Mercedes-Benz 413CDi	Killbeggan Vehicle Converters	M16	2005
12	SN08GJK	Mercedes-Benz 515CDi	Killbeggan Vehicle Converters	M16	2008
17	SN08GXD	Mercedes-Benz 515CDi	Killbeggan Vehicle Converters	M16	2008
18	SN08GYG	Mercedes-Benz 515CDi	Killbeggan Vehicle Converters	C16F	2008
19	YN09EZG	Mercedes-Benz 515CDi	Killbeggan Vehicle Converters	M16	2009
20	YN09EZH	Mercedes-Benz 515CDi	Killbeggan Vehicle Converters	M16	2009
21	RO10ZRV	Mercedes-Benz 516CDI	EVM	M16	2010
22	RO10ZRX	Mercedes-Benz 516CDI	EVM	M16	2010
23	RE10PFG	Mercedes-Benz 516CDI	EVM	M16	2010
	SK07LMF	Mercedes-Benz 515CDi	Killbeggan Vehicle Converters	M16	2007
	SN08GJJ	Mercedes-Benz 515CD	Killbeggan Vehicle Converters	C16	2008
	SN08GJO	Mercedes-Benz 515CDi	Killbeggan Vehicle Converters	C16F	2008
	SN08GXC	Mercedes-Benz 515CDi	Killbeggan Vehicle Converters	C16F	2008

Riverside

Riverside Transport Training Ltd, 15 Carlibar Road, Barrhead G78 1AA

Website
Depot 15 Carlibar Road, Barrhead G78 1AA
Licence PM0002254

M354SDC	Mercedes-Benz 709D	Plaxton Beaver	B25F	1995
N491FDT	Mercedes-Benz 709D	Plaxton Beaver	B27F	1996
N779OGA	Mercedes-Benz 709D	UVG CityStar	B29F	1996
N810PDS	Mercedes-Benz 811D	Marshall C16	B33F	1996
P478TGA —	Mercedes-Benz 811D	Mellor	B33F	1996
P939YSB	Mercedes-Benz 709D	Plaxton Beaver	B29F	1997
PA51LEY —	Dennis Dart 10.7 SLF	Plaxton Pointer 2	B37F	2001
SA02UEX —	Dennis Dart 10.7 SLF	Alexander ALX200	B31F	2002
SA02UEY	Dennis Dart 10.7 SLF	Alexander ALX200	B31F	2002
SA52GXO	Dennis Dart 8.8 SLF	Plaxton Mini Pointer	B29F	2002
SF03ABU —	Dennis Dart 10.7 SLF	Plaxton Pointer 2	B37F	2003
SF03YXP	Mercedes-Benz Vario O.814D	Plaxton Beaver 2	B29F	2003
SF03YXR	Mercedes-Benz Vario O.814D	Plaxton Beaver 2	B29F	2003
SF04LHR	TransBus Dart 8.8 SLF	TransBus Mini Pointer	B29F	2004
SH51KJY	Dennis Dart 8.8 SLF	Plaxton Mini Pointer	B29F	2001
X109RGG —	Dennis Dart 10.7 SLF	Plaxton Pointer	B29F	2000
YN09LCM	Optare Solo M950	Optare	B33F	2009

Roberts of Rothiemay

G&E Roberts, Crossroads Garage, Rothiemay, Huntly AB54 5JT
Website
Depot   Crossroads Garage, Rothiemay, Huntly AB54 5JT
           Heavy Goods Car Park, Keith AB55 6QX
           Market Muir Car Park, Market Street, Huntly AB54 8JY
           Railway Station Yard, Dufftown, Keith AB55 5JW
Licence   PM0001403

*	699NAE	Mercedes-Benz Vario O.814D	Autobus Nouvelle	C33F	2004
*	MKZ1878	Dennis Javelin 10.5SFD	UVG	C33F	1997
*	NIL5906	Volvo B10M-60	Plaxton Paramount 3500 III	C57F	1991
	P153VSU	Mercedes-Benz 611D	Adamson	C24F	1997
	PN03UGA	Optare Alero L7200	Optare	B16F	2003
	PO54MHK	LDV Convoy	Concept	M16	2005

Rowe & Tudhope Coaches

G Rowe, West Hillhead, Western Road, Kilmarnock KA3 1PH
Website   www.roweandtudhope.com
Depot   West Hillhead, Western Road, Kilmarnock KA3 1PH
Licence   PM1071868

	BX05VPT	Mercedes-Benz 413CDI	Elite	M16	2005
	D217NCS	Dennis Dorchester SDA	Alexander TC	B69F	1987
	D220NCS	Dennis Dorchester SDA	Alexander TC	B69F	1987
	D518DSX	Leyland Tiger TRCTL11/3RH	Alexander P	B61F	1987
	D713CSC	Leyland Tiger TRCTL11/3RH	Alexander P	B61F	1987
*	R15SCC	Volvo B10M-62	Berkhof Axial 50	C49FT	1998
*	R913GFF	Volvo B10M-48	Van Hool Alizée	C30FT	1997
	SN04GBY	Mercedes-Benz 413CDI	Killbeggan Vehicle Converters	M16	2004
	SN56FBE	Mercedes-Benz 616CDI	Unvi	C23F	2006
*	V1PEO	Bova FHD12.370	Bova Futura	C49FT	2000
*	VJI3002	Volvo B10M-62	Plaxton Excalibur	C53F	1999
*	VJI9413	Volvo B10M-62	Jonckheere Deauville	C57F	1995
*	VJI9414	Bova FHD10-340	Bova Futura	C36FT	1998

R S Coaches

R Bain, Blackstock, Ordhead, Sauchen, Inerurie AB51 7RD
Website
Depot   Blackstock, Ordhead, Sauchen, Inerurie AB51 7RD
Licence   PM0002871

	BU05DVL	Renault Master	Renault	M15	2005
	BU05DVM	Renault Master	Renault	M15	2005
	BU05DVN	Renault Master	Renault	M15	2005
	BU05DWD	Renault Master	Renault	M15	2005
*	CLZ1838	DAF MB200DKFL600	Plaxton Paramount 3200 II Exp.	C53F	1985
*	EIG9345	MAN 13.220	Berkhof Axial 30	C41F	2000
	G621XLO	Mercedes-Benz 811D	Reeve Burgess Beaver	B26F	1989
	L438FPA	Mercedes-Benz 709D	Plaxton Beaver	B23F	1994
	M131DCS	LDV Convoy	LDV	M16	1995
*	MIL9587	Neoplan N122/3	Neoplan Skyliner	CH57/20CT	1985
	N549NYS	Volvo B10M-62	Van Hool Alizée	C49F	1996
	PO51OLV	LDV Convoy	Onyx	M16	2001
*	UIL1250	MAN 10.180	Caetano Algarve II	C26FT	1992
*	UIL1270	Volvo B10M-60	Plaxton Paramount 3500 III	C49FT	1989

Scotbus

Scotbus Ltd, 5 Darnaway Avenue, Inverness IV2 3HY
Website www.scotbus.co.uk
Depot Old Station Yard, Allangrove, Tore, Muir of Ord IV6 7SD
Licence PM1043672

	Reg	Chassis	Body	Layout	Year
	A357HHG	Leyland Atlantean AN68D/2R	East Lancs	H50/36F	1983
	A361HHG	Leyland Atlantean AN68D/2R	East Lancs	H50/36F	1983
	DRN176Y	Leyland Atlantean AN68D/2R	East Lancs	H50/36F	1983
	F210YHG	Leyland Lynx LX112L10ZR1R	Leyland Lynx	B47F	1989
	G216KRN	Leyland Lynx LX2R11C15Z4R	Leyland Lynx 2	DP45F	1989
*	GFV152W	Leyland Atlantean AN68D/2R	East Lancs	H50/36F	1981
	H23YBV	Leyland Lynx LX2R11C15Z4R	Leyland Lynx 2	DP45F	1990
	H114UYG	Volvo B10M-60	Plaxton Paramount 3500 III	C49F	1991
	K859HRS y	Mercedes-Benz 609D	Devon Conversions	B24FL	1993
	L309YDU	Mercedes-Benz 709D	Alexander (Belfast) Sprint	B23F	1994
*	MJI6254	Volvo B10M-60	Plaxton Premiere 350	C50F	1992
	N224HWX	Volvo B10M-62	Plaxton Premiere 350	C53F	1996
	R649YCR	Mercedes-benz O.810D	UVG	DP23FL	1997
	S378PGB	Mercedes-Benz Vario O.814D	Plaxton Beaver	B27F	1999
	SY52UMS	Renault Master	Mellor	M14	2003
	UHG354Y	Leyland Atlantean AN68D/2R	East Lancs	H49/36F	1982
	URN168Y	Leyland Atlantean AN68B/2R	East Lancs	H50/36F	1982
	URN170Y	Leyland Atlantean AN68B/2R	East Lancs	H50/36F	1982
	W669JOG	Mercedes-Benz 614D	W.J.W.	C24F	2000

Shiel Buses

Shiel Buses Ltd, Blain Garage, Acharacle PH36 4JY
Website www.shielbuses.co.uk
Depot Blain Garage, Acharacle PH36 4JY
Licence PM0002951

	Reg	Chassis	Body	Layout	Year
*	FNZ2300	Volvo B10M-62	Van Hool Alizée	C49FT	1996
*	HSK735	Volvo B10M-46	Van Hool Alizée	C42FT	1990
*	JIL3961	Volvo B10M-48	Van Hool Alizée	C40F	1997
*	K20JCM	Volvo B10M-62	Van Hool Alizée	C49FT	2000
*	K30SBL	Volvo B12M	Van Hool Alizée	C51FT	2002
*	K40SBL —	Mercedes-Benz	Unvi Cimo	C39F	2004
*	K60BSL	Volvo B10M-62	Plaxton Premiere 350	C49FT	2001
	N660WAW	Toyota Coaster HZB50R	Caetano Optimo	C21F	1996
	S670KST	Toyota Coaster BB50R	Caetano Optimo	C26F	1998
	SF53KUT	Mercedes-Benz Vario O.814D	TransBus Beaver 2	DP33F	2004
	SJ51LZA	Mercedes-Benz Sprinter 413CDI	Essbee	M16	2001
	SK07FMP	Mercedes-Benz Atego 1523L	Unvi Cimo	C39FL	2007
	SN09JFU	Mercedes-Benz 515CDI	Killbeggan Vehicle Converters	M16	2009
	SN54FVG	Mercedes-Benz Vario O.814D	Plaxton Cheetah	C33F	2005
	T381RFL	Ford Transit	Ford	M14	1999
	T420JNE	Mercedes-Benz 614D		C16L	1999
	Y20BGS	Volvo B10M-62	Plaxton Premiere 350	C49FT	2001
	YJ05JWX	Optare Solo M920	Optare	B33F	2005
	YN06PCY	Mercedes-Benz Vario O.814D	Plaxton Cheetah	C32FL	2006
	YN06PFA	Mercedes-Benz Vario O.814D	Plaxton Cheetah	C29F	2006

—K10SBL
—K80SBL
—K100SBL

J R & M B Shirran

J Robb & M Shirran, Lumsden Garage, Main Street, Lumsden AB54 4JB
Website
Depot   Lumsden Garage, Main Street, Lumsden AB54 4JB
Licence   PM0000812

BX55FYA	Mercedes-Benz O.815D	Mercedes-Benz	C29F	2005
PO51OLU	LDV Convoy		M16	2001
R128KGD	Mercedes-Benz 614D	Onyx	C24F	1997
SF06FSS	Mercedes-Benz Vario O.814D		C24F	2006
SF57JSY	Mercedes-Benz 311CDI	Onyx	M16	2007
V725GGE	Mercedes-Benz Vario O.814D	Mellor	C33F	1999
* VAV552	Volvo B10M-62	Jonckheere	C53F	1995
VKS910V	Ford R1014	Duple	C43F	1979
* Y178KCS	Volvo B10M-62	Jonckheere	C49FT	2001
YX05AVT	Mercedes-Benz Atego 1223L	Ferqui	C39FL	2005
YY52SSU	LDV Convoy	LDV	M16	2002

Shuttle Buses

Shuttle Buses Ltd, Unit 2, Caledonia House, Longford Avenue, Kilwinning KA13 6EX
Website   www.shuttlebus.39media.co.uk
Depot   Unit 2, Caledonia House, Longford Avenue, Kilwinning KA13 6EX
Licence   PM0001560

8	YX09HRF	Volkswagen	Bluebird	B14F	2009
9	YX09HRG	Volkswagen	Bluebird	B14F	2009
10	YJ09OUP	Optare Solo M780SE	Optare	B21F	2009
13	YX59DZC	Volkswagen Trader	Bluebird	B11FL	2010
14	SF10GKC	Renault Master	Bluebird	B11FL	2010
15	SF10GKD	Renault Master	Bluebird	B11FL	2010
	* 875YYA	AEC Reliance	Plaxton Supreme	C53F	1979
	B208FFS	Leyland Tiger TRTCL11/2RH	Alexander TC	C49F	1985
	G831RDS	Ford Transit	Dormobile Routemaker	B20F	1990
	* GSU551	Volvo B10M-62	Caetano Algarve II	C53F	1995
	K708RNR	Volvo B10M-60	Caetano Algarve II	C49FT	1993
	L384YFT	Optare MetroRider MR13	Optare	B25F	1994
	L746LWA	Mercedes-Benz 709D	Alexander (Belfast)	B25F	1993
	M786VJO	Dennis Javelin 12SDA	Caetano Algarve II	C47FT	1995
	N2SBL	Optare Solo M850	Optare	B29F	2005
	N3SBL	Optare Solo M920	Optare	B33F	2005
	* N5SBL	Optare Solo M850	Optare	B20F	2004
	* N6SBL	Optare Solo M850	Optare	B29F	2004
	* N7SBL	Optare Solo M850	Optare	B29F	2004
	N590GBW	Dennis Javelin 12SDA	Caetano Algarve II	C70F	1996
	S310KNW-w	Optare MetroRider MR17	Optare	B29F	1999

Silver Choice Travel

Silver Choice Travel Ltd, 1 Milton Road, College Milton North, East Kilbride G74 5BU
Website   www.silverchoice.co.uk
Depot   1 Milton Road, College Milton North, East Kilbride G74 5BU
Licence   PM0002593

* 84HER	Volvo B10M-61	Van Hool Alizée	C53F	1987
* BUI5220	Scania K113CRB	Van Hool Alizée	C49FT	1994
* EAZ8407	Volvo B10M-61	Plaxton Paramount 3500 III	C53F	1988
* HDZ8352	Bova FHD12-290	Bova Futura	C49FT	1989
* MIL6548	Volvo B10M-61	Plaxton Paramount 3500 III	C51FT	1988
* PIB277	Volvo B10M-62	Plaxton Premiere 350	C49F	1998
* SIL9988	Iveco EuroRider 391E.12.35	Beulas Stergo E	C49FT	2001

		Silver Choice Travel		
* SIL9991	Bova FHD12-340	Bova Futura	C49FT	2002
* SIL9993	Bova FHD12-340	Bova Futura	C51FT	2003
* SIL9994	Bova FHD12-340	Bova Futura	C49FT	2004
* SIL9996	Volvo B12BT	Van Hool Astrobel	CH57/14CT	1994
* SIL9997	Volvo B12BT	Van Hool Astrobel	CH57/14CT	1996
W875UWO	Mercedes-Benz Vario O.814D	Plaxton Cheetah	C29F	2000

Silver Fox Coaches
Silver Fox Coaches Ltd, Tower Garage, 67 Ferry Road, Renfrew PA4 8SH
Website www.silverfoxcoaches.co.uk
Depot Tower Garage, 67 Ferry Road, Renfrew PA4 8SH
Licence PM0000092

BMA524W	Bristol VRT/SL3/6LXB	Eastern Coach Works	H43/31F	1981
* BXI7437	Scania K92CRB	Duple 320	C59F	1989
KUS244Y	Leyland Tiger TRCTL11/2R	Duple Dominant	b60f	1982
LEO736Y	Leyland Atlantean AN68D/1R	Northern Counties	H43/32F	1983
* MUI4134	Volvo B10M-62	Van Hool Alizée	C44FT	1998
* PIL2172	Volvo B10M-60	Van Hool Alizée	C49FT	1991
PR56BEC	Volvo B7R	Plaxton Profile	C70F	2007
SIL1102	Irisbus EuroRider 391E.12.43	Beulas Cygnus	C49FT	2006
* SIL1103	Volvo B12M	Jonckheere Mistral	C53F	2003
* SIL1104	Volvo B12M	Jonckheere Mistral	C53F	2003
SIL4134	Irisbus EuroRider 397E.12.43	Beulas Cygnus	C49FT	2006

Silverdale Coaches
J Chapman, Jerviston Street, New Stevenston ML1 4JS
Website
Depot Unit 4 Flowerhill Industrial Estate, Airdrie ML6 6BH
Licence PM0000327

BX59KVR	King Long KMQ6127	BMC	C F	2009
GX07ARF	Irisbus Agora Line	Optare	B44F	2007
MX05WZK	Mercedes-Benz Sprinter 413CDI	Concept	M16	2005
MX06AEA	Enterprise Bus Plasma EB01	Plaxton Primo	B28F	2006
SA02UEP	Bova FHD12-340	Bova Futura	C49FT	2002
SF55PSY	Mercedes-Benz Vario O.814D	Plaxton Welfare Beaver 2	DP29FL	2005
* SG03ZEX	Volvo B12M	Jonckheere Mistral	C53F	2003
SG52XKJ	Mercedes-Benz Vario O.814D	Essbee	C24F	2002
YN56OSK	Mercedes-Benz Vario O.814D	Plaxton Cheetah	C33F	2007
YN59BNA	Volvo B12B	Plaxton Panther	C53FT	2009

Simpson of Rosehearty
R Simpson, 21 Union Street, Rosehearty AB43 7JQ
Website
Depot 21 Union Street, Rosehearty AB43 7JQ
Licence PM0001326

5685RWG	Mercedes-Benz Vario O.814D	Plaxton Cheetah	C32F	1999
FJ03VNE	Volvo B12M	Caetano	C49FT	2003
FJ05APZ	Volvo B12M	Berkhof Axial 50	C51FT	2005
* R3JNK	Bova FHD12.340	Bova Futura	C49FT	1997
* R101PWR	Bova FHD12.340	Bova Futura	C69F	1997
SM06SON	Volvo B12B	Caetano Levante	C49FT	2006
SM06SUN	Volvo B12B	Caetano Levante	C49FT	2006
SM08SON	MAN 18.360	Beulas	C FT	2008
SM08SUN	MAN 18.360	Beulas	C FT	2008
* SY54BMV	Mercedes-Benz 413CDI	Excel	M16	2004

Skyline Travel Service

F Dolan, Bay 3, Block F, Westway Development, Westway, Renfrew PA4 8DJ
Website
Depot   Bay 3, Block F, Westway Development, Westway, Renfrew PA4 8DJ
Licence   PM0002831

H151MOB	Dennis Dart 8.5 SDL	Carlyle Dartline	B28F	1990
H154MOB	Dennis Dart 8.5 SDL	Carlyle Dartline	B28F	1990
K720UTT	Fiat Daily 59-12	Mellor	B29F	1993
M318RSO	Mercedes-Benz 709D	Alexander Sprint	B25F	1994
M771TFS	Mercedes-Benz 709D	Alexander Sprint	B25F	1994
M776TFS	Mercedes-Benz 709D	Alexander Sprint	B25F	1994
N345KKH	Mercedes-Benz 709D	Alexander Sprint	B25F	1994
N996CCC	Mercedes-Benz 709D	Alexander Sprint	B27F	1995
N997CCC	Mercedes-Benz 709D	Alexander Sprint	B27F	1995
P477TGA	Mercedes-Benz 811D	Mellor	B31F	1996

Slaemuir Coaches

Slaemuir Coaches Ltd, Unit 2, 11 Dellingburn Street, Greenock PA15 4RN
Website
Depot   11 Dellingburn Street, Greenock PA15 4RN
Licence   PM1001614

*	C6POC	Volvo B10M-62	Caetano Enigma	C49F	2001
*	C7POC	Volvo B10M-62	Plaxton Excalibur	C49FT	2000
*	C11POC	Volvo B10M-62	Van Hool Alizée	C57F	1994
*	C13POC	Volvo B10M-62	Van Hool Alizée	C57F	1994
*	HIL7590	Volvo B10M-61	Van Hool Alizée	C53F	1982
	K239SFJ —	Mercedes-Benz 709D	Plaxton Beaver	B29F	1992
	K369RTY	Dennis Dart 9.8 SDL	Wright Handybus	B40F	1992
	L94LND	Mercedes-Benz 709D	Plaxton Beaver	B27F	1993
	L253YOD	Mercedes-Benz 709D	Plaxton Beaver	B25F	1993
	L254YOD	Mercedes-Benz 709D	Plaxton Beaver	B25F	1993
	L637DNA	Mercedes-Benz 709D	Marshall C19	B29F	1994
	M20BLU	Mercedes-Benz 811D	Marshall C16	B31F	1994
	M345JBO	Mercedes-Benz 709D	Alexander (Belfast) Sprint	B25F	1994
	M349JBO	Mercedes-Benz 709D	Alexander (Belfast) Sprint	B25F	1994
	M660FYS	Mercedes-Benz 709D	Alexander (Belfast) Sprint	B25F	1994
	M707JDG	Mercedes-Benz 709D	Alexander (Belfast) Sprint	B25F	1994
	N616DWY —	Mercedes-Benz 709D	Plaxton Beaver	B27F	1995
	N798PDS	Mercedes-Benz 709D	Marshall C19	B29F	1996
	N948NAP	Mercedes-Benz 709D	Alexander	B23F	1996
*	OAZ9372	Volvo B10M-60	Van Hool Alizée	C50F	1993
	P151LSC —	Mercedes-Benz 709D	Alexander Sprint	B29F	1996
	P224EJW	Mercedes-Benz 811D	Marshall C16	B27F	1997
	P232EJW	Mercedes-Benz 811D	Marshall C16	B27F	1997
	P722EJW	Mercedes-Benz 811D	Marshall C16	B27F	1997
	PN04NPC	MAN 18.360	Marcopolo Viaggio	C57F	2004
	SF03SCV	Mercedes-Benz Vario O.814D	Plaxton Cheetah	C33F	2003
	SF05FNU	Mercedes-Benz Vario O.814D	Plaxton Cheetah	C33F	2005
	SF10GKE	Renault Master	Bluebird	B11FL	2010
*	WDZ4724	Volvo B10M-60	Van Hool Alizée	C50F	1993
	YF02SKX	Optare Solo M920	Optare	B33F	2002
	YF02SKZ	Optare Solo M920	Optare	B33F	2002
	YK05BAO	BMC Falcon 1100FE	BMC	B55FL	2005
	YK05BAV	BMC Falcon 1100FE	BMC	B55FL	2005
	YX09HRW	Volkswagen	Bluebird	B14F	2009
	YX09HRZ	Volkswagen	Bluebird	B14F	2009
	YX09HSA	Volkswagen	Bluebird	B14F	2009
	YX59AAE	Volkswagen	Tucana	B14F	2009
	YX59AAV	Volkswagen	Bluebird	B14F	2009

	Slaemuir Coaches			

YX59AAY	Volkswagen		Bluebird	B14F	2009
YX59ABK	Volkswagen		Bluebird	B-F	2009

Smith & Sons

A Smith & Partners, The Coach Depot, Wester Balgersho, Woodside, Coupar Angus PH13 9LP
Website www.smithandsonscoaches.co.uk
Depot The Coach Depot, Wester Balgersho, Woodside, Coupar Angus PH13 9LP
Mains of Huntingtower Farm, Perth PH1 3JT
The Coach Depot, Woodside, Coupar Angus, Blairgowrie PH13 LP
Licence PM0001044

*	GNZ9360	Volvo B10M-62	Van Hool Alizée	C53F	1998
*	HUI 6828	Volvo B10M-60	Jonckheere Deauville	C51FT	1992
*	K240EUX	Volvo B10M-60	Jonckheere Deauville	C49FT	1992
*	KUI3849	Volvo B10M-62	Jonckheere Deauville	C51FT	1994
	L3LCC	Volvo B10M-60	Van Hool Alizée	C70F	1994
*	L214GJO	Volvo B10M-60	Jonckheere Deauville	C53F	1993
*	L643DNA	Mercedes-Benz 709D	Plaxton Beaver	B27F	1994
	MU51FMV	Mercedes-Benz Sprinter 413CDI	Onyx	M16	2001
*	N627RGD	Volvo B10M-62	Van Hool Alizée	C70F	1996
*	N801RGD	Volvo B10M-62	Van Hool Alizée	C53F	1996
	P681DCK	Ford Transit	Ford	M11	1997
	P871AFV	Ford Transit	Ford	M14	1997
	R28VSM	DAF DE33WSSB3000	Van Hool Alizée	C68FT	1998
	RKZ8286	Mercedes-Benz O.815D	Unvi Cimo	C29F	2006
*	SIL8697	Volvo B10M-62	Van Hool Alizée	C70F	1996
	SK07FYT	Mercedes-Benz Atego 1523L	Unvi Cimo	C37F	2007
	SP06FBG	Mercedes-Benz Vario O.815D	Sitcar Beluga	C33F	2006
	SP07ENX	Mercedes-Benz Vario O.815D	Sitcar Beluga	C33F	2007
	SP07ENY	Mercedes-Benz Vario O.815D	Sitcar Beluga	C33F	2007
	SP07FHA	Bova FHD120-365	Bova Futura	C49FT	2007
	SP08ADZ	Bova FHD120-365	Bova Futura	C49FT	2008
	SP08AET	Bova FHD120-365	Bova Futura	C49FT	2008
	SP58DPE	Optare Versa V1100	Optare	B38F	2008
	SP58DPF	Optare Versa V1100	Optare	B38F	2008
	SP58DPK	Optare Versa V1100	Optare	B38F	2008
*	T25ERS	Bova FHD12-370	Bova Futura	C70F	2000
	T523GSR	Volvo B10M-62	Van Hool Alizée	C53F	1999
	T980OGA	Mercedes-Benz Vario O.814D	Marshall	B31F	1999
	YJ59NOF	Optare Versa V1110	Optare	B39F	2009
	YJ59NOH	Optare Versa V1110	Optare	B39F	2009

Smith's Coaches

A & A Smith, Doonview, Burnfoot, Ayr Road, Patna KA6 7JW
Website
Depot Hillside Garage, Ayr Road, Patna KA6 7JW
Licence PM0003006

	A319GLV	Leyland Olympian ONTL11/1R	Alexander RH	CH40/23F	1983
	C451BKM	Leyland Olympian ONTL11/2R	Eastern Coach Works	CH45/28F	1985
	D522DSX	Leyland Tiger TRSTL11/2	Alexander P	B57F	1987
*	EAZ6207	DAF SBR3000DKZ570	Plaxton Paramount 4000	CH55/19FT	1989
	G761WAS	Volvo B10M-60	Van Hool Alizée	C49FT	1990
	G811WST	Volvo B10M-60	Van Hool Alizée	C53F	1990
*	L628AYS	Volvo B10M-62	Van Hool Alizée	C53F	1994
	L906JRN	Dennis Dart 9 SDL	East Lancs EL2000	B34F	1994
*	PSV223	Volvo B10M-55	Van Hool Alizée	C49FT	1999
	R632EYS	Mercedes-Benz Vario O.810D	Plaxton Beaver 2	B27F	1997

HB10 - Scotland

139

	Smiths Coaches			
T431LGP	Dennis Dart 10.7 SLF	Caetano Compass	B30D	1999
* TJI4024	Volvo B10M-61	Van Hool Alizée	C49DT	1984
V452NGA	Volvo B6BLE	Wright Crusader 2	B37F	2000
X331ABU	Mercedes-Benz Vario O.814D	Plaxton Beaver 2	B31F	2000
* YC02DHZ	Volvo B12M	Jonckheere	C48FT	2002

Southern Coaches
Southern Coaches (NM) Ltd, Barshagra Garage, Lochlibo Road, Barrhead G78 1LF
Website www.southerncoaches.co.uk
Depot Barshagra Garage, Lochlibo Road, Barrhead G78 1LF
Licence PM0000050

SF04SOU	VDL DE40XSSB4000	Van Hool Alizée	C51F	2004
SG04SOU	Volvo B12M	Van Hool Alizée	C51F	2004
SJ05SOU	Volvo B12B	Plaxton Panther	C51F	2004
SK05SOU	Volvo B12M	Van Hool Alizée	C51F	2005
SL06SOU	Volvo B12B	Plaxton Paragon	C51FT	2006
SM06SOU	Volvo B12M	Plaxton Paragon	C57F	2006
SO06SOU	Volvo B12B	Van Hool Alizée	C51F	2006
SP07SOU	Volvo B12B	Plaxton Paragon	C57F	2007
SR07SOU	Volvo B12B	Van Hool Alizée	C51FT	2007
ST09SOU	Volvo B12B	Plaxton Paragon	C51F	2009
* TU07SOU	Volvo B12B	Van Hool Alizée	C51F	2007
UU08SOU	Bova FHD104-365	Bova Futura	C38FT	2008
VU08SOU	Volvo B12B	Van Hool Alizée	C51FT	2008
WU08SOU	Volvo B12B	Plaxton Paragon	C57F	2008
XU05SOU	Toyota Coaster BB50R	Caetano Optimo	C22F	2005
YU07SOU	Mercedes-Benz Vario O.815D	Sitcar Beluga	C29F	2007

Spa Coaches
N McArthur & Partners, Kinettas, Strathpeffer IV14 9AJ
Website www.spacoaches.co.uk
Depot Spa Motors, Strathpeffer IV14 9AJ
Licence PM0002233

* BX53OLE	Toyota Coaster BB50R	Caetano Optimo	C22F	2003
D605MVR	Volvo B10M-61	Van Hool Alizée	C53F	1987
G862RNC	Volvo B10M-60	Van Hool Alizée	C53F	1990
K295ESF	Mercedes-Benz 811D	Dormobile Routemaker	C29F	1993
K481VVR	Volvo B10M-60	Van Hool Alizée	C70F	1993
KN07SPA	Volvo B12B(T)	Van Hool Alizée	C53FT	2007
* OIB3519	Volvo B10M-61	Van Hool Alizée	C51F	1987
P550MSF	Mercedes-Benz Vario O.814D	Plaxton Beaver Coach	C33F	1996
* P974WOS	Volvo B10M-62	Van Hool Alizée	C53F	1997
* PAZ2535	Volvo B10M-60	Van Hool Alizée	C48FT	1994
R73FCA	Mercedes-Benz 412CD	Concept	M16	1998
S21SPA	Volvo B10M-62	Plaxton Premiere 320	C57F	1998
* S22SPA	Toyota Coaster BB50R	Caetano Optimo	C21F	2005
S33SPA	Mercedes-Benz Vario O.814D	Plaxton Cheetah	C31F	2002
SN03NLK	Mercedes-Benz Vario O.814D	Plaxton Cheetah	C33F	2003
T642BSS	Volvo B10M-55	Van Hool Alizée	C49FT	1999
* UHR412	Leyland Tiger TRCTL10/3ARZM	Plaxton Paramount 3200 III	C70F	1989
* VEL374	Volvo B10M-61	Van Hool Alizée	C57F	1983
W251GSE	Volvo B10M-55	Van Hool Alizée	C49FT	2000
* XIB9829	Volvo B10M-61	Jonckheere Bermuda	C49FT	1981
Y5SPA	Volvo B10M-62	Van Hool Alizée	C53F	2001
* Y6SPA	Volvo B10M-55	Van Hool Alizée	C49FT	2001

Stables of Keith
R Stables, 64 Main Street, Newmill AB55 6TS
Depot   74 Main Street, Newmill AB55 3TS
Licence   PM0001916

BT05BJT	Mercedes-Benz Vario O.814D	Plaxton Cheetah	C33F	2005
FN02RXJ	Dennis Javelin 12SFD	Caetano Enigma	C53F	2002
* LUI6840	Mercedes-Benz Vario O.814D	Plaxton Cheetah	C27F	2000
P444TCC	Dennis Javelin 12SFD	Plaxton Premiere 320	C51F	1997
* SIL8572	Volvo B10M-62	Jonckheere	C53F	1995
* SUI1480	Dennis Javelin 12SFD	Plaxton Premiere 320	C53F	1998
* YIL2860	Mercedes-Benz Atego 1223L	Ferqui	C39F	2002

Stagecoach Scotland
Bluebird Buses Ltd, Guild Street, Aberdeen AB11 6NA
Rennies / Fife Scottish Omnibuses Ltd / A A Buses Ltd / Strathtay Scottish Omnibuses Ltd,
Offices 47-51, Evans Business Centre, John Smith Business Park, Kirkcaldy, Fife KY2 6WD
Highland Country Buses Ltd, 6 Burnett Road, Inverness IV1 1TF
Western Buses Ltd / Stagecoach Glasgow Ltd / Schoolbus Ltd, Sandgate, Ayr KA7 1DD
Website   www.stagecoachbus.com
Depots   As per list
Licence   PM0000005 (Aberdeen) / PM0000870 (Rennies) / PM0002511 (Schoolbus Ltd)
           PM0000004 (Fife Scottish Omnibus) / PM0002607 (AA Buses)
           PM0002294 (Inverness) / PM0001799 (Strathtay) / PM0001100 (Stagecoach Scotland)
           PM0001990 (Stagecoach Glasgow Ltd) / PM0000008 (Western Buses Ltd)

10005	WYV5T		GW-rLeyland Titan TNLXB/2RR	Park Royal	H44/26D	1979
10473	KYV473X	w	Leyland Titan TNLXB2RR	Leyland	H44/31F	1982
11083	B83WUV	AY	Leyland Titan TNLXB2RR	Leyland	H44/31F	1984
11093	* NIB5233	S	Leyland Titan TNLXB2RR	Leyland	O44/29F	1984
12060	* EDS50A	p	AEC Routemaster	Park Royal	H40/32R	1960
12444	JJD444D	DS-r	AEC Routemaster	Park Royal	H40/32R	1965
12550	JJD550D	DS-r	AEC Routemaster	Park Royal	H40/32R	1966
13502	* C160HBA	w	Leyland Olympian ONLXCT/3R	Alexander RH	H61/39F	1986
13506	* C170HBA	w	Leyland Olympian ONLXCT/3R	Alexander RH	H61/39F	1986
13518	* C158HBA	w	Leyland Olympian ONLXCT/3R	Alexander RH	H61/39F	1986
13602	* WLT416	AS	Leyland Olympian ON3R49C18Z4	Alexander RH	CH53/31FT	1990
13609	* J701HMY	CK	Leyland Olympian ON3R49C18Z4	Alexander RH	CH53/29FT	1991
13612	* J938MHC	AS	Leyland Olympian ON3R49C18Z4	Alexander RH	DPH53/41F	1991
13616	* G189YRJ	K	Leyland Olympian ON3R49C18Z4	Alexander RH	DPH53/41F	1991
13617	* H445EGU	K-r	Leyland Olympian ON3R49C18Z4	Alexander RH	CH53/39FT	1990
13618	* H522FRP	AS	Leyland Olympian ON3R49C18Z4	Alexander RH	DPH53/41F	1991
13623	* H494LNA	CK	Leyland Olympian ON3R49C18Z4	Alexander RH	DPH53/41F	1991
13624	* TSU638	CK	Leyland Olympian ON3R49C18Z4	Alexander RH	DPH53/41F	1991
13625	* H511FRP	a	Leyland Olympian ON3R49C18Z4	Alexander RH	CH53/41F	1990
13628	* K688CBA	K	Leyland Olympian ON3R49C18Z4	Alexander RH	DPH53/41F	1991
13632	* H778VHL	K	Leyland Olympian ON3R49C18Z4	Alexander RH	DPH53/41F	1991
13636	* G128WGX	AS	Leyland Olympian ON3R49C18Z4	Alexander RH	DPH53/41F	1991
13642	* H625LNA	K	Leyland Olympian ON3R49C18Z4	Alexander RH	DPH53/41F	1989
13643	* G280YRJ	K	Leyland Olympian ON3R49C18Z4	Alexander RH	CH53/39F	1989
13644	* G278YRJ	AY	Leyland Olympian ON3R49C18Z4	Alexander RH	CH53/39F	1989
13647	* H606LNA	AS	Leyland Olympian ON3R49C18Z4	Alexander RH	DPH53/41F	1991
13650	* H627LNA	AS	Leyland Olympian ON3R49C18Z4	Alexander RH	CH53/39FT	1991
13651	* H603LNA	AS	Leyland Olympian ON3R49C18Z4	Alexander RH	CH53/39FT	1991
14392	D142FYM	w	Leyland Olympian ONLXB/1RH	Eastern Coach Works	H42/29F	1986
14701	J801WFS	p	Leyland Olympian ON2R50G13Z4	Alexander RL	H47/32F	1992
14957	G807RTS	z	Leyland Olympian ONLXB/2RZ	Alexander RL	CH51/31F	1989
14964	G214SSL	w	Leyland Olympian ONLXB/2RZ	Alexander RL	DPH51/31F	1989
15299	C799USG	w	Volvo Citybus B10M-50	Alexander RV	H47/37F	1986
15309	H429BNL	w	Scania N113DRB	Alexander RH	H47/31F	1991

15621	SF10CAA	K	Scania N230UD	ADL Enviro 400	H47/29F	2010
15622	SF10CAE	K	Scania N230UD	ADL Enviro 400	H47/29F	2010
15623	SF10CAO	K	Scania N230UD	ADL Enviro 400	H47/29F	2010
15624	SF10CAU	K	Scania N230UD	ADL Enviro 400	H47/29F	2010
15625	SF10CAV	K	Scania N230UD	ADL Enviro 400	H47/29F	2010
15626	SF10CAX	K	Scania N230UD	ADL Enviro 400	H47/29F	2010
15627	SF10CBO	K	Scania N230UD	ADL Enviro 400	H47/29F	2010
15628	SF10CBU	K	Scania N230UD	ADL Enviro 400	H47/29F	2010
15629	SF10CBV	K	Scania N230UD	ADL Enviro 400	H47/29F	2010
15630	SF10CBX	K	Scania N230UD	ADL Enviro 400	H47/29F	2010
15631	SF10CBY	K	Scania N230UD	ADL Enviro 400	H47/29F	2010
15632	SF10CCD	AS	Scania N230UD	ADL Enviro 400	H47/29F	2010
15633	SF10CCE	AS	Scania N230UD	ADL Enviro 400	H47/29F	2010
15634	SF10CCJ	AS	Scania N230UD	ADL Enviro 400	H47/29F	2010
15635	SF10CCK	AS	Scania N230UD	ADL Enviro 400	H47/29F	2010
15636	SF10CCN	AS	Scania N230UD	ADL Enviro 400	H47/29F	2010
15637	SF10CCO	AS	Scania N230UD	ADL Enviro 400	H47/29F	2010
15638	SF10CCU	AS	Scania N230UD	ADL Enviro 400	H47/29F	2010
15639	SF10CCV	AS	Scania N230UD	ADL Enviro 400	H47/29F	2010
15640	SF10CCX	AS	Scania N230UD	ADL Enviro 400	H47/29F	2010
15641	SF10CCY	AS	Scania N230UD	ADL Enviro 400	H47/29F	2010
15642	SF10CCZ	AS	Scania N230UD	ADL Enviro 400	H47/29F	2010
15643	SF10CDE	AS	Scania N230UD	ADL Enviro 400	H47/29F	2010
15644	SF10CDK	AS	Scania N230UD	ADL Enviro 400	H47/29F	2010
15645	SF10CDN	AS	Scania N230UD	ADL Enviro 400	H47/29F	2010
15646	SF10CDO	AS	Scania N230UD	ADL Enviro 400	H47/29F	2010
15647	SF10CDU	AS	Scania N230UD	ADL Enviro 400	H47/29F	2010
16008	P808GMU	G	Volvo Olympian YN2RV18V3	Northern Counties Palatine I	H49/31F	1996
16009	P809GMU	R	Volvo Olympian YN2RV18V3	Northern Counties Palatine I	H49/31F	1996
16045	P645SEV	C	Volvo Olympian OLY-56	Alexander RL	H51/34F	1997
16046	P646SEV	KY-r	Volvo Olympian OLY-56	Alexander RL	H51/34F	1997
16054	R154VPU	R	Volvo Olympian OLY-56	Alexander RL	H51/32F	1997
16057	R157VPU	S	Volvo Olympian OLY-56	Alexander RL	H51/32F	1997
16060	R160VPU	S	Volvo Olympian OLY-56	Alexander RL	H51/34F	1997
16065	R165VPU	D R	Volvo Olympian OLY-56	Alexander RL	H51/32F	1997
16067	R167VPU	A	Volvo Olympian OLY-56	Alexander RL	H51/31F	1997
16068	R168VPU	CK	Volvo Olympian OLY-56	Alexander RL	H51/34F	1997
16073	R173VPU	D R	Volvo Olympian OLY-56	Alexander RL	H51/32F	1997
16074	R174VPU	CK	Volvo Olympian OLY-56	Alexander RL	H51/32F	1997
16075	R175VPU	R	Volvo Olympian OLY-56	Alexander RL	H51/32F	1997
16077	R177VPU	C	Volvo Olympian OLY-56	Alexander RL	H51/32F	1997
16084	R84XNO	A R	Volvo Olympian OLY-56	Northern Counties Palatine I	H45/27F	1997
16092	R92XNO	G	Volvo Olympian OLY-56	Northern Counties Palatine I	H45/27F	1997
16098	R98XNO	A	Volvo Olympian OLY-56	Northern Counties Palatine I	H45/27F	1997
16100	R210XNO	G	Volvo Olympian OLY-56	Northern Counties Palatine I	H45/27F	1997
16101	R101XNO	A R	Volvo Olympian OLY-56	Northern Counties Palatine I	H45/27F	1998
16104	R104XNO	G	Volvo Olympian OLY-56	Northern Counties Palatine I	H45/27F	1998
16107	R107XNO	D	Volvo Olympian OLY-56	Northern Counties Palatine I	H45/27F	1998
16108	R108XNO	D	Volvo Olympian OLY-56	Northern Counties Palatine I	H45/27F	1998
16111	R311XNO	BU	Volvo Olympian OLY-56	Northern Counties Palatine I	H45/27F	1998
16112	R112XNO	SV	Volvo Olympian OLY-56	Northern Counties Palatine I	H45/27F	1998
16114	R114XNO	C	Volvo Olympian OLY-56	Northern Counties Palatine I	H45/27F	1998
16115	R115XNO	D R	Volvo Olympian OLY-56	Northern Counties Palatine I	H45/27F	1998
16116	R116XNO	AB	Volvo Olympian OLY-56	Northern Counties Palatine I	H45/27F	1998
16117	R117XNO	AB	Volvo Olympian OLY-56	Northern Counties Palatine I	H45/27F	1998
16118 ·	R118XNO	FW	Volvo Olympian OLY-56	Northern Counties Palatine I	H45/27F	1998
16119 ·	R119XNO	FW	Volvo Olympian OLY-56	Northern Counties Palatine I	H45/27F	1998
16120 ·	R120XNO	FW	Volvo Olympian OLY-56	Northern Counties Palatine I	H45/27F	1998
16121	R121XNO	AB	Volvo Olympian OLY-56	Northern Counties Palatine I	H45/27F	1998
16132	R132EVX	A	Volvo Olympian OLY-56	Alexander RL	H51/32F	1998
16138	R138EVX	C	Volvo Olympian OLY-56	Alexander RL	H51/32F	1998

16140	R140EVX	DR	Volvo Olympian OLY-56	Alexander RL	H51/32F	1998
16141	R141EVX	A	Volvo Olympian OLY-56	Alexander RL	H51/32F	1998
16144	R144EVX	A	Volvo Olympian OLY-56	Alexander RL	H51/32F	1998
16150	R150HHK	A	Volvo Olympian OLY-56	Northern Counties Palatine I	H49/30F	1998
16152	R152HHK	DR	Volvo Olympian OLY-56	Northern Counties Palatine I	H49/31F	1998
16153 *	LSK545	BU	Volvo Olympian OLY-56	Northern Counties Palatine I	H49/31F	1998
16154	R154HHK	D	Volvo Olympian OLY-56	Northern Counties Palatine I	H49/30F	1998
16155	R155HHK	C	Volvo Olympian OLY-56	Northern Counties Palatine I	H49/30F	1998
16156	R156HHK	C	Volvo Olympian OLY-56	Northern Counties Palatine I	H49/31F	1998
16157	R157HHK	AI	Volvo Olympian OLY-56	Northern Counties Palatine I	H49/30F	1998
16158	R158HHK	D	Volvo Olympian OLY-56	Northern Counties Palatine I	H49/31F	1998
16159	R159HHK	D	Volvo Olympian OLY-56	Northern Counties Palatine I	H49/30F	1998
16160	R160HHK	G	Volvo Olympian OLY-56	Northern Counties Palatine I	H49/30F	1998
16161	R161HHK	C	Volvo Olympian OLY-56	Northern Counties Palatine I	H49/31F	1998
16163	R163HHK	D	Volvo Olympian OLY-56	Northern Counties Palatine I	H49/31F	1998
16165	R165HHK	S	Volvo Olympian OLY-56	Northern Counties Palatine I	H49/30F	1998
16166	R166HHK	D	Volvo Olympian OLY-56	Northern Counties Palatine I	H49/31F	1998
16170	R170HHK	GS	Volvo Olympian OLY-56	Northern Counties Palatine I	H49/31F	1998
16171	R171HHK	KY-r	Volvo Olympian OLY-56	Northern Counties Palatine I	H49/31F	1998
16172	R172HHK	D	Volvo Olympian OLY-56	Northern Counties Palatine I	H49/31F	1998
16173	R173HHK	C	Volvo Olympian OLY-56	Northern Counties Palatine I	H49/31F	1998
16176	R176HHK	A	Volvo Olympian OLY-56	Northern Counties Palatine I	H49/31F	1998
16177	R177HHK	D	Volvo Olympian OLY-56	Northern Counties Palatine I	H49/31F	1998
16178	R178HHK	GS	Volvo Olympian OLY-56	Northern Counties Palatine I	H49/31F	1998
16190	S960URJ	AB	Volvo Olympian OLY-49	Northern Counties Palatine II	H47/30F	1999
16198	L26JSA	P	Volvo Olympian YN2RC18Z4	Northern Counties Palatine II	H47/30F	1993
16200 *	NIB4138	AB	Volvo Olympian YN2RV18Z4	Northern Counties Palatine I	CH43/25F	1993
16244	L244SDY	w	Volvo Olympian YN2RV18Z4	Northern Counties Palatine I	DPH43/25F	1993
16245	L245SDY	P	Volvo Olympian YN2RV18Z4	Northern Counties Palatine I	DPH43/25F	1993
16248	L248SDY	P	Volvo Olympian SLVYNNF21	Northern Counties Palatine I	DPH43/25F	1993
16249	L249SDY	w	Volvo Olympian SLVYNNF21	Northern Counties Palatine I	DPH43/25F	1993
16288	P288VPN	DR	Volvo Olympian YV3YNA41	Alexander RL	DPH47/32F	1997
16289	P289VPN	AY	Volvo Olympian YV3YNA41	Alexander RL	DPH47/32F	1997
16290	P290VPN	CK	Volvo Olympian YV3YNA41	Alexander RL	DPH47/32F	1997
16306	S306CCD	C	Volvo Olympian YV3YNA41	Alexander RL	DPH47/32F	1998
16307	S307CCD	AR	Volvo Olympian YV3YNA41	Alexander RL	DPH47/32F	1998
16308	S308CCD	AS	Volvo Olympian YV3YNA41	Alexander RL	DPH47/32F	1998
16309	S309CCD	AS	Volvo Olympian YV3YNA41	Alexander RL	DPH47/32F	1998
16310	S310CCD	CK	Volvo Olympian YV3YNA41	Alexander RL	DPH47/32F	1998
16311	S311CCD	K	Volvo Olympian YV3YNA41	Alexander RL	DPH47/32F	1998
16312	S312CCD	C	Volvo Olympian YV3YNA41	Alexander RL	DPH47/32F	1998
16313	S313CCD	A	Volvo Olympian YV3YNA41	Alexander RL	DPH47/32F	1998
16319	S319CCD	C	Volvo Olympian YV3YNA41	Alexander RL	DPH47/32F	1998
16320	S320CCD	S	Volvo Olympian YV3YNA41	Alexander RL	DPH47/32F	1998
16322	S322CCD	C	Volvo Olympian YV3YNA41	Alexander RL	DPH47/32F	1998
16323	S323CCD	CR	Volvo Olympian YV3YNA41	Alexander RL	DPH47/32F	1998
16324	S324CCD	CR	Volvo Olympian YV3YNA41	Alexander RL	DPH47/32F	1998
16345	N345MPN	P	Volvo Olympian YN2RC16V3	Alexander RL	DPH43/28F	1996
16354	N354MPN	P	Volvo Olympian YN2RC16V3	Alexander RL	DPH43/28F	1996
16359	N359MPN	R	Volvo Olympian YN2CV16V3	Alexander RL	CH47/28F	1996
16401	M301DGP	DE	Volvo Olympian YN2CV16V3	Northern Counties Palatine I	H45/27F	1995
16402	M302DGP	R	Volvo Olympian YN2CV16V3	Northern Counties Palatine I	H45/27F	1995
16403	M303DGP	R	Volvo Olympian YN2CV16V3	Northern Counties Palatine I	H45/27F	1995
16404	M304DGP	AH	Volvo Olympian YN2CV16V3	Northern Counties Palatine I	H45/27F	1995
16405	M305DGP	AH	Volvo Olympian YN2CV16V3	Northern Counties Palatine I	H45/27F	1995
16406	M306DGP	R	Volvo Olympian YN2RC16V3	Northern Counties Palatine I	H45/27F	1995
16407	M307DGP	R	Volvo Olympian YN2RC16V3	Northern Counties Palatine I	H45/27F	1995
16408	M308DGP	R	Volvo Olympian YN2RC16V3	Northern Counties Palatine I	H45/27F	1995
16409	M309DGP	R	Volvo Olympian YN2RC16V3	Northern Counties Palatine I	H45/27F	1995
16410	M310DGP	R	Volvo Olympian YN2RC16V3	Northern Counties Palatine I	H45/27F	1995
16413	M313DGP	R	Volvo Olympian YN2RC16V3	Northern Counties Palatine I	H45/27F	1995

16414	M314DGP	R	Volvo Olympian YN2RC16V3	Northern Counties Palatine I	H45/27F	1995
16415	M315DGP	w	Volvo Olympian YN2RC16V3	Northern Counties Palatine I	H45/27F	1995
16416	M316DGP	R	Volvo Olympian YN2RC16V3	Northern Counties Palatine I	H45/27F	1995
16417	M317DGP	P	Volvo Olympian YN2RC16V3	Northern Counties Palatine I	H45/27F	1995
16418	M318DGP	w	Volvo Olympian YN2RC16V3	Northern Counties Palatine I	H45/27F	1995
16419	M319DGP	w	Volvo Olympian YN2RC16V3	Northern Counties Palatine I	H45/27F	1995
16420	M320DGP	w	Volvo Olympian YN2RC16V3	Northern Counties Palatine I	H45/27F	1995
16421	N321HGK	R	Volvo Olympian YN2RC16V3	Northern Counties Palatine I	H45/26F	1995
16422	N322HGK	A	Volvo Olympian YN2RC16V3	Northern Counties Palatine I	H45/26F	1995
16423	N323HGK	R	Volvo Olympian YN2RC16V3	Northern Counties Palatine I	H45/26F	1995
16424	N324HGK	R	Volvo Olympian YN2RC16V3	Northern Counties Palatine I	H45/26F	1995
16425	N325HGK	r	Volvo Olympian YN2RC16V3	Northern Counties Palatine I	H45/26F	1995
16426	N326HGK	A	Volvo Olympian YN2RC16V3	Northern Counties Palatine I	H45/26F	1995
16427	N327HGK	A	Volvo Olympian YN2RC16V3	Northern Counties Palatine I	H45/26F	1995
16428	N328HGK	S	Volvo Olympian YN2RC16V3	Northern Counties Palatine I	H45/26F	1995
16429	N329HGK	A	Volvo Olympian YN2RC16V3	Northern Counties Palatine I	H45/26F	1995
16430	N330HGK	r /R	Volvo Olympian YN2RC16V3	Northern Counties Palatine I	H45/26F	1995
16432 *	N332HGK	R	Volvo Olympian YN2RC16V3	Northern Counties Palatine I	H45/26F	1995
16434	N334HGK	R	Volvo Olympian YN2RC16V3	Northern Counties Palatine I	H45/26F	1995
16438	N338HGK	A	Volvo Olympian YN2RC16V3	Northern Counties Palatine I	H45/26F	1995
16439	N339HGK	R	Volvo Olympian YN2RC16V3	Northern Counties Palatine I	H45/26F	1995
16440	N340HGK	R	Volvo Olympian YN2RC16V3	Northern Counties Palatine I	H45/26F	1995
16446	N346HGK	C	Volvo Olympian YN2RV18Z4	Northern Counties Palatine I	H45/23D	1995
16450	N350HGK	S	Volvo Olympian YN2RC16V3	Northern Counties Palatine I	H45/27F	1995
16518	R418XFC	A	Volvo Olympian OLY-56	Alexander RL	H51/36F	1998
16519	R419XFC	A	Volvo Olympian OLY-56	Alexander RL	H51/36F	1998
16520	R420XFC	A	Volvo Olympian OLY-56	Alexander RL	H51/36F	1998
16521	R421XFC	A	Volvo Olympian OLY-56	Alexander RL	H51/36F	1998
16522	R422XFC	AB	Volvo Olympian OLY-56	Alexander RL	H51/36F	1998
16526	R426XFC	AB	Volvo Olympian OLY-56	Alexander RL	H51/36F	1998
16610 *	L100JLB	P	Volvo Olympian YN2RV18Z4	Northern Counties Palatine I	DPH43/25F	1993
16641	P271VPN	R	Volvo Olympian YN2RV18Z4	Alexander RL	H51/36F	1997
16646	R246NBV	A C	Volvo Olympian OLY-56	Alexander RL	H51/36F	1997
16656	R256NBV	A	Volvo Olympian OLY-56	Alexander RL	H51/36F	1997
16658	R258NBV	D C	Volvo Olympian OLY-56	Alexander RL	H51/36F	1997
16686 *	P686JBD	A	Volvo Olympian YN2RV18V3	Alexander RL	H51/36F	1996
16687	P687JBD	G	Volvo Olympian YN2RV18V3	Alexander RL	H51/36F	1996
16688	P688JBD	G	Volvo Olympian YN2RV18V3	Alexander RL	H51/36F	1996
16689	P689JBD	G	Volvo Olympian YN2RV18V3	Alexander RL	H51/36F	1996
16690	P690JBD	G	Volvo Olympian YN2RV18V3	Alexander RL	H51/36F	1996
16712	N712LTN	r	Volvo Olympian YN2RC16V3	Alexander RL	H47/28F	1995
16713	N713LTN	r	Volvo Olympian YN2RC16V3	Alexander RL	H47/28F	1995
16715	N715LTN	w	Volvo Olympian YN2RC16V3	Alexander RL	H47/28F	1995
16716	N716LTN	r P	Volvo Olympian YN2RC16V3	Alexander RL	H47/28F	1995
16718	N718LTN	AH	Volvo Olympian YN2RC16V3	Alexander RL	H47/28F	1995
16720	N720LTN	r P	Volvo Olympian YN2RC16V3	Alexander RL	H47/28F	1995
16724	N724LTN	AH	Volvo Olympian YN2RV16V3	Alexander RL	H47/28F	1995
16725	N725LTN	K	Volvo Olympian YN2RV16V3	Alexander RL	H47/28F	1995
16726	N726LTN	K	Volvo Olympian YN2RV16V3	Alexander RL	H47/28F	1995
16727	N727LTN	CK	Volvo Olympian YN2RV16V3	Alexander RL	H47/28F	1995
16737	N737LTN	A	Volvo Olympian YN2RV16V3	Alexander RL	H47/28F	1996
16809	R955TSL	BL	Volvo Olympian OLY-49	East Lancs Pyoneer	CH43/29F	1998
16810	R956TSL	BL	Volvo Olympian OLY-49	East Lancs Pyoneer	CH43/29F	1998
16811	R957TSL	AH	Volvo Olympian OLY-49	East Lancs Pyoneer	CH43/29F	1998
16812	R958TSL	AH	Volvo Olympian OLY-49	East Lancs Pyoneer	CH43/29F	1998
16813	S959KSR	DE	Volvo Olympian OLY-49	East Lancs Pyoneer	CH43/29F	1998
16814	S960KSR	AH	Volvo Olympian OLY-49	East Lancs Pyoneer	CH43/29F	1998
16815	S961KSR	AH	Volvo Olympian OLY-49	East Lancs Pyoneer	CH43/29F	1998
16816	S962KSR	AHL	Volvo Olympian OLY-49	East Lancs Pyoneer	CH43/29F	1998
16846	M490ASW	R	Volvo Olympian YN2RC16C3	Alexander RL	H47/32F	1995
16849	N849VHH	R	Volvo Olympian YN2RC16V3	Alexander RL	H47/32F	1995

16850	N850VHH	G	Volvo Olympian YN2RC16V3	Alexander RL	H47/32F	1995
16851	N851VHH	G	Volvo Olympian YN2RC16V3	Alexander RL	H47/32F	1995
16852	N852VHH	r	Volvo Olympian YN2RC16V3	Alexander RL	H47/32F	1995
16853	N853VHH	CK	Volvo Olympian YN2RC16V3	Alexander RL	H47/32F	1995
16854	N854VHH	r	Volvo Olympian YN2RC16V3	Alexander RL	H47/32F	1995
16855	N855VHH	G	Volvo Olympian YN2RC16V3	Alexander RL	H47/32F	1995
16856	N856VHH	G	Volvo Olympian YN2RC16V3	Alexander RL	H47/32F	1995
16857	N857VHH	G	Volvo Olympian YN2RC16V3	Alexander RL	H47/32F	1995
16858	N858VHH	G	Volvo Olympian YN2RC16V3	Alexander RL	H47/32F	1995
16859	N859VHH	r	Volvo Olympian YN2RC16V3	Alexander RL	H47/32F	1995
16860	N860VHH	G	Volvo Olympian YN2RC16V3	Alexander RL	H47/32F	1995
16861	N861VHH	P	Volvo Olympian YN2RC16V3	Alexander RL	H47/32F	1995
16862	N862VHH	P	Volvo Olympian YN2RC16V3	Alexander RL	H47/32F	1995
16863	N863VHH	r	Volvo Olympian YN2RC16V3	Alexander RL	H47/32F	1995
16864	N864VHH	r	Volvo Olympian YN2RC16V3	Alexander RL	PO47/32F	1995
16865	N865VHH	CK	Volvo Olympian YN2RC16V3	Alexander RL	H47/32F	1995
16866	N866VHH	K	Volvo Olympian YN2RC16V3	Alexander RL	H47/32F	1995
16881	M951XES	BL	Volvo Olympian YN2RV18Z4	Northern Counties Palatine I	CH43/29F	1995
16882	M952XES	BL	Volvo Olympian YN2RV18Z4	Northern Counties Palatine I	CH43/29F	1995
16883	M953XES	DE	Volvo Olympian YN2RV18Z4	Northern Counties Palatine I	CH43/29F	1995
16884	M954XES	AH	Volvo Olympian YN2RV18Z4	Northern Counties Palatine I	CH43/29F	1995
16894	L964MSC	w	Volvo Olympian YN2RC16Z4	Alexander RL	H51/30D	1994
16921	* WLT427	AH	Volvo B7TL	East Lancs Myllennium Vyking	CH47/29F	2001
16922	* 128NNU	DE	Volvo B7TL	East Lancs Myllennium Vyking	CH47/29F	2001
16923	SP51AWX	AH	Volvo B7TL	East Lancs Myllennium Vyking	CH47/29F	2001
16924	ST52NTL	AH	Volvo B7TL	East Lancs Myllennium Vyking	CH47/29F	2002
16925	ST52NTM	AH	Volvo B7TL	East Lancs Myllennium Vyking	CH47/29F	2002
16926	ST52NTN	AH	Volvo B7TL	East Lancs Myllennium Vyking	CH47/29F	2002
16927	ST52NTO	AH	Volvo B7TL	East Lancs Myllennium Vyking	CH47/29F	2002
16928	ST52NTU	AH	Volvo B7TL	East Lancs Myllennium Vyking	CH47/29F	2002
16929	SP03GDJ	AH	Volvo B7TL	East Lancs Myllennium Vyking	CH47/29F	2003
16930	SP03GDK	DE	Volvo B7TL	East Lancs Myllennium Vyking	CH47/29F	2003
16931	SP03GDU	DE	Volvo B7TL	East Lancs Myllennium Vyking	CH47/29F	2003
16932	* WLT743	AH	Volvo B7TL	East Lancs Myllennium Vyking	CH47/29F	2003
16933	SP05FKG	AH	Volvo B7TL	East Lancs Myllennium Vyking	CH47/29F	2005
16934	SP05FKH	AH	Volvo B7TL	East Lancs Myllennium Vyking	CH47/29F	2005
16935	SP05FKJ	AH	Volvo B7TL	East Lancs Myllennium Vyking	CH47/29F	2005
16936	SP05FKK	AH	Volvo B7TL	East Lancs Myllennium Vyking	CH47/29F	2005
16945	SY07CVA	IS	Volvo B9TL	East Lancs Olympus	CH49/26F	2007
16946	SY07CVB	IS	Volvo B9TL	East Lancs Olympus	CH49/26F	2007
16947	SY07CUW	IS	Volvo B9TL	East Lancs Olympus	CH49/26F	2007
16948	SY07CUX	IS	Volvo B9TL	East Lancs Olympus	CH49/26F	2007
17060	T660KPU	S	Dennis Trident 10.5 SLF	Alexander ALX400	H51/26F	1999
17061	T661KPU	P	Dennis Trident 10.5 SLF	Alexander ALX400	H51/26F	1999
18000	SF53BZG	DS	Dennis Trident 2 10.5 SLF	TransBus ALX400	H47/28F	2003
18001	SF53BZH	DS	Dennis Trident 2 10.5 SLF	TransBus ALX400	H47/28F	2003
18002	SF53BZJ	DS	Dennis Trident 2 10.5 SLF	TransBus ALX400	H47/28F	2003
18003	SF53BYV	DS	Dennis Trident 2 10.5 SLF	TransBus ALX400	H47/28F	2003
18004	SF53BYW	AS	Dennis Trident 2 10.5 SLF	TransBus ALX400	H47/28F	2003
18005	SF53BYX	AS	Dennis Trident 2 10.5 SLF	TransBus ALX400	H47/28F	2003
18006	SF53BYY	AS	Dennis Trident 2 10.5 SLF	TransBus ALX400	H47/28F	2003
18007	SF53BYZ	FRC	Dennis Trident 2 10.5 SLF	TransBus ALX400	H47/28F	2003
18008	SF53BZA	TN	Dennis Trident 2 10.5 SLF	TransBus ALX400	H47/28F	2003
18009	SF53BZB	TN	Dennis Trident 2 10.5 SLF	TransBus ALX400	H47/28F	2003
18010	SF53BZC	TN	Dennis Trident 2 10.5 SLF	TransBus ALX400	H47/28F	2003
18011	SF53BZD	TN	Dennis Trident 2 10.5 SLF	TransBus ALX400	H47/28F	2003
18012	SF53BZE	TN	Dennis Trident 2 10.5 SLF	TransBus ALX400	H47/28F	2003
18013	SF53BYL	TN	Dennis Trident 2 10.5 SLF	TransBus ALX400	H47/28F	2003
18014	SF53BYM	D	Dennis Trident 2 10.5 SLF	TransBus ALX400	H47/28F	2003
18015	SF53BYN	D	Dennis Trident 2 10.5 SLF	TransBus ALX400	H47/28F	2003
18016	SF53BYO	D	Dennis Trident 2 10.5 SLF	TransBus ALX400	H47/28F	2003

18092	SP04DBV	A	Dennis Trident 2 10.5 SLF	TransBus ALX400	H47/28F	2004
18093	SP04DBX	A	Dennis Trident 2 10.5 SLF	TransBus ALX400	H47/28F	2004
18094	SP04DBY	A	Dennis Trident 2 10.5 SLF	TransBus ALX400	H47/28F	2004
18095	SP04DBZ	A	Dennis Trident 2 10.5 SLF	TransBus ALX400	H47/28F	2004
18096	SP04DCE	A	Dennis Trident 2 10.5 SLF	TransBus ALX400	H47/28F	2004
18097	SP04DCF	G	Dennis Trident 2 10.5 SLF	TransBus ALX400	H47/28F	2004
18098	SP04DCU	A	Dennis Trident 2 10.5 SLF	TransBus ALX400	H47/28F	2004
18099	SP04DCV	A	Dennis Trident 2 10.5 SLF	TransBus ALX400	H47/28F	2004
18100	SP04DCX	A	Dennis Trident 2 10.5 SLF	TransBus ALX400	H47/28F	2004
18129	KN04XJD	G	TransBus Trident 2 10.45 SLF	TransBus ALX400	H47/28F	2004
18130	KN04XJE	G	TransBus Trident 2 10.45 SLF	TransBus ALX400	H47/28F	2004
18195	KN54ZXR	C	Dennis Trident 2 10.5 SLF	ADL ALX400	H47/28F	2005
18196	KN54ZXL	C	Dennis Trident 2 10.5 SLF	ADL ALX400	H47/28F	2005
18197	KN54ZXM	C	Dennis Trident 2 10.5 SLF	ADL ALX400	H47/28F	2005
18332	SF55NNZ	K	ADL Trident 2 10.4 SLF	ADL ALX400	H47/28F	2005
18333	SF55NOH	K	ADL Trident 2 10.4 SLF	ADL ALX400	H47/28F	2005
18334	SF55NOU	K	ADL Trident 2 10.4 SLF	ADL ALX400	H47/28F	2005
18350	MX55KOU	BLC	ADL Trident 2 10.4 SLF	ADL ALX400	H47/28F	2005
18351	MX55KOV	AHC	ADL Trident 2 10.4 SLF	ADL ALX400	H47/28F	2005
18352	MX55KOW	AH	ADL Trident 2 10.4 SLF	ADL ALX400	H47/28F	2005
18353	MX55KPA	AH	ADL Trident 2 10.4 SLF	ADL ALX400	H47/28F	2005
18369	SF55TZP	K	ADL Trident 2 10.4 SLF	ADL ALX400	H47/28F	2005
18370	SF55TZR	K	ADL Trident 2 10.4 SLF	ADL ALX400	H47/28F	2005
18371	SF55TZS	K	ADL Trident 2 10.4 SLF	ADL ALX400	H47/28F	2005
18389	MX55KSU	AH	ADL Trident 2 10.4 SLF	ADL ALX400	H47/28F	2006
18390	MX55ZNH	AHC	ADL Trident 2 10.4 SLF	ADL ALX400	H47/28F	2006
18506	SP06EGK	BLA	ADL Trident 2 10.4 SLF	ADL ALX400	DPH47/28F	2006
18507	SP06EGU	BL	ADL Trident 2 10.4 SLF	ADL ALX400	DPH47/28F	2006
18508	SP06EGV	BLA	ADL Trident 2 10.4 SLF	ADL ALX400	DPH47/28F	2006
18509	SP06EGX	BLA	ADL Trident 2 10.4 SLF	ADL ALX400	DPH47/28F	2006
19047	MX56FRP	C	ADL Trident 2 10.6 SLF	ADL Enviro 400	H47/33F	2006
19050	MX56FRV	G	ADL Trident 2 10.6 SLF	ADL Enviro 400	H47/33F	2006
19052	MX56FSA	G	ADL Trident 2 10.6 SLF	ADL Enviro 400	H47/33F	2006
19057	MX56FSG	G	ADL Trident 2 10.6 SLF	ADL Enviro 400	H47/33F	2006
19169	SV57BFP	IS	ADL Trident 2 10.6 SLF	ADL Enviro 400	H47/33F	2007
19170	SV57BFU	FW	ADL Trident 2 10.6 SLF	ADL Enviro 400	H47/33F	2007
19171	SV57BFX	IS	ADL Trident 2 10.6 SLF	ADL Enviro 400	H47/33F	2007
19172	SV57BFY	IS	ADL Trident 2 10.6 SLF	ADL Enviro 400	H47/33F	2007
19173	SV57BFZ	TN	ADL Trident 2 10.6 SLF	ADL Enviro 400	H47/33F	2007
19174	SV57BGE	TN	ADL Trident 2 10.6 SLF	ADL Enviro 400	H47/33F	2007
19175	SV57BGF	TN	ADL Trident 2 10.6 SLF	ADL Enviro 400	H47/33F	2007
19176	SV57BGK	TN	ADL Trident 2 10.6 SLF	ADL Enviro 400	H47/33F	2007
19366 *	SP58CXX	P	ADL Trident 2 10.6 SLF	ADL Enviro 400	H47/33F	2008
19367	SP58CXW	P	ADL Trident 2 10.6 SLF	ADL Enviro 400	H47/33F	2008
19368 *	SP58CXV	PG	ADL Trident 2 10.6 SLF	ADL Enviro 400	H47/33F	2008
19369	SV58BLN	TN	ADL Trident 2 10.6 SLF	ADL Enviro 400	H47/33F	2008
19370	SV58BLX	TN	ADL Trident 2 10.6 SLF	ADL Enviro 400	H47/33F	2008
19371	SV58BLZ	TN	ADL Trident 2 10.6 SLF	ADL Enviro 400	H47/33F	2008
19372	SV58BMO	IS	ADL Trident 2 10.6 SLF	ADL Enviro 400	H47/33F	2008
19373 *	SV58BMU	FW	ADL Trident 2 10.6 SLF	ADL Enviro 400	H47/33F	2008
19374	SV58BMY	SV	ADL Trident 2 10.6 SLF	ADL Enviro 400	H47/33F	2008
19375	SV58BMZ	SV	ADL Trident 2 10.6 SLF	ADL Enviro 400	H47/33F	2008
19376	SV58BNA	SV	ADL Trident 2 10.6 SLF	ADL Enviro 400	H47/33F	2008
19377	SV58BNB	FW	ADL Trident 2 10.6 SLF	ADL Enviro 400	H47/33F	2008
19378	SV58BND	SV	ADL Trident 2 10.6 SLF	ADL Enviro 400	H47/33F	2008
19541	SP59APV	G	ADL Trident 2 10.6 SLF	ADL Enviro 400	H47/33F	2009
19542	SP59APX	G	ADL Trident 2 10.6 SLF	ADL Enviro 400	H47/33F	2009
19543	SP59APY	G	ADL Trident 2 10.6 SLF	ADL Enviro 400	H47/33F	2009
19544	SP59AOU	D	ADL Trident 2 10.6 SLF	ADL Enviro 400	H47/33F	2009
19545	SP59AOV	D	ADL Trident 2 10.6 SLF	ADL Enviro 400	H47/33F	2009
19546	SP59AOW	D	ADL Trident 2 10.6 SLF	ADL Enviro 400	H47/33F	2009

19547	SP59AOX	A	ADL Trident 2 10.6 SLF		ADL Enviro 400	H47/33F	2009
19548	SP59AOY	A	ADL Trident 2 10.6 SLF		ADL Enviro 400	H47/33F	2009
19549	SP59AOZ	A	ADL Trident 2 10.6 SLF		ADL Enviro 400	H47/33F	2009
19550	SP59APF	A	ADL Trident 2 10.6 SLF		ADL Enviro 400	H47/33F	2009
19551	SP59APK	A	ADL Trident 2 10.6 SLF		ADL Enviro 400	H47/33F	2009
19552	SP59APO	A	ADL Trident 2 10.6 SLF		ADL Enviro 400	H47/33F	2009
19553	SP59APU	C	ADL Trident 2 10.6 SLF		ADL Enviro 400	H47/33F	2009
19554	SP59AON	C	ADL Trident 2 10.6 SLF		ADL Enviro 400	H47/33F	2009
19555	SP59AOO	C	ADL Trident 2 10.6 SLF		ADL Enviro 400	H47/33F	2009
19556	SP59AOR	C	ADL Trident 2 10.6 SLF		ADL Enviro 400	H47/33F	2009
19557	SP59AOS	C	ADL Trident 2 10.6 SLF		ADL Enviro 400	H47/33F	2009
19558	SP59AOT	AB	ADL Trident 2 10.6 SLF		ADL Enviro 400	H47/33F	2009
19959	UCS659	*WS-p*	Albion FT39N		Alexander	H40/31F	1963
19982	RCS382	*WS-p*	Leyland PD3A/3		Alexander	L35/32RD	1961
20108	N208LTN	w	Volvo B10M-55		Alexander PS	B49F	1995
20109	N209LTN	w	Volvo B10M-55		Alexander PS	B49F	1995
20113	N213LTN	FR	Volvo B10M-55		Alexander PS	B49F	1995
20118	P118XCN	w	Volvo B10M-55		Alexander PS	B49F	1996
20119	P119XCN	SR	Volvo B10M-55		Alexander PS	B49F	1996
20141	R641LSO	r	Volvo B10M-55		Alexander PS	B49F	1997
20142	R642LSO	r	Volvo B10M-55		Alexander PS	B49F	1997
20143	R643LSO	r	Volvo B10M-55		Alexander PS	B49F	1997
20144	R644LSO	r	Volvo B10M-55		Alexander PS	B49F	1997
20145	R645LSO	DS	Volvo B10M-55		Alexander PS	B49F	1997
20146	R646LSO	DS	Volvo B10M-55		Alexander PS	B52F	1997
20147	R647LSO	*ege*	Volvo B10M-55		Alexander PS	B49F	1997
20148	R648LSO	DE	Volvo B10M-55		Alexander PS	B49F	1997
20149	R649LSO	S	Volvo B10M-55		Alexander PS	B49F	1997
20150	R650LSO	P	Volvo B10M-55		Alexander PS	B49F	1997
20151	R651VSE	P	Volvo B10M-55		Alexander PS	B49F	1998
20152	R652VSE	w	Volvo B10M-55		Alexander PS	B49F	1998
20153	R653VSE	r	Volvo B10M-55		Alexander PS	B49F	1998
20154	R654VSE	P	Volvo B10M-55		Alexander PS	B49F	1998
20191	M591OSO	w	Volvo B10M-55		Alexander PS	B49F	1994
20197	M597OSO	AV	Volvo B10M-55		Alexander PS	B49F	1994
20308	L308PSC	AV	Volvo B10M-55		Alexander PS	B49F	1994
20315	M315PKS	*w P*	Volvo B10M-55		Alexander PS	DP48F	1995
20316	N316VMS	DE	Volvo B10M-55		Alexander PS	B49F	1995
20318	N318VMS	r	Volvo B10M-55		Alexander PS	B49F	1995
20322	N322VMS	BL	Volvo B10M-55		Alexander PS	B49F	1995
20323	N323VMS	r	Volvo B10M-55		Alexander PS	B49F	1995
20324	N324VMS	r	Volvo B10M-55		Alexander PS	B49F	1995
20325	N325VMS	AH	Volvo B10M-55		Alexander PS	B49F	1995
20327	N327VMS	w	Volvo B10M-55		Alexander PS	B49F	1996
20330	R330HFS	G	Volvo B10M-55		Alexander PS	B49F	1997
20331	R331HFS	C	Volvo B10M-55		Alexander PS	B49F	1997
20332	R332HFS	AH	Volvo B10M-55		Alexander PS	B49F	1997
20334	R334HFS	G	Volvo B10M-55		Alexander PS	B49F	1998
20335	R335HFS	G	Volvo B10M-55		Alexander PS	B49F	1997
20336	R336HFS	G	Volvo B10M-55		Alexander PS	B49F	1997
20337	R337HFS	G	Volvo B10M-55		Alexander PS	B49F	1997
20338	R338HFS	G	Volvo B10M-55		Alexander PS	B49F	1997
20339	R339HFS	A	Volvo B10M-55		Alexander PS	B49F	1997
20340	R340HFS	C	Volvo B10M-55		Alexander PS	B49F	1997
20341	R341HFS	*PA*	Volvo B10M-55		Alexander PS	B49F	1997
20342	R342HFS	P	Volvo B10M-55		Alexander PS	B49F	1997
20502	R502KSA	DS	Volvo B10M-55		Alexander PS	B49F	1997
20503	R503KSA	DS	Volvo B10M-55		Alexander PS	B49F	1997
20504	R504KSA	SR	Volvo B10M-55		Alexander PS	B49F	1997
20505	M488ASW	DS	Volvo B10M-55		Alexander PS	B49F	1995
20506	M869ASW	r	Volvo B10M-55		Alexander PS	B49F	1995

20507	M871ASW	AN	Volvo B10M-55	Alexander PS	B49F	1995
20509	M469ASW	GW	Volvo B10M-55	Alexander PS	B49F	1995
20511	M483ASW	TN	Volvo B10M-55	Alexander PS	B49F	1995
20514	R514KSA	GW	Volvo B10M-55	Alexander PS	B49F	1997
20515	R515KSA	GW	Volvo B10M-55	Alexander PS	B49F	1997
20516	R516VSE	rbs	Volvo B10M-55	Alexander PS	B49F	1998
20517	R517VSE	bSGW	Volvo B10M-55	Alexander PS	B49F	1998
20518	R518VSE	GW	Volvo B10M-55	Alexander PS	B49F	1998
20519	R519VSE	GW	Volvo B10M-55	Alexander PS	B49F	1998
20521	R521VSE	DS	Volvo B10M-55	Alexander PS	B49F	1998
20522	R522VSE	GW	Volvo B10M-55	Alexander PS	B49F	1998
20524	R524VSE	AN	Volvo B10M-55	Alexander PS	B49F	1998
20526	R526VSE	AN	Volvo B10M-55	Alexander PS	B49F	1998
20532	P532ESA	K	Volvo B10M-55	Alexander PS	B49F	1997
20535	P535ESA	GW	Volvo B10M-55	Alexander PS	B49F	1997
20536	P536ESA	r	Volvo B10M-55	Alexander PS	B49F	1997
20537	P537ESA	AN	Volvo B10M-55	Alexander PS	B49F	1997
20538	P538ESA	AN	Volvo B10M-55	Alexander PS	B49F	1997
20539	P539ESA	AN	Volvo B10M-55	Alexander PS	B49F	1997
20548	P548ESA	SR	Volvo B10M-55	Alexander PS	B49F	1997
20549	P549ESA	K	Volvo B10M-55	Alexander PS	B49F	1997
20556	P556ESA	SR	Volvo B10M-55	Alexander PS	B49F	1997
20566	M486ASW	AV	Volvo B10M-55	Alexander PS	B49F	1995
20567	M487ASW	r	Volvo B10M-55	Alexander PS	B49F	1995
20569	M482ASW	AV	Volvo B10M-55	Alexander PS	B49F	1995
20570	M470ASW	AV	Volvo B10M-55	Alexander PS	B49F	1995
20572	M472ASW	AV	Volvo B10M-55	Alexander PS	B49F	1995
20579	M479ASW	AV	Volvo B10M-55	Alexander PS	B61F	1995
20584	M784PRS	GW	Volvo B10M-55	Alexander PS	B49F	1994
20586	M786PRS	w	Volvo B10M-55	Alexander PS	B49F	1994
20587	M787PRS	r	Volvo B10M-55	Alexander PS	B49F	1994
20588	M788PRS	w	Volvo B10M-55	Alexander PS	B49F	1994
20589	M789PRS	r	Volvo B10M-55	Alexander PS	B49F	1994
20590	M790PRS	r	Volvo B10M-55	Alexander PS	B49F	1994
20591	M791PRS	TU	Volvo B10M-55	Alexander PS	B61F	1994
20594 ·	M467ASW	FN	Volvo B10M-55	Alexander PS	B49F	1995
20595	R595LSO	AN	Volvo B10M-55	Alexander PS	B49F	1997
20596	R596LSO	AN	Volvo B10M-55	Alexander PS	B49F	1997
20860	P860GND	w	Volvo B10M-55	Alexander PS	B49F	1996
20861	P861GND	AB-r	Volvo B10M-55	Alexander PS	B49F	1996
20862	P862GND	r	Volvo B10M-55	Alexander PS	B49F	1996
20863	P863GND	w	Volvo B10M-55	Alexander PS	B49F	1996
20864	P864GND	w	Volvo B10M-55	Alexander PS	B49F	1996
20865	P865GND	r	Volvo B10M-55	Alexander PS	B49F	1996
20866	P866GND	AB-r	Volvo B10M-55	Alexander PS	B49F	1996
20868	P868GND	r	Volvo B10M-55	Alexander PS	B49F	1996
20875	P875MNE	r	Volvo B10M-55	Northern Counties Paladin	B48F	1997
20878	P878MNE	r	Volvo B10M-55	Northern Counties Paladin	B48F	1997
20879	P879MNE	r	Volvo B10M-55	Northern Counties Paladin	B48F	1997
20881	P881MNE	SV	Volvo B10M-55	Northern Counties Paladin	B48F	1997
20893	P893MNE	w	Volvo B10M-55	Northern Counties Paladin	B48F	1997
20916	R916XVM	P	Volvo B10M-55	Alexander PS	B49F	1997
20920	R920XVM	PO	Volvo B10M-55	Alexander PS	B49F	1997
20922 ·	R922XVM	PO	Volvo B10M-55	Alexander PS	B49F	1997
20925 ·	R925XVM	PO	Volvo B10M-55	Alexander PS	B49F	1997
20926	R926XVM	PO	Volvo B10M-55	Alexander PS	B49F	1997
20927	R927XVM	P	Volvo B10M-55	Alexander PS	B49F	1997
20929	R929XVM	PO	Volvo B10M-55	Alexander PS	B49F	1997
20932	R932XVM	AB	Volvo B10M-55	Alexander PS	B49F	1997
20935	R935XVM	AB	Volvo B10M-55	Alexander PS	B49F	1997
20937	R937XVM	AB	Volvo B10M-55	Alexander PS	B49F	1997

20939	R939XVM	PO	Volvo B10M-55	Alexander PS	B49F	1997
20941	R941XVM	AB	Volvo B10M-55	Alexander PS	B49F	1997
20946	R946XVM	PO	Volvo B10M-55	Alexander PS	B49F	1997
20947	R947XVM	r	Volvo B10M-55	Alexander PS	B49F	1997
20948	R948XVM	AB	Volvo B10M-55	Alexander PS	B49F	1997
20951	R951XVM	r	Volvo B10M-55	Alexander PS	B49F	1997
20953	R953XVM	AB	Volvo B10M-55	Alexander PS	B49F	1997
20954	R954XVM	AB	Volvo B10M-55	Alexander PS	B49F	1997
20957	R957XVM	IS	Volvo B10M-55	Alexander PS	B49F	1997
20958	R958XVM	IS	Volvo B10M-55	Alexander PS	B49F	1997
20964	R964XVM	AH	Volvo B10M-55	Alexander PS	B49F	1997
20988	R988XVM	r	Volvo B10M-55	Plaxton Paladin	B48F	1998
20989	R989XVM	AB	Volvo B10M-55	Plaxton Paladin	B48F	1998
20990	R990XVM	AB	Volvo B10M-55	Plaxton Paladin	B48F	1998
20991	R991XVM	AB	Volvo B10M-55	Plaxton Paladin	B48F	1998
20992	R992XVM	AB	Volvo B10M-55	Plaxton Paladin	B48F	1998
20993	R993XVM	AB	Volvo B10M-55	Plaxton Paladin	B48F	1998
20996	R996XVM	r	Volvo B10M-55	Plaxton Paladin	B48F	1998
21020	P367UUG	r	Volvo B10B-58	Wright Endurance	DP49F	1996
21021	P368UUG	r	Volvo B10B-58	Wright Endurance	DP49F	1996
~~21051~~	~~* M151FGB~~	~~r~~	~~Volvo B10B-58~~	~~Wright Endurance~~	~~B51F~~	~~1994~~
21124	* PSU374	DE	Volvo B10BLE	Wright Renown	B47F	1998
21125	* PSU375	FR	Volvo B10BLE	Wright Renown	DP47F	1998
21126	* PSU376	BL	Volvo B10BLE	Wright Renown	DP47F	1998
21127	R526TWR	BL	Volvo B10BLE	Wright Renown	DP47F	1998
21128	R527TWR	BL	Volvo B10BLE	Wright Renown	DP47F	1998
21168	W747NAS	FW	Volvo B10BLE	Alexander ALX300	B44F	2000
21201	SF55RKA	DS	Volvo B7RLE	Wright Eclipse Urban	C51F	2005
21202	SF55RKE	DS	Volvo B7RLE	Wright Eclipse Urban	C51F	2005
21203	SY07CEX	IS	Volvo B7RLE	Wright Eclipse Urban	B41F	2007
21204	SY07CFA	IS	Volvo B7RLE	Wright Eclipse Urban	B41F	2007
21205	SY07CFD	IS	Volvo B7RLE	Wright Eclipse Urban	B41F	2006
21206	SY07CFU	IS	Volvo B7RLE	Wright Eclipse Urban	B41F	2007
21207	SY07CNJ	IS	Volvo B7RLE	Wright Eclipse Urban	B41F	2007
22109	S109TRJ	AB	MAN 18.220	Alexander ALX300	B42F	1998
22110	S110TRJ	AB	MAN 18.220	Alexander ALX300	B42F	1998
22112	S112TRJ	AB	MAN 18.220	Alexander ALX300	B42F	1998
22252	V252ESX	DE	MAN 18.220	Alexander ALX300	B42F	1999
22254	* GSU950	AB	MAN 18.220	Alexander ALX300	B42F	1999
22255	V255ESX	AB	MAN 18.220	Alexander ALX300	B42F	1999
22258	V258ESX	AY	MAN 18.220	Alexander ALX300	B42F	1999
22259	V259ESX	DE	MAN 18.220	Alexander ALX300	B42F	1999
22261	* BSK756	AB	MAN 18.220	Alexander ALX300	B42F	1999
22262	V262ESX	r	MAN 18.220	Alexander ALX300	B42F	1999
22263	V263ESX	S	MAN 18.220	Alexander ALX300	B42F	1999
22264	V264ESX	P	MAN 18.220	Alexander ALX300	B42F	1999
22265	* NSU132	AB	MAN 18.220	Alexander ALX300	B42F	1999
22266	V266ESX	rS	MAN 18.220	Alexander ALX300	B42F	1999
22267	V267ESX	rG	MAN 18.220	Alexander ALX300	B42F	1999
22268	V268ESX	SE	MAN 18.220	Alexander ALX300	B42F	1999
22271	X271MTS	DE	MAN 18.220	Alexander ALX300	B42F	2000
22272	X272MTS	AB	MAN 18.220	Alexander ALX300	B42F	2000
22273	X273MTS	AB	MAN 18.220	Alexander ALX300	B42F	2000
22276	X276MTS	GS	MAN 18.220	Alexander ALX300	B42F	2000
22277	X277MTS	rc	MAN 18.220	Alexander ALX300	B42F	2000
22349	SV55CCU	C	MAN 18.220	Alexander ALX300	B42F	2005
22350	SV55CCX	C	MAN 18.220	Alexander ALX300	B42F	2005
22351	SV55CCY	AB	MAN 18.220	Alexander ALX300	B42F	2005
22352	SV55CCZ	AB	MAN 18.220	Alexander ALX300	B42F	2005
22353	SV55CAA	AL	MAN 18.220	Alexander ALX300	B42F	2005
22354	SV55CAE	AB	MAN 18.220	Alexander ALX300	B42F	2005

22355	SV55CAO	SV	MAN 18.220	Alexander ALX300	B42F	2005
22356	SV55CAU	SV	MAN 18.220	Alexander ALX300	B42F	2005
22357	SV55CAX	SV	MAN 18.220	Alexander ALX300	B42F	2005
22358	SV55CBF	SV	MAN 18.220	Alexander ALX300	B42F	2005
22359	SV55CBO	SV	MAN 18.220	Alexander ALX300	B42F	2005
22360	SV55CBU	SV	MAN 18.220	Alexander ALX300	B42F	2005
22361	SV55CBX	SV	MAN 18.220	Alexander ALX300	B42F	2005
22362	SV55CBY	SV	MAN 18.220	Alexander ALX300	B42F	2005
22363	SV55EEJ	SV	MAN 18.220	Alexander ALX300	B42F	2005
22364	SV55EEM	SV	MAN 18.220	Alexander ALX300	B42F	2005
22367	SP55EHB	G	MAN 18.220	Alexander ALX300	B42F	2006
22368	SP55EHC	G	MAN 18.220	Alexander ALX300	B42F	2006
22369	SP55EGC	G	MAN 18.220	Alexander ALX300	B42F	2006
22370	SP55EGD	G	MAN 18.220	Alexander ALX300	B42F	2006
22371	SP55EGE	G	MAN 18.220	Alexander ALX300	B42F	2006
22372	SP55EGF	G	MAN 18.220	Alexander ALX300	B42F	2006
22373	SP55EGJ	G	MAN 18.220	Alexander ALX300	B42F	2006
22374	SP55EGK	G	MAN 18.220	Alexander ALX300	B42F	2006
22375	SP55EGU	G	MAN 18.220	Alexander ALX300	B42F	2006
22376	SP55EGV	G	MAN 18.220	Alexander ALX300	B42F	2006
22377	SP55EGX	G	MAN 18.220	Alexander ALX300	B42F	2006
22378	SP55EGY	G	MAN 18.220	Alexander ALX300	B42F	2006
22379	SF55RJV	DS	MAN 18.220	Alexander ALX300	B42F	2006
22380	SF55RJX	DS	MAN 18.220	Alexander ALX300	B42F	2006
22381	SF55RJY	DS	MAN 18.220	Alexander ALX300	B42F	2006
22382	SF55RJZ	DS	MAN 18.220	Alexander ALX300	B42F	2006
22383	SF55RKJ	DS	MAN 18.220	Alexander ALX300	B42F	2006
22384	SF55RKK	AY	MAN 18.220	Alexander ALX300	B42F	2006
22385	SF55RKN	AY	MAN 18.220	Alexander ALX300	B42F	2006
22386	SF55VUM	AY	MAN 18.220	Alexander ALX300	B42F	2006
22387	SF55VUN	AY	MAN 18.220	Alexander ALX300	B42F	2006
22388	SF55VUO	AY	MAN 18.220	Alexander ALX300	B42F	2006
22389	SF55VUP	AY	MAN 18.220	Alexander ALX300	B42F	2006
22390	SF55VUR	AY	MAN 18.220	Alexander ALX300	B42F	2006
22400	SP06DAO	S D	MAN 18.220	Alexander ALX300	B42F	2006
22401	SP06DAU	S C	MAN 18.220	Alexander ALX300	B42F	2006
22402	SP06DBO	S C	MAN 18.220	Alexander ALX300	B42F	2006
22403	SP06DBU	S	MAN 18.220	Alexander ALX300	B42F	2006
22404	SP06DBV	S	MAN 18.220	Alexander ALX300	B42F	2006
22405	SP06DBX	S	MAN 18.220	Alexander ALX300	B42F	2006
22406	SP06DBY	C	MAN 18.220	Alexander ALX300	B42F	2006
22407	SP06DBZ	S	MAN 18.220	Alexander ALX300	B42F	2006
22501	SP56FGO	P	MAN 18.240	East Lancs Kinetic	B43F	2007
22502	SP07EWL	P	MAN 18.240	East Lancs Kinetic	B43F	2007
22503	SP56FGV	P	MAN 18.240	East Lancs Kinetic	B43F	2007
22504	SP56FGX	P	MAN 18.240	East Lancs Kinetic	B43F	2007
22505	SP56FGZ	P	MAN 18.240	East Lancs Kinetic	B43F	2007
22506	SP56AGO	P	MAN 18.240	East Lancs Kinetic	B43F	2007
22507	SP56AGU	P	MAN 18.240	East Lancs Kinetic	B43F	2007
22508	SF56FKL	AY	MAN 18.240	East Lancs Kinetic	B43F	2006
22509	SF56FKM	AY	MAN 18.240	East Lancs Kinetic	B43F	2007
22510	SF56FKN	AY	MAN 18.240	East Lancs Kinetic	B43F	2007
22511	SF56FKO	AY	MAN 18.240	East Lancs Kinetic	B43F	2007
22512	SF56FKP	AY	MAN 18.240	East Lancs Kinetic	B43F	2007
22513	SF56FKR	AY	MAN 18.240	East Lancs Kinetic	B43F	2007
22514	SF56FKS	AY	MAN 18.240	East Lancs Kinetic	B43F	2007
22515	SF56FKT	SR	MAN 18.240	East Lancs Kinetic	B43F	2007
22516	SF56FKU	SR	MAN 18.240	East Lancs Kinetic	B43F	2007
22521	SF57LUB	AS	MAN 18.240	ADL Enviro 300	B45F	2008
22522	SF57LUD	AS	MAN 18.240	ADL Enviro 300	B45F	2008
22523	SF57LUE	AS	MAN 18.240	ADL Enviro 300	B45F	2008

22524		SF57LUH	AS	MAN 18.240	ADL Enviro 300	B45F	2008
22525		SF57LUJ	AS	MAN 18.240	ADL Enviro 300	B45F	2008
22526		SF57LUL	AS	MAN 18.240	ADL Enviro 300	B45F	2008
22527		SF57LUO	AS	MAN 18.240	ADL Enviro 300	B45F	2008
22528		SF57LUP	AY	MAN 18.240	ADL Enviro 300	B45F	2008
22529		SF57LUR	AY	MAN 18.240	ADL Enviro 300	B45F	2008
22530		SF57LUW	AY	MAN 18.240	ADL Enviro 300	B45F	2008
22531		SF57LUY	AY	MAN 18.240	ADL Enviro 300	B45F	2008
22532		SF57LUZ	AY	MAN 18.240	ADL Enviro 300	B45F	2008
22533		SF57LVB	AY	MAN 18.240	ADL Enviro 300	B45F	2008
22534		SF57LVC	CK	MAN 18.240	ADL Enviro 300	B45F	2008
22564		SP08DBY	DE	MAN 18.240	ADL Enviro 300	B45F	2008
22565		SP08DBZ	DE	MAN 18.240	ADL Enviro 300	B45F	2008
22566		SP08DCE	DE	MAN 18.240	ADL Enviro 300	B45F	2008
22567		SP08DCF	DE	MAN 18.240	ADL Enviro 300	B45F	2008
22568		SP08DCO	DE	MAN 18.240	ADL Enviro 300	B45F	2008
22569		SP08DCU	DE	MAN 18.240	ADL Enviro 300	B45F	2008
22570		SP08DCV	DE	MAN 18.240	ADL Enviro 300	B45F	2008
22571		SP08DCX	DE	MAN 18.240	ADL Enviro 300	B45F	2008
22572		SP08DCY	DE	MAN 18.240	ADL Enviro 300	B45F	2008
22573		SP08DCZ	AH	MAN 18.240	ADL Enviro 300	B45F	2008
22574		SP08DDA	FN	MAN 18.240	ADL Enviro 300	B45F	2008
22575		SP08DDE	P	MAN 18.240	ADL Enviro 300	B45F	2008
22576		SP08DDF	P	MAN 18.240	ADL Enviro 300	B45F	2008
22577		SP08DDJ	P	MAN 18.240	ADL Enviro 300	B45F	2008
22578		SP08DDK	AH	MAN 18.240	ADL Enviro 300	B45F	2008
22579		SP08DDL	AH	MAN 18.240	ADL Enviro 300	B45F	2008
22580		SP08DDN	A	MAN 18.240	ADL Enviro 300	B45F	2008
22581		SP08DDO	A	MAN 18.240	ADL Enviro 300	B45F	2008
22582		SF08GOK	CK	MAN 18.240	ADL Enviro 300	B45F	2008
22583		SF08GOU	CK	MAN 18.240	ADL Enviro 300	B45F	2008
22584		SF08GOX	CK	MAN 18.240	ADL Enviro 300	B45F	2008
22585		SF08GPE	CK	MAN 18.240	ADL Enviro 300	B45F	2008
22586		SF08GPJ	CK	MAN 18.240	ADL Enviro 300	B45F	2008
22587		SF08GPK	CK	MAN 18.240	ADL Enviro 300	B45F	2008
22588		SF08GPU	CK	MAN 18.240	ADL Enviro 300	B45F	2008
22589		SF08GPV	CK	MAN 18.240	ADL Enviro 300	B45F	2008
22590		SF08GPX	CK	MAN 18.240	ADL Enviro 300	B45F	2008
22591		SF08GPY	CK	MAN 18.240	ADL Enviro 300	B45F	2008
22592		SF08GPZ	CK	MAN 18.240	ADL Enviro 300	B45F	2008
22593		SF08GRK	CK	MAN 18.240	ADL Enviro 300	B45F	2008
22594		SF08GRU	CK	MAN 18.240	ADL Enviro 300	B45F	2008
22601	*	V601GCS	DS	MAN 18.220	Alexander ALX300	B42F	1999
22602		V602GCS	DS	MAN 18.220	Alexander ALX300	B42F	1999
22603		V603GCS	P	MAN 18.220	Alexander ALX300	B42F	1999
22604		V604GCS	P	MAN 18.220	Alexander ALX300	B42F	1999
22605		V605GCS	AY	MAN 18.220	Alexander ALX300	B42F	1999
22606		V606GCS	DS	MAN 18.220	Alexander ALX300	B42F	1999
22701		V701DSA	AB	MAN 18.220	Alexander ALX300	B42F	1999
22702		V702DSA	AB	MAN 18.220	Alexander ALX300	B42F	1999
22703		V703DSA	AB	MAN 18.220	Alexander ALX300	B42F	1999
22704		V704DSA	SV	MAN 18.220	Alexander ALX300	B42F	1999
22705		V705DSA	AB	MAN 18.220	Alexander ALX300	B42F	1999
22706		V706DSA	AB	MAN 18.220	Alexander ALX300	B42F	1999
22707		V707DSA	AB	MAN 18.220	Alexander ALX300	B42F	1999
22708		V708DSA	AB	MAN 18.220	Alexander ALX300	B42F	1999
22709		V709DSA	AB	MAN 18.220	Alexander ALX300	B42F	1999
22710		V710DSA	AB	MAN 18.220	Alexander ALX300	B42F	1999
22711		V711DSA	AB	MAN 18.220	Alexander ALX300	B42F	1999
22712		V712DSA	DE	MAN 18.220	Alexander ALX300	B42F	1999
22713		V713DSA	DS	MAN 18.220	Alexander ALX300	B42F	1999

|---|---|---|---|---|---|---|
				Stagecoach Scotland		
22714	X714NSE	P	MAN 18.220	Alexander ALX300	B42F	2000
22715	X715NSE	P	MAN 18.220	Alexander ALX300	B42F	2000
22716	X716NSE	P	MAN 18.220	Alexander ALX300	B42F	2000
22717	X717NSE	P	MAN 18.220	Alexander ALX300	B42F	2000
22718	X718NSE	P	MAN 18.220	Alexander ALX300	B42F	2000
22719	X719NSE	P	MAN 18.220	Alexander ALX300	B42F	2000
22722	X722NSE	SC	MAN 18.220	Alexander ALX300	B42F	2000
22802	V802DFV	AB	MAN 18.220	Alexander ALX300	B42F	1999
22803	V803DFV	AB	MAN 18.220	Alexander ALX300	B42F	1999
22850	SF09ADV	AY	MAN 18.240	ADL Enviro 300	B42F	2009
22851	SF09ADX	AY	MAN 18.240	ADL Enviro 300	B42F	2009
22852	SF09ADZ	AY	MAN 18.240	ADL Enviro 300	B42F	2009
22853	SF09AEA	AY	MAN 18.240	ADL Enviro 300	B42F	2009
22854	SF09AEB	AY	MAN 18.240	ADL Enviro 300	B42F	2009
22855	SF09AED	AY	MAN 18.240	ADL Enviro 300	B42F	2009
22856	SF09AEE	AY	MAN 18.240	ADL Enviro 300	B42F	2009
22857	SF09AEG	K	MAN 18.240	ADL Enviro 300	B42F	2009
22858	SF09AEJ	K	MAN 18.240	ADL Enviro 300	B42F	2009
22859	SF09AEK	K	MAN 18.240	ADL Enviro 300	B42F	2009
22860	SF09AEL	AY	MAN 18.240	ADL Enviro 300	B42F	2009
22861	SF09AEM	K	MAN 18.240	ADL Enviro 300	B42F	2009
22862	SF09AEN	K	MAN 18.240	ADL Enviro 300	B42F	2009
22863	SF09AEO	K	MAN 18.240	ADL Enviro 300	DP42F	2009
22864	SF09AEP	K	MAN 18.240	ADL Enviro 300	DP42F	2009
22865	SF09AET	K	MAN 18.240	ADL Enviro 300	DP42F	2009
22866	SF09AEU	K	MAN 18.240	ADL Enviro 300	DP42F	2009
22867	SF09AEV	K	MAN 18.240	ADL Enviro 300	DP42F	2009
22868	SF09AEW	K	MAN 18.240	ADL Enviro 300	DP42F	2009
22869	SF09AEX	K	MAN 18.240	ADL Enviro 300	DP42F	2009
22870	SF09AEY	K	MAN 18.240	ADL Enviro 300	DP42F	2009
22871	SF09AEZ	K	MAN 18.240	ADL Enviro 300	DP42F	2009
22872	SP09DPF	C	MAN 18.240	ADL Enviro 300	B42F	2009
22873	SP09DPK	C	MAN 18.240	ADL Enviro 300	B42F	2009
22874	SP09DPN	C	MAN 18.240	ADL Enviro 300	B42F	2009
22875	SP09DPO	C	MAN 18.240	ADL Enviro 300	B42F	2009
22876	SP09DPU	C	MAN 18.240	ADL Enviro 300	B42F	2009
22877	SP09DPV	C	MAN 18.240	ADL Enviro 300	B42F	2009
22878	SP09DPX	C	MAN 18.240	ADL Enviro 300	B42F	2009
22879	SP09DPY	C	MAN 18.240	ADL Enviro 300	B42F	2009
22880	SP09DPZ	C	MAN 18.240	ADL Enviro 300	B42F	2009
22881	SP09DRO	S	MAN 18.240	ADL Enviro 300	B42F	2009
22882	SP09DRV	C	MAN 18.240	ADL Enviro 300	B42F	2009
22883	SP09DRX	C	MAN 18.240	ADL Enviro 300	B42F	2009
22884	SP09DRZ	C	MAN 18.240	ADL Enviro 300	B42F	2009
22885	SP09DSE	C	MAN 18.240	ADL Enviro 300	B42F	2009
22886	SP09DSO	C	MAN 18.240	ADL Enviro 300	B42F	2009
22887	SP09DOH	C	MAN 18.240	ADL Enviro 300	B42F	2009
22888	SP09DOJ	C	MAN 18.240	ADL Enviro 300	B42F	2009
22889	SP09DOU	C	MAN 18.240	ADL Enviro 300	B42F	2009
22890	SP09DPE	C	MAN 18.240	ADL Enviro 300	B42F	2009
24001	SP57CNE	D	Scania K270UB6	Scania OmniLink	B51F	2007
24002	SP57CNF	D	Scania K270UB6	Scania OmniLink	B51F	2007
24003	SP57CNJ	D	Scania K270UB6	Scania OmniLink	B51F	2007
24004	SP57CNK	D	Scania K270UB6	Scania OmniLink	B51F	2007
24005	SP57CNN	D	Scania K270UB6	Scania OmniLink	B51F	2007
24006	SP57CNO	D	Scania K270UB6	Scania OmniLink	B51F	2007
24007	SP57CNU	D	Scania K270UB6	Scania OmniLink	B51F	2007
24008	SP57CNV	D	Scania K270UB6	Scania OmniLink	B51F	2007
24009	SP57CNX	D	Scania K270UB6	Scania OmniLink	B51F	2007
24183	* B10PSV	K	MAN A70 18.250 HOCL-NL	ADL Enviro 300	B46F	2010
24184	SF10BYV	K	MAN A70 18.250 HOCL-NL	ADL Enviro 300	B46F	2010

24185	SF10BYW	K	MAN A70 18.250 HOCL-NL	ADL Enviro 300	B46F	2010
24186	SF10BYX	K	MAN A70 18.250 HOCL-NL	ADL Enviro 300	B46F	2010
24187	SF10BYY	K	MAN A70 18.250 HOCL-NL	ADL Enviro 300	B46F	2010
24188	SF10BYZ	K	MAN A70 18.250 HOCL-NL	ADL Enviro 300	B46F	2010
24189	SF10BZA	K	MAN A70 18.250 HOCL-NL	ADL Enviro 300	B46F	2010
24190	SF10BZB	K	MAN A70 18.250 HOCL-NL	ADL Enviro 300	B46F	2010
24191	SF10BZC	K	MAN A70 18.250 HOCL-NL	ADL Enviro 300	B46F	2010
25201	SJ57AAE	K	Optare Versa V1100	Optare	B38F	2007
25202	SJ57AAF	K	Optare Versa V1100	Optare	B38F	2007
25218	SF08GOA	K	Optare Versa V1100	Optare	B38F	2008
25219	SF08GOC	K	Optare Versa V1100	Optare	B38F	2008
25220	SF08GOE	K	Optare Versa V1100	Optare	B38F	2008
25221	SF08GOJ	K	Optare Versa V1100	Optare	B38F	2008
25235	SF09AFA	DS	Optare Versa V1100	Optare	B38F	2009
25236	SF09AFE	DS	Optare Versa V1100	Optare	B38F	2009
25475	* OIW7025	K-a	Leyland National 11351A/3R	Leyland National	B44F	1979
25728	* WLT546	WS-p	Leyland Leopard PSU3F/4R	Plaxton Supreme Exp.	C49F	1981
27051	* SY51EHT	SE	Dennis Javelin 12SFD	Plaxton Premiere 320	C70F	2002
27052	SY51EHU	AV	Dennis Javelin 12SFD	Plaxton Premiere 320	C70F	2002
27053	SY51EHV	AV	Dennis Javelin 12SFD	Plaxton Premiere 320	C70F	2002
27054	SY51EHX	CT	Dennis Javelin 12SFD	Plaxton Premiere 320	C70F	2002
27055	SY51EHZ	SE	Dennis Javelin 12SFD	Plaxton Premiere 320	C70F	2002
27056	* MXI694	SE	Dennis Javelin 12SFD	Plaxton Premiere 320	C70F	2002
27057	YX05FEK	TN	Dennis Javelin 12SFD	Plaxton Profile	C70F	2005
27091	* D6BUS	R	Dennis Javelin 12SDA	Wadham Stringer Vanguard II	DP70F	1993
27092	* BHZ9543	R	Dennis Javelin 12SDA	Wadham Stringer Vanguard II	DP70F	1992
27093	* K966SUS	w	Dennis Javelin 12SFD	Wadham Stringer Vanguard II	DP70F	1993
27094	* BHZ9549	R	Dennis Javelin 12SFD	Wadham Stringer Vanguard	DP70F	1994
27095	* N887HSX	w	Dennis Javelin 12SFD	Wadham Stringer Vanguard	DP70F	1995
27096	* NXX451	R	Dennis Javelin 12SFD	Wadham Stringer Vanguard	DP70F	1995
27097	* BHZ9548	R	Dennis Javelin 12SFD	UVG UniStar	DP70F	1997
27098	R849CJS	r	Dennis Javelin 12SFD	UVG UniStar	DP69F	1998
27524	SP57CNY	P	ADL Enviro 300 12.0 SLF	ADL Enviro 300	DP48F	2007
27525	SP57CNZ	P	ADL Enviro 300 12.0 SLF	ADL Enviro 300	DP48F	2007
27526	SP57COA	P	ADL Enviro 300 12.0 SLF	ADL Enviro 300	DP48F	2007
27527	SP57COH	P	ADL Enviro 300 12.0 SLF	ADL Enviro 300	DP48F	2007
27528	SP57COJ	P	ADL Enviro 300 12.0 SLF	ADL Enviro 300	DP48F	2007
27529	SP57COU	P	ADL Enviro 300 12.0 SLF	ADL Enviro 300	DP48F	2007
27530	SP57CPE	P	ADL Enviro 300 12.0 SLF	ADL Enviro 300	DP48F	2007
27531	SP57DFD	P	ADL Enviro 300 12.0 SLF	ADL Enviro 300	DP48F	2007
27532	SV57BYM	AB	ADL Enviro 300 12.0 SLF	ADL Enviro 300	B44F	2007
27533	SV57BYN	AB	ADL Enviro 300 12.0 SLF	ADL Enviro 300	B44F	2007
27534	SV57BYP	AB	ADL Enviro 300 12.0 SLF	ADL Enviro 300	B44F	2007
27535	SV57BYR	AB	ADL Enviro 300 12.0 SLF	ADL Enviro 300	B44F	2007
27536	SV57BYS	AB	ADL Enviro 300 12.0 SLF	ADL Enviro 300	B44F	2007
27537	SV57BYT	AB	ADL Enviro 300 12.0 SLF	ADL Enviro 300	B44F	2007
27538	SV57BYU	AB	ADL Enviro 300 12.0 SLF	ADL Enviro 300	B44F	2007
27539	SV57BYW	ABC	ADL Enviro 300 12.0 SLF	ADL Enviro 300	B44F	2007
27540	SV57BYX	ABC	ADL Enviro 300 12.0 SLF	ADL Enviro 300	B44F	2007
27541	SV57BYY	ABC	ADL Enviro 300 12.0 SLF	ADL Enviro 300	B44F	2007
27545	SP58BYX	P	ADL Enviro 300 12.0 SLF	ADL Enviro 300	DP42F	2008
27546	SP58BYY	P	ADL Enviro 300 12.0 SLF	ADL Enviro 300	DP42F	2008
27547	SP58BZA	DE	ADL Enviro 300 12.0 SLF	ADL Enviro 300	DP42F	2008
27548	SP58BZB	DE	ADL Enviro 300 12.0 SLF	ADL Enviro 300	DP42F	2009
27549	SP58BZC	DE	ADL Enviro 300 12.0 SLF	ADL Enviro 300	DP42F	2009
27550	SP58BZD	FR	ADL Enviro 300 12.0 SLF	ADL Enviro 300	DP42F	2008
27551	SP58BZE	AH	ADL Enviro 300 12.0 SLF	ADL Enviro 300	DP42F	2008
27552	SP58BZF	DE	ADL Enviro 300 12.0 SLF	ADL Enviro 300	DP42F	2008
27586	SN06BSU	SE	ADL Enviro 300 12.5 SLF	ADL Enviro 300	B60F	2006
27587	SN56AXR	SE	ADL Enviro 300 12.5 SLF	ADL Enviro 300	B60F	2007
27588	SN56AXS	CT	ADL Enviro 300 12.5 SLF	ADL Enviro 300	B60F	2007

27589	SN56AXT	SE	ADL Enviro 300 12.5 SLF	ADL Enviro 300		B60F	2007
27590	SN56AXU	CT	ADL Enviro 300 12.5 SLF	ADL Enviro 300		B60F	2007
27591	SN56AXV	CT	ADL Enviro 300 12.5 SLF	ADL Enviro 300		B60F	2007
27596	SN08AEJ	K	ADL Enviro 300 12.5 SLF	ADL Enviro 300		B60F	2008
27597	SN08AEK	K	ADL Enviro 300 12.5 SLF	ADL Enviro 300		B60F	2008
27601	SV59DDZ	MY	ADL Enviro 300 12.0 SLF	ADL Enviro 300		B42F	2009
27602	SV59DEU	MY	ADL Enviro 300 12.0 SLF	ADL Enviro 300		B42F	2009
27603	SP59CTF	D	ADL Enviro 300 12.0 SLF	ADL Enviro 300		B42F	2009
27604	SP59CTK	D	ADL Enviro 300 12.0 SLF	ADL Enviro 300		B42F	2009
27605	SP59CTO	D	ADL Enviro 300 12.0 SLF	ADL Enviro 300		B42F	2009
27606	SP59CTU	D	ADL Enviro 300 12.0 SLF	ADL Enviro 300		B42F	2009
27607	SP59CTV	D	ADL Enviro 300 12.0 SLF	ADL Enviro 300		B42F	2009
27608	SP59CTX	D	ADL Enviro 300 12.0 SLF	ADL Enviro 300		B42F	2009
27609	SP59CTY	C	ADL Enviro 300 12.0 SLF	ADL Enviro 300		B42F	2009
27610	SP59CTZ	G	ADL Enviro 300 12.0 SLF	ADL Enviro 300		B42F	2009
27611	SP59CUA	C	ADL Enviro 300 12.0 SLF	ADL Enviro 300		B42F	2009
27612	SP59CTC	G	ADL Enviro 300 12.0 SLF	ADL Enviro 300		B42F	2009
27613	SP59CTG	G	ADL Enviro 300 12.0 SLF	ADL Enviro 300		B42F	2009
27614	SF59FUT	K	ADL Enviro 300 12.0 SLF	ADL Enviro 300		B42F	2009
27615	SF59FUU	K	ADL Enviro 300 12.0 SLF	ADL Enviro 300		B42F	2009
27631	SV10DMZ	TU	ADL Enviro 300 12.0 SLF	ADL Enviro 300		B42F	2010
27632	SV10DND	TU	ADL Enviro 300 12.0 SLF	ADL Enviro 300		B42F	2010
28955	M100AAB	GW	Scania L113CRL	Northern Counties Paladin	DP49F	1994
29717	SN05FCU	R	BMC Probus 850RE	BMC		C35F	2005
29718	SN05FCX	R	BMC Probus 850RE	BMC		C35F	2005
29862	BX06NZV	R	Autosan A1012T	Autosan Eagle		C70F	2006
29863	BX56XAY	R	Autosan A1012T	Autosan Eagle		C70F	2006
29864	BX56XAZ	R	Autosan A1012T	Autosan Eagle		C70F	2006
30339	M739BSJ	WS-p	Volvo B6-50	Alexander Dash		B40F	1994
31370	P370DSA	r	Volvo B6LE-53	Alexander ALX200		B36F	1997
31377	P377DSA	w	Volvo B6LE-53	Alexander ALX200		B36F	1997
31379	P379DSA	r	Volvo B6LE-53	Alexander ALX200		B36F	1997
31387	Y601TSD	AY	Volvo B6BLE	Wright Crusader		B36F	2001
31388	Y602TSD	AY	Volvo B6BLE	Wright Crusader		B36F	2001
31491	P491BRS	w	Volvo B6LE	Wright Crusader		B36F	1996
31493	P493BRS	w	Volvo B6LE	Alexander ALX200		B36F	1996
31494	P494BRS	w	Volvo B6LE	Alexander ALX200		B36F	1996
31495	P495BRS	w	Volvo B6LE	Alexander ALX200		B36F	1996
31496	P496BRS	w	Volvo B6LE	Alexander ALX200		B36F	1996
31497	P497BRS	P	Volvo B6LE	Alexander ALX200		B36F	1996
31498	P498BRS	w	Volvo B6LE	Alexander ALX200		B36F	1996
31499	P499BRS	w	Volvo B6LE	Alexander ALX200		B36F	1996
32201	K601ESH	p	Dennis Dart 9.8 SDL	Alexander Dash		B40F	1992
32209	P609CMS	w	Dennis Dart 9.8 SFD	Alexander Dash		B40F	1996
32210	P610CMS	w	Dennis Dart 9.8 SFD	Alexander Dash		B40F	1996
32304	N304AMC	w	Dennis Dart 9.8 SDL	Alexander Dash		B36F	1995
32360	R710YWC	w	Dennis Dart 9.8 SFD	Plaxton Pointer		B43F	1997
32361	R711YWC	w	Dennis Dart 9.8 SFD	Plaxton Pointer		B43F	1997
32362	R712YWC	w	Dennis Dart 9.8 SFD	Plaxton Pointer		B43F	1997
32365	R715YWC	w	Dennis Dart 9.8 SFD	Plaxton Pointer		B43F	1997
32366	R716YWC	w	Dennis Dart 9.8 SFD	Plaxton Pointer		B43F	1997
32368	R718YWC	w	Dennis Dart 9.8 SFD	Plaxton Pointer		B43F	1997
32394	P394LPS	AV	Dennis Dart 9.8 SFD	Alexander Dash		B40F	1996
32395	P395BRS	r	Dennis Dart 9.8 SFD	Alexander Dash		DP40F	1996
32805	J805FPS	w	Dennis Dart 9.8 SDL	Alexander Dash		B41F	1992
32905	M307XSN	M-d	Dennis Dart 9.8 SDL	Northern Counties Paladin	B39F	1995
32907	N309DSL	w	Dennis Dart 9.8 SDL	Northern Counties Paladin	B39F	1996
33074	V974DRM	DS	Dennis Dart 8.8 SLF	Plaxton Mini Pointer		B29F	2000
33075	V975DRM	DS	Dennis Dart 10.7 SLF	Plaxton Pointer 2		B29F	2000
33077	X523SHH	DS	Dennis Dart 8.8 SLF	Alexander ALX200		B29F	2000
33078	PY02KTO	DS	Dennis Dart 10.7 SLF	Plaxton Pointer 2		B37F	2002

33079	PY02KTP	DS	Dennis Dart 10.7 SLF	Plaxton Pointer 2	B37F	2002
33089	T36VCS	DS	Dennis Dart 8.8 SLF	Plaxton Mini Pointer	B29F	1999
33139	P820YCW	AB	Dennis Dart 10.7 SLF	Wright Crusader	B36F	1997
33140	P814YCW	u	Dennis Dart 10.7 SLF	Wright Crusader	B36F	1997
33141	P815YCW	AB	Dennis Dart 10.7 SLF	Wright Crusader	B36F	1997
33142	P819YCW	u	Dennis Dart 10.7 SLF	Wright Crusader	B36F	1997
33186	X461UKS	CT	Dennis Dart 11.3 SLF	Alexander ALX200	B43F	2000
33187	X462UKS	w	Dennis Dart 11.3 SLF	Alexander ALX200	B43F	2000
33188	X463UKS	CT	Dennis Dart 11.3 SLF	Alexander ALX200	B43F	2000
33263	R313MSL	MY	Dennis Dart 10.1 SLF	East Lancs Spryte	B37F	1997
33264	V314DSL	r	Dennis Dart 11.3 SLF	East Lancs Spryte	DP43F	1999
33266	V316DSL	w	Dennis Dart 11.3 SLF	East Lancs Spryte	DP43F	1999
33267	V317DSL	w	Dennis Dart 11.3 SLF	East Lancs Spryte	DP43F	1999
33414	R614GFS	IS	Dennis Dart 10.7 SLF	Alexander ALX200	B38F	1997
33415	S615CSC	DE	Dennis Dart 10.7 SLF	Alexander ALX200	B38F	1998
33416	S616CSC	D	Dennis Dart 10.7 SLF	Alexander ALX200	B38F	1998
33417	S617CSC	D	Dennis Dart 10.7 SLF	Alexander ALX200	B38F	1998
33418	S618CSC	D	Dennis Dart 10.7 SLF	Alexander ALX200	B38F	1998
33419	S619CSC	D	Dennis Dart 10.7 SLF	Alexander ALX200	B38F	1998
33428	X428NSE	IS	Dennis Dart 10.7 SLF	Alexander ALX200	B38F	2001
33429	* X429NSE	IS	Dennis Dart 10.7 SLF	Alexander ALX200	B38F	2001
33430	* X441NSE	TN	Dennis Dart 10.7 SLF	Alexander ALX200	B38F	2001
33431	* X431NSE	AB	Dennis Dart 10.7 SLF	Alexander ALX200	B38F	2001
33432	* X432NSE	AB	Dennis Dart 10.7 SLF	Alexander ALX200	B38F	2001
33433	X433NSE	C	Dennis Dart 10.7 SLF	Alexander ALX200	B38F	2001
33434	* TSV718	P	Dennis Dart 10.7 SLF	Alexander ALX200	B38F	2001
33435	X435NSE	G	Dennis Dart 10.7 SLF	Alexander ALX200	B38F	2001
33436	X436NSE	A	Dennis Dart 10.7 SLF	Alexander ALX200	B38F	2001
33437	* X437NSE	AB	Dennis Dart 10.7 SLF	Alexander ALX200	B38F	2001
33438	* TSV722	AB	Dennis Dart 10.7 SLF	Alexander ALX200	B38F	2001
33439	X439NSE	A	Dennis Dart 10.7 SLF	Alexander ALX200	B38F	2001
33443	X613JCS	AY	Dennis Dart 10.7 SLF	Alexander ALX200	B38F	2001
33444	X614JCS	AY	Dennis Dart 10.7 SLF	Alexander ALX200	B38F	2001
33445	X615JCS	AY	Dennis Dart 10.7 SLF	Alexander ALX200	B38F	2001
33446	X616JCS	AY	Dennis Dart 10.7 SLF	Alexander ALX200	B38F	2001
33447	X617JCS	AY	Dennis Dart 10.7 SLF	Alexander ALX200	B38F	2001
33469	T469GPS	AB	Dennis Dart 10.7 SLF	Alexander ALX200	B37F	1999
33470	T470GPS	IS	Dennis Dart 10.7 SLF	Alexander ALX200	B37F	1999
33471	T471GPS	IS	Dennis Dart 10.7 SLF	Alexander ALX200	B37F	1999
33472	S472JSE	r	Dennis Dart 10.7 SLF	Alexander ALX200	B37F	1998
33473	S473JSE	IS	Dennis Dart 10.7 SLF	Alexander ALX200	B37F	1998
33474	S474JSE	IS	Dennis Dart 10.7 SLF	Alexander ALX200	B37F	1998
33476	S476JSE	IS	Dennis Dart 10.7 SLF	Alexander ALX200	B37F	1998
33478	S478JSE	MY	Dennis Dart 10.7 SLF	Alexander ALX200	B37F	1998
33479	S479JSE	MY	Dennis Dart 10.7 SLF	Alexander ALX200	B37F	1998
33772	T402UCS	DS	Dennis Dart 10.7 SLF	Alexander ALX200	B37F	1999
33773	T403UCS	DS	Dennis Dart 10.7 SLF	Alexander ALX200	B37F	1999
33775	X739JCS	AY	Dennis Dart 11.3 SLF	Plaxton Pointer 2	B41F	2000
33776	X741JCS	AY	Dennis Dart 11.3 SLF	Plaxton Pointer 2	B41F	2000
33777	X742JCS	AYC	Dennis Dart 11.3 SLF	Plaxton Pointer 2	B41F	2000
33778	X743JCS	AY	Dennis Dart 11.3 SLF	Plaxton Pointer 2	B41F	2000
33779	X744JCS	AY	Dennis Dart 11.3 SLF	Plaxton Pointer 2	B41F	2000
33780	X59RCS	AY	Dennis Dart 11.3 SLF	Plaxton Pointer 2	B41F	2000
33906	P906SMR	w	Dennis Dart 10.1 SLF	Alexander ALX200	B36F	1996
33907	P907SMR	r	Dennis Dart 10.1 SLF	Alexander ALX200	B36F	1997
33908	P908SMR	AB	Dennis Dart 10.1 SLF	Alexander ALX200	B36F	1997
33909	P909SMR	BU	Dennis Dart 10.1 SLF	Alexander ALX200	B36F	1997
34022	R122VPU	IS	Dennis Dart 10.1 SLF	Alexander ALX200	B33F	1997
34024	R124VPU	w	Dennis Dart 10.1 SLF	Alexander ALX200	B33F	1997
34025	R125VPU	r	Dennis Dart 10.1 SLF	Alexander ALX200	B33F	1997
34026	R126VPU	AY	Dennis Dart 10.1 SLF	Alexander ALX200	B33F	1997

34027	R127VPU	AY	Dennis Dart 10.1 SLF	Alexander ALX200	B33F	1997
34028	R128VPU	MY	Dennis Dart 10.1 SLF	Alexander ALX200	B33F	1997
34029	R129VPU	BU	Dennis Dart 10.1 SLF	Alexander ALX200	B33F	1997
34036	R936FOO	r	Dennis Dart 10.1 SLF	Alexander ALX200	B33F	1998
34039	R939FOO	AB	Dennis Dart 10.1 SLF	Alexander ALX200	B33F	1998
34040	R940FOO	MY	Dennis Dart 10.1 SLF	Alexander ALX200	B33F	1998
34059	S459BWC	P	Dennis Dart 10.1 SLF	Alexander ALX200	B33F	1998
34060	S460BWC	P	Dennis Dart 10.1 SLF	Alexander ALX200	B33F	1998
34061	S461BWC	MY	Dennis Dart 10.1 SLF	Alexander ALX200	B33F	1998
34062	S462BWC	MY	Dennis Dart 10.1 SLF	Alexander ALX200	B33F	1998
34063	S463BWC	AY	Dennis Dart 10.1 SLF	Alexander ALX200	B33F	1998
34069	S469BWC	MY	Dennis Dart 10.1 SLF	Alexander ALX200	B33F	1998
34070	S470BWC	MY	Dennis Dart 10.1 SLF	Alexander ALX200	B33F	1998
34076	S476BWC	MY	Dennis Dart 10.1 SLF	Alexander ALX200	B33F	1999
34082	S482BWC	D	Dennis Dart 10.1 SLF	Alexander ALX200	B36F	1999
34084	S484BWC	D	Dennis Dart 10.1 SLF	Alexander ALX200	B36F	1998
34086	* TSV720	D	Dennis Dart 10.1 SLF	Alexander ALX200	B36F	1998
34087	* WLT415	D	Dennis Dart 10.1 SLF	Alexander ALX200	B36F	1998
34104	S104WHK	D	Dennis Dart 10.1 SLF	Alexander ALX200	B29F	1999
34142	V142MVX	AS	Dennis Dart 9.3 SLF	Plaxton Mini Pointer	B31F	1999
34143	V143MVX	CK	Dennis Dart 9.3 SLF	Plaxton Mini Pointer	B31F	1999
34146	V146MVX	CK	Dennis Dart 9.3 SLF	Plaxton Mini Pointer	B31F	1999
34151	V151MVX	CK	Dennis Dart 9.3 SLF	Plaxton Mini Pointer	B31F	1999
34212	W212DNO	D	Dennis Dart 10.1 SLF	Plaxton Pointer 2	B30F	2000
34213	W213DNO	D	Dennis Dart 10.1 SLF	Plaxton Pointer 2	B30F	2000
34216	W216DNO	G	Dennis Dart 10.1 SLF	Plaxton Pointer 2	B30F	2000
34217	W234DNO	A	Dennis Dart 10.1 SLF	Plaxton Pointer 2	B30F	2000
34482	SV53DDJ	IS	TransBus Dart 10.7 SLF	TransBus Pointer 2	B37F	2004
34483	SV53DDK	IS	TransBus Dart 10.7 SLF	TransBus Pointer 2	B37F	2004
34484	SV53DDL	IS	TransBus Dart 10.7 SLF	TransBus Pointer 2	B37F	2004
34485	SV53DDN	IS	TransBus Dart 10.7 SLF	TransBus Pointer 2	B37F	2004
34486	SV53DDO	IS	TransBus Dart 10.7 SLF	TransBus Pointer 2	B37F	2004
34487	SV53DDU	IS	TransBus Dart 10.7 SLF	TransBus Pointer 2	B37F	2004
34488	SV53DDX	IS	TransBus Dart 10.7 SLF	TransBus Pointer 2	B37F	2004
34489	SV53DDY	IS	TransBus Dart 10.7 SLF	TransBus Pointer 2	B37F	2004
34490	SV53DDZ	IS	TransBus Dart 10.7 SLF	TransBus Pointer 2	B37F	2004
34596	SF04VSV	AY	TransBus Dart 11.3 SLF	TransBus Pointer 2	B38F	2004
34597	SF04VSX	AY	TransBus Dart 11.3 SLF	TransBus Pointer 2	B38F	2004
34598	SF04VSY	AY	TransBus Dart 11.3 SLF	TransBus Pointer 2	B38F	2004
34599	SF04VSZ	AY	TransBus Dart 11.3 SLF	TransBus Pointer 2	B38F	2004
34600	SF04VTA	AY	TransBus Dart 11.3 SLF	TransBus Pointer 2	B38F	2004
34601	SF04VTC	AY	TransBus Dart 11.3 SLF	TransBus Pointer 2	B38F	2004
34602	SF04VTD	AY	TransBus Dart 11.3 SLF	TransBus Pointer 2	B38F	2004
34603	SF04VTE	AY	TransBus Dart 11.3 SLF	TransBus Pointer 2	B38F	2004
34604	SF04VTG	AY	TransBus Dart 11.3 SLF	TransBus Pointer 2	B38F	2004
34725	SP05EKX	D	ADL Dart 10.7 SLF	ADL Pointer 2	B38F	2005
34726	SP05EKY	D	ADL Dart 10.7 SLF	ADL Pointer 2	B38F	2005
34727	SP05EKZ	D	ADL Dart 10.7 SLF	ADL Pointer 2	B38F	2005
34728	SP05ELC	D	ADL Dart 10.7 SLF	ADL Pointer 2	B38F	2005
34729	SP05ELH	C	ADL Dart 10.7 SLF	ADL Pointer 2	B38F	2005
34730	SP05ELJ	D	ADL Dart 10.7 SLF	ADL Pointer 2	B38F	2005
34731	SV55BZF	IS	ADL Enviro Dart 10.7 SLF	ADL Enviro 200	B38F	2005
34732	SV55BZG	IS	ADL Enviro Dart 10.7 SLF	ADL Enviro 200	B38F	2005
34733	SV55BZH	IS	ADL Enviro Dart 10.7 SLF	ADL Enviro 200	B38F	2005
34734	SV55BZJ	IS	ADL Enviro Dart 10.7 SLF	ADL Enviro 200	B38F	2005
34735	SV55BZL	IS	ADL Enviro Dart 10.7 SLF	ADL Enviro 200	B38F	2005
34736	SV55BZM	IS	ADL Enviro Dart 10.7 SLF	ADL Enviro 200	B38F	2005
34737	SV55BZN	IS	ADL Enviro Dart 10.7 SLF	ADL Enviro 200	B38F	2005
34738	SV55CCK	IS	ADL Enviro Dart 10.7 SLF	ADL Enviro 200	B38F	2005
34739	SV55CCN	TN	ADL Enviro Dart 10.7 SLF	ADL Enviro 200	B38F	2005
34740	SV55CCO	MY	ADL Enviro Dart 10.7 SLF	ADL Enviro 200	B38F	2005

34795	SV55GWJ	IS	ADL Enviro Dart 10.7 SLF	ADL Enviro 200	B38F	2006
34796	SV55GWK	IS	ADL Enviro Dart 10.7 SLF	ADL Enviro 200	B38F	2006
35101	SP06FMY	D	ADL Enviro Dart 10.7 SLF	ADL Enviro 200	B38F	2006
35102	SP06FMZ	D	ADL Enviro Dart 10.7 SLF	ADL Enviro 200	B38F	2006
35238	SF56FKV	AS	ADL Enviro Dart 10.7 SLF	ADL Enviro 200	B38F	2006
35239	SF56FKW	AS	ADL Enviro Dart 10.7 SLF	ADL Enviro 200	B38F	2006
35240	SF56FKX	AS	ADL Enviro Dart 10.7 SLF	ADL Enviro 200	B38F	2006
35241	SF56FKY	AS	ADL Enviro Dart 10.7 SLF	ADL Enviro 200	B38F	2006
35242	SF56FKZ	AS	ADL Enviro Dart 10.7 SLF	ADL Enviro 200	B38F	2006
36031	SV07FCC	MY	ADL Enviro Dart 10.7 SLF	ADL Enviro 200	B38F	2007
36032	SV07FCD	MY	ADL Enviro Dart 10.7 SLF	ADL Enviro 200	B38F	2007
36033	SV07FCE	MY	ADL Enviro Dart 10.7 SLF	ADL Enviro 200	B38F	2007
36034	SV07FCF	MY	ADL Enviro Dart 10.7 SLF	ADL Enviro 200	B38F	2007
36035	SV07FCG	MY	ADL Enviro Dart 10.7 SLF	ADL Enviro 200	B38F	2007
36046	SV08GUU	MY	ADL Enviro Dart 10.7 SLF	ADL Enviro 200	B38F	2008
36047	SV08GUV	MY	ADL Enviro Dart 10.7 SLF	ADL Enviro 200	B38F	2008
36048	SV08GUW	MY	ADL Enviro Dart 10.7 SLF	ADL Enviro 200	B38F	2008
36049	SV08GUX	MY	ADL Enviro Dart 10.7 SLF	ADL Enviro 200	B38F	2008
36050	SV08GVA	MY	ADL Enviro Dart 10.7 SLF	ADL Enviro 200	B38F	2008
36066	SY57AXR	IS	ADL Enviro Dart 10.7 SLF	ADL Enviro 200	B37F	2007
36067	SY57AXU	FW	ADL Enviro Dart 10.7 SLF	ADL Enviro 200	B37F	2007
36068	SY57AYF	FW	ADL Enviro Dart 10.7 SLF	ADL Enviro 200	B37F	2007
36069	SY57AYG	FW	ADL Enviro Dart 10.7 SLF	ADL Enviro 200	B37F	2007
36070	SY57AYH	FW	ADL Enviro Dart 10.7 SLF	ADL Enviro 200	B37F	2007
36071	SN56AYF	AS	ADL Enviro Dart 8.9 SLF	ADL Enviro 200	B29F	2006
36072	SN56AYG	AS	ADL Enviro Dart 8.9 SLF	ADL Enviro 200	B29F	2006
36131	SF10BZW	K	ADL Enviro Dart 10.7 SLF	ADL Enviro 200	B38F	2010
36132	SF10BZX	K	ADL Enviro Dart 10.7 SLF	ADL Enviro 200	B38F	2010
36133	SF10BZY	K	ADL Enviro Dart 10.7 SLF	ADL Enviro 200	B38F	2010
36134	SF10BZL	K	ADL Enviro Dart 10.7 SLF	ADL Enviro 200	B38F	2010
36135	SF10BZM	K	ADL Enviro Dart 10.7 SLF	ADL Enviro 200	B38F	2010
36136	SF10BZN	K	ADL Enviro Dart 10.7 SLF	ADL Enviro 200	B38F	2010
36137	SF10BZO	K	ADL Enviro Dart 10.7 SLF	ADL Enviro 200	B38F	2010
36138	SF10BZP	K	ADL Enviro Dart 10.7 SLF	ADL Enviro 200	B38F	2010
36139	SF10BZR	K	ADL Enviro Dart 10.7 SLF	ADL Enviro 200	B38F	2010
36140	SF10BZS	K	ADL Enviro Dart 10.7 SLF	ADL Enviro 200	B38F	2010
36141	SF10BZT	K	ADL Enviro Dart 10.7 SLF	ADL Enviro 200	B38F	2010
36142	SF10BZU	K	ADL Enviro Dart 10.7 SLF	ADL Enviro 200	B38F	2010
36143	SF10BZV	K	ADL Enviro Dart 10.7 SLF	ADL Enviro 200	B38F	2010
36144	SF10BZH	K	ADL Enviro Dart 10.7 SLF	ADL Enviro 200	B38F	2010
36145	SF10BZJ	K	ADL Enviro Dart 10.7 SLF	ADL Enviro 200	B38F	2010
36146	SF10BZK	K	ADL Enviro Dart 10.7 SLF	ADL Enviro 200	B38F	2010
36147	SF10CFA	K	ADL Enviro Dart 10.7 SLF	ADL Enviro 200	B38F	2010
36148	SF10CFD	K	ADL Enviro Dart 10.7 SLF	ADL Enviro 200	B38F	2010
36149	SF10CDZ	K	ADL Enviro Dart 10.7 SLF	ADL Enviro 200	B38F	2010
36150	SF10CEA	K	ADL Enviro Dart 10.7 SLF	ADL Enviro 200	B38F	2010
36151	SF10CEJ	K	ADL Enviro Dart 10.7 SLF	ADL Enviro 200	B38F	2010
36152	SF10CEK	K	ADL Enviro Dart 10.7 SLF	ADL Enviro 200	B38F	2010
39600	S389JPS	w	MAN 11.220	Marshall City	B36F	1998
40041	P341ASO	w	Mercedes-Benz 709D	Alexander Sprint	DP25F	1996
40043	P343ASO	w	Mercedes-Benz 709D	Alexander Sprint	DP25F	1996
40044	P344ASO	KY-d	Mercedes-Benz 709D	Alexander Sprint	DP25F	1996
40051	P351ASO	w	Mercedes-Benz 709D	Alexander Sprint	DP25F	1996
40055	M655FYS	w	Mercedes-Benz 709D	Alexander Sprint	B25F	1995
40056	M656FYS	AY-a	Mercedes-Benz 709D	Alexander Sprint	B25F	1995
40058	M658FYS	r	Mercedes-Benz 709D	Alexander Sprint	B25F	1995
40067	M667FYS	K-a	Mercedes-Benz 709D	Alexander Sprint	B25F	1995
40068	M668FYS	r	Mercedes-Benz 709D	Alexander Sprint	B25F	1995
40098	M648FYS	AN	Mercedes-Benz 709D	Alexander Sprint	B25F	1995
40135	M335LHP	w	Mercedes-Benz 709D	Alexander Sprint	B23F	1995
40136	M336LHP	w	Mercedes-Benz 709D	Alexander Sprint	B23F	1995

40138	M338LHP	w	Mercedes-Benz 709D	Alexander Sprint	B23F	1995
40157	N357AVV	w	Mercedes-Benz 709D	Alexander Sprint	B23F	1996
40158	N358AVV	w	Mercedes-Benz 709D	Alexander Sprint	B23F	1996
40159 •	N359AVV	SE	Mercedes-Benz 709D	Alexander Sprint	B23F	1996
40165	N365AVV	w	Mercedes-Benz 709D	Alexander Sprint	B23F	1996
40166	N366AVV	w	Mercedes-Benz 709D	Alexander Sprint	B23F	1996
40167	N367AVV	w	Mercedes-Benz 709D	Alexander Sprint	B23F	1996
40169	N369AVV	w	Mercedes-Benz 709D	Alexander Sprint	B23F	1996
40170	N370AVV	MY	Mercedes-Benz 709D	Alexander Sprint	B23F	1996
40171	N371AVV	w	Mercedes-Benz 709D	Alexander Sprint	B23F	1996
40176	L321AUT	AH-r	Mercedes-Benz 709D	Alexander Sprint	B25F	1994
40229	M229UTM	w	Mercedes-Benz 709D	Marshall C19	B23F	1995
40496	N496RVK	w	Mercedes-Benz 709D	Alexander Sprint	B25F	1996
40548	M348JBO	SE	Mercedes-Benz 709D	Alexander Sprint	B25F	1994
40611	N611VSS	AN	Mercedes-Benz 709D	Alexander Sprint	B25F	1996
40621	N621VSS	w	Mercedes-Benz 709D	Alexander Sprint	B25F	1996
40624	N624VSS	AS	Mercedes-Benz 709D	Alexander Sprint	B25F	1995
40626	N626VSS	w	Mercedes-Benz 709D	Alexander Sprint	B25F	1995
40627	N627VSS	r	Mercedes-Benz 709D	Alexander Sprint	B25F	1995
40628	N628VSS	w	Mercedes-Benz 709D	Alexander Sprint	B25F	1995
40630	N630VSS	AN	Mercedes-Benz 709D	Alexander Sprint	B25F	1995
40632	N632VSS	AS	Mercedes-Benz 709D	Alexander Sprint	B25F	1995
40633	N633VSS	AN	Mercedes-Benz 709D	Alexander Sprint	B25F	1995
40635	N635VSS	w	Mercedes-Benz 709D	Alexander Sprint	B25F	1995
40636	N636VSS	w	Mercedes-Benz 709D	Alexander Sprint	B25F	1996
40637	N637VSS	w	Mercedes-Benz 709D	Alexander Sprint	B25F	1996
40640	N640VSS	w	Mercedes-Benz 709D	Alexander Sprint	B25F	1996
40735	N735RDD	w	Mercedes-Benz 709D	Alexander Sprint	DP25F	1996
40755	N755CKU	w	Mercedes-Benz 709D	Alexander Sprint	B25F	1995
40756	N756CKU	w	Mercedes-Benz 709D	Alexander Sprint	B25F	1995
40926	N926NAP	BU-a	Mercedes-Benz 709D	Alexander Sprint	B23F	1996
40928	N928NAP	w	Mercedes-Benz 709D	Alexander Sprint	B23F	1996
40929	N929NAP	w	Mercedes-Benz 709D	Alexander Sprint	B23F	1996
40986	M396KVR	AS-a	Mercedes-Benz 709D	Alexander Sprint	B27F	1995
41362	N102WRC	w	Mercedes-Benz 811D	Plaxton Beaver	B33F	1995
41369	N109WRC	w	Mercedes-Benz 811D	Plaxton Beaver	B30F	1995
41507	J407PRW	SV	Mercedes-Benz 811D	Alexander	B31F	1991
41801	K801OMW	w	Mercedes-Benz 811D	Wright Nimbus	B33F	1993
41802	K802OMW	SV	Mercedes-Benz 811D	Wright Nimbus	B33F	1993
42019	V772GCS	TU	Mercedes-Benz Vario O814D	Plaxton Beaver 2	B31F	1999
42020	V773GCS	r	Mercedes-Benz Vario O814D	Plaxton Beaver 2	B31F	1999
42021	V774GCS	TU	Mercedes-Benz Vario O814D	Plaxton Beaver 2	B31F	1999
42022	SN03FHK	SR	Mercedes-Benz Vario O814D	Plaxton Beaver 2	B31F	2003
42023	SN03FHL	r	Mercedes-Benz Vario O814D	Plaxton Beaver 2	B31F	2003
42024 •	SN03FHM	SE	Mercedes-Benz Vario O814D	Plaxton Beaver 2	B31F	2003
42034	Y218BGB	w	Mercedes-Benz Vario O814D	Mellor	C29F	2001
42047 *	S751SCJ	SE	Mercedes-Benz Vario O814D	Plaxton Beaver 2	B31F	1998
42049	W692NST	CT	Mercedes-Benz Vario O814D	Plaxton Beaver 2	B33F	2000
42221	Y484PSR	BL	Mercedes-Benz Vario O814D	Plaxton Beaver 2	B31F	2001
42222	R89EOL	w	Mercedes-Benz Vario O814D	Plaxton Beaver 2	B33F	1998
42223	R91EOL	r	Mercedes-Benz Vario O814D	Plaxton Beaver 2	B33F	1998
42224	SP53EGY	BL	Mercedes-Benz Vario O814D	Plaxton Beaver 2	DP33F	2003
42225	SP53EGZ	BL	Mercedes-Benz Vario O814D	Plaxton Beaver 2	DP33F	2003
42228	S343SWF	r	Mercedes-Benz Vario O814D	Plaxton Beaver 2	B31F	1998
42229	S344SWF	AH	Mercedes-Benz Vario O814D	Plaxton Beaver 2	B31F	1998
42230	S345SWF	FR	Mercedes-Benz Vario O814D	Plaxton Beaver 2	B31F	1998
42231	S346SWF	DE	Mercedes-Benz Vario O814D	Plaxton Beaver 2	B31F	1998
42234	S349SWF	BL	Mercedes-Benz Vario O814D	Plaxton Beaver 2	B31F	1998
42237	T167ATS	BL	Mercedes-Benz Vario O814D	Plaxton Beaver 2	DP25F	1999
42238	T168ATS	AH	Mercedes-Benz Vario O814D	Plaxton Beaver 2	DP25F	1999
42356	S356KEF	S	Mercedes-Benz Vario O814D	Alexander ALX100	B29F	1998

			Stagecoach Scotland				

42357	S357KEF	w	Mercedes-Benz Vario O814D	Alexander ALX100		B29F	1998
42358	S358KEF	w	Mercedes-Benz Vario O814D	Alexander ALX100		B29F	1998
46690	SP54EGF	r	Iveco Daily 50C13			B11FL	2004
46691	SP54EGJ	DE	Iveco Daily 50C13			B7FL	2004
46692	SP54ETX	AH-a	Iveco Daily 50C13			B9FL	2004
47003	KX51CRZ	S	Optare Solo M850	Optare		B27F	2001
47004	KX51CSF	A	Optare Solo M850	Optare		B27F	2001
47051	SV04DVK	P G	Optare Solo M850	Optare		B27F	2004
47052	SV04DVL	P D	Optare Solo M850	Optare		B27F	2004
47053	SV04DVM	P	Optare Solo M850	Optare		B27F	2004
47054	SV04DVN	P R	Optare Solo M850	Optare		B27F	2004
47063	SF04SKD	DS	Optare Solo M850	Optare		B27F	2004
47064	SF04SKE	DS	Optare Solo M850	Optare		B27F	2004
47065	SF04SKJ	DS	Optare Solo M850	Optare		B27F	2004
47066	SF04SKK	DS	Optare Solo M850	Optare		B27F	2004
47067	SF04SKN	DS	Optare Solo M850	Optare		B27F	2004
47068	SF04VFS	DS	Optare Solo M850	Optare		B27F	2004
47078	SV04HLM	AB	Optare Solo M850	Optare		B27F	2004
47079	SV04HLN	BU	Optare Solo M850	Optare		B27F	2004
47080	SV04HLP	AB	Optare Solo M850	Optare		B27F	2004
47111	SV54BYM	AB	Optare Solo M850	Optare		B27F	2004
47150	SF54RJU	AS	Optare Solo M850	Optare		B27F	2004
47156	*	S962BBV	BU	Optare Solo M850	Optare	B27F	1999
47157	*	S964BBV	BU	Optare Solo M850	Optare	B27F	1998
47158	*	S963BBV	P	Optare Solo M850	Optare	B27F	1998
47159	*	S961BBV	BU	Optare Solo M850	Optare	B27F	1999
47160	T552ADN	BU	Optare Solo M850	Optare		B27F	1999
47161	SV05DJU	IS	Optare Solo M850	Optare		B27F	2005
47162	SV05DJX	AB	Optare Solo M850	Optare		B27F	2005
47167	SP05EFF	A	Optare Solo M850	Optare		B27F	2005
47168	SP05EFG	A	Optare Solo M850	Optare		B27F	2005
47169	SP05EFH	G	Optare Solo M850	Optare		B27F	2005
47170	SF05NXD	SR	Optare Solo M850	Optare		B27F	2005
47171	SF05NXE	SR	Optare Solo M850	Optare		B27F	2005
47172	SF05NXG	SR	Optare Solo M850	Optare		B27F	2005
47178	SP05EOH	S	Optare Solo M850	Optare		B27F	2005
47179	SP05EOJ	S	Optare Solo M850	Optare		B27F	2005
47180	SV05DJY	IS	Optare Solo M850	Optare		B27F	2005
47181	SV05DKA	CT	Optare Solo M850	Optare		B27F	2005
47182	SV05DKD	IS	Optare Solo M850	Optare		B27F	2005
47183	SP05EFJ	G	Optare Solo M850	Optare		B27F	2005
47212	SV55BZO	AH	Optare Solo M850	Optare		B27F	2005
47213	SV55BZP	BU	Optare Solo M850	Optare		B27F	2005
47214	SV55BZR	BU	Optare Solo M850	Optare		B27F	2005
47215	SV55BZU	AH	Optare Solo M850	Optare		B27F	2005
47216	SV55BZW	BU	Optare Solo M850	Optare		B27F	2005
47217	SV55BZX	P	Optare Solo M850	Optare		B27F	2005
47218	SV55BZY	P	Optare Solo M850	Optare		B27F	2005
47219	SV55BZB	P	Optare Solo M850	Optare		B27F	2005
47220	SV55BZC	P	Optare Solo M850	Optare		B27F	2005
47221	SV55BZD	P	Optare Solo M850	Optare		B27F	2005
47222	SV55BZE	P	Optare Solo M850	Optare		B27F	2005
47223	SV55CCA	P	Optare Solo M850	Optare		B27F	2005
47224	SV55CCD	S	Optare Solo M850	Optare		B27F	2005
47225	SV55CCE	P	Optare Solo M850	Optare		B27F	2005
47226	SV55CCF	P	Optare Solo M850	Optare		B27F	2005
47227	SV55CCJ	P A	Optare Solo M850	Optare		B27F	2005
47228	SP55CXG	A	Optare Solo M850	Optare		B27F	2005
47229	SP55CXH	D	Optare Solo M850	Optare		B27F	2005
47230	SP55CXJ	D G	Optare Solo M850	Optare		B27F	2005
47231	SP55CXK	D	Optare Solo M850	Optare		B27F	2005

47232	SP55CXL	C	Optare Solo M850	Optare	B27F	2005
47233	SP55CXM	C	Optare Solo M850	Optare	B27F	2005
47234	SP55CXN	D	Optare Solo M850	Optare	B27F	2005
47235	SP55CXO	C	Optare Solo M850	Optare	B27F	2005
47240	SP55EEA	D	Optare Solo M850	Optare	B27F	2005
47246	OA05RKA	DS	Optare Solo M880	Optare	B27F	2005
47250	SP04GZX	BL	Optare Solo M880	Optare	DP27F	2004
47251	SP54ENO	DE	Optare Solo M880	Optare	B25F	2004
47252	SP05ECF	OY	Optare Solo M880	Optare	B27F	2005
47253	SP05ECJ	BL	Optare Solo M880	Optare	B27F	2005
47254	SP05ECN	DE	Optare Solo M880	Optare	B27F	2005
47255	SP05FUJ	FR	Optare Solo M880	Optare	B27F	2005
47256	SP05FUM	AH	Optare Solo M880	Optare	B27F	2005
47257	SP55DDE	SV	Optare Solo M880	Optare	B27F	2005
47258	SP55DND	P	Optare Solo M880	Optare	B27F	2005
47259	YN55KND	P	Optare Solo M880	Optare	B27F	2005
47260	YJ55BHW	FR	Optare Solo M880	Optare	B27F	2005
47281	YS02WVY	AB	Optare Solo M920	Optare	B33F	2002
47301	SP06FCF	A	Optare Solo M850SL	Optare	B28F	2006
47302	SP06FCG	A	Optare Solo M850SL	Optare	B28F	2006
47303	SP06FCJ	A	Optare Solo M850SL	Optare	B28F	2006
47314	SF06OVE	K	Optare Solo M850	Optare	B27F	2006
47356	SF06OVG	AY	Optare Solo M850	Optare	B27F	2006
47357	SF06OVH	K	Optare Solo M850	Optare	B27F	2006
47358	SF06OVJ	K	Optare Solo M850	Optare	B27F	2006
47359	SF06OVK	AY	Optare Solo M850	Optare	B27F	2006
47360	SF06OVL	AY	Optare Solo M850	Optare	B27F	2006
47361	SF06OVM	AY	Optare Solo M850	Optare	B27F	2006
47362	SF06OVN	AY	Optare Solo M850	Optare	B27F	2006
47364	SP06FNA	D	Optare Solo M850	Optare	B27F	2006
47365	SF06OVP	AY	Optare Solo M850	Optare	B27F	2006
47366	SP06FNC	D	Optare Solo M850	Optare	B27F	2006
47367	SP06FND	S	Optare Solo M850	Optare	B27F	2006
47368	SP06FNE	D	Optare Solo M850	Optare	B27F	2006
47386	SF56FLA	CK	Optare Solo M850	Optare	B27F	2006
47387	SF56FLB	CK	Optare Solo M850	Optare	B27F	2006
47388	SF56FLC	GW	Optare Solo M850	Optare	B27F	2006
47391	SP56CXD	IS	Optare Solo M850	Optare	B27F	2006
47392	SP56CXE	P	Optare Solo M850	Optare	B27F	2006
47393	SP56CXF	S	Optare Solo M850	Optare	B27F	2006
47425	W281EYG	AB	Optare Solo M850	Optare	B33F	2000
47426	W294EYG	AB	Optare Solo M850	Optare	B33F	2000
47427	W297EYG	AB	Optare Solo M850	Optare	B33F	2000
47428	W303EYG	AB	Optare Solo M850	Optare	B33F	2000
47495	SF57DRO	AS	Optare Solo M880	Optare	B27F	2007
47496	SF57DNU	AS	Optare Solo M880	Optare	B27F	2007
47497	SF57DNV	AN	Optare Solo M880	Optare	B27F	2007
47498	SF57DNX	AS	Optare Solo M880	Optare	B27F	2007
47499	SF57DOA	GW	Optare Solo M880	Optare	B27F	2007
47500	SF57DOH	GW	Optare Solo M880	Optare	B27F	2007
47501	SF57DOJ	GW	Optare Solo M880	Optare	B27F	2007
47502	SF57DOU	K	Optare Solo M880	Optare	B27F	2007
47503	SF57DPE	K	Optare Solo M880	Optare	B27F	2007
47504	SF57DPK	K	Optare Solo M880	Optare	B27F	2007
47505	SF57DPN	K	Optare Solo M880	Optare	B27F	2007
47506	SF57DPO	AY	Optare Solo M880	Optare	B27F	2007
47507	SF57DPU	AY	Optare Solo M880	Optare	DP27F	2007
47562	YK04KWH	OY	Optare Solo M850	Optare	B28F	2004
47563	YJ05XOA	OY	Optare Solo M950	Optare	B31F	2005
47564	YJ05XOB	SE	Optare Solo M950	Optare	B31F	2005
47565	YJ05XOC	SE	Optare Solo M950	Optare	B31F	2005

47566		YJ05XOD	SE	Optare Solo M950	Optare	B31F	2005
47567		YJ05XOE	IS	Optare Solo M950	Optare	B31F	2005
47568		YJ05XOF	TU	Optare Solo M1020	Optare	B35F	2005
47569		YJ05XOG	OY	Optare Solo M1020	Optare	B35F	2005
47570		YJ05XOH	OY	Optare Solo M990	Optare	B35F	2005
47571		YJ05XOK	OY	Optare Solo M990	Optare	B35F	2005
47572		YJ05XOL	OY	Optare Solo M990	Optare	B31F	2005
47573		YJ05XOM	OY	Optare Solo M990	Optare	B31F	2005
47574		YJ56WVE	OY	Optare Solo M990	Optare	B29F	2006
47601		SV08FZM	MY	Optare Solo M880	Optare	B27F	2008
47602		SV08FZN	MY	Optare Solo M880	Optare	B27F	2008
47603		SV08FZO	AB	Optare Solo M880	Optare	B27F	2008
47604		SV08FZP	AB	Optare Solo M880	Optare	B27F	2008
47605		SV08FZR	AB	Optare Solo M880	Optare	B27F	2008
47606		SV08FZS	r	Optare Solo M880	Optare	B27F	2008
47607		SP08FLZ	G	Optare Solo M880	Optare	B27F	2008
47608		SP08FMA	G	Optare Solo M880	Optare	B27F	2008
47609		SP08FMC	G	Optare Solo M880	Optare	B27F	2008
47610		SP08FMD	G	Optare Solo M880	Optare	B27F	2008
47611		SP08FME	G	Optare Solo M880	Optare	B27F	2008
47612		SF08GUO	K	Optare Solo M880	Optare	B27F	2008
47613		SF08GUU	K	Optare Solo M880	Optare	B27F	2008
47614		SF08GUW	K	Optare Solo M880	Optare	B27F	2008
47615		SF08GUX	K	Optare Solo M880	Optare	B27F	2008
47657		SP58AZC	A	Optare Solo M880SL	Optare	B27F	2008
47732		SF10BZD	AY	Optare Solo M880	Optare	B27F	2010
47733		SF10BZE	AY	Optare Solo M880	Optare	B27F	2010
47734		SF10BZG	AY	Optare Solo M880	Optare	B27F	2010
47807		SV54BYN	OY	Optare Alero L7200	Optare	B16F	2004
49752		SF51JWV	r	Volkswagen Transporter	Volkswagen	M8	2001
49753		SF56DPX	AL	Volkswagen Transporter	Volkswagen	DP??F	2007
49754		SF56DTU	SV	Volkswagen Transporter	Volkswagen	M8	2007
49756		YX07DXC	SV	Volkswagen Transporter	Bluebird	B15F	2007
49802		R251VVX	AB-a	Ford Transit	Ford	M8	1997
50126		SV54ELC	AY	Neoplan N122	Neoplan Skyliner	CH65/24FT	2005
50127	*	WLT720	AY	Neoplan N122	Neoplan Skyliner	CH65/24FT	2005
50128	*	MSU466	AY	Neoplan N122	Neoplan Skyliner	CH65/24FT	2005
50129	*	ESK934	AB	Neoplan N122	Neoplan Skyliner	CH65/24FT	2005
50130	*	YSV730	AY	Neoplan N122	Neoplan Skyliner	CH65/24FT	2005
50131	*	VCS391	AY	Neoplan N122	Neoplan Skyliner	CH65/24FT	2005
50132		SV54ELX	AY	Neoplan N122	Neoplan Skyliner	CH65/24FT	2005
50133		CN05APV	K	Neoplan N122	Neoplan Skyliner	CH65/24FT	2005
50134		CN05APX	AY	Neoplan N122	Neoplan Skyliner	CH65/24FT	2005
50135	*	TSV719	BU	Neoplan N122	Neoplan Skyliner	CH65/24FT	2005
50136		LX05BWL	K	Neoplan N122	Neoplan Skyliner	CH65/24FT	2005
50137	*	ESK932	r	Neoplan N122	Neoplan Skyliner	CH65/24FT	2005
50138		LX05BWN	K	Neoplan N122	Neoplan Skyliner	CH65/24FT	2005
50139		CN05FVU	AY	Neoplan N122	Neoplan Skyliner	CH65/24FT	2005
50140	*	TSV721	AY	Neoplan N122	Neoplan Skyliner	CH65/24FT	2005
50141		KX05HVE	r	Neoplan N122	Neoplan Skyliner	CH65/24FT	2005
50142	*	TSV778	BU	Neoplan N122	Neoplan Skyliner	CH65/24FT	2005
50143		CN05FVW	AY	Neoplan N122	Neoplan Skyliner	CH65/24FT	2005
50144		CN05FVX	BU	Neoplan N122	Neoplan Skyliner	CH65/24FT	2005
50145		YN05WEC	AY	Neoplan N122	Neoplan Skyliner	CH65/24FT	2005
50146		YN05WEF	K	Neoplan N122	Neoplan Skyliner	CH65/24FT	2005
50147	*	TSV781	BU	Neoplan N122	Neoplan Skyliner	CH65/24FT	2005
50149		MX05BWO	AY	Neoplan N122	Neoplan Skyliner	CH65/24FT	2005
50150		YN05WEK	AY	Neoplan N122	Neoplan Skyliner	CH65/24FT	2005
50227		SV59CGG	AB	Van Hool TD927	Van Hool Astromega	CH63/24DT	2009
50228		SV59CGK	AB	Van Hool TD927	Van Hool Astromega	CH63/24DT	2009
50229		SV59CGO	AB	Van Hool TD927	Van Hool Astromega	CH63/24DT	2009

50230	SV59CGU	AB	Van Hool TD927	Van Hool Astromega	CH63/24DT	2009
50231	SV10DDK	AB	Van Hool TD927	Van Hool Astromega	CH63/24DT	2010
50232	SV10DDL	AB	Van Hool TD927	Van Hool Astromega	CH63/24DT	2010
51061	* N561SJF	K-r	Volvo B10MA-55	Jonckheere Modulo	AC70F	1996
51062	* N562SJF	GW-r	Volvo B10MA-55	Jonckheere Modulo	AC70F	1996
51063	* TSU642	BU-r	Volvo B10M-55	Plaxton Premiere 320 Interurban	AC71F	1996
51070	* DSV943	AB	Volvo B10M-55	Plaxton Premiere 320 Interurban	AC71F	1996
51071	* 128ASV	AB	Volvo B10M-55	Plaxton Premiere 320 Interurban	AC71F	1996
51076	P976UBV	AB	Volvo B10M-55	Plaxton Premiere 320 Interurban	AC71F	1996
51092	T640KCS	AS	Volvo B10MA-55	Jonckheere Modulo	AC72F	1999
51093	T641KCS	AS	Volvo B10MA-55	Jonckheere Modulo	AC72F	1999
51094	T642KCS	AS	Volvo B10MA-55	Jonckheere Modulo	AC72F	1999
51095	T95JHN	AS	Volvo B10MA-55	Jonckheere Modulo	AC72F	1999
51096	T96JHN	CK	Volvo B10MA-55	Jonckheere Modulo	AC72F	1999
51097	T97JHN	CK	Volvo B10MA-55	Jonckheere Modulo	AC72F	1999
51098	* CSU920	AB	Volvo B10M-55	Plaxton Premiere 320 Interurban	AC71F	1996
51099	* 127ASV	AB	Volvo B10M-55	Plaxton Premiere 320 Interurban	AC71F	1996
52026	* YSV735	K-t	Volvo B10M-62	Berkhof Excellence 1000LD	C51FT	1995
52044	* 200UWX	CT	Volvo B10M-62	Van Hool Alizée	C55F	1995
52045	* JAZ9850	TU	Volvo B10M-62	Van Hool Alizée	C48F	1996
52046	* KBZ4631	OY	Volvo B10M-62	Van Hool Alizée	C49F	1996
52047	* PSU954	R	Volvo B10M-62	Van Hool Alizée	C41FT	1996
52048	* TFX966	OY	Volvo B10M-62	Van Hool Alizée	C49F	1996
52049	* TRM144	OY	Volvo B10M-62	Van Hool Alizée	C49FT	1996
~~52128~~	~~* A2XXH~~	~~R~~	~~Volvo B10M-60~~	~~Plaxton Premiere 320~~	~~C70F~~	~~1993~~
~~52129~~	~~* A2XXW~~	~~R~~	~~Volvo B10M-60~~	~~Plaxton Premiere 320~~	~~C70F~~	~~1993~~
52137	* FSU331	MY	Volvo B10M-60	Plaxton Premiere 320	C53F	1993
52141	* FSU797	AB	Volvo B10M-60	Plaxton Premiere 320	C53F	1993
52148	* SIL1895	AV	Volvo B10M-60	Plaxton Premiere 350	C70F	1992
52167	* ESK985	AV	Volvo B10M-62	Plaxton Premiere 320	C70F	1994
52173	* L583JSA	w	Volvo B10M-60	Plaxton Premiere 320	C51F	1993
52184	L584HSG	D-t	Volvo B10M-60	Plaxton Premiere 320	TV	1993
52185	L585HSG	IS-t	Volvo B10M-60	Plaxton Premiere 320	TV	1993
52198	DAZ1561	SE	Volvo B10M-62	Plaxton Premiere 320	C53F	1994
52201	DAZ1571	AV	Volvo B10M-62	Plaxton Premiere 320	C70F	1994
52202	EAZ2575	IS	Volvo B10M-62	Plaxton Premiere 320	C70F	1994
52204	EAZ2590	r	Volvo B10M-62	Plaxton Premiere 320	C53F	1994
52205	* ESK981	IS	Volvo B10M-62	Plaxton Premiere 320	C67F	1994
52206	* ESK983	𝒜𝒱	Volvo B10M-62	Plaxton Premiere 320	C53F	1995
52216	* WLT978	SR	Volvo B10M-62	Plaxton Premiere 350	C51FT	1995
52224	* 162EKH	AB-t	Volvo B10M-62	Plaxton Premiere 350	C51FT	1995
52227	* M527RSO	TU	Volvo B10M-62	Plaxton Premiere 320	DP51F	1994
52228	* M528RSO	C	Volvo B10M-62	Plaxton Premiere 320	C51F	1994
52229	* M529RSO	TU	Volvo B10M-62	Plaxton Premiere 320	DP51F	1994
52230	* M530RSO	D-t	Volvo B10M-62	Plaxton Premiere 320	DP51F	1994
52235	* CSU923	MY	Volvo B10M-62	Plaxton Premiere 320	DP51F	1994
52236	M536RSO	w	Volvo B10M-62	Plaxton Premiere 320	DP51F	1994
52237	M537RSO	MY	Volvo B10M-62	Plaxton Premiere 320	DP51F	1994
52238	M538RSO	TN	Volvo B10M-62	Plaxton Premiere 320	DP51F	1994
52239	M539RSO	r	Volvo B10M-62	Plaxton Premiere 320	DP51F	1994
52240	* 673EXA	AB	Volvo B10M-62	Plaxton Premiere 320	DP51F	1994
52242	* OFA990	r	Volvo B10M-62	Plaxton Premiere 320	DP51F	1994
52243	M543RSO	w	Volvo B10M-62	Plaxton Premiere 320	DP51F	1994
52244	* M544RSO	AB-t	Volvo B10M-62	Plaxton Premiere 320	DP51F	1994
52246	M946TSX	K-t	Volvo B10M-62	Plaxton Premiere 320	C51F	1994
52250	M950TSX	BL	Volvo B10M-62	Plaxton Premiere 320	C51F	1994
52252	M952TSX	r	Volvo B10M-62	Plaxton Premiere 320	C51F	1994
52253	M953TSX	G-t	Volvo B10M-62	Plaxton Premiere 320	TV	1994
52254	M954TSX	BL	Volvo B10M-62	Plaxton Premiere 320	C51F	1994
52255	M955TSX	K-t	Volvo B10M-62	Plaxton Premiere 320	C51F	1994
52256	M956TSX	BL	Volvo B10M-62	Plaxton Premiere 320	DP51F	1994

52258	M944TSX	r	Volvo B10M-62	Plaxton Premiere 320	C51F	1994
52261	M161CCD	GW	Volvo B10M-62	Plaxton Premiere 320	C51F	1994
52269	M808JTY	AV	Volvo B10M-62	Plaxton Premiere 350	C44FT	1995
52279 *	WLT809	SR	Volvo B10M-62	Plaxton Premiere 350	C44FT	1996
52284	N144XSA	GW-jv	Volvo B10M-62	Plaxton Premiere 320	C51F	1996
52285 *	283URB	C	Volvo B10M-62	Plaxton Premiere 320	C46FT	1996
52287	N247XSA	AN	Volvo B10M-62	Plaxton Premiere 320	C51F	1996
52288	N148XSA	C	Volvo B10M-62	Plaxton Premiere 320	C51F	1996
52294	N154XSA	MY	Volvo B10M-62	Plaxton Premiere 320	C70F	1996
52297	N447XVA	r	Volvo B10M-62	Plaxton Premiere 350	C49FT	1995
52307 *	WLT447	R	Volvo B10M-62	Plaxton Premiere 350	C44FT	1995
52308 *	GSU341	C-jv	Volvo B10M-62	Plaxton Premiere 350	C44FT	1995
52309 *	N620USS	r	Volvo B10M-62	Plaxton Premiere 350	C44FT	1995
52312	N582XSA	MY	Volvo B10M-62	Plaxton Premiere 320	DP51F	1996
52313	N583XSA	MY	Volvo B10M-62	Plaxton Premiere 320	DP51F	1996
52314	N584XSA	OY	Volvo B10M-62	Plaxton Premiere 320	DP51F	1996
52328	N128VAO	AN	Volvo B10M-62	Plaxton Premiere 350	C46FT	1995
52334 *	650GXJ	OY	Volvo B10M-62	Plaxton Premiere 350	C46FT	1996
52336 *	900HKU	OY	Volvo B10M-62	Plaxton Premiere 350	C52F	1997
52338 *	LTU284	OY	Volvo B10M-62	Plaxton Premiere 320	C52F	1997
52348	P148ASA	GW	Volvo B10M-62	Plaxton Premiere 320	C51F	1996
52349	P149ASA	AS	Volvo B10M-62	Plaxton Premiere 320	C51F	1996
52350 .	P150ASA	GW	Volvo B10M-62	Plaxton Premiere 320	C51F	1996
52352	P152ASA	MY	Volvo B10M-62	Plaxton Premiere 320	C51F	1996
52353 *	IIL3504	R	Volvo B10M-62	Plaxton Premiere 320	DP51F	1996
52354	P154ASA	GW-jv	Volvo B10M-62	Plaxton Premiere 320	C51F	1996
52355	P255ASA	r	Volvo B10M-62	Plaxton Premiere 320	C51F	1996
52356	P156ASA	r	Volvo B10M-62	Plaxton Premiere 320	C51F	1996
52359 *	P159ASA	GW	Volvo B10M-62	Plaxton Premiere 320	C51F	1996
52360	P160ASA	GW	Volvo B10M-62	Plaxton Premiere 320	C51F	1996
52361	P568MSX	r	Volvo B10M-62	Plaxton Premiere 320	C51F	1996
52362	P569MSX	AB-t	Volvo B10M-62	Plaxton Premiere 320	DP51F	1996
52386 *	FSU739	P-jv	Volvo B10M-62	Plaxton Premiere 350	C44FT	1996
52392 *	703DYE	OY	Volvo B10M-62	Plaxton Premiere 320	C47FT	1996
52416	R116OPS	AS	Volvo B10M-62	Plaxton Premiere 320	DP51F	1997
52418	R118OPS	AS	Volvo B10M-62	Plaxton Premiere 320	DP51F	1997
52419	R119OPS	GW-jv	Volvo B10M-62	Plaxton Premiere 320	DP51F	1997
52420	R120OPS	D	Volvo B10M-62	Plaxton Premiere 320	DP51F	1997
52422	R112OPS	MY	Volvo B10M-62	Plaxton Premiere 320	DP51F	1997
52425	R103LSO	CK	Volvo B10M-62	Plaxton Premiere 320	DP51F	1997
52426	R104LSO	G	Volvo B10M-62	Plaxton Premiere 320	DP51F	1997
52427	R105LSO	GW-jv	Volvo B10M-62	Plaxton Premiere 320	DP51F	1997
52429 *	YSU882	TU	Volvo B10M-62	Plaxton Premiere 350	C50FT	1998
52431	R451MSL	P	Volvo B10M-62	Plaxton Premiere 320	C49FT	1997
52432 *	YJU694	DE-jv	Volvo B10M-62	Plaxton Premiere 320	C49FT	1997
52433 *	143CLT	P	Volvo B10M-62	Plaxton Premiere 320	C49FT	1997
52456	R636RSE	MY	Volvo B10M-62	Plaxton Premiere 320	C51F	1997
52460	R640RSE	S	Volvo B10M-62	Plaxton Premiere 320	DP51F	1997
52463 *	WLT915	MY	Volvo B10M-62	Plaxton Premiere 320	C51F	1997
52464	R84SEF	GW-jv	Volvo B10M-62	Plaxton Premiere 320	C51F	1997
52465	R85SEF	GW	Volvo B10M-62	Plaxton Premiere 320	C51F	1997
52474	R174DNH	r	Volvo B10M-62	Plaxton Premiere 320	C51F	1997
52475	R175DNH	r	Volvo B10M-62	Plaxton Premiere 320	C51F	1997
52476	R176DNH	C	Volvo B10M-62	Plaxton Premiere 320	C51F	1997
52477	R177DNH	G p	Volvo B10M-62	Plaxton Premiere 320	C51F	1997
52478	R178DNH	G	Volvo B10M-62	Plaxton Premiere 320	C51F	1997
52479	R179DNH	GC	Volvo B10M-62	Plaxton Premiere 320	C51F	1997
52481	R181DNH	S	Volvo B10M-62	Plaxton Premiere 320	C51F	1997
52510	S860VAT	OY	Volvo B10M-62	Plaxton Premiere 320	DP51F	1998
52518 *	T536EUB	r	Volvo B10M-62	Plaxton Premiere 350	C48FT	1999
52519 *	T535EUB	OY	Volvo B10M-62	Plaxton Premiere 350	C49FT	1999

52523	W743NAS	TN	Volvo B10M-62	Plaxton Paragon	C49FT	2000
52524	W745NAS	OY	Volvo B10M-62	Plaxton Paragon	C49FT	2000
52525	* X466SAS	TU	Volvo B10M-62	Plaxton Paragon	C49FT	2000
52528	Y285VST	TU	Volvo B10M-62	Plaxton Excalibur	C49FT	2001
52530	* OXI413	FW	Volvo B10M-62	Plaxton Premiere 350	C49FT	2000
52531	* OXI459	CT	Volvo B10M-62	Plaxton Premiere 350	C49FT	2000
52532	* XIJ602	FW	Volvo B10M-62	Plaxton Paragon	C49FT	2000
52533	* 444VNX	FW	Volvo B10M-62	Plaxton Paragon	C49FT	2000
52534	* DSU707	TN	Volvo B10M-62	Plaxton Paragon	C49FT	2001
52535	* 900RWX	R	Volvo B10M-62	Plaxton Paragon	C49FT	2001
52536	* KLZ2317	CT	Volvo B10M-62	Plaxton Premiere 350	C49FT	2001
52602	* S174SVK	OY	Volvo B10M-62	Jonckheere Mistral	C53F	1998
52603	S133KRM	OY	Volvo B10M-62	Jonckheere Mistral	C44FT	1998
52605	S655JSE	OY	Volvo B10M-62	Jonckherre Modulo	C51F	1998
52606	S656JSE	OY	Volvo B10M-62	Jonckherre Modulo	C51F	1998
52607	S657JSE	OY	Volvo B10M-62	Jonckherre Modulo	C51F	1998
52608	S658JSE	OY	Volvo B10M-62	Jonckherre Modulo	C51F	1998
52609	S659JSE	OY	Volvo B10M-62	Jonckherre Modulo	C51F	1998
52610	S660JSE	OY	Volvo B10M-62	Jonckherre Modulo	C51F	1998
52611	S661JSE	OY	Volvo B10M-62	Jonckherre Modulo	C51F	1998
52612	S662JSE	OY	Volvo B10M-62	Jonckherre Modulo	C51F	1998
52638	S808BTT	OY	Volvo B10M-62	Jonckherre Modulo	C51F	1998
52655	* NSU133	DE-jv	Volvo B10M-62	Jonckheere Mistral	C49FT	1999
52656	V906DPN	DE-jv	Volvo B10M-62	Jonckheere Mistral	C49FT	1999
52666	X676NSE	DE-jv	Volvo B10M-62	Jonckheere Mistral	C49FT	2000
52667	* PIB9211	R	Volvo B10M-62	Jonckherre Mistral	C49FT	2000
52668	X678NSE	DE-jv	Volvo B10M-62	Jonckheere Mistral	C49FT	2000
52669	* GDZ3363	R	Volvo B10M-62	Jonckheere Mistral	C49FT	2000
52670	* LSK479	R	Volvo B10M-62	Jonckheere Deauville	C49FT	1995
52671	* LSK478	R	Volvo B10M-62	Jonckheere Deauville	C49FT	1995
52672	* CCZ5837	R	Volvo B10M-62	Jonckheere Mistral	C49FT	1998
52675	* MIL5573	CT	Volvo B10M-62	Jonckheere Mistral	C43FT	1998
52676	* 540FFX	CT	Volvo B10M-62	Plaxton Premiere 350	C53FT	1997
52679	* UIL7808	OY	Volvo B10M-60	Jonckherre Mistral	C53F	1992
53038	FJ04ESU	R	Volvo B12M	Sunsundegui Sideral	C49FT	2004
53101	SV08GXM	TU	Volvo B12B	Plaxton Panther	C49FTL	2008
53102	SV08GXN	TU	Volvo B12B	Plaxton Panther	C49FTL	2008
53103	SV08GXO	IS	Volvo B12B	Plaxton Panther	C49FTL	2008
53104	SV08GXP	IS	Volvo B12B	Plaxton Panther	C49FTL	2008
53105	SF08GTY	GW-jv	Volvo B12B	Plaxton Panther	C49FTL	2008
53106	SF08GTZ	GW-jv	Volvo B12B	Plaxton Panther	C49FTL	2008
53107	SP08FUV	C-jv	Volvo B12B	Plaxton Panther	C49FTL	2008
53108	SV09EGY	FW-jv	Volvo B12M	Plaxton Panther	C49FTL	2009
53109	SV09EGD	FW-jv	Volvo B12M	Plaxton Panther	C49FTL	2009
53110	SV09EGE	FW-jv	Volvo B12M	Plaxton Panther	C49FTL	2009
53111	SV09EGF	FW-jv	Volvo B12M	Plaxton Panther	C49FTL	2009
53112	SV09EGJ	FW-jv	Volvo B12M	Plaxton Panther	C49FTL	2009
53113	SV09EGK	TN	Volvo B12M	Plaxton Panther	C49FTL	2009
53114	SF09ADO	GW-jv	Volvo B12B	Plaxton Panther	C49FTL	2009
53201	SV54BYO	TU	Volvo B7R	Plaxton Profile	C51F	2004
53202	SV54BYP	TU	Volvo B7R	Plaxton Profile	C51F	2004
53203	SV54BYR	TU	Volvo B7R	Plaxton Profile	C51F	2004
53204	SV54BYT	AS	Volvo B7R	Plaxton Profile	C51F	2004
53205	SV54BYU	OY	Volvo B7R	Plaxton Profile	C51F	2004
53206	SV54BYW	TU	Volvo B7R	Plaxton Profile	C51F	2004
53207	SV54BYY	TU	Volvo B7R	Plaxton Profile	C51F	2004
53208	SV54BYZ	AS	Volvo B7R	Plaxton Profile	C51F	2004
53209	SV54EKP	TU	Volvo B7R	Plaxton Profile	C51F	2004
53210	SV54EKR	AS	Volvo B7R	Plaxton Profile	C51F	2004
53211	SV54EKT	OY	Volvo B7R	Plaxton Profile	C51F	2004
53212	SV54EKU	TU	Volvo B7R	Plaxton Profile	C51F	2005

53213	SV54EKW	AS	Volvo B7R	Plaxton Profile	C51F	2005
53214	SV54EKX	TU	Volvo B7R	Plaxton Profile	C51F	2005
53215	SV54EKY	AS	Volvo B7R	Plaxton Profile	C51F	2005
53216	SV54EKZ	AS	Volvo B7R	Plaxton Profile	C51F	2005
53217	SV54EMF	AS	Volvo B7R	Plaxton Profile	C51F	2005
53218	SV54EMJ	AS	Volvo B7R	Plaxton Profile	C51F	2005
53219	SV54EMK		Volvo B7R	Plaxton Profile	C51F	2005
53220	SV54ENC	TU	Volvo B7R	Plaxton Profile	C51F	2005
53221	SV55EEP	BU	Volvo B7R	Plaxton Profile	C49FL	2005
53222	SV55EER	BU	Volvo B7R	Plaxton Profile	C49FL	2005
53223	SV55EES	BU	Volvo B7R	Plaxton Profile	C49FL	2005
53225	SV55EEU	BU	Volvo B7R	Plaxton Profile	C49FL	2005
53226	SV55FKA	AB	Volvo B7R	Plaxton Profile	C49FL	2005
53227	SV55FKB	IS	Volvo B7R	Plaxton Profile	C49FL	2005
53228	SV55FKD	IS	Volvo B7R	Plaxton Profile	C49FL	2005
53229	SV55FKE	IS	Volvo B7R	Plaxton Profile	C49FL	2005
53230	SV55FKF	TN	Volvo B7R	Plaxton Profile	C49FL	2005
53231	SV55FKG	TN	Volvo B7R	Plaxton Profile	C49FL	2005
53232	SV55FKH	BU	Volvo B7R	Plaxton Profile	C49FL	2005
53233	SV55FKJ	BU	Volvo B7R	Plaxton Profile	C49FL	2005
53234	SV55FKK	MY	Volvo B7R	Plaxton Profile	C49FL	2005
53235	SV55FKL	AB	Volvo B7R	Plaxton Profile	C49FL	2006
53236	SV55FKM	MY	Volvo B7R	Plaxton Profile	C49FL	2006
53237	SV55FKN	MY	Volvo B7R	Plaxton Profile	C49FL	2006
53238	SV55FKO	MY	Volvo B7R	Plaxton Profile	C49FL	2006
53239	SV55FJN	MY	Volvo B7R	Plaxton Profile	C49FL	2006
53240	SV55FJO	MY	Volvo B7R	Plaxton Profile	C49FL	2006
53241	SV55FJP	MY	Volvo B7R	Plaxton Profile	C49FL	2006
53242	SV55FJU	MY	Volvo B7R	Plaxton Profile	C49FL	2006
53243	SV55FJX	MY	Volvo B7R	Plaxton Profile	C49FL	2006
53244	SV55FJY	MY	Volvo B7R	Plaxton Profile	C49FL	2006
53245	SV55FJZ	MY	Volvo B7R	Plaxton Profile	C49FL	2006
53246	SV06FTF	MY	Volvo B7R	Plaxton Profile	C49FL	2006
53247	SV06FTJ	MY	Volvo B7R	Plaxton Profile	C49FL	2006
53248	SP06FVA	D	Volvo B7R	Plaxton Profile	C49FL	2006
53249	SP06FVB	D	Volvo B7R	Plaxton Profile	C49FL	2006
53250	SP06FVC	D	Volvo B7R	Plaxton Profile	C49FL	2006
53251	SP06FVD	D	Volvo B7R	Plaxton Profile	C49FL	2006
53252	SP06FVE	D	Volvo B7R	Plaxton Profile	C49FL	2006
53253	SP06FVF	D	Volvo B7R	Plaxton Profile	C49FL	2006
53254	SP06FVG	D	Volvo B7R	Plaxton Profile	C49FL	2006
53255	SP06FVH	A	Volvo B7R	Plaxton Profile	C49FL	2006
53256	SP06FVJ	A	Volvo B7R	Plaxton Profile	C49FL	2006
53257	SP56EBL	A	Volvo B7R	Plaxton Profile	C49FL	2006
53258	SP56EBM	A	Volvo B7R	Plaxton Profile	C49FL	2006
53259	SP56EBN	A	Volvo B7R	Plaxton Profile	C49FL	2006
53260	SP56EBO	A	Volvo B7R	Plaxton Profile	C49FL	2006
53261	SP56EBU	A	Volvo B7R	Plaxton Profile	C49FL	2006
53262	SV56BVR	MY	Volvo B7R	Plaxton Profile	C49FL	2006
53263	SV56BVS	MY	Volvo B7R	Plaxton Profile	C49FL	2006
53264	SV56BVT	MY	Volvo B7R	Plaxton Profile	C49FL	2006
53265	SV56BVU	MY	Volvo B7R	Plaxton Profile	C49FL	2006
53266	SV56BVW	MY	Volvo B7R	Plaxton Profile	C49FL	2006
53267	SV56BVX	MY	Volvo B7R	Plaxton Profile	C49FL	2006
53268	SV56BVY	MY	Volvo B7R	Plaxton Profile	C49FL	2006
53269	SV56BVZ	MY	Volvo B7R	Plaxton Profile	C49FL	2006
53270	SV56BWA	MY	Volvo B7R	Plaxton Profile	C49FL	2006
53275	KX56JZN	R	Volvo B7R	Plaxton Profile	C67FL	2006
53276	KX56JZO	R	Volvo B7R	Plaxton Profile	C49FL	2006
53277	SP07HHD	A	Volvo B7R	Plaxton Profile	C49FL	2007
53278	SP07HHE	A	Volvo B7R	Plaxton Profile	C49FL	2007

53279	SP07HHF	A	Volvo B7R	Plaxton Profile	C49FL	2007
53280	SP07HHG	A	Volvo B7R	Plaxton Profile	C49FL	2007
53281	SP07HHJ	A	Volvo B7R	Plaxton Profile	C49FL	2007
53282	SP07HHK	A	Volvo B7R	Plaxton Profile	C49FL	2007
53283	SP07HHL	A	Volvo B7R	Plaxton Profile	C49FL	2007
53284	SP07HHM	A	Volvo B7R	Plaxton Profile	C49FL	2007
53285	SP07HHN	A	Volvo B7R	Plaxton Profile	C49FL	2007
53286 *	SP07HHO	G	Volvo B7R	Plaxton Profile	C49FL	2007
53287	SP07HHR	G	Volvo B7R	Plaxton Profile	C49FL	2007
53288	SP07HHS	G	Volvo B7R	Plaxton Profile	C49FL	2007
53289	SP07HHT	G	Volvo B7R	Plaxton Profile	C49FL	2007
53290	SP07HHU	G	Volvo B7R	Plaxton Profile	C49FL	2007
53291	SP07HHV	G	Volvo B7R	Plaxton Profile	C49FL	2007
53292	SP07HHW	G	Volvo B7R	Plaxton Profile	C49FL	2007
53293	SP07HHX	G	Volvo B7R	Plaxton Profile	C49FL	2007
53294	SP07HHY	G	Volvo B7R	Plaxton Profile	C49FL	2007
53295	SP07HHZ	G	Volvo B7R	Plaxton Profile	C49FL	2007
53296	SP57CNC	A	Volvo B7R	Plaxton Profile	C49FL	2007
53297	SJ57AAK	R	Volvo B7R	Plaxton Profile	C67FL	2007
53298	SJ57AAN	K	Volvo B7R	Plaxton Profile	C49FL	2007
53299	SJ57AAO	K	Volvo B7R	Plaxton Profile	C49FL	2007
53300	SJ57AAU	K	Volvo B7R	Plaxton Profile	C49FL	2007
53301	SJ57AAV	K	Volvo B7R	Plaxton Profile	C49FL	2007
53302	SF07LCJ	DS	Volvo B7R	Plaxton Profile	C49FL	2007
53303	SF07LCK	SR	Volvo B7R	Plaxton Profile	C49FL	2007
53304	SP07FCY	A	Volvo B7R	Plaxton Profile	C49FL	2007
53305	SP07FCZ	A	Volvo B7R	Plaxton Profile	C49FL	2007
53306	SV08DHE	SV	Volvo B7R	Plaxton Profile	C49FL	2008
53307	SV08DHF	SV	Volvo B7R	Plaxton Profile	C49FL	2008
53308	SV08DHG	SV	Volvo B7R	Plaxton Profile	C49FL	2008
53309	SV08DHJ	SV	Volvo B7R	Plaxton Profile	C49FL	2008
53310	SV08DHK	SV	Volvo B7R	Plaxton Profile	C49FL	2008
53311	SV08DHL	SV	Volvo B7R	Plaxton Profile	C49FL	2008
53312	SV08DHM	SV	Volvo B7R	Plaxton Profile	C49FL	2008
53313	SV08DHN	SV	Volvo B7R	Plaxton Profile	C49FL	2008
53314	SV08DHO	SV	Volvo B7R	Plaxton Profile	C49FL	2008
53315	SV08DHP	r	Volvo B7R	Plaxton Profile	C49FL	2008
53316	SV08DHU	SV	Volvo B7R	Plaxton Profile	C49FL	2008
53317	SV08DHX	SV	Volvo B7R	Plaxton Profile	C49FL	2008
53318	SV08DHY	TN	Volvo B7R	Plaxton Profile	C49FL	2008
53319	SV08DHZ	TN	Volvo B7R	Plaxton Profile	C49FL	2008
53320	SV08DJD	TN	Volvo B7R	Plaxton Profile	C49FL	2008
53321	SV09BHL	MY	Volvo B7R	Plaxton Profile	C49FL	2009
53322	SF09ACV	AY	Volvo B7R	Plaxton Profile	C49FL	2009
53323	SF09ACX	AY	Volvo B7R	Plaxton Profile	C49FL	2009
53324	SF09ACY	DS	Volvo B7R	Plaxton Profile	C49FL	2009
53325	SF09ACZ	SR	Volvo B7R	Plaxton Profile	C49FL	2009
53331	SV09EGZ	TN	Volvo B7R	Plaxton Profile	C49FL	2009
53332	SV09EHB	IS	Volvo B7R	Plaxton Profile	C49FL	2009
53333	SV09EHC	IS	Volvo B7R	Plaxton Profile	C49FL	2009
53334	SV09EFZ	MY	Volvo B7R	Plaxton Profile	C49FL	2009
53335 *	9637EL	MY	Volvo B7R	Plaxton Profile	C49FL	2009
54008	SV56BWB	AB	Volvo B12B(T)	Plaxton Panther	C65FLT	2007
54009	SV56BWC	AB	Volvo B12B(T)	Plaxton Panther	C65FLT	2007
54010	SV56BWD	AB	Volvo B12B(T)	Plaxton Panther	C65FLT	2007
54011	SV56BWE	AB	Volvo B12B(T)	Plaxton Panther	C65FLT	2007
54012	SV56BWF	IS	Volvo B12B(T)	Plaxton Panther	C65FLT	2007
54013	SV07ACX	IS	Volvo B12B(T)	Plaxton Panther	C65FLT	2007
54014	SV07ACY	IS	Volvo B12B(T)	Plaxton Panther	C65FLT	2007
54015	SV07ACZ	IS	Volvo B12B(T)	Plaxton Panther	C65FLT	2007
54016	SV07ADO	IS	Volvo B12B(T)	Plaxton Panther	C65FLT	2007

54017	SV07ADU	IS	Volvo B12B(T)	Plaxton Panther	C65FLT	2007
54018	SP07CAA	P	Volvo B12B(T)	Plaxton Panther	C65FLT	2007
54019	SP07CAE	P	Volvo B12B(T)	Plaxton Panther	C65FLT	2007
54020	SP07CAO	P	Volvo B12B(T)	Plaxton Panther	C65FLT	2007
54021	SP07CAU	P	Volvo B12B(T)	Plaxton Panther	C65FLT	2007
54022	SP07CAV	P	Volvo B12B(T)	Plaxton Panther	C65FLT	2007
54027	SF07AMV	GW-jv	Volvo B12B(T)	Plaxton Panther	C65FLT	2007
54028	SF07AMX	GW-jv	Volvo B12B(T)	Plaxton Panther	C65FLT	2007
54029	SF07ANP	GW-jv	Volvo B12B(T)	Plaxton Panther	C65FLT	2007
54030	SF07ANR	GW-jv	Volvo B12B(T)	Plaxton Panther	C65FLT	2007
54031	SF07ANU	GW-jv	Volvo B12B(T)	Plaxton Panther	C65FLT	2007
54032	SF07ANV	GW-jv	Volvo B12B(T)	Plaxton Panther	C65FLT	2007
54033	SF07ANX	DE-jv	Volvo B12B(T)	Plaxton Panther	C65FLT	2007
54034	SF07AOA	JS	Volvo B12B(T)	Plaxton Panther	C65FLT	2007
54035	SP07FCX	P	Volvo B12B(T)	Plaxton Panther	C65FLT	2007
54036	SV07FKY	IS	Volvo B12B(T)	Plaxton Panther	C65FLT	2007
54037	SF07LCG	IS	Volvo B12B(T)	Plaxton Panther	C65FLT	2007
54038	SJ57AAX	CK	Volvo B12B(T)	Plaxton Panther	C69FL	2008
54039	SJ57AAY	CK	Volvo B12B(T)	Plaxton Panther	C69FL	2008
54040	SJ57AAZ	CK	Volvo B12B(T)	Plaxton Panther	C69FL	2008
54041	SF57DPV	CK	Volvo B12B(T)	Plaxton Panther	C69FL	2008
54042	SF57DPX	CK	Volvo B12B(T)	Plaxton Panther	C69FL	2008
54043	SF57DPY	CK	Volvo B12B(T)	Plaxton Panther	C69FL	2008
54044	SF57DPZ	CK	Volvo B12B(T)	Plaxton Panther	C69FL	2008
54045	SF57DRV	CK	Volvo B12B(T)	Plaxton Panther	C69FL	2008
54046	* 448GWL	AB	Volvo B12B(T)	Plaxton Panther	C65FLT	2008
54047	SP08FPF	GW-jv	Volvo B12B(T)	Plaxton Panther	C65FLT	2008
54048	SP08FPJ	DE-jv	Volvo B12B(T)	Plaxton Panther	C65FLT	2008
54049	SF08GTU	GW-jv	Volvo B12B(T)	Plaxton Panther	C65FLT	2008
54062	SV59CGX	BU	Volvo B12B(T)	Plaxton Panther	C65FLT	2009
54063	SV59CGY	BU	Volvo B12B(T)	Plaxton Panther	C65FLT	2009
54064	SV59CGZ	BU	Volvo B12B(T)	Plaxton Panther	C65FLT	2009
54065	SV59CHC	BU	Volvo B12B(T)	Plaxton Panther	C65FLT	2009
54066	SV59CHD	BU	Volvo B12B(T)	Plaxton Panther	C65FLT	2009
54067	SV59CHF	BU	Volvo B12B(T)	Plaxton Panther	C65FLT	2009
54068	SV59CHG	BU	Volvo B12B(T)	Plaxton Panther	C65FLT	2009
54069	SV59CHJ	GW-jv	Volvo B12B(T)	Plaxton Panther	C65FLT	2009
54070	SV59CHK	BU	Volvo B12B(T)	Plaxton Panther	C65FLT	2009
54071	SV59CHL	GW-jv	Volvo B12B(T)	Plaxton Panther	C65FLT	2009
54072	SV59CHN	BU	Volvo B12B(T)	Plaxton Panther	C65FLT	2009
54073	SV59CHO	BU	Volvo B12B(T)	Plaxton Panther	C65FLT	2009
54074	SV59CHX	BU	Volvo B12B(T)	Plaxton Panther	C65FLT	2009
54075	SV59CHY	BU	Volvo B12B(T)	Plaxton Panther	C65FLT	2009
54076	SF59FYV	GW	Volvo B12B(T)	Plaxton Panther	C65FLT	2009
54077	SF59FYW	DS	Volvo B12B(T)	Plaxton Panther	C65FLT	2009
54078	SF59FYX	K	Volvo B12B(T)	Plaxton Panther	C65FLT	2009
54079	SF59FYY	DS	Volvo B12B(T)	Plaxton Panther	C65FLT	2009
59111	* BHZ9546	R	Dennis Javelin 12SDA	Caetano Algarve II	C53F	1992
59112	* A19RNY	R	Dennis Javelin 12SDA	Caetano Algarve II	C53F	1995
59113	* A16RNY	R	Dennis Javelin 12SDA	Caetano Algarve II	C67F	1995
59114	* C12RNY	R	Dennis Javelin 12SDA	Caetano Algarve II	C53F	1996
59115	* A17RNY	R	Dennis Javelin 12SFD	Caetano Algarve II	C53F	1997
59171	* XIB3473	w	Dennis Javelin 12SDA	Plaxton Premiere 320	C70F	1992
59173	* 719CEL	r	Dennis Javelin 12SDA	Plaxton Premiere 320	C70F	1994
59175	* FSU718	CT	Dennis Javelin 12SFD	Plaxton Premiere 320	DP67F	1998
59176	* JAZ9852	SE	Dennis Javelin 12SFD	Plaxton Premiere 320	C67F	1998
59177	* JAZ9855	CT	Dennis Javelin 12SFD	Plaxton Premiere 320	C67F	1998
59178	* S690RWG	SE	Dennis Javelin 12SFD	Plaxton Premiere 320	DP67F	1998
59602	* C13RNY	R	Mercedes-Benz 614D	Autobus Nouvelle	C24F	1999
59603	* PIJ601	R	Mercedes-Benz Sprinter	Onyx	C24F	1999
59614	MX06ONV	R	Mercedes-Benz Vario O814D	Excel	C24F	2006

59615		MX06ONW	R	Mercedes-Benz Vario O814D	Onyx	C23FL	2006
59621	*	N401LTL	R	Bova FHD12.280	Bova Futura	C53F	1995
59642	*	EKZ469	R	Mercedes-Benz Touro	Mercedes-Benz	C49FT	2004
59643	*	439BUS	R	Mercedes-Benz Touro 1836RL	Mercedes-Benz	C49FT	2003
59661		T993PFH	w	Toyota Coaster BB50R	Caetano Optimo	C21F	1999
59671	*	LIJ595	R	Setra S250	Setra Special	C55FT	1995
59793	*	YBZ818	R	DAF SB3000XMG	Van Hool Alizée	C50FT	1997
59950		YSD350L	WS-p	Leyland Leopard PSU3/3R	Alexander AY	C49F	1973
60004		SW03OYE	GW-a	Mercedes-Benz Vito 110CDi	Mercedes-Benz	M8	2003
60005		SW03OYF	DS-a	Mercedes-Benz Vito 110CDi	Mercedes-Benz	M8	2003
60010		SW03OYL	IS-a	Mercedes-Benz Vito 110CDi	Mercedes-Benz	M8	2003
60014		SF54CSU	R	Mercedes-Benz Vito 110CDi	Mercedes-Benz	M8	2004
80013		BK10MGE		Volvo B7RLE	Wright Eclipse Urban	B43F	2010

Starline Travel

Starline Travel (Scotland) Ltd, 249 Greengairs Road, Greengairs ML6 7SZ
Website
Depot   249 Greengairs Road, Greengairs ML6 7SZ
Licence   PM1086532

*	A201MFR	Leyland Tiger TRCTL11/3R	Plaxton Paramount 3500 I	C53F	1983
*	B16SCJ	Scania K113CRB	Berkhof	C30FT	1998
*	F969RSE	Volvo B10M-60	Duple 320	C57F	1989
*	J229NNC	Volvo B10M-60	Van Hool Alizée	C49FT	1991
*	K600SOU	Volvo B10M-60	Jonckheere Deauville P599	C53F	1992
*	MAZ8433	Volvo B10M-62	Caetano Algarve II	C49FT	1994
	SS07JAY	Bova FHD13.340	Bova Futura	C36FT	2007
*	XCZ4150	Bova FHD12.340	Bova Futura	C49FT	1996

Stepend Coaches

S Chapman, 106 High Street, Motherwell ML1 5JH
Website
Depot   Unit 4 Flowerhill Industrial Estate, Airdrie ML6 6BH
Licence   PM0002154

	BU08ACZ		Enterprise Bus Plasma EB01	Plaxton Primo	B28F	2008
	BX04MZT		Mercedes-Benz Atego 1223L	Mercedes-Benz	C49FT	2004
	GX07BAU		Irisbus Agora Line	Optare	B44F	2007
	L2SBC	w	Mercedes-Benz 811D	Plaxton Beaver	B31F	1993
	MX04VLS		Optare Solo M850	Optare	B26F	2004
	MX53FDE		Optare Solo M850	Optare	B29F	2003
	N264JUG		Mercedes-Benz 709D	Plaxton Beaver	B22F	1996
	N768EWG		Mercedes-Benz 709D	Alexander Sprint	B25F	1996
	NK53KGJ		Mercedes-Benz Vario O.814D	TransBus Beaver 2	B33F	2003
	P233EJW		Mercedes-Benz 811D	Marshall C16	B27F	1997
	P234EJW		Mercedes-Benz 811D	Marshall C16	B27F	1997
	R971MGB		Mercedes-Benz Vario O.814D	Alexander Sprint	B27F	1998
	S13ORO		Volvo B10M-62	Plaxton Premiere 350	C49F	1999
	SF54HVZ		Mercedes-Benz Vario O.814D	Plaxton Beaver 2	DP33F	2004
	SF57JTX		Optare Solo M950	Optare	B33F	2007
	T877SSF		Mercedes-Benz Vario O.810D	Plaxton Beaver 2	B31F	1999
	T976OGA		Mercedes-Benz Vario O.814D	Plaxton Beaver 2	B27F	1999
	W10CAE		Volvo B10M-55	Van Hool Alizée	C49FT	1999
	Y407DAB		Dennis R	Plaxton Panther	C49FT	2001
	YE52KPT		Optare Solo M850	Optare	B29F	2002
*	YIL7775		MAN 11.190	Optare Vecta	B41F	1994
	YJ55BKD		Optare Solo M850	Optare	B F	2005
	YJ55YHH		Optare Solo M780SL	Optare	B23F	2005
	YJ55YHL		Optare Solo M780SL	Optare	B23F	2005

Stepend Coaches				
YN03NDX	Optare Solo M850	Optare	B29F	2003
YN53YGZ	Optare Solo M850	Optare	B29F	2003

William Stokes & Sons

William Stokes & Sons Ltd, 22 Carstairs Road, Carstairs ML11 8QD
Website www.stokescoaches.co.uk
Depot 22 Carstairs Road, Carstairs ML11 8QD
Licence PM0000018

	F343GUS ~ z	Leyland Tiger TRBTL11/2RP	Plaxton Paramount 3500 III	B54F	1988
	L292USU ~	Dennis Dart 9 SDL	Plaxton Pointer	B35F	1993
	L293USU ~	Dennis Dart 9 SDL	Plaxton Pointer	B35F	1993
	M530DPN	DAF SB220LT550	Ikarus Citibus 480	B48F	1995
	N753LSU ~	Volvo B6-50	Alexander Dash	B40F	1995
	N971MGG	Volvo B6-50	Alexander Dash	B40F	1995
	T80LRT ~	Dennis Javelin 12SFD	Berkhof Axial 50	C53F	1999
	T409BGB ~	Mercedes-Benz Vario O.814D	Marshall Master	B31F	1999
*	WSU557	Dennis Javelin 12SFD	Berkhof Axial 50	C51FT	1998
*	WSU858	Volvo B12B	Jonckheere Mistral	C51FT	2007
*	WSU859	Volvo B10M-60	Ikarus Blue Danube VL	C49FT	1989
*	WSU860	Volvo B12B	Jonckheere Mistral	C51FT	2007
*	WSU871	Mercedes-Benz Atego	Unvi Cimo	C37F	2004

Stonehouse Coaches

Stonehouse Coaches Ltd, 2 Ayr Road, Ashgill, Larkhall ML9 3AD
Website
Depot 2 Ayr Road, Ashgill, Larkhall ML9 3AD
48 New Street, Stonehouse ML9 3LT
Licence PM1049208

	F155DET	Scania N113CRB	Alexander RH	H47/33F	1989
	G47FKG	Scania N113CRB	Alexander RH	H47/33F	1989
	G49FKG	Scania N113CRB	Alexander RH	H47/33F	1989
	G616OTV	Volvo B10M-60	Alexander RV	H47/37F	1989
	G808LAG	Scania N113CRB	East Lancs	H55/37F	1989
	KE54FUV	Mercedes-Benz Vario O.814D	Plaxton Beaver 2	DP33F	2004
	KE54FVL	Mercedes-Benz Vario O.814D	Plaxton Beaver 2	DP31F	2004
	L487NTO	Volvo Olympian YN2RV18Z5	East Lancs Pyoneer	H49/38F	1994
*	N289RGD	Dennis Javelin 12SFD	Wadham Stringer Vanguard III	C50FA	1995
*	N465AAO	Dennis Javelin 10SDA	Wadham Stringer	C60F	1995
	YP52KSJ	Mercedes-Benz Vario O.814D	Plaxton Beaver	DP30FL	2002

Stuarts of Carluke
Stuarts Coaches Ltd, Airdrie Road, Carluke ML8 5EP
Website
Depot   Castlehill Garage, Carluke ML8 5EP
Licence   PM1029048

*	2450PP	Mercedes-Benz Vario O.814D	Plaxton Cheetah	C33F	2002
*	BSV216	Volvo B10M-62	Van Hool Alizée	C46FT	1995
	C806USG	Volvo B10M-50	Alexander RV	H47/37F	1986
*	CSV651	Volvo B10M-62	Van Hool Alizée	C51FT	1997
*	DSV246	Volvo B12M	Jonckheere Mistral	C53F	2003
	E324BVO	Volvo B10M-50	East Lancs	H47/38D	1988
*	EYN165	Volvo B10M-62	Van Hool Alizée	C70F	1996
	F103TML	Volvo B10M-50	Alexander RV	H47/32F	1989
	F104TML	Volvo B10M-50	Alexander RV	H47/33F	1989
*	FSV864	Mercedes-Benz Vario O.814D	Plaxton Beaver 2	C33F	2002
	G653EKA z	Volvo B10M-50	East Lancs	H49/39F	1990
*	HSV782	Volvo B12M	Jonckheere Mistral	C53F	2004
*	KXG661	Leyland Tiger TRCTL11/3ARZ	Plaxton Paramount 3200 III	C70F	1998
*	LSV380	Volvo B10M-62	Van Hool Alizée	C49FT	2000
*	MSV452	Bova FHD12-340	Bova Futura	C49FT	2003
	MX06ACF	Optare Solo M850	Optare	B29F	2006
	MX07BCK	Optare Solo M780	Optare	B24F	2007
	MX54KXU	Optare Solo M850	Optare	B24F	2004
	MX54KYN	Optare Solo M850	Optare	B24F	2004
*	NSV224	Volvo B10M-55	Alexander	B51F	1990
*	OBZ2241	Volvo B10M-61	Van Hool Alizée	C53F	1986
*	RSU585	Volvo B12M	Jonckheere Mistral	C53F	2004
*	RSV533	Volvo B10M-60	Plaxton Paramount 3200 III	C57F	1989
	S776RNE	Dennis Dart 10.7 SLF	Plaxton Pointer 2	B41F	1998
	SF09HKH	Bova FHD127-365	Bova Futura	C63FLT	2009
	SF10GXK	Bova FHD127-365	Bova Futura	C53FLT	2010
	SF10GXL	Bova FHD127-365	Bova Futura	C53FLT	2010
	SN08AEL	ADL Enviro 300 12.5 SLF	ADL Enviro 300	B53F	2008
	SN08AEO	ADL Enviro 300 12.5 SLF	ADL Enviro 300	B53F	2008
*	UVS158	Volvo B10M-62	Jonckheere Mistral	C49FT	2000
*	VIL4027	Volvo B10M-50	Alexander RV	H46/33F	1990
*	WJI2321	Volvo B10M-60	Van Hool Alizée	C57F	1989
*	WSV238	Bova FHD12-340	Bova Futura	C49FT	2002
	X705UKS	Dennis Dart 10.7 SLF	Plaxton Pointer	B29F	2001
	YJ07VRR	Optare Solo M710SE	Optare	B21F	2007
	YJ55YHG	Optare Solo M780SL	Optare	B24F	2005
*	YKJ798	Volvo B10M-62	Caetano Enigma	C49F	2000
	YN54AGO	Scania K114EB4	Irizar Century	C49FT	2005

Telfords Coaches
Telford's Coaches Ltd, 26 North Hermitage Street, Newcastleton TD9 0RA
Website   www.telfordscoaches.com
Depot   Tweedon Brae, Newcastleton TD9 0TL
               Auction Mart, North Hermitage Street, Newcastleton TD9 0RG
Licence   PM1016939

	B134BBV	Ford R1115	Plaxton Paramount 3200 II	C53F	1985
	E318XGB	Mercedes-Benz 609D	PMT	C24F	1987
*	K700BUL	Dennis Javelin 11SDA	Duple 320	C53F	1993
*	L710ADS	Volvo B10M-62	Van Hool Alizée	C53F	1994
	N501AWB	Mercedes-Benz 609D	Crystals	C24F	1996
	N791NYS	Mercedes-Benz Vario O.814D	Plaxton Beaver Coach	C33F	1996
*	NIL1235 —	Volvo B10M-60	Plaxton Excalibur	C47FT	1993
*	NIL4979 —	Volvo B10M-62	Plaxton Excalibur	C53F	1998

		Telfords Coaches		

P28KWA —	Volvo B10M-62	Plaxton Premiere 350	C49FT	1996
P119RSF	Volvo B10M-62	Plaxton Premiere 350	C53F	1997
* PIJ2799	Mercedes-Benz Vario O.814D	TransBus Cheetah	C29F	2003
R457VSD	Mercedes-Benz 410D	Adamson	M16	1998
* R951RCH —	Volvo B10M-62	Plaxton Premiere 320	C57F	1997
* SF05XDG	Volvo B12M	Jonckheere Mistral	C53F	2005
* SF06WKE	Volvo B12M	Jonckheere Mistral	C53F	2005
* T717UOS	Volvo B10M-62	Jonckheere Mistral	C51FT	1999
* WSU864	Volvo B10M-62	Berkhof Axial 50	C51FT	2002
Y502TNB	Mercedes-Benz Vario O.814D	Onyx	C24F	2001
YN56DZF—	Mercedes-Benz Vario O.814D	Plaxton Beaver	DP29FL	2006

Tramontana
W Telfer, Chapleknowe Road, Carfin, Motherwell ML1 5SE
Website
Depot   Chapleknowe Road, Carfin, Motherwell ML1 5SE
Licence   PM0002277

* 688EYV	Volvo B10M-62	Caetano Algarve II	C53F	1994
* 887TTT	Volvo B10M-62	Caetano Algarve II	C53F	1994
* AAZ3305	Volvo B10M-61	Plaxton Paramount 3500 I	C53F	1984
JSU626Y	Volvo B58-56	Plaxton Supreme V	C53F	1982
* VXI8302	Volvo B10M-61	Irlzar Pyrennean	C49FT	1984
* WXI2245	Volvo B10M-56	Plaxton Paramount 3200 I Exp.	C53F	1983

Travel Direct / Fairway Coaches
W Hutchison, 9 Lochy Avenue, Renfrew PA4 0XT
Website
Depot   8A Underwood Road, Paisley PA3 1TD
Licence   PM1023195

* AHZ9360	Mercedes-Benz 709D	Alexander Sprint	DP25F	1991
G289TSL	Mercedes-Benz 709D	Alexander Sprint	B23F	1990
G290TSL	Mercedes-Benz 709D	Alexander Sprint	B25F	1990
G301WHP	Mercedes-Benz 709D	PMT	B25F	1989
* J20JPT	Mercedes-Benz 609D	Made to Measure	B21F	1991
J209KTT	Mercedes-Benz 709D	Reeve Burgess	B25F	1991
J212KTT	Mercedes-Benz 709D	Reeve Burgess	B25F	1991
K114XHG	Mercedes-Benz 709D	Alexander Sprint	B25F	1993
K620UFR	Mercedes-Benz 709D	Alexander Sprint	B25F	1993
K871ODY	Mercedes-Benz 709D	Alexander Sprint	B25F	1993
L188SDY	Mercedes-Benz 709D	Alexander (Belfast)	B25F	1993
L249YOD	Mercedes-Benz 709D	Plaxton Beaver	B25F	1993
L250YOD	Mercedes-Benz 709D	Plaxton Beaver	B25F	1993
L502FVU	Mercedes-Benz 709D	Marshall	DP27F	1993
L658MYG	Mercedes-Benz 711D	Plaxton Beaver	B27F	1993
M261HOD	Mercedes-Benz 709D	Plaxton Beaver	B25F	1994
M263HOD	Mercedes-Benz 709D	Plaxton Beaver	B25F	1994
M264HOD	Mercedes-Benz 709D	Plaxton Beaver	B25F	1994
M265HOD	Mercedes-Benz 709D	Plaxton Beaver	B25F	1994
M266HOD	Mercedes-Benz 709D	Plaxton Beaver	B25F	1994
M267HOD	Mercedes-Benz 709D	Plaxton Beaver	B25F	1994
M269HOD	Mercedes-Benz 709D	Plaxton Beaver	B25F	1994
M272HOD	Mercedes-Benz 709D	Plaxton Beaver	B25F	1994
N908NAP	Mercedes-Benz 709D	Alexander Sprint	B25F	1996
N923NAP	Mercedes-Benz 709D	Alexander Sprint	B25F	1996

Travel Dundee

Tayside Public Transport Company Ltd, 44-48 Dock Street , Dundee DD1 3JS
Website www.traveldundee.co.uk
Depot 44-48 Dock Street , Dundee DD1 3JS
Licence PM0001793

300	T130UOX	DU	Optare Solo M850	Optare	B27F	1999
0301	T301UOX	DU	Optare Solo M850	Optare	B27F	1999
321	YT51EBC	DU	Optare Solo M850	Optare	B21F	2001
322	YT51EBD	DU	Optare Solo M850	Optare	B21F	2001
1352	N352WOH	DU	Volvo B10B-58	Wright Endurance	B48F	1996
1366	N366WOH	DU	Volvo B10B-58	Wright Endurance	B48F	1996
7001	SP54CHF	DU	Volvo B7TL	Wright Eclipse Gemini	H45/29F	2004
7002	SP54CHG	DU	Volvo B7TL	Wright Eclipse Gemini	H45/29F	2004
7003	SP54CHH	DU	Volvo B7TL	Wright Eclipse Gemini	H45/29F	2004
7004	SP54CHJ	DU	Volvo B7TL	Wright Eclipse Gemini	H45/29F	2004
7005	SP54CHK	DU	Volvo B7TL	Wright Eclipse Gemini	H45/29F	2004
7006	SP54CHL	DU	Volvo B7TL	Wright Eclipse Gemini	H45/29F	2004
7007	SP54CHN	DU	Volvo B7TL	Wright Eclipse Gemini	H45/29F	2004
7008	SP54CHO	DU	Volvo B7TL	Wright Eclipse Gemini	H45/29F	2004
7009	SP54CGG	DU	Volvo B7TL	Wright Eclipse Gemini	H45/29F	2004
7010	SP54CGK	DU	Volvo B7TL	Wright Eclipse Gemini	H45/29F	2004
7011	SP54CGO	DU	Volvo B7TL	Wright Eclipse Gemini	H45/29F	2004
7012	SP54CGU	DU	Volvo B7TL	Wright Eclipse Gemini	H45/29F	2004
7013	SP54CGV	DU	Volvo B7TL	Wright Eclipse Gemini	H45/29F	2004
7014	SP54CGX	DU	Volvo B7TL	Wright Eclipse Gemini	H45/29F	2004
7015	SP54CGY	DU	Volvo B7TL	Wright Eclipse Gemini	H45/29F	2004
7016	SP54CGZ	DU	Volvo B7TL	Wright Eclipse Gemini	H45/29F	2004
7017	SP54CHC	DU	Volvo B7TL	Wright Eclipse Gemini	H45/29F	2004
7018	SP54CHD	DU	Volvo B7TL	Wright Eclipse Gemini	H45/29F	2004
7019	SP10CXA	DU	Scania K230UB	Scania OmniCity	B43F	2010
7020	SP10CXB	DU	Scania K230UB	Scania OmniCity	B43F	2010
7021	SP10CXC	DU	Scania K230UB	Scania OmniCity	B43F	2010
7022	SP10CXD	DU	Scania K230UB	Scania OmniCity	B43F	2010
7023	SP10CXE	DU	Scania K230UB	Scania OmniCity	B43F	2010
7024	SP10CXF	DU	Scania K230UB	Scania OmniCity	B43F	2010
7026	SP10CXH	DU	Scania K230UB	Scania OmniCity	B43F	2010
7027	SP10CXJ	DU	Scania K230UB	Scania OmniCity	B43F	2010
7028	SP10CXK	DU	Scania K230UB	Scania OmniCity	B43F	2010
7029	SP10CWV	DU	Scania K230UB	Scania OmniCity	B43F	2010
7030	SP10CWW	DU	Scania K230UB	Scania OmniCity	B43F	2010
7031	SP10CWX	DU	Scania K230UB	Scania OmniCity	B43F	2010
7032	SP10CWY	DU	Scania K230UB	Scania OmniCity	B43F	2010
7033	SP10CWZ	DU	Scania K230UB	Scania OmniCity	B43F	2010
7059	P521EJW	DU	Volvo B6LE-53	Wright Crusader	B37F	1996
7060	P522EJW	DU	Volvo B6LE-53	Wright Crusader	B37F	1996
7061	P523EJW	DU	Volvo B6LE-53	Wright Crusader	B37F	1996
7062	P527EJW	DU	Volvo B6LE-53	Wright Crusader	B37F	1996
7063	P531EJW	DU	Volvo B6LE-53	Wright Crusader	B37F	1996
7067	Y722CJW	DU	Volvo B7L	Wright Eclipse	B40F	2001
7085	R85GNW	DU	Dennis Dart 10.1 SLF	Wright Crusader	B36F	1998
7088	S742JRX	DU	Dennis Dart 10.1 SLF	Plaxton Pointer 2	B38F	1998
7089	S743JRX	DU	Dennis Dart 10.1 SLF	Plaxton Pointer 2	B38F	1998
7122	P122KSL	DU	Volvo B10L	Wright Liberator	B43F	1997
7124	P124KSL	DU	Volvo B10L	Wright Liberator	B43F	1997
7130	P130KSL	DU	Volvo B10L	Wright Liberator	B43F	1997
7131	P131KSL	DU	Volvo B10L	Wright Liberator	B43F	1997
7132	P132KSL	DU	Volvo B10L	Wright Liberator	B43F	1997
7133	P133KSL	DU	Volvo B10L	Wright Liberator	B43F	1997
7134	P134KSL	DU	Volvo B10L	Wright Liberator	B43F	1997

Travel Dundee

7135		P135KSL	DU	Volvo B10L	Wright Liberator	B43F	1997
7136		P136KSL	DU	Volvo B10L	Wright Liberator	B43F	1997
7137		P137KSL	DU	Volvo B10L	Wright Liberator	B43F	1997
7138		P138KSL	DU	Volvo B10L	Wright Liberator	B43F	1997
7139		P139KSL	DU	Volvo B10L	Wright Liberator	B43F	1997
7140		P140KSL	DU	Volvo B10L	Wright Liberator	B43F	1997
7141		P141KSL	DU	Volvo B10L	Wright Liberator	B43F	1997
7142		R142RSN	DU	Volvo B10L	Wright Liberator	B43F	1997
7143		R143RSN	DU	Volvo B10L	Wright Liberator	B43F	1997
7144		R144RSN	DU	Volvo B10L	Wright Liberator	B43F	1997
7145		R145RSN	DU	Volvo B10L	Wright Liberator	B43F	1997
7146		R146RSN	DU	Volvo B10L	Wright Liberator	B43F	1997
7147		R147RSN	DU	Volvo B10L	Wright Liberator	B43F	1997
7148		R148RSN	DU	Volvo B10L	Wright Liberator	B43F	1997
7149		R149RSN	DU	Volvo B10L	Wright Liberator	B43F	1997
7150		R150RSN	DU	Volvo B10L	Wright Liberator	B43F	1997
7151		R151RSN	DU	Volvo B10L	Wright Liberator	B43F	1997
7152		R152RSN	DU	Volvo B10BLE	Wright Renown	B43F	1998
7153		R153RSN	DU	Volvo B10BLE	Wright Renown	B43F	1998
7154		R154RSN	DU	Volvo B10BLE	Wright Renown	B43F	1998
7155		R155RSN	DU	Volvo B10BLE	Wright Renown	B43F	1998
7156		R156RSN	DU	Volvo B10BLE	Wright Renown	B43F	1998
7157		R157RSN	DU	Volvo B10BLE	Wright Renown	B43F	1998
7158		R158RSN	DU	Volvo B10BLE	Wright Renown	B43F	1998
7159		R159RSN	DU	Volvo B10BLE	Wright Renown	B43F	1998
7160		R160RSN	DU	Volvo B10BLE	Wright Renown	B43F	1998
7161		R161RSN	DU	Volvo B10BLE	Wright Renown	B43F	1998
7162		R162TSR	DU	Volvo B6LE-53	Wright Crusader	B38F	1998
7163		R163TSR	DU	Volvo B6LE-53	Wright Crusader	B38F	1998
7165		V165ESL	DU	Volvo B10BLE	Wright Renown	B43F	1999
7166		V166ESL	DU	Volvo B10BLE	Wright Renown	B43F	1999
7167		V167ESL	DU	Volvo B10BLE	Wright Renown	B43F	1999
7168		V168ESL	DU	Volvo B10BLE	Wright Renown	B43F	1999
7169		V169ESL	DU	Volvo B10BLE	Wright Renown	B43F	1999
7170		V170ESL	DU	Volvo B10BLE	Wright Renown	B43F	1999
7171		V171ESL	DU	Volvo B10BLE	Wright Renown	B43F	1999
7172		V172ESL	DU	Volvo B10BLE	Wright Renown	B43F	1999
7173		V173ESL	DU	Volvo B10BLE	Wright Renown	B43F	1999
7174		V174ESL	DU	Volvo B10BLE	Wright Renown	B43F	1999
7175		V175ESL	DU	Volvo B10BLE	Wright Renown	B43F	1999
7176		V176ESL	DU	Volvo B10BLE	Wright Renown	B43F	2000
7177		V177ESL	DU	Volvo B10BLE	Wright Renown	B43F	2000
7178		V178ESL	DU	Volvo B10BLE	Wright Renown	B43F	2000
7179		V179ESL	DU	Volvo B10BLE	Wright Renown	B43F	2000
7200		T304UOX	DU	Optare Solo M850	Optare	B27F	1999
7201		S282AOX	DU	Optare Solo M850	Optare	B27F	1999
7211		R991EWU	DU	Optare Excel L1000	Optare	B33F	1998
7236	*	2133PL	FR	Volvo B10M-62	Plaxton Premiere 350	C49FT	1995
7241		S233EWU	FR	Optare Solo M850	Optare	B29f	1998
7242		S231EWU	FR	Optare Solo M850	Optare	B29F	1998
7243		S235EWU	FR	Optare Solo M850	Optare	B29F	1998
7245	*	PYJ136	FR	Volvo B10M-62	Plaxton Premiere 350	C49FT	1996
7246	*	A8TPT	FR	Mercedes-Benz Vario O.814D	Plaxton Cheetah	C29F	1999
7259	*	NSV621	FR	Volvo B10M-62	Plaxton Premiere 350	C49FT	1999
7260	*	NSV622	FR	Volvo B10M-62	Plaxton Premiere 350	C49FT	1999
7269		R91GTM	DU	Volvo Olympian OLY-50	Northern Counties Palatine I	CH39/29F	1998
7270	*	USU662	DU	Volvo Olympian OLY-50	Northern Counties Palatine I	CH39/29F	1998
7271	*	VSR591	FR	Volvo Olympian YN2RV18Z4	Alexander R	CH43/21FL	1995
7272		N125YRW	DU	Volvo Olympian YN2RV18Z4	Alexander R	CH43/21FL	1995
7273		N126YRW	DU	Volvo Olympian YN2RV18Z4	Alexander R	CH43/21FL	1995

7274		Y823HHE	FR	Volvo B10M-62	Plaxton Panther	C49FT	2001
7275		Y824HHE	FR	Volvo B10M-62	Plaxton Panther	C49FT	2001
7305	*	LVG263	FR	Mercedes-Benz Vario O.814D	Plaxton Cheetah	C29F	1999
7306	*	JSU542	FR	Mercedes-Benz Vario O.814D	Plaxton Beaver Coach	C32F	1997
7307	*	5414PH	FR	Mercedes-Benz Vario O.814D	Plaxton Beaver Coach	C32F	1997
7308		T577ASN	FR	Optare Solo M920	Optare	B31F	1999
7309		T307UOX	FR	Optare Solo M850	Optare	B27F	1999
7345		YP02LCE	FR	Optare Solo M850	Optare	B28F	2002
7349		Y825HHE	FR	Volvo B10M-62	Plaxton Panther	C49FT	2001
7350	*	K5KFC	FR	Volvo B10M-62	Berkhof Axial 50	C53F	2000
7351	*	M8KFC	FR	Volvo B10M-62	Berkhof	C53F	2000
7352	*	H3KFC	FR	Volvo B10M-62	Berkhof	C49FT	2000
7353		YX06AWM	FR	Mercedes-Benz 413CDI	Ferqui	C16F	2006
7419		N23FWU	DU-t	DAF DE02LTSB220	Ikarus Citibus 480	B41F	1995

Victoria Executive

E Mowat, Braiklaw Farm, Forehill, Peterhead AB42 3LA
Website www.victoriacoaches.co.uk
Depot Braiklaw Farm, Forehill, Peterhead AB42 3LA
Licence PM0002649

*	IXI1337	Volvo B10M-61	Jonckheere Jubilee P599	C49F	1984
*	K14AMC	Mercedes-Benz 709D	Alexander Sprint	B25F	1993
	LN52LLK	Ford Transit	Ford	M16	2002
	MX54KLF	Mercedes-Benz Vario O.814D	Onyx	C24F	2005
*	NIW252	Volvo B10M-62	Van Hool Alizée	C53F	1999
*	NIW525	Mercedes-Benz Atego 1223L	Unvi Cimo	C39F	2004
*	NIW1422	Volvo B10M-60	Van Hool Alizée	C53F	1993
*	NIW1951	Volvo B10M-62	Van Hool Alizée	C51FT	1995
*	NIW2531	Volvo B10M-62	Van Hool Alizée	C53F	1994
*	NIW6712	Scania K114FB	Irizar	C49FT	2004
	P372XGG	Mercedes-Benz Vario O.814D	Mellor	C33F	1997
	P914PGF	Mercedes-Benz 609D	Pilcher Greene	B16F	1996
	S12AMC	Mercedes-Benz Vario O.814D	Plaxton Cheetah	C32F	1998
	S14AMC	Mercedes-Benz Vario O.814D	Plaxton Cheetah	C32F	1998
	SF59BXP	Mercedes-Benz O.816D	Plaxton Cheetah	C33F	2009
*	TIW2316	Mercedes-Benz 411CDI	Frank Guy	M8L	2002
*	TIW8406	Mercedes-Benz Vario O.815D	Sitcar Beluga	C27F	2001

Vision Travel

J Campbell, 53 Mill Road, Linlithgow Bridge, Linlithgow EH49 7QJ
Website
Depot c/o Trailerdec, Unit 6 Whitecross Industrial Park, Linlithgow EH49 6LH
Licence PM1070628

*	E278YPS	Volvo B10M-46	Plaxton Paramount 3200 III	C35F	1987
*	FIG8241	Volvo B10M-62	Berkhof	C49FT	2001
*	FIG822	Volvo B10M-62	Jonckheere	C49FT	1999
*	K400JCD	Volvo B10M-62	Plaxton Premiere 350	C46FT	1994
*	K662CBA	Bova FHD12.290	Bova Futura	C44FT	1992
	L4HOD	Mercedes-Benz 711D	TBP	C29FL	1993
*	L297ORS	Volvo B10M-62	Plaxton Premiere 350	C49FT	1993
*	L700JPC —	Volvo B10M-62	Plaxton Premiere 350	C46FT	1994
*	MAZ8439	Volvo B10M-62	Berkhof Axial 50	C51FT	1997
*	OWW618	Volvo B10M-60	Plaxton Paramount 3500 III	C48FT	1988
	P451FVV	LDV Convoy	LDV	M16	1996

Alexander Wait & Son

J Andrew & A Cockburn, West End Garage, Chirnside TD11 3UJ
Website
Depot Craigswell Farm, Chirnside TD11 3PZ
Licence PM0003009

DSV698	Volvo B10M-61	Berkhof Esprite 350	C53F	1985
* E32HSH	Volvo B10M-61	Van Hool	C53F	1987
* J8LWC	Volvo B10M-60	Jonckheere	C53F	1992
MX07DHA	Iveco Daily 45C14	Elite	M16	2007
NK55EHT	LDV Convoy	Olympus	M16	2005
P231XKS	Iveco Daily 49.10	Nuova	C19F	1996
R818GSF	Mercedes-Benz Vario O.814D	Plaxton Cheetah	C33F	1997
R821HDS	Mercedes-Benz 614D	Crest	C24F	1997
SN51LUZ	Mercedes-Benz Vario O.814D	Plaxton Cheetah	C33F	2001
SN7CCD	Irisbus 65C17	Indcar	C24F	2007

Watermill Coaches

Watermill Coaches Ltd, 88 College Bounds, Fraserburgh AB43 9QS
Website
Depot Townhead Quarry, Ythanbank, Ellon AB41 7TE
Unit 6, Blackhouse Industrial Estate, Peterhead AB42 1BW
Barrasgate Road, Fraserburgh AB43 9QS
Licence PM1012789

* BS8362	Mercedes-Benz 614D	Onyx	C24F	2001
G800GSX	Leyland Olympian ON2R56C13Z4	Alexander RH	H51/30D	1990
G801GSX	Leyland Olympian ON2R56C13Z4	Alexander RH	H51/30D	1990
* HSV725	Volvo B12M	Van Hool Alizée	C49FT	2002
* J222BER	Dennis Javelin 12SDA	Wadham Stringer	DP70F	1995
* J999BER	Dennis Javelin 12SDA	Wadham Stringer	DP70F	1995
* JIL8207	Mercedes-Benz Vario O.814D	Plaxton Beaver Coach	C32F	1996
* LAZ9205	Bova FHD12.340	Bova Futura	C49FT	2002
* LUI 3026	Bova FHD10.340	Bova Futura	C48FT	1999
* M516TVM	Dennis Javelin 12SDA	Wadham Stringer	C70F	1995
* M783ASL	Dennis Javelin 12SDA	Wadham Stringer	DP70F	1995
* M788ASL	Dennis Javelin 12SDA	Wadham Stringer	DP57F	1995
* M796ASL	Dennis Javelin 12SDA	Wadham Stringer	DP57F	1995
* M808ASL	Dennis Javelin 12SDA	Wadham Stringer	DP70F	1995
* M823ASL	Dennis Javelin 12SDA	Wadham Stringer	DP70F	1995
ML02PFN	Mercedes-Benz 614D	Onyx	C24F	2002
MV54GGE	Mercedes-Benz Vario O.814D	Onyx	C24F	2005
MX55HXP	Mercedes-Benz Vario O.814D	Onyx	C24F	2005
N5BUS	Mercedes-Benz 811D	Marshall C16	B33F	1996
* N30BUS	Volvo B10M-48	Van Hool Alizée	C38FT	1997
* N87FHL	Dennis Javelin 10SDA	Wadham Stringer	C49FT	1996
* N195RGD	Dennis Javelin 12SDA	Wadham Stringer	DP70F	1996
* N245RGD	Dennis Javelin 12SDA	Wadham Stringer	DP70F	1996
N350VSO	Mercedes-Benz 711D	Devon Conversions	DP23F	1995
* NT05MXL	Volvo B12M	Plaxton Paragon	C53F	2005
P787BJU	Mercedes-Benz 709D	Leicester Carriage Builders	C29F	1996
R43ALS x	Ford Transit	Ford	M8	1998
* R888WMC	Volvo B10M-62	Plaxton Premiere 320	C55F	1997
* SA51CTF	Bova FHD12.340	Bova Futura	C49FT	2002
SF54CHO	Mercedes-Benz Vario O.814D	Plaxton Beaver 2	DP33F	2004
SH04YZB	Ford Transit	Ford	M16	2004
SJ55VCE	Ford Transit	Ford	M16	2005
SK02OAA	Mercedes-Benz Vario O.814D	Plaxton Beaver 2	C33F	2002
SK03ANV	Mercedes-Benz Atego 1223L	Unvi Cimo	C37F	2003
* SN03TOA	Mercedes-Benz O.815D	Sitcar Beluga	C33F	2003
SN03ZCE	Mercedes-Benz 413CDI	Killbeggan Vehicle Converters	M16L	2003

SN51LVB		Mercedes-Benz Vario O.814D	Plaxton Beaver 2		C33F	2001
SV05ZKT		Ford Transit	Ford		M14	2005
SV05ZPP		Ford Transit	Ford		M16	2005
SV54EPJ		Mercedes-Benz Vario O.815D	Sitcar Beluga		C33F	2004
* SW02VFX		Dennis Javelin 12SDA	Wadham Stringer		DP70F	1996
* SW02VGY		Dennis Javelin 12SDA	Wadham Stringer		DP70F	1996
T111WCS		Mercedes-Benz Vario O.814D	Plaxton Beaver 2		C31F	1999
* TIB5004		Volvo B10M-62	Caetano Algarve II		C49FT	1998
V169NGE	x	Ford Transit	Mayflower		M8	2000
* VRY357		Volvo B10M-62	Caetano Algarve II		C70F	1996
VU06XKX		Mercedes-Benz Vario O.814D	Plaxton Cheetah		C33F	2006
* W409OSS	x	Ford Transit			M14	2000
W777WCS —		Volvo B10M-62	Plaxton Premiere 350		C53F	2000
W885NNT	x	Ford Transit	Mayflower		M8	2000
YN53EJC		Mercedes-Benz Vario O.814D	Plaxton Cheetah		C33F	2003
YN55LMO		Mercedes-Benz Vario O.814D	Plaxton Cheetah		C33F	2005
YP52KRG		Volvo B7R	Plaxton Profile		C70F	2002

W J C Buses

J Carson, 9 Bank View, Chapelhall, Airdrie ML6 8UB
Website www.wjcbuses.biz
Depot Greenside Farm, High Street, Newhouse, Motherwell ML1 5ST
Henderson Travel, 4 Whisltleberry Industrial Estate, Hamilton ML3 0ED
Licence PM1003541 PM1003541

DD658	ULS658T	p	Leyland Fleetline FE30AGR	Eastern Coach Works	H43/32F	1979
H8	* LSG27N		Leyland Leopard PSU3B/3R	East Lancs	C55F	1974
H258	XOI2258	p	Leyland Leopard PSU3E/4R	Wright	DP53F	1982
L331	B331LSA		Leyland Tiger TRCTL11/2RP	Alexander TC	C51F	1985
L516	D516DSX		Leyland Tiger TRCTL11/3RH	Alexander P	B61F	1987
N41	DOC41V		Leyland National NL116L11/1R(DAF)	Leyland National	B50F	1980
N90	EGB90T		Leyland National 11351A/1R (Volvo)	Leyland National	B52F	1979
N104	KSX104X		Leyland National NL116L11/2R	Leyland National	B42D	1982
T468	RLS468T		Ford R1014	Alexander AYS	B45F	1979
V5	XSA5Y —		Volvo B57-60	Alexander AYS	B65F	1983
V97	* G9WJC		Volvo B10M-50	Alexander RV	H47/37F	1989
W1	* TRR814R		Volvo Ailsa B55-10	Alexander AV	H43/34F	1977
W865	* E7WJC		Volvo B10M-50	Alexander RV	H45/35F	1987
XC95	* G95YFW		Setra S210H	Setra	C32FT	1990
XCV20	* P20WJC		Volvo B10M-62	Van Hool Alizée	C51FT	1987
XLL764	* LJZ6056		Leyland Tiger TRCTL11/3R	Jonckheere	CH47/12	1984
XV02	* T90WJC		DAF SB4000	Van Hool Alizée	C51FT	2002
YV03	* SC03WJC		Volvo B7R	Jonckheere Mistral	C53F	2003
YV506	D506GHY		Volvo B10M-61	Van Hool Alizée	C48FT	1987
ZK336	* Y3WJC		Scania L94UB	Wright Solar	DP43F	2001
ZLL201	F201FHH		Leyland Olympian ON6LXCT/3RZ	Alexander RL	CH55/41F	1989
ZLL202	* F202FHH		Leyland Olympian ON6LXCT/3RZ	Alexander RL	CH55/41F	1989
ZLL645	* BIG9871		Leyland Olympian ON3R49C18Z4	Alexander RH	CH57/47F	1992
ZV947	* A15RBL		Volvo B10M-56	Van Hool	DP64F	1984
	B145GSC		Leyland Olympian ONTL11/2R	Alexander	CH / F	1984
	B321CGG		Volvo B10M-61	Van Hool Alizée	C49F	1985
	* E9WJC		MCW MetroBus DR140/4	MCW	CH53/20DT	1988
	F631BKD	r	Dennis Dominator DDA	East Lancs	CH43/25F	1989
	* G452FVX		Dennis Condor DDA1702	Duple Metsec	H63/44F	1989
	G700PNS		Volvo b10M-50	Alexander RV	H47/37F	1989
	* N88WJC		Volvo Olympian YN2RV18Z4	Alexander R	CH49/33F	1995
	* R111WJC		Volvo B12(T)	Van Hool Astrobel	CH57/14CT	1998
	VMP10G —p		AEC Reliance	Alexander Y	DP57F	1969
	* WJ08BUS		MAN 14.240	MCV Evolution	B43F	2008
	* XSU913		Leyland Olympian ONTL11/2RSP	Eastern Coach Works	CH47/30DT	1982

Waverley Travel
R Jack, Building 5 Ligget Syke Place, east Mains Industrial Estate, Broxburn EH52 5NA
Website
Depot   Unit 11, Turnhouse Business Park, Turnhouse Road, Edinburgh Airport EH12 9DN
Licence   PM0002288

BU05EGD		BMC Probus 850RE	BMC	C35F	2005
KX06LYS		ADL Enviro Dart 8.8 SLF	ADL Enviro 200	B29F	2006
KX06LYT		ADL Enviro Dart 8.8 SLF	ADL Enviro 200	B29F	2006
KX08UXU		ADL Enviro Dart 8.9 SLF	ADL Enviro 200	B29F	2008

West Coast Motor Services
Craig of Campbeltown Ltd, Benmhor, Saddel Street, Campbeltown, PA28 6DN
Website   www.westcoastmotors.co.uk
Depots   As per list
Licence   PM0000019

* 109ASV —		Mercedes-Benz Vario O.814D	Killbeggan Vehicle Converters	C24F	2004
B79WUV	D	Leyland Titan TNLXB2RR	Leyland	O44/24D	1984
B108CCS	w	Volvo B10M-50	Alexander RV	H47/37F	1985
CUL197V	O	Leyland Titan TNLXB2RRSP	Park Royal	H44/24D	1980
DK05FWB		ADL Enviro Dart 8.8 SLF	ADL Enviro 200	B29F	2005
* E68EKG		Scania N113CRB	Alexander	B48F	1994
E870BGG	R	Volvo B10M-56	Duple 300	B53F	1988
E871BGG	R	Volvo B10M-56	Duple 300	B53F	1988
F727ASB	D	Volvo B10M-61	Plaxton Paramount 3200 III	C53F	1989
* FSU318		Volvo B10M-61	Plaxton Paramount 3200 III	C57F	1988
* FSU319		Mercedes-Benz Vario O.814D	Plaxton Cheetah	C33F	2006
GX08AUR		ADL Enviro 300 12.0 SLF	ADL Enviro 300	B55F	2008
GX08AUT		ADL Enviro 300 12.0 SLF	ADL Enviro 300	B55F	2008
* J70WCM		Dennis Dart 9.8 SFD	Plaxton Pointer	B40F	1998
* J80WCM		Dennis Dart 9.8 SFD	Plaxton Pointer	B40F	1998
* J90WCM		Dennis Dart 9.8 SFD	Plaxton Pointer	B40F	1998
* J100WCM		Dennis Dart 9.8 SFD	Plaxton Pointer	B40F	1998
J301BRM	R	Dennis Dart 9.8 SDL	Alexander Dash	B40F	1992
J303BRM	A	Dennis Dart 9.8 SDL	Alexander Dash	B40F	1992
J304BRM	w	Dennis Dart 9.8 SDL	Alexander Dash	B40F	1992
J305BRM	R	Dennis Dart 9.8 SDL	Alexander Dash	B40F	1992
J308BRM	D	Dennis Dart 9.8 SDL	Alexander Dash	B40F	1992
J309BRM	R	Dennis Dart 9.8 SDL	Alexander Dash	B40F	1992
J807HSB	C	MAN 11.190	Optare Vecta	B41F	1992
* K79SYS		DAF SB3000DKVF601	Van Hool Alizée	C53F	1993
K103XHG	C	Dennis Dart 9.8 SDL	Alexander Dash	B40F	1993
* K200WCM	G	DAF DE40XSSB4000	Van Hool Alizée	C49FT	2003
* K300WCM	G	DAF DE40XSSB4000	Van Hool Alizée	C49FT	2003
* K400WCM		Mercedes-Benz Vario O.814D	Plaxton Beaver	DP31F	2006
* K500WCM	C	DAF DE33WSSB3000	Van Hool Alizée	C49FT	1998
* L100WCM	G	VDL DE40XSSB4000	Van Hool Alizée	C49FT	2005
L146VRH	D	Dennis Dart 9 SDL	Plaxton Pointer	B34F	1993
* L200WCM	G	VDL DE40XSSB4000	Van Hool Alizée	C49FT	2005
* L400WCM		DAF DE33WSSB3000	Van Hool Alizée	C53F	1998
L700WCM	A	DAF SB3000WS601	Van Hool Alizée	C53F	1994
L932CTY		DAF SB3000DKVF601	Van Hool Alizée	C51FT	1993
* L990ASU	A	Volvo B10M-60	Jonckheere Deauville	C53F	1994
* M100WCM	G	DAF DE33WSSB3000	Van Hool Alizée	C48FT	2001
M227VSX		Volvo YN2RC16Z4	Alexander RH	H51/30D	1995
M300WCM	C	DAF SB3000WS601	Van Hool Alizée	C53F	1995
M400WCM		DAF SB3000WS601	Van Hool Alizée	C51FT	1995
M500WCM	C	Optare MetroRider MR15	Optare	B30F	1995
* M600WCM	G	DAF DE33WSSB3000	Van Hool Alizée	C48FT	2001
* M700WCM		DAF SB3000DKVF601	Van Hool Alizée	C51FT	1995

*	M800WCM	O	DAF SB3000WS601	Van Hool Alizée	C51FT	1995
*	MSL276X		Leyland Leopard PSU3G/4R	Plaxton Supreme V Exp.	B53F	1982
	MX57NTK		Mercedes-Benz 515CDI	Onyx	M16	2007
*	N200WCM	O	DAF DE33WSSB3000	Van Hool Alizée	C49FT	1996
	N300WCM	A	Volvo B10M-48	Van Hool Alizée	C45F	1996
	N401GSX		Volvo Olympian YN2RV18Z4	Alexander Royale	H51/30D	1996
	N603VSS	R	Mercedes-Benz 709D	Alexander Sprint	B25F	1995
	N629VSS	R	Mercedes-Benz 709D	Alexander Sprint	B18FL	1995
	N901PFC		Dennis Lance 11SDA	Plaxton Pointer	B49F	1996
	NDZ3024	A	Dennis Dart 9 SDL	Wright Handybus	B35F	1993
*	NDZ3026	C	Leyland Tiger TRCTL11/3RZM	Plaxton Paramount 3200 III	C70F	1988
	P87BPL		Dennis Lance 11SDA	Northern Counties Paladin	B49F	1996
	P100WCM		DAF DE33WSSB3000	Van Hool Alizée	C49FT	1997
	P200WCM	C	DAF DE33WSSB3000	Van Hool Alizée	C49FT	1997
	P281PSX		Volvo Olympian OLY-56	Alexander Royale	H51/30D	1997
	P430KSX		Volvo Olympian YN2RV18Z4	Alexander Royale	H51/33F	1996
*	P600WCM		Optare Solo M710SE	Optare	B21F	2007
	R100WCM	G	DAF DE33WSSB3000	Van Hool Alizée	C49FT	1998
	R200WCM	G	DAF DE33WSSB3000	Van Hool Alizée	C49FT	1998
	R300WCM	G	DAF DE33WSSB3000	Van Hool Alizée	C49FT	1998
	R846FDM		Mercedes-Benz 614D	Onyx	C24F	1998
*	R900WCM	G	DAF DE40XSSB4000	Van Hool Alizée	C53F	2002
*	S200WCM		Optare Solo M880SL	Optare	B27F	2004
*	S300WCM		Optare Solo M880SL	Optare	B27F	2004
	S400WCM	G	DAF DE33WSSB3000	Van Hool Alizée	C49FT	1999
*	S555WCM		Optare Solo M880SL	Optare	B27F	2004
*	S600WCM		Optare Solo M880SL	Optare	B27F	2004
*	S900WCM	G	DAF DE40XSSB4000	Van Hool Alizée	C49FT	2002
	SC02HHE		Mercedes-Benz Vito 108CDI		M8	2002
	SF04WME		Mercedes-Benz Vario O.814D	Plaxton Beaver 2	DP31	2004
	SF06ODT		Mercedes-Benz Vario O.814D	Plaxton Beaver 2	DP29FL	2006
	SF54HWA	D	Mercedes-Benz Vario O.814D	Plaxton Beaver 2	DP33F	2004
	SK07HMC	C	ADL Enviro Dart 8.9 SLF	ADL Enviro 200	DP29F	2007
	SK07HMD	D	ADL Enviro Dart 8.9 SLF	ADL Enviro 200	DP29F	2007
	SK07HME	O	ADL Enviro Dart 8.9 SLF	ADL Enviro 200	DP29F	2007
	SK07HMF	R	ADL Enviro Dart 10.2 SLF	ADL Enviro 200	DP29F	2007
	SN54FCE		Dennis Dart 10.1 SLF	Alexander ALX200	B39F	2004
	SN57DXF		ADL Enviro Dart 10.7 SLF	ADL Enviro 200	B37F	2007
*	T600WCM	C	Mercedes-Benz Vario O.814D	Onyx	C24F	2002
*	T900WCM	G	DAF DE40XSSB4000	Van Hool Alizée	C49FT	2002
*	V100WCM		Enterprise Bus Plasma EB03	Plaxton Primo	B28F	2008
*	W100WCM	O	DAF DE33WSSB3000	Van Hool Alizée	C53F	2000
	Y80WCM	C	DAF DE40XSSB4000	Van Hool Alizée	C53F	2003
	YJ05PVF	D	DAF DE12BSSB120	Wright Cadet	B39F	2005
	YJ05PVK	D	DAF DE12BSSB120	Wright Cadet	B39F	2005
	YJ05PVL	D	DAF DE12BSSB120	Wright Cadet	B39F	2005
	YJ05PWU	R	DAF DE12BSSB120	Wright Cadet	B39F	2005
	YJ06YSD		Optare Solo M880SL	Optare	B20F	2006
	YJ54ZYK	A	Optare Solo M880SL	Optare	B27F	2005
	YJ54ZYL	A	Optare Solo M880SL	Optare	B27F	2005
	YJ54ZYM	R	Optare Solo M880SL	Optare	B27F	2005

West Lothian Transport

Davidson Buses Ltd, PO Box 12542, Bathgate EH48 2YD
Website
Depot   Unit C, Westwood Works, by West Calder EH55 8PY
Licence   PM0002363

P692RWU	—	Dennis Dart 10.1 SLF	Plaxton Pointer	B35F	1997
P698RWU	—	Dennis Dart 10.1 SLF	Plaxton Pointer	B35F	1997
SN05HDD		Dennis Dart 8.8 SLF	Alexander ALX200	B29F	2005
SN05HDE	—	Dennis Dart 8.8 SLF	Alexander ALX200	B29F	2005

Westerbus

M MacKenzie & I MacLennan, The Garage, Gairloch IV21 2BH
Website
Depot   The Garage, Gairloch IV21 2BH
Licence   PM0001172

* DAZ4298	w	MAN MT8.136	Reeve Burgess	C32F	1986
L676JSX		Mercedes-Benz 811D	Dormobile Routemaker	DP33F	1993
* MKZ585		Scania K113CRB	Van Hool	C49FT	1992
MV02UMF		Volvo B12M	Van Hool	C46FT	2002
* SIL8761		Van Hool T815	Van Hool Acron	C53F	1985
* TIL2360		Volvo B10M-46	Plaxton Paramount 3200 III	C39F	1988
* UIL4223		Mercedes-Benz Sprinter 411CDI		M16	2002
* VIL8250		Volvo B10M-46	Plaxton Paramount 3200 II	C35F	1986
* W297UGX		Setra S315GT-HD	Setra	C48FT	2000
* WSU892		Volvo B10M-62	Van Hool Alizée	C46FT	1995
* XIL5755		MAN 10.180	Caetano Algarve II	C35F	1994
* YIL2041		Mercedes-Benz Vario O.814D	Autobus Classique	C29F	1996
* YIL4029		Volvo B10M-60	Jonckheere Deauville	C51FT	1992

Whitelaws Coaches

G Whitelaw & Partners, Lochpark Industrial Estate, Stonehouse, Larkhall ML9 3LR
Website
Depot   Lochpark Industrial Estate, Stonehouse, Larkhall ML9 3LR
Licence   PM1076402

191WHW		Volvo B12B(T)	Volvo 9700 Prestige	C55F	2008
7173WW		Volvo B12B(T)	Sunsundegui Sideral	C55FT	2003
7994WW		Volvo B12B	Volvo 9700 Prestige	C48FT	2006
9398WW		Volvo B12B(T)	Volvo 9700	C55FT	2009
AE07DZL		MAN 14.220	MCV Evolution	B35F	2007
AE07DZM	—	MAN 14.220	MCV Evolution	B35F	2007
AE07DZN	—	MAN 14.220	MCV Evolution	B35F	2007
AE07DZO		MAN 14.220	MCV Evolution	B35F	2007
AE08KTD		MAN 14.240	MCV Evolution	B40F	2008
AE08KTF		MAN 14.240	MCV Evolution	B40F	2008
AE08KTG		MAN 14.240	MCV Evolution	B40F	2008
AF53EUW		MAN 14.220	MCV Evolution	B36F	2003
CU56AVP	—	MAN 18.240	East Lancs Kinetic	B43F	2006
D280JME		Volvo B10M-61	Plaxton Paramount 3200 II	C53F	1986
R335RWK		Leyland Tiger TRBTL11/2RP	Plaxton Verde	B69F	1988
F336RWK		Leyland Tiger TRBTL11/2RP	Plaxton Verde	B69F	1988
FAS374X	—	Leyland Leopard PSU3G/4R	Alexander AYS	B62F	1982
* LIW4270		Volvo B10M-60	Plaxton Paramount 3500 III	C53F	1990
OLS539P	— w	Leyland Leopard PSU3C/3R	Alexander AY	B53F	1975
OSJ614R	w	Leyland Leopard PSU3C/3R	Alexander AY	B52F	1977
OSJ631R	t	Leyland Leopard PSU3C/3R	Alexander AY	B52F	1977
S947NGB		Iveco 391.12.29	Marshall	B51F	1998
SF08RNY		MAN NL273F	Wright Meridian	B44F	2008

SF08RNZ	MAN NL273F		Wright Meridian	B44F	2008
SF08ROH	MAN NL273F		Wright Meridian	B44F	2008
SF08ROU	MAN NL273F		Wright Meridian	B44F	2008
SF08RRO	MAN NL273F		Wright Meridian	B44F	2008
SF09LZV	MAN A22		Wright	B44F	2009
SF10GCK	Volvo B12B		Volvo 9700	C49FT	2010
SF10GCL	Volvo B12B		Volvo 9700	C49FT	2010
SF55HHC	Volvo B7RLE		Wright Eclipse Urban	B43F	2005
SF55HHD	Volvo B7RLE		Wright Eclipse Urban	B43F	2005
SF55HHE	Volvo B7RLE		Wright Eclipse Urban	B43F	2005
SF57FZY	MAN NL273F		Wright Meridian	B44F	2007
SF58OHO	MAN A22		Wright Meridian	B44F	2008
SF60FPP	MAN		MCV Evolution	B F	2010
SF60FPT	MAN		MCV Evolution	B F	2010
SF60FPV	MAN		MCV Evolution	B F	2010
SF60FPX	MAN		MCV Evolution	B F	2010
SF60FPY	MAN		MCV Evolution	B F	2010
SN59AXA	ADL Enviro Dart 8.9 SLF		ADL Enviro 200	B29F	2010
SN59AXB	ADL Enviro Dart 8.9 SLF		ADL Enviro 200	B29F	2010
SN59AXC	ADL Enviro Dart 8.9 SLF		ADL Enviro 200	B29F	2010
* VIL 8578	Volvo B10M-60		Van Hool Alizée	C55F	1991
W674WGG	Volvo B10M-55		Van Hool Alizée	C49FT	2000
W675WGG	Volvo B10M-55		Van Hool Alizée	C49FT	2000
WFS152W	Leyland Leopard PSU3F/4R		Alexander AYS	B62F	1980
* WSU857	Volvo B10M-60		Van Hool Alizée	C53F	1989
* XIL7307	Volvo B10M-61		Van Hool	C52F	1988
* XIL8125	Volvo B10M-60		Van Hool Alizée	C49FT	1992

— YXII CGY

Whitestar

B McGowan, 37 Manse Road, Neilston G78 3EX
Website www.whitestarcoaches.co.uk
Depot Braefort Garage, 72 Holhouse Brae, Neilston G78 3LX
Unit 2A Shanks Industrial Estate, Kirktonfield Garage, Glasgow G78 3NG
Licence PM0001228

* BLZ589	Volvo B10M-62		Van Hool Alizée	C53F	1995
BX56AYP	LDV Convoy		Excel	M16	2006
C194CYO	Volvo B10M-46		Plaxton Paramount 3200 II	C28F	1986
* HDZ8349	Bova FHD12-340		Bova Futura	C49FT	2002
PE55WML	MAN 18.350		Marcopolo Viaggio	C55F	2006
PN06KME	MAN 18.310		Marcopolo Viaggio	C57F	2006
PN08CNO	MAN A91		Marcopolo Viaggio	C70F	2008
* RG02NMN	Bova FHD12-340		Bova Futura	C49FT	2002
SF10KOE	Van Hool T915		Van Hool Astron	C51F	2010
SK06FFO	Mercedes-Benz Vario O.814D		Killbeggan Vehicle Converters	C24F	2007
SN57MBO	Mercedes-Benz Sprinter 515CDI		Killbeggan Vehicle Converters	C19F	2008
SN57MEV	Mercedes-Benz Sprinter 616CDI		Unvi	C33F	2008
SN60BFV	Mercedes-Benz O.816D		Unvi	C31F	2010
W537XNS	Bova FHD12-370		Bova Futura	C75F	2000
* WSC267	Volvo B10M-62		Van Hool Alizée	C51F	2000
* WSC471	Volvo B10M-62		Plaxton Premiere 350	C70F	1998
* WSC700	Volvo B12B		Van Hool Alizée	C53F	2002
YJ04BYB	DAF SB4000		Van Hool Alizée	C49FT	2004

Whyte's Coaches

Whytes Coaches Ltd, Scotstown Road, Newmachar, Aberdeen AB21 7PP
Website www.whytescoachtours.co.uk
Depot Scotstown Road, Newmachar, Aberdeen AB21 7PP
Licence PM1078024

KX08UXA	Mercedes-Benz Vario O.816D	Plaxton Cheetah	C33F	2008
KX08UXB	Mercedes-Benz Vario O.816D	Plaxton Cheetah	C33F	2008
KX08UXC	Mercedes-Benz Vario O.816D	Plaxton Cheetah	C33F	2008
KX08UXD	Mercedes-Benz Vario O.816D	Plaxton Cheetah	C33F	2008
KX08UXE	Mercedes-Benz Vario O.816D	Plaxton Cheetah	C33F	2008
KX08UXF	Mercedes-Benz Vario O.816D	Plaxton Cheetah	C33F	2008
KX08UXG	Mercedes-Benz Vario O.816D	Plaxton Cheetah	C33F	2008
S591ACT	Mercedes-Benz Vario O.814D	Autobus Nouvelle	C33F	1999
SF06LKU	Bova FHD12-340	Bova Futura	C49FT	2006
SF06LKV	Bova FHD12-340	Bova Futura	C49FT	2006
SF06OKT	Bova FHD12-340	Bova Futura	C49FT	2006
SJ58AEG	Mercedes-Benz Atego 1022L	Unvi Cimo	C35F	2008
SN04GUF	Volkswagen LT46	Killbeggan Vehicle Converters	M16	2004
SN04MJS	Ford Transit	Ford	M16	2004
SN09AKV	Bova MHD131-460	Bova Magiq	C49FT	2009
SN09AKX	Bova MHD131-460	Bova Magiq	C49FT	2009
SN10ANR	Bova MHD131-460	Bova Magiq	C49FT	2010
SN10ANU	Bova MHD131-460	Bova Magiq	C49FT	2010
SN57ERZ	Mercedes-Benz Atego 1022L	Unvi Cimo	C33F	2007
SN57EXD	Mercedes-Benz Sprinter 515CDI	Killbeggan Vehicle Converters	M16	2007
SN60AOX	Bova FHD120.365	Bova Futura	C49FT	2010
SN60AOY	Bova FHD120.365	Bova Futura	C49FT	2010
SV06CEK	Bova FHD12-340	Bova Futura	C49FT	2006
X622CWN	Mercedes-Benz 614D	Cymric	C24F	2001
YN09BXW	Mercedes-Benz 515CDI	Killbeggan Vehicle Converters	M16	2009

Wilson's Coaches

R Wilson, 15 Dellingburn Street, Greenock PA15 4RN
Website www.wilsonscoaches.co.uk
Depot 15 Dellingburn Street, Greenock PA15 4RN
Licence PM0001458

	AE54JPX	MAN 14.220	MCV Evolution	B39F	2004
	AE54JPY	MAN 14.220	MCV Evolution	B39F	2004
*	HSL660	AEC Routemaster	Park Royal	PO45/28R	1961
	J615XHL	y	Dennis Dart 9 SDL	Plaxton Pointer	B34F	1991
	JJD432D	AEC Routemaster	Park Royal	H40/32R	1966
	L233TKA	Volvo B6-50	Plaxton Pointer	B38F	1994
	M121YCM	Mercedes-Benz 709D	Alexander Sprint	B27F	1995
	M126YCM	Mercedes-Benz 709D	Alexander Sprint	B29F	1995
	M327TSF	Mercedes-Benz 709D	Alexander Sprint	B29F	1994
	M378EFD	Mercedes-Benz 709D	Alexander Sprint	B27F	1995
	M394KVR	y	Mercedes-Benz 709D	Alexander Sprint	B27F	1995
	M815HCU	Dennis Dart 9.8 SDL	Plaxton Pointer	B40F	1994
	N345OBC	Mercedes-Benz 709D	Alexander Sprint	B27F	1995
	N470SPA	Mercedes-Benz 709D	Alexander Sprint	B27FL	1995
*	R17GCT	Volvo Olympian-55	Alexander	H / D	1998
	S432NSB	Volvo Olympian-55	Alexander	H47/27D	1988
	S433NSB	Volvo Olympian-55	Alexander	H47/27D	1988
	SMK697F	AEC Routemaster	Park Royal	H40/32R	1967
*	V649PHJ	Volvo B6BLG	Wright Crusader	B33F	1994
*	WIL6457	Mercedes-Benz 709D	Alexander Sprint	B25F	1996
*	WIL6957	Volvo B10M-61	Jonckheere Jubilee	C51FT	1988
*	WIL6981	Mercedes-Benz 709D	Alexander Sprint	B25F	1994
*	WIL9217	Volvo B6BLG	Wright Crusader	B33F	1994
	YJ55YGD	Optare Solo M880	Optare	B29F	2006

Wilson of Rhu

Wilson of Rhu Ltd, Manse Brae, Rhu G84 8RE
Website www.wilsonsofrhu.co.uk
Depot Manse Brae, Rhu G84 8RE
Woodlea Garage, Main Road, Garelochhead G84 0EG
Birchwood, 22 Rhu Road Higher, Rhu, Helensburgh G84 8JZ
Licence PM1012693

*	641RHU	Volvo B10M-62	Van Hool Alizée	C51F	2001
	K76OCR —	Mercedes-Benz 811D	Alexander AM	B31F	1992
	N604VSS	Mercedes-Benz 709D	Alexander Sprint	B25F	1995
	YJ10EXX	Optare Solo M950	Optare	B F	2010
	YJ10EXZ	Optare Solo M950	Optare	B F	2010
	YJ57EGV	Optare Solo M950	Optare	B33F	2007
	YJ57EHL	Optare Solo M780SE	Optare	B27F	2007
	YJ59NNX —	Optare Solo M850	Optare	B28F	2009
	YN08NXW	Volvo B7R	Plaxton Profile	C70F	2008
	YN09AOV	Mercedes-Benz O.811D	Plaxton Cheetah	C33F	2009
	YN09EXC	Mercedes-Benz 515CDI	Killbeggan Vehicle Converters	M16	2009
	YN09EZD	Mercedes-Benz 515CDI	Unvi	C29F	2009
*	YN58FXO	Mercedes-Benz O.816D	Plaxton Cheetah	C33F	2008

Woods of Tillicoultry

J Woods, 2 Golf View, Tillicoultry FK13 6BL
Website
Depot Oakmill, Lower Mill Street, Tillicoultry FK13 6BP
Licence PM0001078

*	JW02BUS	Mercedes-Benz 413CDI		M16	2004
*	S20FMC	Mercedes-Benz 616CDI	Unvi	C16F	2007
	SK02VTC	Ford Transit	Ford	M14	2002
	SK07FZS	Mercedes-Benz 616CDI	Unvi	C16F	2007
	SK07JYA	Mercedes-Benz 616CDI	Unvi	C12F	2007
	SK07LBE	Mercedes-Benz Atego 1523L	Unvi Cimo	C22F	2007
	SK07LZD	Mercedes-Benz Atego 1523L	Unvi Cimo	C41F	2007
	SN05FBB	Bova FHD12.340	Bova Futura	C49FT	2005
	SN06ABO	Mercedes-Benz 413cdl	Killbeggan Vehicle Converters	M16	2006
	SN10AHJ	Mercedes-Benz O.813D	Unvi	C16F	2010
	SN10AUV	Bova FHD120.365	Bova Futura	C49FT	2010
	SN10ENV	Mercedes-Benz Atego 1223L	Unvi Cimo	C30F	2010
	SN58FXB	Mercedes-Benz 515CDI	Killbeggan Vehicle Converters	C16F	2008
	SP57XKL	Ford Transit	Ford	M8	2007

Elizabeth Yule

E Yule, Station Road Crossing Garage, Pitlochry PH16 5AN
Website
Depot Station Road Crossing Garage, Pitlochry PH16 5AN
Licence PM0000757

	101RTD —	Volvo B10M-62	Van Hool Alizée	C53F	1996
	L15YUL	Volvo B10M-62	Van Hool Alizée	C49FT	2001
	SF54CFO	Mercedes-Benz Vario O.814D	Plaxton Beaver 2	DP33F	2004
*	SK05BYX	Mercedes-Benz Vario O.814D	Killbeggan Vehicle Converters	C28F	2005
	SN55FDC	Ford Transit	Killbeggan Vehicle Converters	M16	2005
	SN55FLJ	Mercedes-Benz Vario O.814D	Killbeggan Vehicle Converters	C29F	2005
	SP53PYG x	Renault Master	Gleneagles	M8	2003
	UDL453 —	Volvo B10M-60	Van Hool Alizée	C53F	1993
	Y15AMS	Volvo B10M-62	Van Hool Alizée	C49FT	2001

Registration Number Index

A&B	Allan & Black	ETN	Elite Transportation; North Fife Travel
AAA	AAA Coaches	EVE	Eve Coaches
AAM	Mason, A&A	FAB	First Aberdeen
ABK	ABC Travel	FCC	Fitzcharles Coaches
ABO	Abbot Travel	FED	First Edinburgh
ACM	Ace Travel / McLeans Coaches	FG	First Glasgow
ACN	Abbey Coaches	FIR	Firth Coaches
ALA	Allander Travel	FIT	Fishers Tours
ALG	Allan's	GCB	Glasgow Citybus
AMS	Aberfeldy Motor Services	GCT	Glasgow Corporation Transport
ANN	Ann's Coaches	GEC	Golden Eagle Coaches
APE	Fairline Coaches / Airport Express	GEM	GEM Coaches
ARC	Arthurs Coaches	GIB	Gibson Direct Minibus Service
ASW	Arriva Scotland West	GIC	Gillens Coaches
AUS	Austin Travel	GLC	Glen Coaches
AVD	Avondale Coaches	GMC	Garlochhead Minibuses & Coaches
AYR	Ayrways Coach Travel	GSM	Galson-Stornoway Motor Services
BBD	Stagecoach Bluebird	GUM	United / McGills
BCD	Bryans Coaches	HAO	Halls Coaches
BCM	Bowman Coaches (Mull)	HCC	Crawford H
BDC	Billy Davies Coaches	HCO	Harrold Coaches
BEK	Bennetts of Kilwinning	HEB	Hebridean Coaches
BLS	Blue Bus	HHL	Highland Heritage
BLY	Blyth Coaches	HLO	Hunter's Coaches / William Hunter
BNA	Bus Na Cormhairie	HOR	Horsburgh, E&M
BRU	Bruce Coaches	HOU	Houston
BRW	Brownings (Whitburn)	HQD	Harlequin Coaches (Dunblane
BUT	Burns of Tarves	HQL	Harlequin Coaches (Livingston)
CAM	John Campbell Coaches	HTR	Hebridean Transport
CBC	Coakley Bus & Coach	HUC	Hunter's Executive
CCC	Clyde Coast Coaches	HVB	Henderson Travel
CCG	Campbells Coaches (Dumbarton)	IRB	Irvines Coaches; Law Bus & Coach
CCI	Colchri	JDT	JD Travel
CFM	Frasers Coaches	JJT	J J Travel / McNairns Coaches
CFT	Crieff Travel	JMC	Morrow, John Coaches
CHE	Cheyne Coaches	JPM	JP Minicoaches
CHI	Irons (Charlie) Coaches	JTK	King, James T
CIC	City Circle	KCO	KC Transport
CNV	Canavan P Coaches	KEY	Key Coaches
CSA	City Sprinter / S&A Coaches	KIN	Kineil Coaches
CSR	City Sightseeing Stirling	KOA	Keenan of Ayr
CSS	City Sightseeing Glasgow	LAG	Lochs & Glens Holidays
D&B	Bain's Coaches	LAK	L A Travel
D&E	D&E Coaches	LID	Liddell, James
DBT	D B Travel	LIP	Lippen Coaches
DCA	Dunns Coaches	LOT	Lothian Buses
DEV	Deveron Coaches	LSK	Leask John & Son
DIC	Dickson of Erskine	M&C	M&C Coaches
DJI	D J International	MAT	Marbill Travel
DMC	Docherty's Midland Coaches	MAY	Mayne's Coaches
DOI	Doigs of Glasgow	MCC	McKendry Coaches
DOT	Dodds of Troon	MCD	McDade Travel
DPC	Prentice Don Coaches	MCL	McCall's Coaches
DPG	Dunn's Coaches; C & M Coaches	MCM	MCT Group Travel
DWF	Dewar Coaches	MCO	McColl Coaches
EAR	Earnside Coaches	MCR	McCreadie Coaches
ECL	Edinburgh Coach Lines	MCS	Millers Coaches Scotland Ltd
ERT	Easter Ross Coach Company	MDO	MacDonalds Coaches
ESB	Essbee Coaches	MEW	MacEwans Coach Services

MEX	Mearns Exclusive Travel	
MFW	Moffat & Williamson	
MIT	Milligan Coach Travel	
MLC	MacLeod's Coaches	
MLI	M-Line International Coaches	
MLS	MacLennan	
MOA	Mackie of Alloa	
MOB	Marshall of Ballieston	
MPC	MacPhails Coaches	
MUN	Munro's of Jedburgh	
NAT	NCP	
NIC	Nicoll	
NXD	Travel Dundee	
OAD	Oban & District Buses	
ORD	Order of Malta	
PHO	Photoflash Services	
POC	Pride of the Clyde Executive Coaches	
POH	Park's of Hamilton	
PSK	Peace JD & Co (Aberdeen)	
PTW	Passenger Travel, Whitburn	
PUM	Puma Coaches	
PWW	Prentice Westwood	
RAB	Rabbies Trailburners	
ROR	Roberts of Rothiemay	
ROW	Rowe & Tudhope Coaches	
RSS	R S Coaches, Sauchen	
RTT	Riverside Transport Training	
SAA	A & C Coaches	
SAB	Aberfoyle Coaches	
SAD	ARAYS Travel	
SAF	A Trip In Time	
SAH	Bee-Line Travel	
SAJ	Caber Coaches	
SAM	Clan Travel	
SAP	Courtney Travel	
SAQ	S.J.Douglas / SD Travel	
SAW	Festival Travel	
SAY	Fountain Execuive	
SAZ	H.Gordon	
SBG	Hardies Coaches	
SBJ	Jenkins Travel	
SBO	MacBackpackers	
SBP	MacPherson Luxury Travel	
SBQ	McKechnie of Bathgate	
SBZ	J.R.& M.B.Shirran	
SCB	Scotbus	
SCD	Simpson of Rosehearty	
SCJ	Starline Travel	
SCK	Stables of Keith	
SCK	Vision Travel	
SCM	Alexander Wait & Son	
SCN	Woods of Tillicoultry	
SCP	Kelvin Valley Coaches	
SEC	Silverdale Executive Coaches	
SHB	Shuttle Buses	
SHC	Stonehouse Coaches	
SHI	Shiel Buses	
SHIC	Stagecoach Highlands	
SIC	Silver Fox Coaches	
SKY	Skyline	
SLA	Slaemuir Coaches	
SMI	Smith & Sons	
SMK	Central Coaches	
SMP	Smith's Coaches	
SOK	Stables of Keith	
SOU	Southern Coaches	
SPA	Spa Coaches	
SREN	Stagecoach East Scotland	
STAY	Stagecoach Strathtay & Perth	
STK	Stokes William & Sons	
STP	Stepend Coaches	
STU	Stuarts of Carluke	
SVC	Silver Choice Travel	
SWSC	Stagecoach West Scotland	
TED	Docherty T&E	
TEL	Telford's Coaches	
TRD	Travel Direct / Fairway Coaches	
TTA	Tramontana	
VIC	Victoria Coaches	
WAV	Waverley Travel	
WCG	Wilsons Coaches	
WCM	West Coast Motor Services	
WHI	Whitestar	
WHY	Whyte's Coaches	
WJC	W J C Buses	
WLC	Whitelaws Coaches	
WLO	West Lothian Transport	
WMC	Watermill Coaches	
WRH	Wilson of Rhu	
WTB	Westerbus	
YUL	Yule, Elizabeth	

Reg	Op		Reg	Op		Reg	Op	
98-D-20408	MCO		7MCB	MAY	24	151EWU	LID	
99-D-504	MCO		12HM	POH		162EKH	BBD	52224
99-D-519	MCO		15RWM	POH		191WHW	WLC	
99-D-544	MCO		81CBK	PWW		200UWX	SHIC	52044
99-D-60017	MCO		84HER	SVC		246AJF	KOA	
			101RTD	YUL		283URB	SREN	52285
1RWM	POH		109ASV	WCM		361EKH	BLY	
2GRT	FAB	20011	121ASV	MFW		367NHA	PWW	
2HAN	POH		123TRL	IRB		408UFC	ESB	
2HW	POH		127ASV	BBD	51099	410KGG	ANN	PE1
2RWM	POH		128ASV	BBD	51071	439BUS	SREN	59643
2WR	POH		128NNU	STAY	16922	444VNX	SHIC	52533
3HWS	POH		138ASV	PWW		448GWL	BBD	54046
3RWM	POH		143CLT	STAY	52433	479DKH	LID	

B5VOL	KOA		B305KVO	IRB		BU04EZC	CIC	9
B5YST	D&E		B307KVO	IRB		BU04EZE	CIC	11
B6YST	D&E		B321CGG	WJC		BU04EZZ	POC	
B7YST	D&E		B331LSA	WJC	L331	BU04UTF	MLI	
B8OVA	SAZ		B417CVH	HCO		BU04ZYT	HOR	
B8YST	D&E		B494UNB	FIT		BU05DVL	RSS	
B9PRE	ALA	AT115	B496MFS	MOA		BU05DVM	RSS	
B9YST	D&E		B500MPY	MEW		BU05DVN	RSS	
B10MBC	BUT		B758GSC	PWW		BU05DWD	RSS	
B10MGR	EAR		B759GSC	PWW		BU05EGD	WAV	
B10MKF	ALA	AT 98	B762GSC	MAT		BU05EHB	D&B	
B10MSC	ALA	AT 96	B774AOC	MCO		BU05HFN	BEK	
B10MSE	ALA	AT 97	B777AOC	MCO		BU06CTE	GUM	
B10PSV	SWSC	24183	B806AOP	MCO	3004	BU06CUH	SAB	
B10SBP	FIT		B848AOP	MCO		BU06HSV	GUM	310
B10VOL	KOA		B851KRY	HCO		BU08ACZ	STP	
B10YST	D&E		B852OSB	MCO		BU51AYL	MCD	
B11DWA	ALG		B853AOP	MCO		BU51DEC	D&E	
B12ABT	ABO		B858AOP	MCO	3027	BU52LAS	MLI	
B12BGR	EAR		B867DOM	MCO		BU53AXJ	SBG	
B12DWA	ALG		B884DOM	MCO		BU53DEC	D&E	
B12GEC	GEC		B885DOM	MEW		BU56DEC	D&E	
B12YST	D&E		B899RSH	LID		BU58DEC	D&E	
B13DWA	ALG		B964WRN	JDT		BUI5220	SVC	
B13YST	D&E		BAZ7912	GLC		BV04AFA	LID	
B14DWA	ALG		BAZ7916	JJT		BV04CZJ	HOR	
B14PCH	DPC		BAZ7918	GLC		BV08ZWC	GUM	306
B14YST	D&E		BB05DOT	DOT		BV08ZWG	GUM	307
B15DWA	ALG		BD04XVU	SAP		BV08ZWP	GUM	308
B15KCT	KCO		BHZ1255	FIT		BV57JYG	GUM	304
B15YST	D&E		BHZ1256	FIT		BV57JYH	GUM	305
B16SCJ	SCJ		BHZ1257	FIT		BV57XLJ	MLS	
B17DWA	ALG		BHZ8809	SAH		BVS118	A&B	
B17YST	D&E		BHZ9543	SREN	27092	BW05LGW	NAT	1022
B18DWA	ALG		BHZ9546	SREN	59111	BX03OVA	GUM	228
B19DWA	ALG		BHZ9548	SREN	27097	BX04MZT	STP	
B19WCS	AYR		BHZ9549	SREN	27094	BX05UVL	CIC	12
B20DWA	ALG		BIG6153	ARC		BX05UVM	CIC	14
B21DWA	ALG		BIG9871	WJC	ZLL645	BX05UVN	CIC	15
B79WUV	WCM		BJ59CWM	SAJ		BX05VPT	ROW	
B83WUV	SWSC	11083	BJI6863	MAT		BX06NZV	SREN	29862
B94PLU	GCT	BS94	BJZ6602	HQD		BX06OAJ	FIR	
B100XTW	MEW		BK10MGE	SWSC	80013	BX06OCZ	D&B	
B108CCS	WCM		BLZ589	WHI		BX06UMU	LID	
B114SJA	JJT		BLZ8582	A&B		BX06UNP	GUM	300
B132CGG	HAO		BM10WSM	MIT		BX06UNR	GUM	301
B134BBV	TEL		BMA524W	SIC		BX10DHF	HOU	
B145GSC	WJC		BMC2T	D&B		BX10DHG	HOU	
B183FFS	MCO	3038	BP54WYH	BCM		BX10DHJ	HOU	
B184FFS	MCO		BS07JDS	DMC		BX10DHK	HOU	
B185FFS	MCO		BS09JDS	DMC		BX53OLE	SPA	
B208FFS	SHB		BS60JDS	DMC		BX53SOC	HOU	
B220WEU	NIC		BS8362	WMC		BX54VNV	D&B	
B238ANK	MCS		BSJ931T	KOA		BX54VTZ	FIR	
B252CVX	KOA		BSK756	BBD	22261	BX55FYA	SBZ	
B269LPH	JJT		BSK790	MFW		BX55XGV	LID	
B301KVO	IRB		BSV216	STU		BX56AYP	WHI	
B302KVO	IRB		BT05BJT	SOK		BX56VTK	GUM	302
B303KVO	IRB		BU04EZA	CIC	7	BX56VTL	GUM	303
B304KVO	IRB		BU04EZB	CIC	8	BX56VUM	AUS	

Reg	Code	Extra	Reg	Code	Extra	Reg	Code	Extra
DEZ9611	MPC		E775NVT	PWW		EYN165	STU	
DFC568	SAJ		E870BGG	WCM		F1MMM	SBP	
DH55MCT	MCM		E871BGG	WCM		F11MMM	SBP	
DJZ4676	DEV		E916NAC	MAT		F46XOF	MCO	3033
DK04LWN	MLC		E917NAC	MAT		F49MCA	HAO	
DK05FWB	WCM		E918NAC	MAT		F69LNU	DPG	
DKS20X	JJT		E937XSB	CCI		F73GYB	SAH	
DLS520Y	MOA		E949JJN	ESB		F76TFU	GEC	
DM10GSM	MAY		E987VUK	MCO		F89GGC	ARC	
DOC41V	WJC	N41	E996FRA	NIC		F95XEM	ARC	
DRN176Y	SCB		EAZ2575	SHIC	52202	F96XEM	ARC	
DSU355	PWW		EAZ2590	SHIC	52204	F97XEM	ARC	
DSU707	BBD	52534	EAZ6207	SMP		F99XEM	ARC	
DSV246	STU		EAZ8407	SVC		F103TML	STU	
DSV698	SCM		EB54MTB	MFW		F104TML	STU	
DSV707	CHE		ECZ9120	LAK		F104XEM	ARC	
DSV943	BBD	51070	ECZ9122	LAK		F106TML	GMC	
DWU37T	LID		EDS50A	SWSC	12060	F107TML	LID	
DX03XEA	GUM	223	EGB60T	APE		F108TML	LID	
DX03XEB	GUM	224	EGB90T	WJC	N90	F109TML	LID	
DX03XEC	GUM	225	EH03EMH	HOR		F110TML	LID	
DX04WKT	CHE		EIG1433	HOR		F119PHM	LID	
DX05CZE	HOR		EIG1434	HOR		F122PHM	AYR	
DY56LYZ	SAJ		EIG1435	ESB		F135PHM	AYR	
E7WJC	WJC	W865	EIG1436	ESB		F155DET	SHC	
E9WJC	WJC		EIG1437	ESB		F189RRF	DPG	
E11MMM	SBP		EIG4966	SMK		F201FHH	WJC	ZLL201
E32HSH	SCM		EIG6554	PHO		F201HSO	MEW	
E51UKL	JJT		EIG9345	RSS		F202FHH	WJC	ZLL202
E68EKG	WCM		EIL584	ANN		F210YHG	SCB	
E100LBC	MDO		EJR109W	SAH		F212TAN	GEM	
E107DJR	LID		EJR115W	ACM		F219DCC	DBT	
E132YUD	D&B		EKS69X	MCD		F264YTJ	SAD	
E156XHS	DCA		EKZ469	SREN	59642	F274JWL	JJT	
E173FRA	NIC		EM04EMH	HOR		F281GNB	DPG	
E205YGC	DPG		EM05EMH	HOR		F311DET	AVD	
E214WBG	GEM		EM06EMH	HOR		R335RWK	WLC	
E225WBG	MLI		EM07EMH	HOR		F336RWK	WLC	
E235WMB	HCO		EM08EMH	HOR		F337RWK	MAT	
E278YPS	SCK		EM09EMH	HOR		F343GUS	STK	
E309MSG	CSS		EM10GSM	MAY	1	F348WSC	JJT	
E310MSG	CSS		EM59GSM	MAY	11	F351FGA	M&C	
E316MSG	HOR		ENV827X	HQL		F357MGB	DCA	
E318MSG	LOT	TB318	EPK1V	APE		F357TSX	CBC	
E318XGB	TEL		ESK880	ABK		F357WSC	LOT	357
E319MSG	LOT	TB319	ESK932	BBD	50137	F358WSC	LOT	358
E320MSG	LOT	TB320	ESK934	BBD	50129	F364WSC	PWW	
E321MSG	HOR		ESK981	SHIC	52205	F366WSC	MCD	
E322MSG	LOT	TB322	ESK983	SHIC	52206	F371WSC	LOT	371
E324BVO	STU		ESK985	SHIC	52167	F427DUG	AYR	
E326BVO	MCO	3011	ESU974	AUS		F427EJC	DBT	
E359NEG	JJT		EU06KDJ	IRB		F428GAT	DBT	
E444ANN	ANN	M2	EUE512	EVE	1	F455BKF	GEC	
E555UHS	DCA		EV07EVE	EVE		F459BKF	GEC	
E559MSE	SMK		EV08EVE	EVE		F481WFX	AYR	
E564YBU	DPG		EVE4	EVE		F484CAL	CSA	
E643KCK	SMK		EY54BPX	FED	56004	F489GGG	MCC	
E701GCU	SAQ		EY54BRV	FAB	56007	F523UVW	PWW	
E711CDS	SAQ		EY54BRX	FAB	56008	F550TMH	JTK	

Reg	Code	Extra		Reg	Code	Extra		Reg	Code	Extra
F572SMG	CBC			FJ06URK	MAY			FSU739	STAY	52386
F575SMG	CBC			FJ07AAZ	HOR			FSU797	BBD	52141
F624XMS	DBT			FJ07ABF	SAB			FSV864	STU	
F631BKD	WJC			FJ07ACV	DOI			FT03COS	FIT	
F644XMS	SAM			FJ07ADV	DOI			FT10KUP	BRU	
F651GNT	AAM			FJ07AED	LAG			FX03GKV	BCM	
F694ACX	A&B			FJ07AEE	LAG			FX51BVF	ERT	
F703COA	AAM			FJ07AEF	LAG			FXI194	SAY	
F725USF	MCS			FJ08BZA	LAG			FXI249	SAY	
F727ASB	WCM			FJ08BZB	LAG			FXI253	SAY	
F727VAC	DEV			FJ08BZC	LAG			FXI457	SAY	
F737FDV	SAM			FJ08BZD	LAG			FXI724	SAY	
F771JYS	LID			FJ08BZE	LAG			FXI782	SAY	
F772JYS	LID			FJ08BZF	LAG			G5LAT	LAK	
F774JYS	MOA			FJ08BZG	LAG			G5WJC	ACM	
F830XAJ	ABK			FJ08BZL	HUC			G7BUS	SAH	
F850NJO	GEM			FJ08FYD	DOI			G7WJC	ACM	
F854LTU	MLI			FJ08FYT	FCC			G9WJC	WJC	V97
F869TLJ	JPM			FJ08FYU	FCC			G21KVH	CSA	
F878RFP	HEB			FJ08FYW	HQD			G21RHG	FIT	
F935ENV	MIT			FJ10DPY	ECL			G38SSR	HEB	
F945PFW	DCA			FJ10DPZ	ECL			G47FKG	SHC	
F956HWB	LID			FJ10EZX	DOT			G49FKG	SHC	
F969RSE	SCJ			FJ10EZZ	DOT			G49TGW	PUM	
F990HGE	HCO			FJ56KUH	AAA			G89GOJ	ANN	M4
FAS374X	WLC			FJ57KGY	BRU	SC31		G94VFP	MCS	
FC04UZK	BCD			FJ57KHB	BRU	SC34		G95YFW	WJC	XC95
FC52AFC	FAB	20021		FJ57KHU	BRU			G103KUB	ANN	
FCZ9700	GIC			FJ57KJF	BRU			G107NGN	EVE	
FE02FBG	ACN			FJ58AKK	BRU			G115NGN	ARC	
FE02FBK	JTK			FJ58AKY	BRU			G118KUB	MCO	
FE51RFF	GLC			FJ58LSC	AYR			G128WGX	SWSC	13636
FHJ83Y	SAJ			FJ58LSD	CCC			G135PGK	ARC	
FHZ2188	FCC			FJ58LSK	AAA			G169LET	JJT	
FHZ3530	FCC			FJZ9714	LID			G189YRJ	SWSC	13616
FHZ3531	FCC			FL02LSK	AAA			G194PAO	KEY	
FHZ4134	FCC			FLZ6854	SBJ			G195PAO	DJI	
FHZ4170	FCC			FN02RXJ	SOK			G197PAO	MDO	
FHZ4171	FCC			FN02VBG	MCR			G203PAO	DJI	
FHZ4190	FCC			FN09AOC	DOI			G214SSL	SWSC	14964
FHZ4191	FCC			FN09AOD	DOI			G216KRN	SCB	
FHZ6882	FCC			FN09AOE	DOI			G233FJC	DPG	
FHZ8395	FCC			FN09AOF	DOI			G249GCC	HQL	
FHZ9593	FCC			FN52GUF	GLC			G278BEL	HEB	
FHZ9599	FCC			FNZ2300	SHI			G278YRJ	SWSC	13644
FIG8241	SCK			FNZ5671	HQL			G280YRJ	SWSC	13643
FIG822	SCK			FNZ5672	HQL			G281OGE	FED	30358
FIL4166	MCL			FNZ5833	HTR			G285TSL	MCO	
FIL7615	CAM			FNZ5834	HTR			G288TSL	DIC	
FIL8613	MDO			FP53ESO	ORD			G289TSL	TRD	
FJ03VNE	SCD			FP53JYO	BCD			G290TSL	TRD	
FJ04ESU	SREN	53038		FSU318	WCM			G293TSL	AVD	
FJ04ETY	MOA			FSU319	WCM			G301WHP	TRD	
FJ04PXX	PSK			FSU331	BBD	52137		G315TKO	BLY	
FJ05APZ	SCD			FSU335	JPM			G326PEW	PWW	
FJ05HXX	IRB			FSU371	GEC			G337KKW	MCO	3039
FJ06BNU	AAA			FSU375	MFW			G339CSG	HOR	
FJ06BPK	FCC			FSU382	FAB	20207		G340CSG	HOR	
FJ06BPO	FCC			FSU394	MFW			G341CSG	HOR	
FJ06BSX	LAG			FSU718	SHIC	59175		G342CSG	HOR	

G345CSG	MCD		G901ANR	BDC		GXI53	IRB	
G369RTO	A&B		G907PKK	EAR		H3KFC	NXD	7352
G373RTO	LID		G924TCU	HOU		H4KDY	SBG	
G452FVX	WJC		G926TCU	LID		H23YBV	SCB	
G454TST	CFM		G926WGS	KEY		H71MOB	PUM	
G470CEH	BLY		G932TVO	HCO		H81PTG	ANN	M1
G504SFT	CBC		G934TTV	HOU		H101HDV	CCI	
G504XLO	DCA		G954WNR	M&C		H113ABV	KOA	
G505SFT	GIB		G970KTX	MLI		H114UYG	SCB	
G567PRM	CSR		G973KTX	MCC		H122MOB	CNV	
G577XAE	JJT		G999OKK	SMK		H129FLX	FED	34329
G601NWA	FG	61256	G999SJR	MCS		H139FLX	FED	34339
G609NWA	FG	60464	GBZ7212	DPG		H149SKU	MAT	
G611NWA	FG	61259	GBZ7213	JPM		H150SKU	MAT	
G612NWA	FG	60138	GBZ8812	LIP		H151MOB	SKY	
G613NWA	FG	60466	GBZ9059	LIP		H151SKU	MAT	
G614NWA	FG	61260	GCS38V	KOA		H152SKU	MAT	
G615NWA	FG	61261	GCS48V	KOA		H153SKU	MAT	
G616NWA	FG	61262	GDZ3363	SREN	52669	H154MOB	SKY	
G616OTV	SHC		GEZ1277	MCL		H154SKU	MAT	
G621NWA	FG	61266	GFA955	MPC		H155SKU	MAT	
G621XLO	RSS		GFM882	MEW		H156SKU	MAT	
G638NWA	FG	60483	GFV152W	SCB		H157SKU	MAT	
G645EVV	GEC		GHZ8752	PWW		H158SKU	MAT	
G647ONH	DCA		GIB6135	GIB		H159SKU	MAT	
G649EVV	GEC		GIL1685	ALA	AT 89	H171EJF	SAW	
G653EKA	STU		GIL2754	CCC		H178EJF	M&C	
G700PNS	WJC		GIL5407	DOT		H195DVM	JTK	
G761WAS	SMP		GIL6540	MLI		H201LOM	ARC	
G774DSK	M&C		GJI627	MAT		H202LOM	PWW	
G799RNC	MCL		GJI926	KIN		H202LRF	TED	
G800GSX	WMC		GK53EBP	ORD		H207LOM	ARC	
G801GSX	WMC		GK53EBU	ORD		H219LOM	LID	
G803GSX	HOR		GLZ5081	GIC		H223VKU	ACM	
G807RTS	SREN	14957	GM04GSM	GUM	701	H224LOM	AYR	
G808GSX	CBC		GM10GSM	MAY	2	H242MUK	CBC	
G808LAG	SHC		GM57GSM	MAY	4	H289VRP	FED	38089
G809HRN	JPM		GN03PVT	SAD		H291VRP	FED	38091
G811WST	SMP		GN55XTD	GMC		H292VRP	FED	38092
G812GSX	CBC		GNZ9360	SMI		H429BNL	SREN	15309
G813GSX	HOR		GOG208W	GEC		H432EFT	SAD	
G814GSX	MCD		GS54EVE	EVE		H433EFT	LID	
G815GSX	CBC		GSO84V	APE		H445EGU	SWSC	13617
G816GSX	JJT		GSU341	SREN	52308	H470KSG	EVE	
G818GSX	CFM		GSU347	ASW	3001	H494LNA	SWSC	13623
G820GSX	CBC		GSU370	EVE		H511FRP	BBD	13625
G821GSX	CBC		GSU551	SHB		H522FRP	SWSC	13618
G823GSX	CBC		GSU950	BBD	22254	H533XGK	CBC	
G824GSX	CBC		GX02AHN	JTK		H551EVM	JPM	
G825GSX	CBC		GX04LWR	GUM	508	H558GKX	CAM	
G826GSX	MCD		GX04LWS	GUM	509	H562GKX	CAM	
G827GSX	MCD		GX04LWT	GUM	510	H603LNA	SWSC	13651
G829GSX	GEC		GX04LWU	GUM	511	H606LNA	SWSC	13647
G831RDS	SHB		GX04LWV	GUM	512	H617LNA	ARC	
G833GSX	MCD		GX04LWW	GUM	513	H625LNA	SWSC	13642
G834GSX	MCD		GX07ARF	SEC		H627LNA	SWSC	13650
G835GSX	MCD		GX07BAU	STP		H648RKU	FG	60492
G862RNC	SPA		GX08AUR	WCM		H660UWE	JTK	
G864RNC	JTK		GX08AUT	WCM		H665GPF	GEC	
G879TVS	MLI		GX51CFF	MLS		H668GPF	MOB	

H676GPF	PWW		HSK641	POH		J212KTT	TRD	
H678GPF	LID		HSK642	POH		J222BER	WMC	
H678THL	FG	60520	HSK644	POH		J229NNC	SCJ	
H679GPF	GEC		HSK645	POH		J235NNC	MCS	
H699PVW	BDC		HSK646	POH		J249LLB	SAP	
H708PVW	BDC		HSK647	POH		J296GNV	FED	38096
H709PVW	BDC		HSK648	POH		J301BRM	WCM	
H717LOL	JJT		HSK649	POH		J303BRM	WCM	
H718PVW	BDC		HSK650	POH		J304BRM	WCM	
H719LOL	JJT		HSK651	POH		J305BRM	WCM	
H757DTM	JTK		HSK655	POH		J306BRM	OAD	
H778VHL	SWSC	13632	HSK656	POH		J308BRM	WCM	
H890LOX	CNV		HSK735	SHI		J309BRM	WCM	
H912JVR	AYR		HSK857	IRB		J316XVX	CBC	
H916XYT	CBC		HSL660	WCG		J388GKH	SAQ	
H921XYT	CBC		HSO61N	FAB	62120	J407PRW	BBD	41507
H922XYT	CBC		HSU247	FAB	20206	J414PRW	ERT	
HCC100	HCC		HSU983	IRB		J420JBV	ESB	
HCC296	HCC		HSV725	WMC		J422JBV	ESB	
HCC440	HCC		HSV782	STU		J442JBV	SCP	
HCC551	HCC		HUI 6828	SMI		J500CCH	AYR	
HCC882	HCC		HUI8156	IRB		J512FPS	CCI	
HDB355V	GCT	LS355	HV02PAO	HVB		J607KGB	JJT	
HDZ8349	WHI		IIB379	SBG		J612XHL	CBC	
HDZ8352	SVC		IIB457	FIR		J615XHL	WCG	
HF53GVJ	BDC		IIL3481	CAM		J619KCU	GCB	
HG08OVA	SAZ		IIL3504	SREN	52353	J627KCU	CSA	
HGD214T	KOA		IJI336	MLI		J635KCU	CSA	
HIG2461	HEB		IUI2129	PWW		J638KCU	CSA	
HIG2462	HEB		IUI9890	DJI		J642CWJ	LAK	
HIG7793	BLS		IXI1337	VIC		J701HMY	SWSC	13609
HIG7814	AAM		J3EGT	SBJ		J734MFY	JPM	
HIL2148	ASW	1436	J3PUB	HUC		J773HMX	SAA	
HIL2160	SBJ		J5EGT	SBJ		J801WFS	SREN	14701
HIL2464	ABO		J7EGT	SBJ		J805FPS	STAY	32805
HIL2702	HLO		J8LWC	SCM		J807HSB	WCM	
HIL2720	HLO		J10WBT	AVD		J818HMC	MLI	
HIL3318	HLO		J10WCM	OAD		J848TSC	HOR	
HIL4336	HLO		J11GRT	FAB	20013	J857TSC	PWW	
HIL5063	HLO		J15GEC	GEC		J862TSC	MCD	
HIL5184	DEV		J17BUS	MCM		J864XFS	JTK	
HIL5345	HLO		J20JPT	TRD		J869TSC	MCD	
HIL5346	HLO		J20WCM	OAD		J870TSC	MCD	
HIL5347	HLO		J24MCW	MCO		J880RHA	MDO	
HIL5348	HLO		J25MCW	MCO	2002	J882UNA	JJT	
HIL5349	HLO		J30WCM	OAD		J938MHC	SWSC	13612
HIL6256	ABO		J40WCM	OAD		J938WHJ	KEY	
HIL6462	MCS		J50WCM	OAD		J999BER	WMC	
HIL6570	MOB		J55BUS	DPG		JA5515	DMC	
HIL7590	SLA		J60WCM	OAD		JAZ3285	MCR	
HIL8129	LID		J70WCM	WCM		JAZ4886	AAM	
HIL8441	MCC		J77GEC	GEC		JAZ9850	SHIC	52045
HIL8617	HLO		J80WCM	WCM		JAZ9852	SHIC	59176
HIL9155	LID		J90WCM	WCM		JAZ9855	SHIC	59177
HJI565	MAT		J100WCM	WCM		JBZ3675	PWW	
HJZ3949	AAM		J119DUV	DCA		JBZ4910	MCD	
HMU118	HQL		J120AHH	AAM		JCZ2065	HOU	
HOI364	SAD		J127MTY	FIR		JDS77J	DMC	
HRS265V	GCT		J168CTO	MLC		JEZ4096	DOT	
HRS271V	GCT		J209KTT	TRD		JEZ8980	DOT	

JFR9W	JJT			K101UJR	MUN	955	K538ORH	CBC	
JH54BUS	HCC			K103OMW	PUM		K540ORH	CBC	
JHZ4804	PWW			K103XHG	WCM		K543ORH	ASW	1693
JIB82	BEK			K106XHG	CCI		K544RJX	MCC	
JIB292	BEK			K112XHG	BLS		K574LTS	MCO	2008
JIB3032	BEK			K114SRH	CBC		K578LTS	MCO	2010
JIL2159	CAM			K114XHG	TRD		K579MGT	LIP	
JIL2161	ESB			K118CSG	CFT		K579PHU	JPM	
JIL2165	CAM			K118XHG	KEY		K580YOJ	GUM	129
JIL2566	HCO			K119SRH	CNV		K581MGT	AVD	
JIL2949	D&B			K120CSG	CFT		K583MGT	AVD	
JIL3757	SAW			K121CSG	SAH		K590MGT	LIP	
JIL3961	SHI			K122CSG	SAH		K593BEG	DPG	
JIL5623	CFM			K122SRH	PUM		K593MGT	AVD	
JIL7656	D&B			K123CSG	CFT		K600AYR	AYR	
JIL8206	LID			K132XRE	CSA		K600JLS	LSK	
JIL8207	WMC			K151LGO	AVD		K600SOU	SCJ	
JIL8256	CFM			K153LGO	AVD		K601ESH	SREN	32201
JIL8560	GEC			K174EUX	FG	30107	K601LAE	FED	30216
JIL8561	GEC			K200AYR	AYR		K605LAE	FG	30220
JIL8562	GEC			K200WCM	WCM		K618UFR	BLS	
JJD365D	GCT			K209OHS	SAH		K619UFR	BLS	
JJD432D	WCG			K221VTB	AVD		K620UFR	TRD	
JJD444D	SWSC	12444		K222AYR	AYR		K655VNF	AYR	
JJD486D	GCT			K222VTB	AVD		K662CBA	SCK	
JJD550D	SWSC	12550		K223VTB	AVD		K688CBA	SWSC	13628
JJD553D	GCT			K224VTB	AVD		K700AYR	AYR	
JJI3316	SCP			K225VTB	AVD		K700BUL	TEL	
JSJ746	LOT	4		K226BJA	DPG		K708RNR	SHB	
JSJ747	LOT	5		K239SFJ	SLA		K711EDT	FG	61347
JSJ748	LOT	6		K240EUX	SMI		K714DAO	DJI	
JSJ749	LOT	1		K242SFJ	CSA		K715DAO	MCO	2011
JSU384	KIN			K244SUS	AVD		K718DAO	MCO	2009
JSU542	NXD	7306		K295ESF	SPA		K719DAO	DJI	
JSU550	DPC			K300AYR	AYR		K720UTT	SKY	
JSU626Y	TTA			K300WCM	WCM		K724DAO	DJI	
JSV362	KIN			K315MWV	GEC		K732DAO	DJI	
JSV440	PWW			K322BTM	DPG		K764CSG	ECL	
JSV486	GSM	GS69		K333AYR	AYR		K766DAO	MEW	
JW02BUS	SCN			K369RTY	SLA		K788DAO	MEW	
JXI317	BRU			K400AYR	AYR		K797PLM	BLY	
K1WGD	DCA			K400JCD	SCK		K800AYR	AYR	
K5KFC	NXD	7350		K400WCM	WCM		K801OMW	BBD	41801
K5SKY	KIN			K433OKH	CBC		K802OMW	BBD	41802
K7SKY	A&B			K434DRW	ETN		K807DJN	DIC	
K10EVE	EVE			K438XRF	DBT		K827HUM	MAY	
K14AMC	VIC			K440HWY	BEK		K851RBB	MEW	
K14BUS	ARC			K446XRF	DBT		K852RBB	MEW	
K20JCM	SHI			K464PNR	JDT		K859HRS	SCB	
K30SBL	SHI			K470SKO	CBC		K866ODY	DIC	
K40SBL	SHI			K477SSM	MEW		K871LGN	CBC	
K60BSL	SHI			K478SSM	MEW		K871ODY	TRD	
K70AYR	AYR			K481VVR	SPA		K873CSF	LOT	
K76OCR	WRH			K491FFS	GUM	107	K875CSF	LOT	
K79SYS	WCM			K495OSU	JJT		K875ODY	HVB	
K85DTM	GUM	122		K498PGN	DEV		K876CSF	LOT	
K96RGA	KEY			K500AYR	AYR		K877CSF	HOR	
K98SAG	CBC			K500WCM	WCM		K879CSF	HOR	
K100AYR	AYR			K505WNR	SBQ		K881CSF	LOT	

Reg	Code	Number
K888BFG	FG	30226
K888ELR	FG	30222
K917RGE	JTK	
K918RGE	AAM	
K944OPX	HTR	
K947SGG	CBC	
K949OEM	DIC	
K966SUS	SREN	27093
K977XND	SBJ	
K987SUS	MLI	
KAO238V	MCL	
KBZ4631	SHIC	52046
KC02BUS	KCO	
KC51BUS	KCO	
KCT50	KCO	
KDZ5801	CBC	
KDZ6277	MCR	
KE54FUV	SHC	
KE54FVL	SHC	
KIW1102	JTK	
KKG109W	ESB	
KKN752	MAY	
KLZ2317	SHIC	52536
KM07GSM	MAY	7
KM10GSM	MAY	
KM57GSM	MAY	3
KN04XJD	SREN	18129
KN04XJE	SREN	18130
KN07SPA	SPA	
KN54ZXL	SREN	18196
KN54ZXM	SREN	18197
KN54ZXR	SREN	18195
KNL665	AUS	
KSD103W	JJT	
KSK933	MPC	
KSK934	MPC	
KSK976	POH	
KSK977	POH	
KSK978	POH	
KSK979	POH	
KSK980	POH	
KSK985	POH	
KSU175	AUS	
KSV803	CHE	
KSX104X	WJC	N104
KU02YUL	MEW	
KU02YUN	MEW	
KUI2759	BLS	
KUI3849	SMI	
KUS244Y	SIC	
KW56LZU	MOA	
KX05HVE	SWSC	50141
KX06LYS	WAV	
KX06LYT	WAV	
KX07HDE	POC	
KX07HDF	FIR	
KX07KNY	CCI	702
KX07UGE	CCI	
KX07UGF	CCI	
KX08HMK	PUM	
KX08HMO	PUM	
KX08UXA	WHY	
KX08UXB	WHY	
KX08UXC	WHY	
KX08UXD	WHY	
KX08UXE	WHY	
KX08UXF	WHY	
KX08UXG	WHY	
KX08UXU	WAV	
KX09CGU	PWW	
KX09CHY	FIR	
KX10DVF	ORD	
KX10DVG	ORD	
KX10DVH	ORD	
KX10DVJ	ORD	
KX10DVM	ORD	
KX10DVN	ORD	
KX51CRZ	SREN	47003
KX51CSF	SREN	47004
KX56JZN	SREN	53275
KX56JZO	SREN	53276
KX57OVA	NAT	1030
KX57OVB	NAT	1031
KX57OVC	NAT	1027
KXG661	STU	
KXI244	BRU	
KXI599	AYR	
KYV473X	SWSC	10473
L1PPN	LIP	
L2PPN	LIP	
L2SBC	STP	
L3LCC	SMI	
L3OBS	JJT	
L4HOD	SCK	
L4LCC	KIN	
L4PHF	CFM	
L5PPN	LIP	
L8PPN	LIP	
L9NCP	CNV	
L9PPN	LIP	
L11JDT	JDT	
L11PPN	LIP	
L12PPN	LIP	
L15PPN	LIP	
L15YUL	YUL	
L17ATS	DEV	
L18TVL	LID	
L21LSG	SBQ	
L25LSX	ASW	270
L26JSA	STAY	16198
L26LSG	CSA	
L33NMS	MCL	
L34ULA	BLS	
L36ULA	JJT	
L58YJF	HQD	
L64GSE	SMK	
L65ORB	NIC	
L82RHL	BRW	
L94LND	SLA	
L98PTW	EVE	
L98WSW	HCC	
L100JLB	STAY	16610
L100WCM	WCM	
L114YVK	CBC	
L123DRN	DBT	
L125DRN	CSA	
L128DRN	DBT	
L129YVK	CBC	
L132YVK	PTW	
L136VRH	CNV	
L138VRH	PUM	
L139XDS	AVD	
L142VRH	CNV	
L143VRH	CNV	
L146VRH	WCM	
L149YVK	CBC	
L151WAG	CBC	
L152YVK	CBC	
L154YVK	PTW	7
L156UNS	FED	31732
L157UNS	FED	31733
L158UNS	FED	31734
L159UNS	FED	31735
L166YAT	CBC	
L188SDY	TRD	
L188SUB	ABK	
L200WCM	WCM	
L201TKA	ASW	4531
L202ONU	DBT	
L203ONU	DBT	
L204JSX	HAO	
L205JSX	HAO	
L210TKA	ASW	4532
L214GJO	SMI	
L216TKA	ASW	4533
L228SWM	CBC	
L229SWM	CBC	
L230SWM	CBC	
L231TKA	CBC	
L232SWM	CBC	
L233SWM	CBC	
L233TKA	WCG	
L234SWM	CBC	
L235TKA	ASW	4537
L244SDY	STAY	16244
L245SDY	STAY	16245
L248SDY	SREN	16248
L249SDY	SREN	16249
L249YOD	TRD	
L250YOD	TRD	
L252YOD	HVB	
L253YOD	SLA	
L254YOD	SLA	
L258YOD	DIC	
L270ULX	CNV	
L273FVN	ASW	7273
L274FVN	ASW	7274
L278JAO	BLS	
L292USU	STK	

Reg	Code	Num	Reg	Code	Num	Reg	Code	Num
L293USU	STK		L642DNA	DIC		LEO736Y	SIC	
L297ORS	SCK		L643DNA	SMI		LEZ3945	PHO	
L300WCM	OAD		L644AFJ	HOU		LEZ9446	CHE	
L304PSC	PUM		L644VCV	DPG		LF51EKX	LID	
L306HPP	ASW	4534	L647SEU	FED	34147	LIB8921	CFM	
L308AUT	CBC		L648SEU	FED	34148	LIJ595	SREN	59671
L308PSC	SHIC	20308	L649SEU	FED	34149	LIL2173	BLY	
L309YDU	SCB		L651SEU	FED	34151	LIL4398	PHO	
L316JSA	CCI		L652SEU	FED	34152	LIL8050	JJT	
L321AUT	STAY	40176	L656MYG	CNV		LIL8970	MEW	
L345ERU	GSM	GS60	L658MYG	TRD		LIL9814	KOA	
L374BGA	AVD		L665MSF	BLS		LIL9970	GCT	
L375BGA	AVD		L676JSX	WTB		LIW4270	WLC	
L376BGA	AVD		L700JPC	SCK		LIW4290	SBJ	
L384YFT	SHB		L700WCM	WCM		LJ04JFZ	LID	
L388YNV	LSK		L701AGA	CNV		LJI978	MAT	
L395BGA	AVD		L703AGA	DIC		LJZ6056	WJC	XLL764
L400WCM	WCM		L710ADS	TEL		LK51UYS	FG	33015
L404BBC	MCO	1001	L715WCC	DPG		LK51UYT	FG	33016
L404LHE	BLY		L717ERU	HQD		LK51UYU	FG	33017
L405BBC	MCO		L717WCC	DPG		LK51UYV	FG	33018
L407BBC	MCO	1002	L730MWW	DBT		LK51UZF	FG	33008
L416BGA	AVD		L733MWW	DBT		LK51UZG	FG	33009
L416UNJ	CBC		L738PUA	DBT		LK51UZH	FG	33010
L417UUF	CBC		L740PUA	CCI		LK51UZJ	FG	33011
L421ORS	MCO	4006	L741LWA	CSA		LK51UZL	FG	33012
L438FPA	RSS		L742NHE	GMC		LK51UZM	FG	33013
L452HOE	AYR		L745LWA	CSA		LK51UZN	FG	33014
L464BGA	AVD		L746LWA	SHB		LKU618	PSK	
L465BGA	AVD		L748LWA	Dic		LKZ4453	ACN	
L481BGA	AVD		L776AUS	LIP		LN51DWE	FG	33040
L485NTO	IRB		L869LFS	JJT		LN51GMV	FG	33089
L486NTO	IRB		L870LFS	CBC		LN52LLK	VIC	
L487NTO	SHC		L881SDY	CSA		LOI1454	GEM	
L489NTO	IRB		L906ANS	CBC		LS04OSL	MOA	
L493BGA	AVD		L906JRN	SMP		LSG27N	WJC	H8
L500WEN	DPG		L910JRN	GUM	434	LSK444	POH	
L501OAL	CSA		L930UGA	MDO		LSK478	SREN	52671
L502FVU	TRD		L931NWW	JTK		LSK479	SREN	52670
L502OAL	CSA		L932CTY	WCM		LSK483	POH	
L504BNX	CBC		L942LBV	BRW		LSK495	POH	
L505OAL	CSA		L945HTM	JPM		LSK496	POH	
L508BNX	CBC		L964MSC	SREN	16894	LSK498	POH	
L508OAL	CSA		L970VGE	GUM	109	LSK499	POH	
L509OAL	DBT		L973MSC	HOR		LSK500	POH	
L551USU	FED	31728	L974MSC	HOR		LSK501	POH	
L554USU	FED	31731	L975MSC	MLI		LSK502	POH	
L583JSA	STAY	52173	L976MSC	MLI		LSK503	POH	
L584HSG	SREN	52184	L977MSC	MLI		LSK505	POH	
L585HSG	SHIC	52185	L978MSC	MLI		LSK507	POH	
L586JSA	MIT		L990ASU	WCM		LSK510	POH	
L605BNX	CBC		LAZ4120	JJT		LSK512	POH	
L619SES	SAJ		LAZ4470	JDT		LSK513	POH	
L628AYS	SMP		LAZ7403	LAK		LSK530	JPM	
L630BFV	BLS		LAZ9205	WMC		LSK545	BBD	16153
L635BFV	BLS		LB10BUS	LOT	950	LSK555	POH	
L636SEU	FED	34136	LCA381	ABO		LSK570	FAB	20014
L637AYS	MCR		LCN36	MCR		LSK571	FAB	20015
L637DNA	SLA		LCZ1890	MCC		LSK614	POH	
L641DNA	GUM	125	LCZ3677	JTK		LSK813	POH	

M346JGB	MCO	3018	M538RSO	BBD	52238	M772BCS	MCO	2005
M348JBO	SHIC	40548	M539RSO	SHIC	52239	M772PRS	FG	61378
M349JBO	SLA		M543RSO	BBD	52243	M773PRS	FG	61379
M354SDC	RTT		M544RSO	BBD	52244	M774PRS	FG	61380
M358LFX	MCC		M547GNS	CNV		M775PRS	FG	61381
M362LAX	AVD		M553WTJ	IRB		M776PRS	FG	61382
M363KVR	MCS		M568TJL	JJT		M776TFS	SKY	
M363LAX	AVD		M578BSM	MEW		M778XHW	FIT	
M364LAX	AVD		M591OSO	SWSC	20191	M779PRS	FG	61384
M365AMA	BNA	B115	M593OSO	HOR		M780XHW	FIT	
M365LAX	AVD		M597OSO	SHIC	20197	M783ASL	WMC	
M366AMA	BNA	B116	M600WCM	WCM		M784PRS	SWSC	20584
M367KVR	HVB		M602BCA	BNA	B117	M785PRS	DMC	
M367LAX	AVD		M609WFS	HVB		M786PRS	SWSC	20586
M371LAX	AVD		M611YSF	ECL		M786VJO	SHB	
M378EFD	WCG		M623RCP	HQL		M787PRS	SWSC	20587
M381JGB	MCO	3028	M627RCP	BCM		M788ASL	WMC	
M394KVR	WCG		M629WBV	MCR		M788PRS	SWSC	20588
M396JGB	MCO		M631RCP	MUN	631	M789PRS	SWSC	20589
M396KVR	SWSC	40986	M634FJF	GMC		M790PRS	SWSC	20590
M400WCM	WCM		M648FYS	SWSC	40098	M791EUS	CBC	
M406KOA	SMK		M649FYS	KEY		M791PRS	SHIC	20591
M409TCK	CBC		M655FYS	SWSC	40055	M793PRS	DMC	
M410TCK	CBC		M656FYS	SWSC	40056	M796ASL	WMC	
M413DEU	FED	20438	M658FYS	SWSC	40058	M800WCM	WCM	
M438ECS	JTK		M658ROS	GSM	GS62	M802ASL	GEC	
M454VCW	HOR		M660FYS	SLA		M804GFT	PUM	
M464YAS	JTK		M662USX	HVB		M805GFT	GUM	426
M467ASW	SHIC	20594	M663FYS	KEY		M806GFT	GUM	428
M468ASW	HOR		M664UCT	HOR		M807GFT	GUM	429
M469ASW	SWSC	20509	M667FYS	SWSC	40067	M808ASL	WMC	
M470ASW	SHIC	20570	M668FYS	SWSC	40068	M808JTY	SHIC	52269
M471ASW	HOR		M677SSX	CSA		M809GFT	PUM	
M472ASW	SHIC	20572	M677TBF	HAO		M811HCU	PUM	
M477ASW	HOR		M685MRP	M&C		M811PGM	FG	64811
M479ASW	SHIC	20579	M700WCM	WCM		M812GFT	GUM	431
M480ASW	HOR		M701EDD	AVD		M812PGM	FG	64812
M481FGG	HOR		M704JDG	AVD		M813GFT	GUM	424
M482ASW	SHIC	20569	M707JDG	SLA		M815GFT	GUM	427
M482CSD	JTK		M719BCS	CSA		M815HCU	WCG	
M483ASW	BBD	20511	M721BCS	CSA		M815JKU	AVD	
M486ASW	SHIC	20566	M722BCS	MCO	2004	M818GFT	GUM	430
M487ASW	SWSC	20567	M736BSJ	CSA		M819GFT	PUM	
M488ASW	SWSC	20505	M739BSJ	SWSC	30339	M821YSC	ABK	
M490ASW	SREN	16846	M742UUA	CBC		M823ASL	WMC	
M498XSP	BEK		M743UUA	CBC		M831HNS	KIN	
M500WCM	WCM		M744UUA	CBC		M831SDA	ASW	7267
M506ALP	CSA		M745UUA	CBC		M832SDA	ASW	7268
M516TVM	WMC		M748PRS	BLS		M833SDA	ASW	7269
M527RSO	SHIC	52227	M756LAX	JMC		M834DUS	FG	31421
M527UGS	JTK		M760ASL	BRW		M835DUS	FG	31422
M528RSO	SREN	52228	M760GGE	KIN		M836DUS	FG	31423
M529RSO	SHIC	52229	M765PRS	FG	61371	M838DUS	FG	31425
M530DPN	STK		M766PRS	FG	61372	M839DUS	FG	31426
M530RSO	SREN	52230	M767PRS	FG	61373	M840DUS	FG	31427
M534CEY	DEV		M768PRS	FG	61374	M841DUS	FG	31428
M534NCG	GSM	GS67	M769PRS	FG	61375	M846DUS	FG	31516
M536RSO	BBD	52236	M770PRS	FG	61376	M867FSU	FG	
M537JRY	SMK		M771PRS	FG	61377	M868FSU	MCM	
M537RSO	BBD	52237	M771TFS	SKY		M869ASW	SWSC	20506

M871ASW	SWSC	20507	MIL7622	ESB		MX06ACF	STU	
M876DDS	GIB		MIL7795	MIT		MX06ACZ	MFW	
M877DDS	DIC		MIL8028	MIT		MX06ADO	MFW	
M877PRS	FG	61387	MIL9145	MIT		MX06AEA	SEC	
M879DDS	SCP		MIL9587	RSS		MX06ONV	SREN	59614
M880DDS	CBC		MJI6254	SCB		MX06ONW	SREN	59615
M907XWA	GEM		MK02GAU	BUT		MX06OOA	SBG	
M922UYG	FG	34202	MK02GZU	CFM		MX06YXN	FG	69181
M923UYG	FG	34203	MK02VFM	MFW		MX06YXO	FG	69182
M925UYG	FG	34205	MK52XNS	ASW	2603	MX06YXP	FG	69183
M937JGB	MCO		MKZ585	WTB		MX06YXR	FG	69184
M939EYS	FG	31429	MKZ1878	ROR		MX07BCK	STU	
M940EYS	FG	31430	MKZ7183	AUS		MX07BCU	IRB	
M941EYS	FG	31431	MKZ7184	BLY		MX07DHA	SCM	
M942EYS	FG	31432	ML02ONH	HTR		MX07MPV	SBG	
M943UDT	DIC		ML02PFN	WMC		MX07NUA	IRB	
M944TSX	SREN	52258	MLL948	GCT		MX08DHP	GMC	
M946TSX	SWSC	52246	MM06GSM	MAY	5	MX08DJF	IRB	
M950TSX	STAY	52250	MM54GSM	MAY	22	MX08MYK	HOR	
M951XES	STAY	16881	MNZ9303	HUC		MX08MYL	HOR	
M952TSX	STAY	52252	MP51BUZ	JMC		MX09MKE	HOU	
M952XES	STAY	16882	MRJ40W	AAM		MX10DDK	MIT	
M953TSX	SREN	52253	MRJ55W	AAM		MX10DEU	MEX	
M953XES	STAY	16883	MSL276X	WCM		MX10DFJ	CIC	25
M954TSX	STAY	52254	MSU466	SWSC	50128	MX10DFK	CIC	26
M954XES	STAY	16884	MSV452	STU		MX10DXO	HVB	210
M955TSX	SWSC	52255	MTU118Y	MLI		MX10DXP	HOU	
M955USC	SAQ		MU51FMV	SMI		MX10DXS	HOU	
M956TSX	STAY	52256	MUD490	MCO	4002	MX10DXW	SAB	
M994HHS	SMK		MUI4134	SIC		MX51VCT	EVE	
M996CYS	ABK		MUI5346	HQD		MX53FDE	STP	
MAZ6509	MIT		MUI5348	HQD		MX53ZWE	DEV	
MAZ8433	SCJ		MV02UGA	HQD		MX54KLF	VIC	
MAZ8439	SCK		MV02UMF	WTB		MX54KXP	IRB	
MBZ1758	SAZ		MV02UMG	ACN		MX54KXU	STU	
MBZ9374	CCI		MV02VDZ	FG	66349	MX54KYG	MFW	
MC02BLU	GCB		MV02XYJ	ASW	2601	MX54KYN	STU	
MC03LWX	GIB		MV02XYK	ASW	2602	MX54PJU	MCD	
MDM371	HUC		MV08CNN	ABO		MX55BYH	IRB	
MFS444P	DPC		MV54GGE	WMC		MX55HXP	WMC	
MH03EMH	HOR		MW08DCW	MFW		MX55KOU	STAY	18350
MIB653	SAB		MW08JPW	MFW		MX55KOV	STAY	18351
MIL1053	POC		MW08LEW	MFW		MX55KOW	STAY	18352
MIL1085	SAZ		MW10JFR	MFW		MX55KPA	STAY	18353
MIL1846	MIT		MW58HGW	MFW		MX55KSU	STAY	18389
MIL1920	MIT		MW59JAV	MFW		MX55WDT	NAT	
MIL2410	MIT		MX03OCB	MUN	C5	MX55XKK	MFW	
MIL2515	MIT		MX03YCV	HVB	503	MX55ZNH	STAY	18390
MIL 2979	MIT		MX03YCW	HVB	403	MX56ACZ	FG	69187
MIL3218	MIT		MX04DSZ	JPM		MX56ADO	FG	69188
MIL3606	MIT		MX04VBL	SBJ		MX56ADU	FG	69189
MIL3725	BRW		MX04VLS	STP		MX56ADV	FG	69190
MIL4314	MIT		MX05BWO	SWSC	50149	MX56ADZ	FG	69191
MIL5016	MCS		MX05CWL	SAZ		MX56AEA	FG	69192
MIL5573	SHIC	52675	MX05EMF	DEV		MX56AEB	FG	69193
MIL5575	MLI		MX05ENC	GMC		MX56AEC	FG	69194
MIL5830	MIT		MX05FPL	HUC		MX56FRP	SREN	19047
MIL6548	SVC		MX05OTE	DEV		MX56FRV	SREN	19050
MIL6676	ESB	20	MX05WZK	SEC		MX56FSA	SREN	19052
MIL7620	ESB		MX06ABV	DEV		MX56FSG	SREN	19057

Reg	Op	No	Reg	Op	No	Reg	Op	No
MX56FWE	MUN	D3	N94OGG	FG	61434	N204LTN	DBT	
MX56NMA	IRB		N95OGG	FG	61445	N205EFS	DMC	
MX56YNU	GCB		N96OGG	FG	61456	N205LTN	LID	
MX56YOV	GCB		N97ALS	PUM		N206LTN	LID	
MX57CCJ	DMC		N97OGG	FG	61467	N207GCS	DIC	
MX57CDN	MAY	23	N98OGG	FG	61477	N208GCS	PUM	
MX57NTK	WCM		N100SAS	HAO		N208LTN	SWSC	20108
MX57UPV	GMC		N102WRC	SHIC	41362	N209LTN	SWSC	20109
MX58AAF	HOR		N102XNU	SBQ		N213LTN	STAY	20113
MX58AAJ	HOR		N103CSN	JTK		N215LTN	LID	
MX58AAN	HOR		N105WRC	HOR		N217LTN	LID	
MX58AAO	HOR		N107WRC	HOR		N221MUS	DJI	
MX58AVN	MFW		N108AVN	M&C		N224HWX	SCB	
MX59BLV	MEX		N109WRC	BBD	41369	N224THO	GSM	GS61
MX59FYM	GLC		N114DWE	MEW		N226HWX	ACN	
MXI694	SHIC	27056	N117FSM	MEW		N228MUS	GUM	102
N1GRT	FAB	20012	N119WBR	GUM	432	N245RGD	WMC	
N2CLL	NIC		N120OGG	FG	61388	N247CKY	FG	60584
N2SBL	SHB		N120WBR	D&B		N247XSA	SWSC	52287
N3CLL	NIC		N121OGG	FG	61389	N249PGD	CSA	
N3SBL	SHB		N121RJF	MCC		N250PGD	CSA	
N5BUS	WMC		N122OGG	FG	61390	N256PGD	GUM	104
N5SBL	SHB		N122WBR	GUM	433	N258PGD	GUM	105
N6SBL	SHB		N123OGG	FG	61391	N264DSF	ETN	
N7CTL	KCO		N123WBR	GUM	425	N264JUG	STP	
N7SBL	SHB		N124OGG	FG	61392	N276HSD	JTK	
N10CLL	NIC		N125OGG	FG	61393	N289RGD	SHC	
N11JCR	EAR		N125YRW	NXD	7272	N296YOA	SAP	
N14FUG	D&B		N126OGG	FG	61394	N300SAS	ANN	M3
N18OVA	ACM		N126YRW	NXD	7273	N300WCM	WCM	
N20JLS	LSK		N127OGG	FG	61395	N304AMC	SREN	32304
N22CLL	NIC		N128OGG	FG	61396	N306JBV	FG	34006
N23FWU	NXD	7419	N128VAO	SWSC	52328	N307JBV	FG	34007
N26KYS	CBC		N129OGG	FG	61397	N308AMC	CCI	
N27KYS	CBC		N130OGG	FG	61398	N308JBV	FG	34008
N30BUS	WMC		N131OGG	FG	61399	N309DSL	STAY	32907
N33CLL	NIC		N132OGG	FG	61400	N309JBV	FG	34009
N34GSX	GUM	112	N133GRE	ABK		N316VMS	STAY	20316
N38FWU	BCM		N133OGG	FG	61401	N317DAG	MEW	
N46FWU	MUN	46	N134OGG	FG	61402	N318VMS	SREN	20318
N62CSC	FED	62363	N135OGG	FG	61403	N321DAG	MEW	
N65CSC	FED	62366	N136OGG	FG	61404	N321HGK	SREN	16421
N66CSC	FED	62367	N137OGG	FG	61405	N322HGK	SREN	16422
N68CSC	FED	62400	N138OGG	FG	61406	N322VMS	STAY	20322
N69CSC	FED	62401	N142PTG	CBC		N323HGK	SREN	16423
N74ESX	AAA		N144XSA	SWSC	52284	N323VMS	SWSC	20323
N77JDS	DMC		N148XSA	SREN	52288	N324HGK	SREN	16424
N78LGD	MCD		N154XSA	BBD	52294	N324VMS	STAY	20324
N79LGD	MCD		N171WNF	GCB		N325HGK	SREN	16425
N81LGD	MCD		N178DWM	AVD		N325VMS	STAY	20325
N81PUS	CBC		N189GFR	SAQ		N326HGK	SREN	16426
N85FWU	MUN	85	N190OGG	FG	61407	N327HGK	SREN	16427
N86FHL	MFW		N191EMJ	SAF		N327VMS	BBD	20327
N87FHL	WMC		N195RGD	WMC		N328HGK	SREN	16428
N88WJC	WJC		N199OGG	FG	61408	N329HGK	SREN	16429
N89OGG	FG	61409	N200BUS	JJT		N330HGK	SREN	16430
N91OGG	FG	61410	N200CHA	CHI		N332HGK	SREN	16432
N92OGG	FG	61412	N200WCM	WCM		N334HGK	SREN	16434
N93HSJ	SMK		N202WSB	GCB		N338HGK	SREN	16438
N93OGG	FG	61423	N203LTN	DBT		N339HGK	SREN	16439

N340HGK	SREN	16440	N500TCC	FED	62268	N677GUM	ASW	1608
N343KKH	PUM		N501AWB	TEL		N681GUM	ASW	1603
N345CJA	FG	48045	N501KCD	GUM	413	N683GUM	ASW	1609
N345KKH	SKY		N502KCD	GUM	414	N685GUM	ASW	1610
N345MPN	STAY	16345	N503KCD	GUM	415	N686GUM	ASW	1614
N345OBC	WCG		N504LUA	PWW		N687GUM	ASW	1615
N346HGK	SREN	16446	N506KCD	GUM	417	N688GUM	ASW	1619
N347WPT	SMK		N511BJA	AVD		N691GUM	ASW	1620
N348EHJ	JTK		N511KCD	GUM	418	N700CHA	CHI	
N350HGK	SREN	16450	N513KCD	GUM	419	N702FLN	HCC	
N350VSO	WMC		N516KCD	GUM	420	N708GUM	ASW	1786
N352WOH	NXD	1352	N518KCD	GUM	422	N709GUM	ASW	1787
N354MPN	STAY	16354	N519KCD	GUM	423	N710GUM	ASW	1780
N357AVV	BBD	40157	N535VSA	FED	62282	N711GUM	ASW	1781
N358AVV	BBD	40158	N536SJF	AUS		N712GUM	ASW	1782
N359AVV	SHIC	40159	N536VSA	FED	62283	N712LTN	BBD	16712
N359MPN	SREN	16359	N538VSA	FED	62286	N713LTN	BBD	16713
N362AVV	DPG		N549NYS	RSS		N715LTN	BBD	16715
N365AVV	BBD	40165	N554SJF	MCC		N716LTN	BBD	16716
N366AVV	BBD	40166	N561SJF	SWSC	51061	N716UVR	LID	
N366WOH	NXD	1366	N562SJF	SWSC	51062	N718LTN	STAY	16718
N367AVV	BBD	40167	N582XSA	BBD	52312	N720LTN	SWSC	16720
N369AVV	BBD	40169	N583XSA	BBD	52313	N724LTN	STAY	16724
N370AVV	BBD	40170	N584XSA	SHIC	52314	N725LTN	SWSC	16725
N371AVV	BBD	40171	N590GBW	SHB		N726LTN	SWSC	16726
N371JGS	SAF		N591GBW	GLC		N727LTN	SWSC	16727
N380PNY	DPG		N600CHA	CHI		N728HSX	DEV	
N400CHA	CHI		N603VSS	WCM		N731RGD	MCO	3019
N400WCM	OAD		N604VSS	WRH		N732RGD	MCO	3021
N401GSX	WCM		N608OGE	MCM		N735RDD	BBD	40735
N401LTL	SREN	59621	N611VSS	SWSC	40611	N737LTN	SREN	16737
N406ENW	FED	62299	N611XJM	FG	40947	N741CKY	FED	60578
N406SPC	HTR		N612APU	FED	20112	N742CKY	FED	60579
N407ENW	FED	62295	N616APU	FED	20116	N743CKY	FG	60580
N407SPC	HTR		N616DWY	SLA		N744CKY	FED	60581
N408ENW	FED	62296	N620USS	STAY	52309	N744LUS	DIC	
N409ENW	FED	62381	N621VSS	SWSC	40621	N745CKY	FG	60582
N409MWO	HOU		N622VSS	KEY		N745LUS	HUC	
N409SPC	HTR		N624VSS	SWSC	40624	N746CKY	FED	60583
N410ENW	FED	62382	N626VSS	SWSC	40626	N746YVR	DIC	
N411ENW	FED	62298	N626XJM	FED	40910	N748CKY	FED	60585
N416CBU	AVD		N627RGD	SMI		N749CKY	FG	60586
N431GBV	CBC		N627VSS	SWSC	40627	N750CKY	FG	60587
N436WKL	SAH		N628VSS	SWSC	40628	N751CKY	FED	60588
N439GHG	CBC		N629VSS	WCM		N752CKY	FED	60589
N440GHG	CBC		N630VSS	SWSC	40630	N752LUS	GUM	101
N447XVA	STAY	52297	N631CDY	CBC		N753CKY	FED	60590
N465AAO	SHC		N632VSS	SWSC	40632	N753LSU	STK	
N465RVK	DPG		N633VSS	SWSC	40633	N754CKY	FED	60591
N468RVK	PUM		N635VSS	SWSC	40635	N754OAP	IRB	
N470PYS	MDO		N636VSS	BBD	40636	N755CKU	BBD	40755
N470SPA	WCG		N637VSS	BBD	40637	N755CKY	FED	60592
N472RVK	CCI		N639LGG	MCD		N756CKU	BBD	40756
N473MUS	CBC		N640LGG	MCD		N756CKY	FG	60593
N474PYS	MCD		N640VSS	BBD	40640	N757CKY	FG	60594
N479VPA	HTR		N642VSS	CCI		N758CKY	FG	60595
N491FDT	RTT		N660WAW	SHI		N759CKY	FED	60596
N495RVK	DPG		N662KCW	MUN	662	N764CKY	FED	60601
N496RVK	STAY	40496	N672GUM	ASW	1606	N768EWG	STP	
N500CHA	CHI		N675GUM	ASW	1607	N779OGA	RTT	

N781PEC	DEV		N932NAP	CCI		N966LSU	FG	61452
N791NYS	TEL		N933LSU	FG	61416	N967LSU	FG	61453
N792SJU	AAA		N934LSU	FG	61417	N968LSU	FG	61454
N796PDS	DBT		N935LSU	FG	61418	N969LSU	FG	61455
N798FSD	DIC		N936LSU	FG	61419	N970LSU	FG	61457
N798PDS	SLA		N937LSU	FG	61420	N971LSU	FG	61458
N799FSD	PUM		N938LSU	FG	61421	N971MGG	STK	
N779PDS	GUM	127	N939LSU	FG	61422	N972LSU	FG	61459
N800CHA	CHI		N940LSU	FG	61424	N973LSU	FG	61460
N800SAS	MCC		N941LSU	FG	61425	N974LSU	FG	61461
N801FSD	PUM		N942LSU	FG	61426	N975LSU	FG	61462
N801RGD	SMI		N943LSU	FG	61427	N976LSU	FG	61463
N802PDS	GUM	120	N943MGG	GUM	124	N977LSU	FG	61464
N804BKN	ASW	2741	N944LSU	FG	61428	N978LSU	FG	61465
N810PDS	RTT		N944SOS	FG	31433	N979LSU	FG	61466
N812KHW	DIC		N945SOS	FG	31434	N980LSU	FG	61468
N835XRP	HOU		N946LSU	FG	61430	N981LSU	FG	61469
N838LGA	MCD		N946SOS	FG	31435	N982LSU	FG	61470
N839LGA	MCD		N947LSU	FG	61431	N983LSU	FG	61471
N840LGA	MCD		N947SOS	FG	31436	N984LSU	FG	61472
N841LGA	MCD		N948LSU	FG	61432	N985LSU	FG	61473
N842LGA	CSA		N948NAP	SLA		N986LSU	FG	61474
N843LGA	MCD		N948SOS	FG	31437	N987LSU	FG	61475
N849VHH	SREN	16849	N949LSU	FG	61433	N988LSU	FG	61476
N850VHH	SREN	16850	N949MGG	DIC		N990FNK	GUM	111
N851VHH	SREN	16851	N949SOS	FG	31438	N991FNK	GUM	114
N852VHH	SWSC	16852	N950LSU	FG	61435	N992KUS	GIB	
N853VHH	SWSC	16853	N950MGG	DIC		N993THO	DEV	
N854VHH	SWSC	16854	N950SOS	FG	31439	N996CCC	SKY	
N855VHH	SREN	16855	N951LSU	FG	61436	N996XNT	MCL	
N856VHH	SREN	16856	N951SOS	FG	31440	N997CCC	SKY	
N857VHH	SREN	16857	N952LSU	FG	61437	NA04ZJU	HEB	
N858VHH	SREN	16858	N952SOS	FG	31441	NBZ1357	LID	
N859VHH	SWSC	16859	N953LSU	FG	61438	NC04NHG	DEV	
N860VHH	SREN	16860	N953SOS	FG	31442	NC56AYM	AAA	
N861VHH	STAY	16861	N954LSU	FG	61439	NCC745	SBJ	
N862VHH	STAY	16862	N954SOS	FG	31443	NCH868	PWW	
N863VHH	SWSC	16863	N955LSU	FG	61440	ND53YFV	PHO	
N864VHH	SWSC	16864	N955SOS	FG	31444	NDL869	MEW	
N865VHH	SWSC	16865	N956LSU	FG	61441	NDZ3024	WCM	
N866VHH	SWSC	16866	N956SOS	FG	31445	NDZ3026	WCM	
N868MSU	CNV		N957LSU	FG	61442	NDZ3146	PUM	
N869MSU	CNV		N957NAP	DPG		NDZ7927	CBC	
N881AVV	DIC		N957SOS	FG	31446	NDZ7928	CBC	
N887HSX	SREN	27095	N958LSU	FG	61443	NDZ7930	CBC	
N901PFC	WCM		N958SOS	FG	31447	NGH456	PWW	
N905AAS	MCO	4007	N959LSU	FG	61444	NHG550	EAR	
N908NAP	TRD		N959NAP	DPG		NHG551	EAR	
N920RGD	MCO	3030	N959SOS	FG	31448	NIB2796	ESB	
N923NAP	TRD		N960LSU	FG	61446	NIB4138	BBD	16200
N926NAP	BBD	40926	N960SOS	FG	31449	NIB5233	SREN	11093
N928NAP	BBD	40928	N961LSU	FG	61447	NIB6535	ESB	
N929NAP	BBD	40929	N961SOS	FG	31450	NIL1235	TEL	
N930LSU	FG	61413	N962LSU	FG	61448	NIL2266	PWW	
N930NAP	CCI		N963ESD	SAZ		NIL3296	SBQ	
N931LSU	FG	61414	N963LSU	FG	61449	NIL3416	MLI	
N931NAP	CCI		N964LSU	FG	61450	NIL3792	MCR	
N931RGD	MCO	3031	N965LHS	MCD		NIL4979	TEL	
N932LSU	FG	61415	N965LSU	FG	61451	NIL5906	ROR	

NIL7707	ESB		OIL5265	MDO		P106MFS	FG	61478
NIL8646	MCO	4004	OIL5315	DEV		P106OLX	CBC	
NIW252	VIC		OIW7025	SWSC	25475	P107MFS	FG	61479
NIW525	VIC		OJI5506	BRW		P107OLX	CBC	
NIW1422	VIC		OJI7161	LID		P108MFS	FG	61480
NIW1951	VIC		OJU106	PWW		P109MFS	FG	61481
NIW2531	VIC		OLS539P	WLC		P113YSH	FG	61482
NIW6712	VIC		ONR314	PWW		P118XCN	BBD	20118
NIW8920	AAM		OO03HCC	HCC		P119RSF	TEL	
NJ07LRV	HEB		OO04HCC	HCC		P119XCN	SWSC	20119
NJ08BHW	ORD		OO05EVE	EVE		P122KSL	NXD	7122
NK02EXB	DEV		OO5HCC	HCC		P123HCH	SAQ	
NK53KGJ	STP		OO06EVE	EVE		P124KSL	NXD	7124
NK55EHT	SCM		OO06HCC	HCC		P125HCH	PTW	
NL58ZZK	ORD		OO07HCC	HCC		P126HCH	PTW	4
NM02AUJ	ABO		OO08HCC	HCC		P127FRS	NIC	
NMY634E	LOT	20	OO56EVE	EVE		P130KSL	NXD	7130
NNF922	HCC		OOB32X	APE		P131KSL	NXD	7131
NOC598R	HCO		ORJ393W	KOA		P132KSL	NXD	7132
NSK919	HCC		ORJ395W	JJT		P133KSL	NXD	7133
NSK920	HCC		ORJ396W	JJT		P134KSL	NXD	7134
NSK921	HCC		OSJ614R	WLC		P135KSL	NXD	7135
NSU132	BBD	22265	OSJ631R	WLC		P136KSL	NXD	7136
NSU133	STAY	52655	OSN857Y	MCD		P137KSL	NXD	7137
NSV224	STU		OSU638	HUC		P138KSL	NXD	7138
NSV621	NXD	7259	OTC950	CHE		P139KSL	NXD	7139
NSV622	NXD	7260	OUI3813	HEB		P140KSL	NXD	7140
NT05MXL	WMC		OUJ969	PWW		P141KSL	NXD	7141
NTC640M	ESB	9	OUR610	PWW		P148ASA	SWSC	52348
NTF9	TED		OWW618	SCK		P149ASA	SWSC	52349
NU03VWA	GMC		OXI413	SHIC	52530	P150ASA	SWSC	52350
NUI1247	MCO	3023	OXI459	SHIC	52531	P150HBG	DPG	
NUI1582	FIT		P1MCT	MCM		P151LSC	SLA	
NUI2416	HEB		P2KLT	ABK		P152ASA	BBD	52352
NUI2420	CHE		P2UVG	FG	40724	P152LSC	KEY	
NUI2572	HEB		P3KON	A&B		P153VSU	ROR	
NUI4223	MLC		P6KET	A&B		P154ASA	SWSC	52354
NUI6046	GIC		P8OVA	SAZ		P156ASA	SWSC	52356
NV56WVH	DEV		P9MCT	MCM		P157XNW	M&C	
NX04MCL	ACM		P10MCT	MCM		P159ASA	SWSC	52359
NXI4616	LID		P11JDT	JDT		P160ASA	SWSC	52360
NXI6842	BLS		P11RVN	IRB		P161RWR	BUT	
NXI9004	MDO		P17LJE	HAO		P171DMS	FED	62369
NXX451	SREN	27096	P17PHO	PHO		P172DMS	FED	62370
OA02RKA	GUM	201	P20GSG	CCG		P173DMS	FED	62371
OA05RKA	SWSC	47246	P20JLS	ABK		P179FNF	DIC	
OAZ1372	MCL		P20WJC	WJC	XCV20	P180FNF	DIC	
OAZ9372	SLA		P22GSG	CCG		P180GND	AVD	
OBA695	BRW		P28KWA	TEL		P188AJU	SAP	
OBX51	APE		P30BLU	CBC		P192TGD	FED	30740
OBZ2241	STU		P40BLU	CBC		P193TGD	FED	30741
OFA990	BBD	52242	P50BLU	CBC		P194TGD	FED	30742
OFS676Y	MLI		P55HMC	ACN		P195TGD	FED	30743
OFS686Y	MAT		P66BUS	IRB		P196TGD	FED	30744
OFS687Y	MAT		P73MRE	LID		P197TGD	FED	30745
OFS700Y	JJT		P74HMC	SCP		P198TGD	FED	30746
OFV21X	MCC		P80BMC	D&B		P199TGD	FED	30747
OIB3519	SPA		P87BPL	WCM		P200WCM	WCM	
OIL2946	HCO		P100WCM	WCM		P201NSC	FED	40887
OIL5079	MCL		P105OLX	CBC		P201TGD	FED	30748

Reg	Op	No	Reg	Op	No	Reg	Op	No
P202NSC	FED	40888	P253PSX	ARC		P451FVV	SCK	
P202TGD	FED	30749	P254PSX	ARC		P451LSR	MFW	
P203NSC	FED	40912	P255ASA	SWSC	52355	P454MFS	HVB	
P203OLX	CBC		P258PS	IRB		P459LSR	MFW	
P203TGD	FED	30750	P264PSX	LOT	264	P477TGA	SKY	
P204NSC	FED	40913	P271VPN	SREN	16641	P478FKJ	LID	
P204OLX	CBC		P279VUS	MDO		P478TGA	RTT	
P204RUM	OAD		P281PSX	WCM		P479MBY	CSS	
P204TGD	FED	30751	P285PSX	LOT	285	P480MBY	CSS	
P205NSC	FED	40914	P288VPN	SREN	16288	P481MBY	CSS	
P205OLX	CBC		P289VPN	SWSC	16289	P483CAL	CSA	
P206GSR	JPM		P290VPN	SWSC	16290	P484GEF	PHO	
P206NSC	FED	40915	P291MLD	CBC		P485MBY	CSS	
P206OLX	CBC		P294MLD	CSA		P486TGA	HOR	
P207NSC	FED	40916	P295MLD	CBC		P487MBY	CSS	
P207OLX	CBC		P301MLD	CBC		P488CAL	CSA	
P208NSC	FED	40917	P301VWR	HUC		P491BRS	SREN	31491
P208OLX	CBC		P314CVE	DEV		P491CVO	IRB	
P209NSC	FED	40918	P318MLD	CBC		P491MBY	CSS	
P210LKJ	ASW	1466	P322VWR	ACM		P492FRR	IRB	
P210NSC	FED	40919	P331LCC	SAM		P492LSR	MFW	
P210OLX	CBC		P334TGS	SAF		P493BRS	SREN	31493
P211LKJ	ASW	1467	P341ASO	BBD	40041	P494BRS	SREN	31494
P211NSC	FED	40920	P343ASO	BBD	40043	P495BRS	SREN	31495
P211OLX	CBC		P344ASO	SREN	40044	P496BRS	SREN	31496
P212LKJ	ASW	1468	P349ASO	PUM		P497BRS	STAY	31497
P212NSC	FED	40921	P351ASO	SHIC	40051	P498BRS	SREN	31498
P213NSC	FED	40922	P364JJU	DEV		P499BRS	SREN	31499
P213RWR	MUN	213	P366DSA	MCO	2041	P503XSH	FED	62291
P214NSC	FED	40889	P367DSA	MCO	2042	P504XSH	FED	62292
P215JKL	SAF		P367UUG	STAY	21020	P506XSH	FED	62294
P218LKK	SAF		P368DSA	MCO	2043	P511RYM	CBC	
P218YSH	FED	40890	P368UUG	STAY	21021	P519TYS	FG	61489
P222GSM	BRW		P369DSA	MCO	2044	P520RDS	DJI	
P224EJW	SLA		P370DSA	SWSC	31370	P520TYS	FG	61490
P226SGB	CBC		P371DSA	MCO	2045	P521EJW	NXD	7059
P227AAP	MCO	2023	P372DSA	MCO	2046	P521TYS	FG	61491
P227EJW	AVD		P372XGG	VIC		P522EJW	NXD	7060
P228EJW	AVD		P373DSA	MCO	2040	P522TYS	FG	61492
P230AAP	MCO		P374DSA	MCO	2047	P523EJW	NXD	7061
P231AAP	MCO	2034	P375DSA	MCO	2048	P523TYS	FG	61493
P231XKS	SCM		P377DSA	SWSC	31377	P524TYS	FG	61494
P232EJW	SLA		P378DSA	MCO	2049	P525TYS	FG	61495
P233EJW	STP		P379DSA	SWSC	31379	P526TYS	FG	61496
P234EJW	STP		P380DSA	MCO	2050	P526UGA	GUM	100
P238AAP	MCO	2035	P382DSA	MCO	2051	P527EJW	NXD	7062
P238EJW	JPM		P384DSA	MCO	2052	P527TYS	FG	61497
P239AAP	MCO	2036	P393NSC	BLY		P527UGA	GUM	121
P241AAP	MCO	2033	P394LPS	SHIC	32394	P528TYS	FG	61498
P242AAP	MCO	2025	P395BRS	SHIC	32395	P528UGA	CBC	
P242UCW	FG	34042	P408RGG	LIP		P529TYS	FG	61499
P243AAP	MCO		P413TNG	DEV		P529UGA	CBC	
P245AAP	MCO	2027	P420MEH	FAB	50077	P530PNE	AVD	
P246AAP	MCO	2028	P430KSX	WCM		P530TYS	FG	61500
P247UCW	FED	34047	P432YSH	FED	61052	P531EJW	NXD	7063
P248AAP	MCO	2029	P433KSX	LOT	433	P531TYS	FG	61501
P248UCW	FED	34048	P433YSH	FED	61053	P532ESA	SWSC	20532
P249AAP	MCO	2030	P444GSM	BRW		P532RGG	SAY	
P250AAP	MCO		P444TCC	SOK		P532TYS	FG	61502

Reg	Op	Fleet		Reg	Op	Fleet		Reg	Op	Fleet
P833KES	ASW	1443		PAZ6344	ESB			PSU315	FED	90147
P834KES	ASW	1444		PCZ2674	GSM	GS58		PSU317	FED	90146
P835KES	ASW	1445		PDX782	KIN			PSU374	STAY	21124
P835YUM	FED	40701		PDZ5772	BCD			PSU375	STAY	21125
P836KES	ASW	1446		PDZ6277	BEK			PSU376	STAY	21126
P837KES	ASW	1447		PE55WML	WHI			PSU610	ECL	
P838KES	ASW	1448		PE57KFU	ORD			PSU611	ECL	
P839KES	ASW	1449		PEZ4338	CBC			PSU612	ECL	
P840HRM	MCD			PEZ4562	CBC			PSU613	ECL	
P840KES	ASW	1450		PEZ4563	CBC			PSU614	ECL	
P860GND	BBD	20860		PFG362	MOA			PSU615	ECL	
P861GND	BBD	20861		PGD216F	MEW			PSU616	ECL	
P862GND	BBD	20862		PGD220F	MEW			PSU617	ECL	
P863GND	BBD	20863		PH54PCH	DPC			PSU618	ECL	
P864GND	BBD	20864		PIB277	SVC			PSU619	ECL	
P865GND	BBD	20865		PIB9211	SREN	52667		PSU620	ECL	
P866GND	BBD	20866		PIJ601	SREN	59603		PSU621	ECL	
P868GND	BBD	20868		PIJ2799	TEL			PSU623	FIT	
P871AFV	SMI			PIL2167	MDO			PSU627	FAB	20016
P875MNE	BBD	20875		PIL2172	SIC			PSU628	FAB	20017
P875YKS	FED	62402		PIL3750	DPG			PSU629	FAB	20018
P876YKS	FED	62403		PIL3752	DPG			PSU698	ECL	705
P877YKS	FED	62404		PIL6351	CCG			PSU755	KIN	
P878MNE	BBD	20878		PIL7835	AYR			PSU954	SREN	52047
P878YKS	FED	62405		PIL9740	AYR			PSV223	SMP	
P879MNE	BBD	20879		PIW2633	DEV			PUF249M	MAY	
P879YKS	FED	62373		PJI5631	LID			PV55GNX	LID	
P881MNE	BBD	20881		PJI7756	DJI			PVY569	SBG	
P889TCV	FG	40782		PJY534	LID			PWV693	JJT	
P890TCV	FG	40783		PK02PUO	MFW			PX07BEY	ALA	AT100
P893MNE	BBD	20893		PK02WVV	GMC			PX07BFA	ALA	AT101
P894RSF	HOR			PKZ5753	SBG			PX07BFE	ALA	AT102
P896EEC	SAA			PN03UGA	ROR			PX07GXT	HUC	
P906SMR	BBD	33906		PN04NPC	SLA			PX09APO	MEW	
P907SMR	BBD	33907		PN06KME	WHI			PX09APU	MEW	
P908SMR	BBD	33908		PN06KSO	AAA			PX53ZLY	JPM	
P909SMR	BBD	33909		PN06TTE	AAA			PX56NNC	LID	
P913PWW	ASW	1783		PN06TVV	AAA			PXI5517	DOT	
P914PGF	VIC			PN08CNO	WHI			PXI5523	DOT	
P914PWW	ASW	1784		PN09CWO	AAA			PY02KTO	SWSC	33078
P915PWW	ASW	1785		PN10FNP	DOI			PY02KTP	SWSC	33079
P915XUG	GCB			PN57CVA	CHI			PY52PHN	MFW	
P931YSB	CBC			PNB800W	MFW			PYJ136	NXD	7245
P937YSB	CBC			PNR723	AAM			R3JNK	SCD	
P939YSB	RTT			PO51OLU	SBZ			R8OVA	SAZ	
P962RUL	ASW	1401		PO51OLV	RSS			R11JDT	JDT	
P963RUL	ASW	1402		PO54MHK	ROR			R15SCC	ROW	
P964RUL	ASW	1403		PO56PCZ	MCO			R16DAB	ORD	
P965RUL	ASW	1404		PO58HRF	AAA			R17GCT	WCG	
P966RUL	ASW	1405		PO60HZA	AAA			R18BLU	D&B	
P967RUL	ASW	1406		POG477Y	MCO	3024		R20JLS	LSK	
P968RUL	ASW	1407		POG568Y	LID			R24GNW	OAD	
P974WOS	SPA			POG601Y	MCO			R27HNS	PSK	
P976UBV	BBD	51076		PP04BUS	IRB			R27VSM	FG	
P984JBC	IRB			PP06BUS	IRB			R28VSM	SMI	
P994VOS	HQD			PR06PET	MFW			R35WDA	DIC	
P995RHS	MCM			PR56BEC	SIC			R43ALS	WMC	
PA51LEY	RTT			PSD281H	LID			R49SCH	CSA	
PAZ2535	SPA			PSU314	FAB	20036		R56EDW	BDC	

Registration Number Index

R59DJS	DEV		R121RLY	CBC		R155HHK	SREN	16155
R73FCA	SPA		R121XNO	BBD	16121	R155RSN	NXD	7155
R74GNW	OAD		R122GSF	FG	61534	R156GSF	FED	62360
R74VVP	JPM		R122VPU	SHIC	34022	R156HHK	SREN	16156
R84NNJ	SAF		R123GSF	FG	61535	R156RSN	NXD	7156
R84SEF	SWSC	52464	R124VPU	SWSC	34024	R156UAL	SAF	
R84XNO	SREN	16084	R125VPU	SWSC	34025	R157GSF	FED	62361
R85GNW	NXD	7085	R126VPU	SWSC	34026	R157HHK	SREN	16157
R85SEF	SWSC	52465	R127VPU	SWSC	34027	R157RSN	NXD	7157
R89EOL	BBD	42222	R128GSF	FG	61537	R157VPU	SREN	16057
R91EOL	SREN	42223	R128KGD	SBZ		R158GSF	FG	61543
R91GTM	NXD	7269	R128VPU	BBD	34028	R158HHK	SREN	16158
R92XNO	SREN	16092	R129VPU	BBD	34029	R158RSN	NXD	7158
R98XNO	SREN	16098	R130GSF	FG	61539	R159GSF	FG	61544
R100DJD	AAM		R131GSF	FG	61540	R159HHK	SREN	16159
R100WCM	WCM		R132EVX	SREN	16132	R159RSN	NXD	7159
R101PWR	SCD		R132LNR	JMC		R160GSF	FG	61545
R101VLX	PTW		R133GSF	FG	65533	R160HHK	SREN	16160
R101XNO	SREN	16101	R135GSF	FG	65535	R160RSN	NXD	7160
R102HUA	MEW		R136GSF	FG	65536	R160TCH	DEV	
R103LSO	SWSC	52425	R137LNR	HAO		R160VPU	SREN	16060
R103NTA	AVD		R138EVX	SREN	16138	R161GSF	FG	61546
R104LSO	SREN	52426	R139EHS	FG	31485	R161HHK	SREN	16161
R104VLX	PTW	16	R140EHS	FED	31670	R161RSN	NXD	7161
R104XNO	SREN	16104	R140EVX	SREN	16140	R162GSF	FG	61547
R105LSO	SWSC	52427	R141EHS	FED	31671	R162TSR	NXD	7162
R105NTA	AVD		R141EVX	SREN	16141	R163GNW	MUN	163
R107NTA	CSA		R142EHS	FED	31672	R163GSF	FG	61548
R107XNO	SREN	16107	R142RSN	NXD	7142	R163HHK	SREN	16163
R108XNO	SREN	16108	R143EHS	FG	31486	R163TSR	NXD	7163
R110GSF	FG	61524	R143RSN	NXD	7143	R164GSF	FG	61549
R110NTA	CSA		R144EHS	FG	31487	R165GSF	FG	61550
R110VLX	PTW	13	R144EVX	SREN	16144	R165HHK	SREN	16165
R111WJC	WJC		R144RSN	NXD	7144	R165VPU	SREN	16065
R112GSF	FG	61525	R145EHS	FG	31488	R166HHK	SREN	16166
R112OPS	BBD	52422	R145RSN	NXD	7145	R167GSF	FG	61552
R112VLX	PTW		R146EHS	FG	31489	R167VPU	SREN	16067
R112XNO	BBD	16112	R146RSN	NXD	7146	R168VPU	SWSC	16068
R113RLY	CBC		R147EHS	FG	31490	R170HHK	SREN	16170
R114GSF	FG	61526	R147RSN	NXD	7147	R171HHK	SREN	16171
R114NTA	AVD		R148EHS	FG	31491	R172GSX	FG	61557
R114VLY	CBC		R148RSN	NXD	7148	R172HHK	SREN	16172
R114XNO	SREN	16114	R149EHS	FG	31492	R173HHK	SREN	16173
R115RLY	CBC		R149RSN	NXD	7149	R173VPU	SREN	16073
R115XNO	SREN	16115	R150EHS	FG	31493	R174DNH	SREN	52474
R116NTA	AVD		R150GSF	FG	65530	R174GSX	FG	61234
R116OPS	SWSC	52416	R150HHK	SREN	16150	R174VPU	SWSC	16074
R116RLY	CBC		R150RSN	NXD	7150	R175DNH	SWSC	52475
R116XNO	BBD	16116	R151EHS	FG	31494	R175GSX	FG	61158
R117XNO	BBD	16117	R151RSN	NXD	7151	R175VPU	SREN	16075
R118OPS	SWSC	52418	R152EHS	FG	31200	R176DNH	SREN	52476
R118RLY	CBC		R152HHK	SREN	16152	R176HHK	SREN	16176
R118XNO	SHIC	16118	R152RSN	NXD	7152	R176VLA	CBC	
R119OPS	SWSC	52419	R153EHS	FG	31495	R177DNH	SREN	52477
R119RLY	CBC		R153RSN	NXD	7153	R177HHK	SREN	16177
R119XNO	SHIC	16119	R154GSF	FED	62359	R177VPU	SREN	16077
R120GSF	FG	61532	R154HHK	SREN	16154	R178DNH	SREN	52478
R120OPS	SREN	52420	R154RSN	NXD	7154	R178HHK	SREN	16178
R120RLY	CBC		R154VPU	SREN	16054	R178VLA	CBC	
R120XNO	SHIC	16120	R155GSF	FED	62398	R179DNH	SREN	52479

Reg	Code	Num		Reg	Code	Num		Reg	Code	Num
R518VSE	SWSC	20518		R651HYG	FED	30831		R898WOC	SAJ	
R519BMS	FED	62306		R651VSE	STAY	20151		R900WCM	WCM	
R519VSE	SWSC	20519		R652HYG	FED	30832		R901WEC	DEV	
R521BMS	FED	62308		R652VSE	SWSC	20152		R909YBA	FIT	
R521VSE	SWSC	20521		R653HYG	FED	30833		R913GFF	ROW	
R522BMS	FED	62384		R653VSE	BBD	20153		R916XVM	STAY	20916
R522VSE	SWSC	20522		R654DUS	FG	31496		R917HTW	BNA	B126
R524BMS	FED	62310		R654VSE	STAY	20154		R920XVM	SHIC	20920
R524VSE	SWSC	20524		R655DUS	FG	31497		R922XVM	SHIC	20922
R526TWR	STAY	21127		R656DUS	FG	31498		R925XVM	SHIC	20925
R526VSE	SWSC	20526		R657DUS	FG	31499		R926XVM	SHIC	20926
R527TWR	STAY	21128		R658DUS	FG	31500		R927XVM	STAY	20927
R544ALS	FED	62301		R659DUS	FG	31501		R929XVM	SHIC	20929
R549MSS	MDO			R661DUS	FG	31503		R932XVM	BBD	20932
R551UOT	GCB			R662DUS	FG	31504		R934AMB	SAQ	
R557UOT	GCB			R663DUS	FG	31505		R935XVM	BBD	20935
R582YMS	FED	62393		R664DUS	FG	40828		R936FOO	BBD	34036
R583YMS	FED	62394		R665DUS	FG	40829		R937XVM	BBD	20937
R584YMS	FED	62395		R667DUS	FG	40830		R939FOO	BBD	34039
R585HDS	JMC			R668DUS	FG	40831		R939XVM	SHIC	20939
R585YMS	FED	62396		R669DUS	FG	40832		R940FOO	BBD	34040
R587BMS	FED	62350		R671DUS	FG	40834		R940UWE	KCO	
R588BMS	FED	62351		R676DUS	FG	40839		R941XVM	BBD	20941
R589BMS	FED	62352		R677DUS	FG	40840		R946XVM	SHIC	20946
R590BMS	FED	62353		R682OYS	CBC			R947XVM	SHIC	20947
R591BMS	FED	62354		R684MEW	SCP			R948XVM	BBD	20948
R591USJ	BCM			R685WRN	M&C			R951RCH	TEL	
R595LSO	SWSC	20595		R687TTS	MFW			R951XVM	BBD	20951
R596LSO	SWSC	20596		R688FYG	JPM			R953XVM	BBD	20953
R598EAB	MCC			R692OYS	CBC			R954XVM	BBD	20954
R614GFS	SHIC	33414		R694OYS	CBC			R955FYS	DIC	
R626ULX	M&C			R703MHN	CBC			R955TSL	STAY	16809
R629VYB	DEV			R707MHN	CBC			R956TSL	STAY	16810
R631DUS	FG	40814		R710YWC	BBD	32360		R957TSL	STAY	16811
R632DUS	FG	40815		R711YWC	BBD	32361		R957XVM	SHIC	20957
R632EYS	SMP			R712YWC	BBD	32362		R958FYS	MFW	
R633DUS	FG	40816		R715YWC	BBD	32365		R958TSL	STAY	16812
R634DUS	FG	40817		R716TRV	JMC			R958XVM	SHIC	20958
R636DUS	FG	40818		R716YWC	BBD	32366		R964XVM	STAY	20964
R636RSE	BBD	52456		R718YWC	BBD	32368		R967MGB	HCO	
R637DUS	FG	40819		R730EGD	PTW	9		R971MGB	STP	
R638DUS	FG	40820		R733EGD	KEY			R971XBC	SAJ	
R640RSE	SREN	52460		R757DYS	FG	40842		R984SSA	MCO	2014
R641LSO	BBD	20141		R776MGB	LIP			R985EWU	MCO	2022
R642LSO	BBD	20142		R777GSM	BNA	B114		R985SSA	MCO	2016
R643LSO	BBD	20143		R797OYS	CBC			R986SSA	MCO	2017
R644LSO	BBD	20144		R801JFS	SAD			R988XVM	BBD	20988
R645LSO	SWSC	20145		R801KCU	KCO			R989XVM	BBD	20989
R646HYG	FED	30826		R803JFS	SAD			R990EWU	BEK	
R646LSO	SWSC	20146		R804YJC	AVD			R990XVM	BBD	20990
R647HYG	FED	30827		R818GSF	SCM			R991EWU	NXD	7211
R647LSO	SREN	20147		R821HDS	SCM			R991XVM	BBD	20991
R648HYG	FED	30828		R846FDM	WCM			R992XVM	BBD	20992
R648LSO	STAY	20148		R849CJS	BBD	27098		R993SSA	MCO	2015
R649HYG	FED	30829		R849HSC	BLY			R993XVM	BBD	20993
R649LSO	SREN	20149		R853SDT	HQL			R996XVM	BBD	20996
R649YCR	SCB			R878FGE	DPG			RAR777W	MEW	
R650HYG	FED	30830		R886YOM	POC			RAX19Y	A&B	
R650LSO	STAY	20150		R888GSM	HAO			RCS382	SWSC	19982
R650VNN	HLO			R888WMC	WMC			RDZ4286	GLC	

RE10PFG	RAB	23	S33SPA	SPA		S284AOX	JPM	
RG02NMN	WHI		S55ECH	MLI		S285AOX	JPM	
RG03BSY	ALA	AT118	S104WHK	SREN	34104	S286AOX	JPM	
RG03BVK	ALA	AT116	S106CSG	FG	61291	S287NRB	MCO	1010
RG03BVW	ALA	AT117	S107CSG	FG	61292	S288NRB	MCO	1011
RG1173	FAB	62121	S108CSG	FG	61293	S300WCM	WCM	
RIB2901	JDT		S109CSG	FG	61294	S306CCD	SREN	16306
RIB6563	BDC		S109TRJ	BBD	22109	S306EWU	FED	50275
RIB7742	KIN		S110CSG	FG	61295	S306KNW	D&B	
RIB8036	LID		S110TNB	FED	60163	S307CCD	SREN	16307
RIB8847	SBQ		S110TRJ	BBD	22110	S308CCD	SWSC	16308
RIB8848	SBQ		S112TNB	FED	60165	S309CCD	SWSC	16309
RIJ774	MOB		S112TRJ	BBD	22112	S310CCD	SWSC	16310
RIL2576	DJI		S113CSG	FG	61298	S310KNW	SHB	
RIL3690	DJI		S113TNB	FED	60166	S311CCD	SWSC	16311
RIL3693	DJI		S114CSG	FG	61299	S312CCD	SREN	16312
RIL3998	AYR		S114TNB	FED	60167	S313CCD	SREN	16313
RJI2162	PHO		S115CSG	FG	61300	S319CCD	SREN	16319
RJI2719	FIT		S115TNB	FED	60168	S320CCD	SREN	16320
RJI5715	FIT		S116CSG	FG	61017	S322CCD	SREN	16322
RJI5716	AAM		S117CSG	FG	61018	S323CCD	SREN	16323
RJI6395	JTK		S118CSG	FG	61019	S324CCD	SREN	16324
RJI8711	PHO		S119CSG	FG	61020	S332CSF	HAO	
RKZ8284	NIC		S131JSO	SAD		S343SWF	STAY	42228
RKZ8286	SMI		S132JSO	SAF		S344SWF	STAY	42229
RLS468T	WJC	T468	S133KRM	SHIC	52603	S345SWF	STAY	42230
RM03GSM	JJT		S137JSO	NIC		S346SWF	STAY	42231
RO06ART	MLC		S151JUA	FIT		S349SWF	STAY	42234
RO10ZRV	RAB	21	S152JUA	FIT		S353CSF	CFT	
RO10ZRX	RAB	22	S174SVK	SHIC	52602	S356KEF	SREN	42356
ROX638Y	MEW		S200WCM	WCM		S357KEF	SREN	42357
ROX641Y	MEW		S211CSG	FG	61296	S358KEF	SREN	42358
RRS303X	HQL		S220GKS	FG	61021	S369PGB	MCR	
RRY342	HLO		S231EWU	NXD	7242	S373PGB	OAD	
RSJ812Y	MEW		S233EWU	NXD	7241	S374PGB	GIB	
RSU585	STU		S235EWU	NXD	7243	S378PGB	SCB	
RSV533	STU		S236EWU	JPM		S389JPS	SHIC	39600
RUI2184	JPM		S236KLM	FG	41236	S400EVE	EVE	
RUI2185	JPM		S237KLM	FG	41237	S400WCM	WCM	
RUI9469	JPM		S240CSF	FED	40893	S432NSB	WCG	
RUI9470	JPM		S242KLM	FG	41242	S433NSB	WCG	
RUI9480	BEK		S243CSF	FED	40895	S445OGB	APE	
RUI9481	BEK		S243KLM	FG	41243	S456LGN	HOR	
RX03HNN	APE		S244CSF	FED	40938	S457LGN	HOR	
RX06WPP	GUM	220	S244KLM	FG	41244	S458LGN	HOR	
RX06WPT	GUM		S245KLM	FG	41245	S459BWC	STAY	34059
RX06WPR	GUM	221	S246KLM	FG	41246	S460BWC	STAY	34060
S1YST	D&E		S248CSF	FED	40896	S461ATV	IRB	
S2HMC	MFW		S249CSF	FED	40897	S461BWC	BBD	34061
S4DPC	MFW		S250CSF	FED	40898	S461LGN	BCD	
S7CED	MLI		S251CSF	FED	40899	S462BWC	BBD	34062
S10MCT	MCM		S266JUG	MOA		S463BWC	SWSC	34063
S12AMC	VIC		S268NRB	PWW		S463LGN	HOR	
S13ORO	STP		S268RBC	TED		S469BWC	BBD	34069
S14AMC	VIC		S273LGA	SBP		S470BWC	BBD	34070
S20FMC	SCN		S276LGA	JPM		S471HOK	D&B	
S20JLS	LSK		S279AOX	JPM		S472JSE	SHIC	33472
S21SPA	SPA		S282AOX	NXD	7201	S473JSE	SHIC	33473
S22SPA	SPA		S282NRB	PTW		S474JSE	SHIC	33474
S33AAM	AAM					S476BWC	BBD	34076

S476JSE	SHIC	33476	S699BFS	FG	61585	SA02BZJ	FG	61592
S478JSE	BBD	33478	S701BFS	FG	61586	SA02BZK	FG	61593
S479JSE	BBD	33479	S742JRX	NXD	7088	SA02BZL	FG	61594
S482BWC	SREN	34082	S743JRX	NXD	7089	SA02BZM	FG	61595
S484BWC	SREN	34084	S751SCJ	SHIC	42047	SA02BZN	FG	61596
S503BFS	HOR		S775RNE	CBC		SA01BZP	PTW	5
S520UMS	FED	62383	S776RNE	STU		SA02CCN	LID	
S523UMS	FED	62309	S778RNE	CBC		SA02CCV	GUM	226
S524LGA	ABO		S808BTT	SHIC	52638	SA02CDF	GUM	227
S525UMS	FED	62311	S860OGB	ASW	1456	SA02CJO	OAD	
S526UMS	FED	62312	S860VAT	SHIC	52510	SA02ECW	LID	
S550JSE	FG	61567	S861OGB	ASW	1457	SA02EDC	HOR	
S551JSE	FG	61568	S862OGB	ASW	1458	SA02EDF	LID	
S552JSE	FG	61569	S863OGB	ASW	1459	SA02EDO	LID	
S553JSE	FG	61570	S864OGB	ASW	1460	SA02OWW	JJT	
S554JSE	FG	61571	S865OGB	ASW	1461	SA02UEP	SEC	
S555JSE	FG	61572	S866OGB	ASW	1462	SA02UEX	RTT	
S555WCM	WCM		S867OGB	ASW	1463	SA02UEY	RTT	
S556JSE	FG	61573	S868OGB	ASW	1464	SA02UUH	HOR	
S557JSE	FG	61574	S869OGB	ASW	1465	SA03YDB	MEW	
S558JSE	FG	61575	S887KRG	M&C		SA04AGT	BCM	
S559JSE	FG	61576	S900WCM	WCM		SA07VUG	HAO	
S579RGA	HOU		S904DUB	SHB		SA51CTF	WMC	
S581ACT	GIC		S905DUB	HVB		SA52DVR	FG	31506
S581PGB	GIB		S924AKS	FED	31655	SA52DVT	FG	31507
S582ACT	ABK		S925AKS	FED	31656	SA52DVU	FG	31508
S588ACT	DEV		S926AKS	FED	31657	SA52DVV	FG	31509
S591ACT	WHY		S928AKS	FED	31659	SA52DVW	FG	31510
S600WCM	WCM		S929AKS	FED	31660	SA52DVX	FG	31511
S613HGD	HOU		S930AKS	FED	31661	SA52DVY	FG	31512
S615CSC	STAY	33415	S931AKS	FED	31662	SA52DVZ	FG	31513
S616CSC	SREN	33416	S932AKS	FED	31663	SA52DWC	FG	31514
S617CSC	SREN	33417	S933AKS	FED	31664	SA52DWD	FG	31515
S617LRN	FIT		S934AKS	FED	31665	SA52EXD	GUM	400
S618CSC	SREN	33418	S935AKS	FED	31666	SA52GXO	RTT	
S618HGD	PTW	2	S936AKS	FED	31667	SA56VMT	AAM	
S619CSC	SREN	33419	S937AKS	FED	31668	SC02DPC	DPC	
S624KHN	ASW	1624	S938AKS	FED	31669	SC02HHA	LID	
S639RJA	BEK		S940UAL	HOR		SC02HHE	WCM	
S642KHN	ASW	1642	S943UAL	HOR		SC02VCD	LID	
S643KHN	ASW	1643	S944UAL	HOR		SC03WJC	WJC	YV03
S655JSE	SHIC	52605	S947NGB	WLC		SC05ONS	GSM	GS66
S656JSE	SHIC	52606	S955TGB	LID		SC09ALL	EVE	
S657JSE	SHIC	52607	S959KSR	STAY	16813	SC53VOM	AAA	
S658JSE	SHIC	52608	S960KSR	STAY	16814	SC56DPC	DPC	
S659JSE	SHIC	52609	S960URJ	BBD	16190	SC57DPC	DPC	
S660JSE	SHIC	52610	S961BBV	BBD	47159	SD02RZK	LID	
S661JSE	SHIC	52611	S961KSR	STAY	16815	SD55WXK	LID	
S662JSE	SHIC	52612	S962BBV	BBD	47156	SD58LKP	HTR	
S663KSN	HQD		S962KSR	STAY	16816	SE02TWJ	KCO	
S670KST	SHI		S963BBV	STAY	47158	SF03ABU	RTT	
S679ASX	SBQ		S964BBV	BBD	47157	SF03ABX	BCM	
S687BFS	FG	61577	S975CSG	JMC		SF03ACU	IRB	
S690RWG	SHIC	59178	S987ERR	HQD		SF03AUC	GUM	
S692BFS	FG	61579	SA02BOU	ESB	11	SF03PZC	SAD	
S693BFS	FG	61580	SA02BZD	FG	61587	SF03SCV	SLA	
S694BFS	FG	61581	SA02BZE	FG	61588	SF03YXP	RTT	
S696BFS	FG	61582	SA02BZF	FG	61589	SF03YXR	RTT	
S697BFS	FG	61583	SA02BZG	FG	61590	SF04EMW	NIC	
S698BFS	FG	61584	SA02BZH	FG	61591	SF04ETE	GIC	

SF04ETK	KOA		SF06GXG	FG	69039	SF06HAE	FG	69115
SF04EWL	CFT		SF06GXH	FG	69059	SF06HAO	FG	69116
SF04HXN	DEV		SF06GXJ	FG	69038	SF06HAU	FG	69117
SF04HXP	GSM	GS71	SF06GXK	FG	69040	SF06HAX	FG	69118
SF04HXW	FG	69295	SF06GXL	FG	69041	SF06HBA	FG	69119
SF04HXX	FG	69296	SF06GXM	FG	69057	SF06HBB	FG	69120
SF04LHR	RTT		SF06GXN	FG	69058	SF06HBC	FG	69121
SF04LHU	JMC		SF06GXO	FG	69060	SF06HHN	IRB	
SF04LKG	DMC		SF06GXP	FG	69061	SF06LKD	MAT	
SF04RHK	GUM	446	SF06GXR	FG	69062	SF06LKE	MAT	
SF04SKD	SWSC	47063	SF06GXS	FG	69063	SF06LKU	WHY	
SF04SKE	SWSC	47064	SF06GXT	FG	69064	SF06LKV	WHY	
SF04SKJ	SWSC	47065	SF06GXU	FG	69065	SF06NBY	PSK	
SF04SKK	SWSC	47066	SF06GXV	FG	69072	SF06NYG	HUC	
SF04SKN	SWSC	47067	SF06GXW	FG	69073	SF06ODS	MUN	431
SF04SOU	SOU		SF06GXX	FG	69074	SF06ODT	WCM	
SF04VFS	SWSC	47068	SF06GXZ	FG	69076	SF06OEA	BDC	
SF04VSV	SWSC	34596	SF06GYA	FG	69077	SF06OKJ	POC	
SF04VSX	SWSC	34597	SF06GYB	FG	69066	SF06OKT	WHY	
SF04VSY	SWSC	34598	SF06GYC	FG	69067	SF06OVE	SWSC	47314
SF04VSZ	SWSC	34599	SF06GYD	FG	69068	SF06OVG	SWSC	47356
SF04VTA	SWSC	34600	SF06GYE	FG	69069	SF06OVH	SWSC	47357
SF04VTC	SWSC	34601	SF06GYG	FG	69070	SF06OVJ	SWSC	47358
SF04VTD	SWSC	34602	SF06GYH	FG	69071	SF06OVK	SWSC	47359
SF04VTE	SWSC	34603	SF06GYJ	FG	69078	SF06OVL	SWSC	47360
SF04VTG	SWSC	34604	SF06GYK	FG	69079	SF06OVM	SWSC	47361
SF04WME	WCM		SF06GYN	FG	69080	SF06OVN	SWSC	47362
SF04WMX	MAT		SF06GYO	FG	69081	SF06OVP	SWSC	47365
SF04WMY	ACM		SF06GYP	FG	69082	SF06PHK	POC	
SF04ZPE	FG	69297	SF06GYR	FG	69083	SF06PHN	POC	
SF04ZPG	FG	69298	SF06GYS	FG	69084	SF06WDZ	MFW	
SF04ZXC	GIB		SF06GYT	FG	69085	SF06WKE	TEL	
SF04ZXD	BLS		SF06GYU	FG	69086	SF07AMV	SWSC	54027
SF05AKK	SHB		SF06GYV	FG	69087	SF07AMX	SWSC	54028
SF05AXW	HAO		SF06GYW	FG	69088	SF07ANP	SWSC	54029
SF05BEJ	APE		SF06GYX	FG	68089	SF07ANR	SWSC	54030
SF05FNS	JTK		SF06GYY	FG	69090	SF07ANU	SWSC	54031
SF05FNT	JTK		SF06GYZ	FG	69091	SF07ANV	SWSC	54032
SF05FNU	SLA		SF06GZA	FG	69092	SF07ANX	STAY	54033
SF05FNV	GIB		SF06GZB	FG	69093	SF07AOA	SHIC	54034
SF05FNZ	SHB		SF06GZC	FG	69094	SF07DLU	FIR	
SF05HPJ	GUM		SF06GZD	FG	69095	SF07DLV	FIR	
SF05KUH	FG	10183	SF06GZE	FG	69096	SF07DMO	POC	
SF05KUJ	FG	53202	SF06GZG	FG	69097	SF07DMV	POC	
SF05KUK	FG	53203	SF06GZH	FG	69098	SF07FCC	FG	37188
SF05KWM	MAT		SF06GZJ	FG	69099	SF07FCD	FG	37189
SF05KWO	MAT		SF06GZK	FG	69100	SF07FCE	FG	37190
SF05KXJ	FG	42885	SF06GZL	FG	69101	SF07FCG	FG	37191
SF05KXK	FG	42886	SF06GZM	FG	69102	SF07FCJ	FG	37192
SF05KXL	FG	42887	SF06GZN	FG	69103	SF07FCL	FG	37199
SF05KXM	FG	42888	SF06GZO	FG	69104	SF07FCM	FG	37201
SF05LFT	GUM		SF06GZP	FG	69105	SF07FCO	FG	37202
SF05LFU	GUM	466	SF06GZR	FG	69106	SF07FCP	FG	37166
SF05LFV	GUM	467	SF06GZS	FG	69107	SF07FCV	FG	37167
SF05LFW	GUM	468	SF06GZT	FG	69108	SF07FCX	FG	37168
SF05NXD	SWSC	47170	SF06GZV	FG	69109	SF07FCY	FG	37169
SF05NXE	SWSC	47171	SF06GZX	FG	69111	SF07FCZ	FG	37170
SF05NXG	SWSC	47172	SF06GZY	FG	69112	SF07FDA	FG	37171
SF05XDG	TEL		SF06GZZ	FG	69113	SF07FDC	FG	37172
SF06FSS	SBZ		SF06HAA	FG	69114	SF07FDD	FG	37173

SF07FDE	FG	37174	SF08GUO	SWSC	47612	SF09LDD	FG	37736
SF07FDG	FG	37175	SF08GUU	SWSC	47613	SF09LDE	FG	37737
SF07FDJ	FG	37176	SF08GUW	SWSC	47614	SF09LDJ	FG	37738
SF07FDK	FG	37177	SF08GUX	SWSC	47615	SF09LDK	FG	37739
SF07FDL	FG	37178	SF08HHC	MEX		SF09LDL	FG	37740
SF07FDM	FG	37179	SF08JDO	PSK		SF09LDN	FG	37741
SF07FDN	FG	37180	SF08MKV	MPC		SF09LDO	FG	37742
SF07FDO	FG	37181	SF08OKK	MAT		SF09LDU	FG	37743
SF07FDP	FG	37182	SF08RNY	WLC		SF09LDV	FG	37744
SF07FDU	FG	37183	SF08RNZ	WLC		SF09LDX	FG	37745
SF07FDV	FG	37184	SF08ROH	WLC		SF09LDY	FG	37746
SF07FDX	FG	37185	SF08ROU	WLC		SF09LDZ	FG	37747
SF07FDY	FG	37186	SF08RRO	WLC		SF09LEJ	FG	37748
SF07FDZ	FG	37187	SF08SMU	FG	37530	SF09LEU	FG	37749
SF07FEG	FG	37193	SF08SMV	FG	37531	SF09LFA	FG	37750
SF07FEH	FG	37194	SF08SMX	FG	37532	SF09LFB	FG	37751
SF07FEJ	FG	37195	SF08SNJ	FG	37533	SF09LNZ	HVB	
SF07FEK	FG	37196	SF08SNK	FG	37534	SF09LOA	HVB	
SF07FEM	FG	37197	SF08SNN	FG	37535	SF09LOD	ASW	2801
SF07FEO	FG	37198	SF08SNU	FG	37536	SF09LYZ	SBJ	
SF07FEP	FG	37200	SF08SNX	FG	37537	SF09LZV	WLC	
SF07FET	FG	37203	SF08SNY	FG	37538	SF09LZW	SBJ	
SF07FEU	FG	37204	SF08SNZ	FG	37539	SF10AZT	KIN	
SF07KGE	SBG		SF08SNZ	FG	37540	SF10BYV	SWSC	24184
SF07LCG	SHIC	54037	SF08UZJ	NAT		SF10BYW	SWSC	24185
SF07LCJ	SWSC	53302	SF08VVE	ABO		SF10BYX	SWSC	24186
SF07LCK	SWSC	53303	SF08VVG	BCD		SF10BYY	SWSC	24187
SF07NLU	MAT		SF09ACV	SWSC	53322	SF10BYZ	SWSC	24188
SF07NLV	MAT		SF09ACX	SWSC	53323	SF10BZA	SWSC	24189
SF07NLX	MAT		SF09ACY	SWSC	53324	SF10BZB	SWSC	24190
SF07NLY	MAT		SF09ACZ	SWSC	53325	SF10BZC	SWSC	24191
SF07NLZ	MAT		SF09ADO	SWSC	53114	SF10BZD	SWSC	47732
SF07ODH	MPC		SF09ADV	SWSC	22850	SF10BZE	SWSC	47733
SF07URJ	HVB	307	SF09ADX	SWSC	22851	SF10BZG	SWSC	47734
SF07URL	HVB	407	SF09ADZ	SWSC	22852	SF10BZH	SWSC	36144
SF07VOB	HVB		SF09AEA	SWSC	22853	SF10BZJ	SWSC	36145
SF08FDK	ESB		SF09AEB	SWSC	22854	SF10BZK	SWSC	36146
SF08FDL	ESB		SF09AED	SWSC	22855	SF10BZL	SWSC	36134
SF08FSU	GIB		SF09AEE	SWSC	22856	SF10BZM	SWSC	36135
SF08FTA	APE		SF09AEG	SWSC	22857	SF10BZN	SWSC	36136
SF08GOA	SWSC	25218	SF09AEJ	SWSC	22858	SF10BZO	SWSC	36137
SF08GOC	SWSC	25219	SF09AEK	SWSC	22859	SF10BZP	SWSC	36138
SF08GOE	SWSC	25220	SF09AEL	SWSC	22860	SF10BZR	SWSC	36139
SF08GOJ	SWSC	25221	SF09AEM	SWSC	22861	SF10BZS	SWSC	36140
SF08GOK	SWSC	22582	SF09AEN	SWSC	22862	SF10BZT	SWSC	36141
SF08GOU	SWSC	22583	SF09AEO	SWSC	22863	SF10BZU	SWSC	36142
SF08GOX	SWSC	22584	SF09AEP	SWSC	22864	SF10BZV	SWSC	36143
SF08GPE	SWSC	22585	SF09AET	SWSC	22865	SF10BZW	SWSC	36131
SF08GPJ	SWSC	22586	SF09AEU	SWSC	22866	SF10BZX	SWSC	36132
SF08GPK	SWSC	22587	SF09AEV	SWSC	22867	SF10BZY	SWSC	36133
SF08GPU	SWSC	22588	SF09AEW	SWSC	22868	SF10CAA	SWSC	15621
SF08GPV	SWSC	22589	SF09AEX	SWSC	22869	SF10CAE	SWSC	15622
SF08GPX	SWSC	22590	SF09AEY	SWSC	22870	SF10CAO	SWSC	15623
SF08GPY	SWSC	22591	SF09AEZ	SWSC	22871	SF10CAU	SWSC	15624
SF08GPZ	SWSC	22592	SF09AFA	SWSC	25235	SF10CAV	SWSC	15625
SF08GRK	SWSC	22593	SF09AFE	SWSC	25236	SF10CAX	SWSC	15626
SF08GRU	SWSC	22594	SF09GWL	SBG		SF10CBO	SWSC	15627
SF08GTU	SWSC	54049	SF09GWM	GIB		SF10CBU	SWSC	15628
SF08GTY	SWSC	53105	SF09HKH	STU		SF10CBV	SWSC	15629
SF08GTZ	SWSC	53106	SF09JWE	MEX		SF10CBX	SWSC	15630

Reg	Op	Number	Reg	Op	Number	Reg	Op	Number
SF10CBY	SWSC	15631	SF51YBP	FG	61623	SF54OSO	FG	32551
SF10CCD	SWSC	15632	SF51YBR	FG	61624	SF54OSP	FG	32552
SF10CCE	SWSC	15633	SF51YBS	FG	61625	SF54OSR	FG	32553
SF10CCJ	SWSC	15634	SF51YBT	FG	61626	SF54OSU	FG	32554
SF10CCK	SWSC	15635	SF52EBD	PSK		SF54OSV	FG	32555
SF10CCN	SWSC	15636	SF53BYL	BBD	18013	SF54OSW	FG	32556
SF10CCO	SWSC	15637	SF53BYM	SREN	18014	SF54OSX	FG	32557
SF10CCU	SWSC	15638	SF53BYN	SREN	18015	SF54OSY	FG	32558
SF10CCV	SWSC	15639	SF53BYO	SREN	18016	SF54OSZ	FG	32559
SF10CCX	SWSC	15640	SF53BYV	SWSC	18003	SF54OTA	FG	32560
SF10CCY	SWSC	15641	SF53BYW	SWSC	18004	SF54OTB	FG	32561
SF10CCZ	SWSC	15642	SF53BYX	SWSC	18005	SF54OTC	FG	32562
SF10CDE	SWSC	15643	SF53BYY	SWSC	18006	SF54OTD	FG	32563
SF10CDK	SWSC	15644	SF53BYZ	STAY	18007	SF54OTE	FG	32564
SF10CDN	SWSC	15645	SF53BZA	BBD	18008	SF54OTG	FG	32565
SF10CDO	SWSC	15646	SF53BZB	BBD	18009	SF54OTH	FG	32566
SF10CDU	SWSC	15647	SF53BZC	BBD	18010	SF54OTJ	FG	32567
SF10CDZ	SWSC	36149	SF53BZD	BBD	18011	SF54OTK	FG	32568
SF10CEA	SWSC	36150	SF53BZE	BBD	18012	SF54OTL	FG	32569
SF10CEJ	SWSC	36151	SF53BZG	SWSC	18000	SF54OTM	FG	32570
SF10CEK	SWSC	36152	SF53BZH	SWSC	18001	SF54OTN	FG	32571
SF10CFA	SWSC	36147	SF53BZJ	SWSC	18002	SF54OTP	FG	32572
SF10CFD	SWSC	36148	SF53JXJ	GUM	504	SF54OTR	FG	32573
SF10DJJ	DOT		SF53JXK	GUM	505	SF54OTT	FG	32574
SF10DJK	DOT		SF53JXL	GUM	506	SF54OTU	FG	32575
SF10GCK	WLC		SF53JXM	GUM	507	SF54OTV	FG	32576
SF10GKC	SHB	14	SF53KGE	GUM	500	SF54OTW	FG	32577
SF10GKD	SHB	15	SF53KGG	GUM	501	SF54OTX	FG	32578
SF10GKE	SLA		SF53KGJ	GUM	502	SF54OTY	FG	32579
SF10GCL	WLC		SF53KGK	GUM	503	SF54OTZ	FG	32580
SF10GXK	STU		SF53KUK	GUM	442	SF54OUA	FG	32581
SF10GXL	STU		SF53KUN	GUM	443	SF54OUB	FG	32582
SF10KOE	WHI		SF53KUR	DEV		SF54OUC	FG	32583
SF51JWV	BBD	49752	SF53KUT	SHI		SF54OUD	FG	32584
SF51YAA	FG	61597	SF54CFO	YUL		SF54OUE	FG	32585
SF51YAD	FG	61598	SF54CHK	SHB		SF54OUG	FG	32586
SF51YAE	FG	61599	SF54CHO	WMC		SF54OUH	FG	32587
SF51YAG	FG	61600	SF54CSU	SREN	60014	SF54OUJ	FG	32588
SF51YAH	FG	61601	SF54HVZ	STP		SF54OUK	FG	32589
SF51YAJ	FG	61602	SF54HWA	WCM		SF54OUL	FG	32590
SF51YAK	FG	61603	SF54HWG	GIB		SF54OUM	FG	32591
SF51YAO	FG	61604	SF54HWH	GIB		SF54OUN	FG	32592
SF51YAU	FG	61605	SF54KHP	BLS		SF54OUO	BLS	
SF51YAV	FG	61606	SF54KHV	IRB		SF54OUU	GIB	
SF51YAW	FG	61607	SF54ORA	HOU		SF54OVB	BLS	
SF51YAX	FG	61608	SF54ORC	AYR		SF54OVC	BLS	
SF51YAY	FG	61609	SF54ORJ	GIB		SF54RHX	GIB	
SF51YBA	FG	61610	SF54ORK	GIB		SF54RJU	SWSC	47150
SF51YBB	FG	61611	SF54ORL	AYR		SF54THV	FG	32593
SF51YBC	FG	61612	SF54ORN	GIB		SF54THX	FG	32594
SF51YBD	FG	61613	SF54ORO	GIB		SF54THZ	FG	32595
SF51YBE	FG	61614	SF54ORP	HOU		SF54TJO	FG	32596
SF51YBG	FG	61615	SF54OSD	FG	32543	SF54TJU	FG	32597
SF51YBH	FG	61616	SF54OSE	FG	32544	SF54TJV	FG	32598
SF51YBJ	FG	61617	SF54OSG	FG	32545	SF54TJX	FG	32599
SF51YBK	FG	61618	SF54OSJ	FG	32546	SF54TJY	FG	32600
SF51YBL	FG	61619	SF54OSK	FG	32547	SF54TJZ	FG	32601
SF51YBM	FG	61620	SF54OSL	FG	32548	SF54TKA	FG	32602
SF51YBN	FG	61621	SF54OSM	FG	32549	SF54TKC	FG	32603
SF51YBO	FG	61622	SF54OSN	FG	32550	SF54TKD	FG	32604

Reg	Op	No	Reg	Op	No	Reg	Op	No
SF54TKE	FG	32605	SF55VUR	SWSC	22390	SF57LUY	SWSC	22531
SF54TKJ	FG	32606	SF56DPX	BBD	49753	SF57LUZ	SWSC	22532
SF54TKK	FG	32607	SF56DTU	BBD	49754	SF57LVB	SWSC	22533
SF54TKN	FG	32609	SF56FKL	SWSC	22508	SF57LVC	SWSC	22534
SF54TKO	FG	32608	SF56FKM	SWSC	22509	SF57MKA	FG	37205
SF54TKT	FG	32610	SF56FKN	SWSC	22510	SF57MKC	FG	37206
SF54TKU	FG	32611	SF56FKO	SWSC	22511	SF57MKD	FG	37207
SF54TKV	FG	32612	SF56FKP	SWSC	22512	SF57MKG	FG	37208
SF54TKX	FG	32613	SF56FKR	SWSC	22513	SF57MKJ	FG	37209
SF54TKY	FG	32614	SF56FKS	SWSC	22514	SF57MKK	FG	37210
SF54TKZ	FG	32615	SF56FKT	SWSC	22515	SF57MKL	FG	37211
SF54TLJ	FG	32616	SF56FKU	SWSC	22516	SF57MKM	FG	37212
SF54TLK	FG	32617	SF56FKV	SWSC	35238	SF57MKN	FG	37213
SF54TLN	FG	32618	SF56FKW	SWSC	35239	SF57MKO	FG	37214
SF54TLO	FG	32619	SF56FKX	SWSC	35240	SF57MKP	FG	37215
SF54TLU	FG	32620	SF56FKY	SWSC	35241	SF57MKU	FG	37216
SF54TLX	FG	32621	SF56FKZ	SWSC	35242	SF57MKV	FG	37217
SF54TLY	FG	32622	SF56FLA	SWSC	47386	SF57MKX	FG	37218
SF54TLZ	FG	32623	SF56FLB	SWSC	47387	SF57MKZ	FG	37219
SF54TMO	FG	32624	SF56FLC	SWSC	47388	SF57MLE	FG	37220
SF54TMU	FG	32625	SF56GYP	FG	66988	SF57MLJ	FG	37221
SF54TMV	FG	32626	SF56GYR	FG	66989	SF57MLK	FG	37222
SF55BKA	MCD		SF56GYS	FG	66990	SF57MLL	FG	37223
SF55FVR	DPC		SF56GYT	FG	66991	SF57MLN	FG	37224
SF55HBD	CBC		SF56LUP	ESB		SF57MLO	FG	37225
SF55HHC	WLC		SF57DNU	SWSC	47496	SF57MLU	FG	37226
SF55HHD	WLC		SF57DNV	SWSC	47497	SF57MLV	FG	37227
SF55HHE	WLC		SF57DNX	SWSC	47498	SF57NMM	ASW	4409
SF55NNZ	SWSC	18332	SF57DOA	SWSC	47499	SF57NMO	ASW	4408
SF55NOH	SWSC	18333	SF57DOH	SWSC	47500	SF57NPK	ASW	4401
SF55NOU	SWSC	18334	SF57DOJ	SWSC	47501	SF57NPN	ASW	4402
SF55PSY	SEC		SF57DOU	SWSC	47502	SF58ATY	FG	37541
SF55RJV	SWSC	22379	SF57DPE	SWSC	47503	SF58ATZ	FG	37542
SF55RJX	SWSC	22380	SF57DPK	SWSC	47504	SF58AUA	FG	37543
SF55RJY	SWSC	22381	SF57DPN	SWSC	47505	SF58AUC	FG	37544
SF55RJZ	SWSC	22382	SF57DPO	SWSC	47506	SF58DHA	SAB	
SF55RKA	SWSC	21201	SF57DPU	SWSC	47507	SF58FTX	SBG	
SF55RKE	SWSC	21202	SF57DPV	SWSC	54041	SF58JFV	KCO	
SF55RKJ	SWSC	22383	SF57DPX	SWSC	54042	SF58OHO	WLC	
SF55RKK	SWSC	22384	SF57DPY	SWSC	54043	SF59BXM	CCC	
SF55RKN	SWSC	22385	SF57DPZ	SWSC	54044	SF59BXP	VIC	
SF55TXC	FG	68566	SF57DRO	SWSC	47495	SF59FUT	SWSC	27614
SF55TZP	SWSC	18369	SF57DRV	SWSC	54045	SF59FUU	SWSC	27615
SF55TZR	SWSC	18370	SF57FXB	HAO		SF59FVA	AAM	
SF55TZS	SWSC	18371	SF57FZK	HVB	157	SF59FYV	SWSC	54076
SF55UAG	FG	69014	SF57FZY	WLC		SF59FYW	SWSC	54077
SF55UAH	FG	69015	SF57FZZ	CCC		SF59FYX	SWSC	54078
SF55UAJ	FG	69016	SF57JRX	APE		SF59FYY	SWSC	54079
SF55UAM	FG	69019	SF57JSY	SBZ		SF59GZA	GMC	
SF55UAO	FG	69021	SF57JTX	STP		SF59KUW	ESB	
SF55UAV	FG	69027	SF57LUB	SWSC	22521	SF60AAX	ESB	
SF55UBB	FG	69042	SF57LUD	SWSC	22522	SF60FPP	WLC	
SF55UBU	FG	69034	SF57LUE	SWSC	22523	SF60FPT	WLC	
SF55UBV	FG	69035	SF57LUH	SWSC	22524	SF60FPV	WLC	
SF55UBW	FG	69036	SF57LUJ	SWSC	22525	SF60FPX	WLC	
SF55UBX	FG	69037	SF57LUL	SWSC	22526	SF60FPY	WLC	
SF55VUM	SWSC	22386	SF57LUO	SWSC	22527	SF60FSO	SHB	
SF55VUN	SWSC	22387	SF57LUP	SWSC	22528	SG03ZEL	ABO	
SF55VUO	SWSC	22388	SF57LUR	SWSC	22529	SG03ZEX	SEC	
SF55VUP	SWSC	22389	SF57LUW	SWSC	22530	SG04SOU	SOU	

Reg	Code	No	Reg	Code	No	Reg	Code	No
SG52VFJ	SAZ		SJ03DPE	FG	50461	SJ57AAK	SREN	53297
SG52XKJ	SEC		SJ03DPF	FG	50462	SJ57AAN	SWSC	53298
SG52XMK	GUM	404	SJ03DPN	FG	50463	SJ57AAO	SWSC	53299
SG52XML	GUM	405	SJ03DPU	FG	50464	SJ57AAU	SWSC	53300
SG52XMO	GUM	401	SJ03DPV	FG	50465	SJ57AAV	SWSC	53301
SG52XMP	GUM	402	SJ03DPZ	FAB	50468	SJ57AAX	SWSC	54038
SG52XMR	GUM	403	SJ03FPW	MFW		SJ57AAY	SWSC	54039
SG58EFC	HTR		SJ04FLA	SHB		SJ57AAZ	SWSC	54040
SG59XGS	GSM	GS72	SJ04MFV	MEW		SJ57DDN	ASW	4411
SH03XBE	MLI		SJ05SOU	SOU		SJ57DDO	ASW	4410
SH04YZB	WMC		SJ06CBV	DOI		SJ57DDU	ASW	4407
SH10PCV	GSM	GS74	SJ06CBX	MAT		SJ57DDV	ASW	4406
SH51KJY	RTT		SJ09GDV	MEW		SJ57DDX	ASW	4405
SH51MHV	PTW	20	SJ10AVR	HVB	410	SJ57DDY	ASW	4404
SH51MHY	FG	61627	SJ10AVT	HVB	510	SJ57DDZ	ASW	4403
SH51MHZ	FG	61628	SJ10AVX	HVB	710	SJ57FYL	ESB	
SH51MJE	FG	61629	SJ10NLJ	HVB	610	SJ58AEG	WHY	
SH51MJF	FG	61630	SJ51DHE	FG	61637	SJ60GBF	MEW	
SH51MKG	FG	61632	SJ51DHK	FG	61640	SJI8112	MLI	
SH51MKK	FG	61634	SJ51DHL	FG	61641	SJW515	DOT	
SH51MKL	FG	61635	SJ51DHM	FG	61642	SK02NYU	GSM	GS57
SH58VKP	HTR		SJ51DHN	FG	61643	SK02OAA	WMC	
SH60PCH	DPC		SJ51DHO	FG	61644	SK02VCG	NIC	
SHE622Y	ARC		SJ51DHP	FG	61645	SK02VCL	NIC	
SIA637	MCM		SJ51DHV	FG	61646	SK02VTC	SCN	
SIB2284	BEK		SJ51DHX	FG	61647	SK02ZYG	FG	65755
SIB3933	GEM		SJ51DHZ	FG	61648	SK02ZYH	FG	65756
SIB4458	CCI		SJ51DJD	FG	61649	SK03ANV	WMC	
SIB6297	BEK		SJ51DJE	FG	61650	SK03FDL	ECL	
SIB7357	BEK		SJ51DJF	FG	61651	SK03ZXU	AYR	
SIB8045	AAM		SJ51DJK	FG	61652	SK05BYX	YUL	
SIL1075	MCD		SJ51DJO	FG	61653	SK05SOU	SOU	
SIL1102	SIC		SJ51DJU	FG	61654	SK06AHF	LOT	995
SIL1103	SIC		SJ51DJX	FG	61656	SK06AHG	LOT	996
SIL1104	SIC		SJ51DJY	FG	61657	SK06AHJ	LOT	997
SIL1598	MCD		SJ51DJZ	FG	61306	SK06AHL	LOT	998
SIL1895	SHIC	52148	SJ51DKA	FG	61658	SK06AHN	LOT	999
SIL2292	ACM		SJ51DKD	FG	61659	SK06BZN	PSK	
SIL4134	SIC		SJ51DKE	FG	61660	SK06FFO	WHI	
SIL4860	D&E		SJ51DKF	FG	61661	SK07CAA	LOT	826
SIL6715	MCD		SJ51DKL	FG	61663	SK07CAE	LOT	827
SIL7566	MCD		SJ51DKN	FG	61664	SK07CAO	LOT	828
SIL8013	SBJ		SJ51LPA	DOI		SK07CAU	LOT	829
SIL8572	SCK		SJ51LZA	SHI		SK07CAV	LOT	830
SIL8697	SMI		SJ51MXY	LID		SK07CAX	LOT	831
SIL8753	HAO		SJ51NVY	HUC		SK07CBF	LOT	832
SIL8761	WTB		SJ52XJF	AYR		SK07CBO	LOT	833
SIL9637	SMK		SJ52XLC	DEV		SK07CBU	LOT	834
SIL9988	SVC		SJ53AWW	SAJ		SK07CBV	LOT	835
SIL9991	SVC		SJ53CUU	PWW		SK07CBX	LOT	836
SIL9993	SVC		SJ53CUV	PWW		SK07CBY	LOT	837
SIL9994	SVC		SJ53LTU	CHE		SK07CCA	LOT	838
SIL9996	SVC		SJ54CCN	BRU		SK07CCD	LOT	839
SIL9997	SVC		SJ54GBE	ACM		SK07CFO	LOT	141
SIW1940	DEV		SJ54GDA	JMC		SK07CFP	LOT	142
SIW9154	MCO		SJ54GDE	JMC		SK07CFU	LOT	143
SJ03AVG	SBQ		SJ55VCE	WMC		SK07CFV	LOT	144
SJ03DNY	FG	40965	SJ56BFL	GIB		SK07CFX	LOT	145
SJ03DOA	FG	40966	SJ57AAE	SWSC	25201	SK07CFY	LOT	146
SJ03DOH	FAB	50460	SJ57AAF	SWSC	25202	SK07CFZ	LOT	147

SK07CGE	LOT	148	SK52OHT	LOT	634	SM06SUN	SCD	
SK07CGF	LOT	149	SK52OHU	LOT	TB51	SM06VJN	CFT	
SK07CGG	LOT	150	SK52OHV	LOT	TB52	SM07GSM	MAY	10
SK07CGO	LOT	136	SK52OHW	LOT	TB53	SM08SON	SCD	
SK07CGU	LOT	137	SK52OHX	LOT	54	SM08SUN	SCD	
SK07CGV	LOT	138	SK52OHY	LOT	55	SM10GSM	MAY	
SK07CGX	LOT	139	SK52OHZ	LOT	56	SMK697F	WCG	
SK07CGY	LOT	140	SK52OJA	LOT	57	SN02AAA	AAA	
SK07FBB	ETN		SK52OJB	LOT	58	SN03AXM	HUC	
SK07FCF	D&E		SK52OJC	LOT	59	SN03CLX	FG	65757
SK07FMP	SHI		SK52OJD	LOT	60	SN03CLY	FG	65758
SK07FOM	IRB		SK52OJE	LOT	61	SN03FHK	SWSC	42022
SK07FXV	ETN		SK52OJF	LOT	62	SN03FHL	SWSC	42023
SK07FYO	SAP		SK52OJG	LOT	63	SN03FHM	SHIC	42024
SK07FYP	DOI		SK52OJH	LOT	64	SN03JWG	DEV	
SK07FYT	SMI		SK52OJJ	LOT	65	SN03LFV	AVD	
SK07FZS	SCN		SK52OJL	LOT	66	SN03LFW	AVD	
SK07FZV	BUT		SK52OJM	LOT	67	SN03LFX	AVD	
SK07HMC	WCM		SK52OJN	LOT	68	SN03NLJ	APE	
SK07HMD	WCM		SK52OJO	LOT	69	SN03NLK	SPA	
SK07HME	WCM		SK52OJP	LOT	70	SN03SWY	SAA	
SK07HMF	WCM		SK52OJR	LOT	71	SN03SXJ	SAA	
SK07HMG	GCB		SK52OJS	LOT	72	SN03TOA	WMC	
SK07HMH	GCB		SK52OJT	LOT	73	SN03UBJ	GIC	
SK07JVN	FED	69254	SK52OJU	LOT	74	SN03WMJ	FED	62411
SK07JVO	FED	69255	SK52OJW	LOT	76	SN03WMU	FED	62412
SK07JVP	FED	69256	SK52OJX	LOT	77	SN03ZCE	WMC	
SK07JYA	SCN		SK52OJY	LOT	78	SN04AAE	LOT	662
SK07LBE	SCN		SK52OJZ	LOT	79	SN04AAF	LOT	663
SK07LFP	SAB		SK52OKA	LOT	80	SN04AAJ	LOT	664
SK07LMF	RAB		SK52OKB	LOT	81	SN04AAK	LOT	665
SK07LZD	SCN		SK52OKC	LOT	82	SN04AAU	LOT	666
SK07MMV	EVE		SK52OKD	LOT	83	SN04AAV	LOT	667
SK07NKN	DOI		SK52OKE	LOT	84	SN04AAX	LOT	668
SK51AYD	MUN	469	SK52OKF	LOT	85	SN04AAY	LOT	669
SK51VVW	PHO		SK57ADO	FED	69257	SN04AAZ	LOT	670
SK52AUK	PSK		SK57ADU	FED	69258	SN04ABF	LOT	671
SK52HYP	GUM	211	SK57ADV	FED	69259	SN04ABK	LOT	672
SK52OCO	NIC		SK57ADX	FED	69260	SN04ABU	LOT	673
SK52OGT	LOT	635	SK57ADZ	FED	69261	SN04ABV	LOT	674
SK52OGU	LOT	636	SK57AEA	FED	69262	SN04ABX	LOT	675
SK52OGV	LOT	637	SK57AEB	FED	69263	SN04ABZ	LOT	676
SK52OGW	LOT	638	SK57AEC	FED	69264	SN04ACJ	LOT	677
SK52OGX	LOT	639	SK57BEY	AAA		SN04ACU	LOT	678
SK52OGY	LOT	640	SK57BHX	ETN		SN04ACV	LOT	679
SK52OGZ	LOT	641	SL02LMO	GIC		SN04ACX	LOT	680
SK52OHA	LOT	642	SL04OLS	MOA		SN04ACY	LOT	681
SK52OHB	LOT	643	SL06SOU	SOU		SN04ACZ	LOT	682
SK52OHC	LOT	644	SL07RVY	AAA		SN04ADU	LOT	683
SK52OHD	LOT	645	SL52AFC	NIC		SN04ADV	LOT	684
SK52OHE	LOT	646	SL52AKN	NIC		SN04ADX	LOT	685
SK52OHG	LOT	647	SL52CPE	BCD		SN04ADZ	LOT	686
SK52OHH	LOT	648	SL54OSL	MOA		SN04AEA	LOT	687
SK52OHJ	LOT	649	SL6069	HQD		SN04AEB	LOT	688
SK52OHL	LOT	650	SL9483	MOA		SN04AEC	LOT	689
SK52OHN	LOT	651	SM02GSM	KIN		SN04AED	LOT	690
SK52OHO	LOT	652	SM04GSM	GUM	702	SN04AEE	LOT	691
SK52OHP	LOT	653	SM06GSM	MAY	16	SN04AEF	LOT	692
SK52OHR	LOT	654	SM06SON	SCD		SN04AEG	LOT	693
SK52OHS	LOT	655	SM06SOU	SOU		SN04AEJ	LOT	694

Reg	Op	No	Reg	Op	No	Reg	Op	No
SN04AEK	LOT	695	SN05DWC	HHL	16	SN06BSU	SHIC	27586
SN04AEL	LOT	696	SN05DWD	HHL	17	SN06GGJ	MOA	
SN04AEM	LOT	697	SN05DWE	HHL	18	SN06GGK	MOA	
SN04AEP	LOT	698	SN05DWF	HHL	19	SN06KAA	ETN	
SN04AET	LOT	699	SN05DWG	HHL	20	SN06KHO	DOI	
SN04AEU	LOT	700	SN05DWJ	HHL	21	SN06OWV	PWW	
SN04AEV	LOT	656	SN05DWK	HHL	22	SN07FVO	RAB	5
SN04AEW	LOT	657	SN05DWL	HHL	23	SN08AEJ	SWSC	27596
SN04AEX	LOT	658	SN05EOV	MOA		SN08AEK	SWSC	27597
SN04AEY	LOT	659	SN05EOW	MOA		SN08AEL	STU	
SN04AEZ	LOT	660	SN05FBB	SCN		SN08AEO	STU	
SN04AFA	LOT	661	SN05FCU	SREN	29717	SN08BWJ	LOT	876
SN04CKX	FED	65701	SN05FCX	SREN	29718	SN08BWK	LOT	877
SN04CKY	FED	65700	SN05FHM	DMC		SN08BWL	LOT	878
SN04CLF	FED	65702	SN05FTK	SAA		SN08BWM	LOT	879
SN04CNK	FED	65703	SN05HCX	GUM	407	SN08BWO	LOT	880
SN04EFY	FED	43843	SN05HCY	GUM	408	SN08BWP	LOT	881
SN04EFZ	FED	43844	SN05HCZ	GUM	409	SN08BWU	LOT	882
SN04GBY	ROW		SN05HDA	GUM	410	SN08BWV	LOT	883
SN04GFE	KIN		SN05HDD	WLO		SN08BWW	LOT	884
SN04GUE	ETN		SN05HDE	WLO		SN08BWX	LOT	885
SN04GUF	WHY		SN05HSY	ETN		SN08BWY	LOT	886
SN04MJS	WHY		SN05HWD	FED	36023	SN08BWZ	LOT	887
SN04NFZ	LOT	101	SN05HWE	FED	36022	SN08BXA	LOT	888
SN04NGE	LOT	102	SN05HWF	FED	36020	SN08BXB	LOT	889
SN04NGF	LOT	103	SN05HWG	FED	36018	SN08BXC	LOT	890
SN04NGG	LOT	104	SN05HWH	FED	36019	SN08BXD	LOT	891
SN04NGJ	LOT	105	SN05HWK	FED	36014	SN08BXE	LOT	892
SN04NGU	LOT	106	SN05HWL	FED	36013	SN08BXF	LOT	893
SN04NGX	LOT	107	SN05HWM	FED	36016	SN08BXG	LOT	894
SN04NGY	LOT	108	SN05HWO	FED	36015	SN08BXH	LOT	895
SN04NGZ	LOT	109	SN05HWP	FED	36021	SN08BXJ	LOT	896
SN04NHA	LOT	110	SN05HWR	FED	36024	SN08BXK	LOT	897
SN04NHB	LOT	111	SN05HWS	FED	36025	SN08BXL	LOT	898
SN04NHC	LOT	112	SN05HWT	FED	36028	SN08BXM	LOT	899
SN04NHD	LOT	113	SN05HWU	FED	36026	SN08BXO	LOT	900
SN04NHE	LOT	114	SN05HWV	FED	36027	SN08BXP	LOT	901
SN04NHF	LOT	115	SN05HWW	FED	36007	SN08BXR	LOT	902
SN04NHG	LOT	116	SN05HWX	FED	36008	SN08BXS	LOT	903
SN04NHH	LOT	117	SN05HWY	FED	36009	SN08BXU	LOT	904
SN04NHJ	LOT	118	SN05HWZ	FED	36010	SN08BXV	LOT	905
SN04NHK	LOT	119	SN05HXA	FED	36011	SN08BXW	LOT	906
SN04NHL	LOT	120	SN05HXB	FED	36012	SN08BXX	LOT	907
SN04NHM	LOT	121	SN05JWZ	SAY		SN08BXY	LOT	908
SN04NHP	LOT	122	SN05JXA	SAY		SN08BXZ	LOT	909
SN04NHT	LOT	123	SN05LFD	RAB	10	SN08BYA	LOT	910
SN04NHU	LOT	124	SN06ABO	SCN		SN08BYB	LOT	911
SN04NHV	LOT	125	SN06ACO	HHL		SN08BYC	LOT	912
SN04NHX	LOT	126	SN06ACU	HHL	2	SN08BYD	LOT	913
SN04NHY	LOT	127	SN06AEF	PWW		SN08BYF	LOT	914
SN04NHZ	LOT	128	SN06AEY	ETN		SN08BYG	LOT	915
SN04NJE	LOT	129	SN06AHK	FED	65754	SN08BYH	LOT	916
SN04NJF	LOT	130	SN06ASU	LAK		SN08BYK	LOT	917
SN04VUR	FIT		SN06AVT	PSK		SN08BYL	LOT	918
SN05DMV	AYR		SN06AZB	IRB		SN08BYM	LOT	919
SN05DVW	HHL	11	SN06AZP	SAZ		SN08BYO	LOT	920
SN05DVX	HHL	12	SN06AZV	FIR		SN08BYP	LOT	921
SN05DVY	HHL	13	SN06BRZ	HOR		SN08BYR	LOT	922
SN05DVZ	HHL	14	SN06BSO	HOR		SN08BYT	LOT	923
SN05DWA	HHL	15				SN08BYU	LOT	924

SN08BYV	LOT	925	SN09CTX	LOT	305	SN10AUV	SCN		
SN08BYW	LOT	35	SN09CTY	LOT	306	SN10AVG	MPC		
SN08BYY	LOT	36	SN09CTZ	LOT	307	SN10AZP	MAT		
SN08BYZ	LOT	37	SN09CUA	LOT	308	SN10AZR	MAT		
SN08BZA	LOT	38	SN09CUC	LOT	309	SN10CAE	BDC		
SN08BZB	LOT	39	SN09CUG	LOT	310	SN10CAO	BCD		
SN08BZC	LOT	40	SN09CUH	LOT	311	SN10CAU	HVB	110	
SN08CNJ	DOI		SN09CUJ	LOT	312	SN10CXH	MEX		
SN08EHE	ORD		SN09CUK	LOT	313	SN10DKE	LOT	937	
SN08GJJ	RAB		SN09CUO	LOT	314	SN10DKF	LOT	938	
SN08GJK	RAB	12	SN09CUU	LOT	315	SN10DKJ	LOT	939	
SN08GJO	RAB		SN09CUV	LOT	316	SN10DKK	LOT	940	
SN08GXC	RAB		SN09CUW	LOT	317	SN10DKL	LOT	941	
SN08GXD	RAB	17	SN09CUX	LOT	318	SN10DKO	LOT	942	
SN08GYG	RAB	18	SN09CUY	LOT	319	SN10DKU	LOT	943	
SN08GYH	ETN		SN09CVA	LOT	320	SN10DKV	LOT	944	
SN08HUH	MEX		SN09CVB	LOT	321	SN10DKX	LOT	945	
SN08HUV	MEX		SN09CVC	LOT	322	SN10DKY	LOT	946	
SN08KBY	ECL		SN09CVD	LOT	323	SN10DLD	LOT	947	
SN08KBZ	ECL		SN09CVE	LOT	324	SN10DLE	LOT	948	
SN08NWH	PWW		SN09CVF	LOT	325	SN10DLF	LOT	949	
SN08NWJ	PWW		SN09CVG	LOT	326	SN10EMP	ETN		
SN09AKV	WHY		SN09CVH	LOT	327	SN10ENH	SBO		
SN09AKX	WHY		SN09CVJ	LOT	328	SN10WNT	SBO		
SN09AZP	LAG		SN09CVK	LOT	329	SN10ENU	SBO		
SN09AZR	LAG		SN09CVL	LOT	926	SN10ENV	SCN		
SN09AZT	LAG		SN09CVM	LOT	927	SN51AXF	LOT	601	
SN09AZU	LAG		SN09CVO	LOT	928	SN51AXG	LOT	602	
SN09AZV	LAG		SN09CVP	LOT	929	SN51AXH	LOT	603	
SN09CAU	FG	38201	SN09CVR	LOT	930	SN51AXJ	LOT	604	
SN09CAV	FG	38202	SN09CVS	LOT	931	SN51AXK	LOT	605	
SN09CAX	FG	38203	SN09CVT	LOT	932	SN51AXO	LOT	606	
SN09CBF	FG	38204	SN09CVU	LOT	933	SN51AXP	LOT	607	
SN09CBO	FG	38205	SN09CVV	LOT	934	SN51AXR	LOT	608	
SN09CBU	FG	38206	SN09CVW	LOT	935	SN51AXS	LOT	609	
SN09CBV	FG	38207	SN09CVX	LOT	936	SN51AXT	LOT	610	
SN09CBX	FG	38208	SN09EZW	FED	69402	SN51AXU	LOT	611	
SN09CBY	FG	38209	SN09EZX	FED	69403	SN51AXV	LOT	612	
SN09CCA	FG	38210	SN09FAU	FED	69404	SN51AXW	LOT	613	
SN09CCD	FG	38211	SN09FBA	FED	69405	SN51AXX	LOT	614	
SN09CCE	FG	38212	SN09FBB	FED	69406	SN51AXY	LOT	615	
SN09CCF	FG	38213	SN09FBC	FED	69407	SN51AXZ	LOT	616	
SN09CCJ	FG	38214	SN09FBD	FED	69408	SN51AYA	LOT	617	
SN09CCK	FG	38215	SN09FBE	FED	69409	SN51AYB	LOT	618	
SN09CCO	FG	38216	SN09FBF	FED	69410	SN51AYD	LOT	620	
SN09CCU	FG	38217	SN09FFA	CSS		SN51AYE	LOT	621	
SN09CCV	FG	38218	SN09FFB	CSS		SN51AYF	LOT	622	
SN09CCX	FG	38219	SN09FFD	MIT		SN51AYG	LOT	623	
SN09CCY	FG	38220	SN09FFE	MIT		SN51AYH	LOT	624	
SN09CCZ	FG	38221	SN09FUW	ECL		SN51AYJ	LOT	625	
SN09CDE	FG	38222	SN09FUY	ECL		SN51AYK	LOT	626	
SN09CDF	FG	38223	SN09JFU	SHI		SN51AYL	LOT	627	
SN09CDK	FG	38224	SN09JUV	AAA		SN51AYM	LOT	628	
SN09CDO	FG	38225	SN09JUW	AAA		SN51AYO	LOT	599	
SN09CGY	GUM	455	SN09JUX	AAA		SN51AYP	LOT	600	
SN09CGZ	GUM	456	SN10AHJ	SCN		SN51FKG	GIB		
SN09CTK	LOT	301	SN10AJO	SBO		SN51FZB	LOT	192	
SN09CTO	LOT	302	SN10ANR	WHY		SN51LUZ	SCM		
SN09CTU	LOT	303	SN10ANU	WHY		SN51LVB	WMC		
SN09CTV	LOT	304	SN10AOA	DWF		SN51MSU	FED	62356	

Reg	Op	No	Reg	Op	No	Reg	Op	No
SN51MSV	FED	62355	SN54KFA	FED	65719	SN55BPK	LOT	749
SN51MSX	FED	62358	SN54KFC	FED	65720	SN55BPO	LOT	750
SN51MSY	FED	62357	SN54KFD	FED	65721	SN55DUU	IRB	
SN51SXC	GUM		SN54KFE	FED	65722	SN55FDC	YUL	
SN51SXD	GUM	447	SN54KFF	FED	65723	SN55FEF	AAA	
SN51SXP	GUM	450	SN54LRL	HHL	24	SN55FLJ	YUL	
SN51SXR	GUM	451	SN54LRO	HHL	25	SN55HDZ	FED	32669
SN51SXS	GUM	452	SN55BJJ	LOT	131	SN55HEJ	FED	32670
SN51SXT	GUM	453	SN55BJK	LOT	132	SN55HEU	FED	32671
SN51SXW	GUM	454	SN55BJO	LOT	133	SN55HEV	FED	32672
SN51UCE	GCB		SN55BJU	LOT	134	SN55HFA	FED	32673
SN51UMC	HOR		SN55BJV	LOT	135	SN55HFB	FED	32674
SN51WYC	NIC		SN55BJX	LOT	701	SN55HFC	FED	32675
SN53AUW	LOT	86	SN55BJY	LOT	702	SN55HFD	FED	32676
SN53AUX	LOT	87	SN55BJZ	LOT	703	SN55HFE	FED	32677
SN53AUY	LOT	88	SN55BKA	LOT	704	SN55HFF	FED	32678
SN53AVC	LOT	89	SN55BKD	LOT	705	SN55HFG	FED	32679
SN53AVD	LOT	90	SN55BKE	LOT	706	SN55HFH	FED	32680
SN53AVE	LOT	91	SN55BKF	LOT	707	SN55HFJ	FED	32681
SN53AVF	LOT	92	SN55BKG	LOT	708	SN55HFK	FED	32682
SN53AVG	LOT	93	SN55BKJ	LOT	709	SN55HFL	FED	32683
SN53AVK	LOT	94	SN55BKK	LOT	710	SN55JVA	FED	65750
SN53AVL	LOT	95	SN55BKL	LOT	711	SN55JVC	FED	65751
SN53AVM	LOT	96	SN55BKU	LOT	712	SN55JVD	FED	65752
SN53AVO	LOT	97	SN55BKV	LOT	713	SN55JVE	FED	65753
SN53AVP	LOT	98	SN55BKX	LOT	714	SN55JVG	FED	65742
SN53AVR	LOT	99	SN55BKY	LOT	715	SN55JVH	FED	65743
SN53AVT	LOT	100	SN55BKZ	LOT	716	SN55JVJ	FED	65744
SN53AVU	LOT	629	SN55BLF	LOT	717	SN55JVK	FED	65745
SN53AVV	LOT	630	SN55BLJ	LOT	718	SN55JVL	FED	65746
SN53AVW	LOT	631	SN55BLK	LOT	719	SN55JVM	FED	65747
SN53AVX	LOT	632	SN55BLV	LOT	720	SN55JVO	FED	65748
SN53AVZ	LOT	633	SN55BLX	LOT	721	SN55JVP	FED	65749
SN53BKU	ACN		SN55BLZ	LOT	722	SN55JZR	SAP	
SN53DYA	KIN		SN55BMO	LOT	723	SN55KKE	FED	36029
SN53JNO	LOT	75	SN55BMU	LOT	724	SN55KKF	FED	36030
SN53KHH	FED	65693	SN55BMV	LOT	725	SN56AAE	LOT	751
SN53KHJ	FED	65694	SN55BMY	LOT	726	SN56AAF	LOT	752
SN53KHK	FED	65695	SN55BMZ	LOT	727	SN56AAJ	LOT	753
SN53KHL	FED	65696	SN55BNA	LOT	728	SN56AAK	LOT	754
SN53KHM	FED	65697	SN55BNB	LOT	729	SN56AAO	LOT	755
SN53KHO	FED	65698	SN55BND	LOT	730	SN56AAU	LOT	756
SN53KHP	FED	65699	SN55BNE	LOT	731	SN56AAV	LOT	757
SN53KYO	PHO		SN55BNF	LOT	732	SN56AAX	LOT	758
SN54FBX	AMS		SN55BNJ	LOT	733	SN56AAY	LOT	759
SN54FCE	WCM		SN55BNK	LOT	734	SN56AAZ	LOT	760
SN54FCF	OAD		SN55BNL	LOT	735	SN56ABF	LOT	761
SN54FVG	SHI		SN55BNO	LOT	736	SN56ABK	LOT	762
SN54GWV	SAP		SN55BNU	LOT	737	SN56ABO	LOT	763
SN54KDF	FED	65708	SN55BNV	LOT	738	SN56ABU	LOT	764
SN54KDJ	FED	65709	SN55BNX	LOT	739	SN56ABV	LOT	765
SN54KDK	FED	65710	SN55BNY	LOT	740	SN56ABX	LOT	766
SN54KDO	FED	65711	SN55BNZ	LOT	741	SN56ABZ	LOT	767
SN54KDU	FED	65712	SN55BOF	LOT	742	SN56ACF	LOT	768
SN54KDV	FED	65713	SN55BOH	LOT	743	SN56ACJ	LOT	769
SN54KDX	FED	65714	SN55BOJ	LOT	744	SN56ACO	LOT	770
SN54KDZ	FED	65715	SN55BOU	LOT	745	SN56ACU	LOT	771
SN54KEJ	FED	65716	SN55BOV	LOT	746	SN56ACV	LOT	772
SN54KEK	FED	65717	SN55BPE	LOT	747	SN56ACX	LOT	773
SN54KEU	FED	65718	SN55BPF	LOT	748	SN56ACZ	LOT	774

SN56ADO	LOT	775	SN56AYG	SWSC	36072	SN57EEP	AAA	
SN56ADU	LOT	776	SN56FBE	ROW		SN57EFG	SAQ	
SN56ADV	LOT	777	SN56FWT	HHL		SN57EGV	PWW	
SN56ADX	LOT	778	SN56GBZ	MEW		SN57EHX	HUC	
SN56AEO	LOT	779	SN56GTZ	SAZ		SN57EOD	ETN	
SN56AEA	LOT	780	SN56NSD	SAQ		SN57ERZ	WHY	
SN56AEB	LOT	781	SN57BJU	DMC		SN57EWJ	MUN	403
SN56AEC	LOT	782	SN57BKL	DMC		SN57EXD	WHY	
SN56AED	LOT	783	SN57BLK	DMC		SN57EXE	MUN	404
SN56AEE	LOT	784	SN7CCD	SCM		SN57EZP	SAP	
SN56AEF	LOT	785	SN57DAA	LOT	985	SN57GMO	LOT	865
SN56AEG	LOT	786	SN57DAO	LOT	986	SN57GMU	LOT	866
SN56AEJ	LOT	787	SN57DAU	LOT	987	SN57GMV	LOT	867
SN56AEK	LOT	788	SN57DBO	LOT	988	SN57GMX	LOT	868
SN56AEL	LOT	789	SN57DBU	LOT	989	SN57GMY	LOT	869
SN56AEM	LOT	790	SN57DBV	LOT	990	SN57GMZ	LOT	870
SN56AEO	LOT	791	SN57DBX	LOT	991	SN57GNF	LOT	871
SN56AEP	LOT	792	SN57DBY	LOT	992	SN57GNJ	LOT	872
SN56AET	LOT	793	SN57DBZ	LOT	993	SN57GNK	LOT	873
SN56AEU	LOT	794	SN57DCE	LOT	994	SN57GNO	LOT	874
SN56AEV	LOT	795	SN57DCF	LOT	151	SN57GNP	LOT	875
SN56AEW	LOT	796	SN57DCO	LOT	152	SN57HCP	FED	37135
SN56AEX	LOT	797	SN57DCU	LOT	153	SN57HCU	FED	37136
SN56AEY	LOT	798	SN57DCV	LOT	154	SN57HCV	FED	37137
SN56AEZ	LOT	799	SN57DCX	LOT	155	SN57HCX	FED	37138
SN56AFA	LOT	800	SN57DCY	LOT	156	SN57HCY	FED	37139
SN56AFE	LOT	801	SN57DCZ	LOT	157	SN57HCZ	FED	37140
SN56AFF	LOT	802	SN57DDA	LOT	158	SN57HDA	FED	37141
SN56AFJ	LOT	803	SN57DDE	LOT	159	SN57HDC	FED	37142
SN56AFK	LOT	804	SN57DDF	LOT	160	SN57HDD	FED	37143
SN56AFO	LOT	805	SN57DDJ	LOT	840	SN57HDE	FED	37144
SN56AFU	LOT	806	SN57DDK	LOT	841	SN57HDF	FED	37145
SN56AFV	LOT	807	SN57DDL	LOT	842	SN57HDG	FED	37266
SN56AFX	LOT	808	SN57DDO	LOT	843	SN57HDH	FED	37133
SN56AFY	LOT	809	SN57DDU	LOT	844	SN57HDJ	FED	37134
SN56AFZ	LOT	810	SN57DDV	LOT	845	SN57HZX	FED	69292
SN56AGO	LOT	811	SN57DDX	LOT	846	SN57HZY	FED	69293
SN56AGU	LOT	812	SN57DDY	LOT	847	SN57HZZ	FED	69294
SN56AGX	LOT	814	SN57DDZ	LOT	848	SN57JAO	FED	37267
SN56AGY	LOT	815	SN57DEU	LOT	849	SN57JAU	FED	37268
SN56AGZ	LOT	816	SN57DFA	LOT	850	SN57JBE	FED	37269
SN56AHA	LOT	817	SN57DFC	LOT	851	SN57JBO	FED	37270
SN56AHC	LOT	818	SN57DFD	LOT	852	SN57JBU	FED	37271
SN56AHD	LOT	819	SN57DFE	LOT	853	SN57JBV	FED	37272
SN56AHE	LOT	820	SN57DFF	LOT	854	SN57JBX	FED	37273
SN56AHF	LOT	821	SN57DFG	LOT	855	SN57JBZ	FED	69281
SN56AHG	LOT	822	SN57DFJ	LOT	856	SN57JCJ	FED	69282
SN56AHJ	LOT	823	SN57DFK	LOT	857	SN57JCO	FED	69283
SN56AHK	LOT	824	SN57DFL	LOT	858	SN57JCU	FED	69284
SN56AHL	LOT	825	SN57DFO	LOT	859	SN57JCV	FED	69285
SN56AWZ	IRB		SN57DFP	LOT	860	SN57JCX	FED	69286
SN56AXR	SHIC	27587	SN57DFU	LOT	861	SN57JCY	FED	69287
SN56AXS	SHIC	27588	SN57DFV	LOT	862	SN57JCZ	FED	69288
SN56AXT	SHIC	27589	SN57DFX	LOT	863	SN57JDF	FED	69289
SN56AXU	SHIC	27590	SN57DFY	LOT	864	SN57JDJ	FED	69290
SN56AXV	SHIC	27591	SN57DXF	WCM		SN57JDK	FED	69291
SN56AXW	MUN	561	SN57DXG	GCB		SN57MBO	WHI	
SN56AXX	MUN	562	SN57DXJ	HUC		SN57MEV	WHI	
SN56AYA	CCI		SN57DXL	GUM	444	SN57MSU	FED	69280
SN56AYF	SWSC	36071	SN57DXM	GUM	445	SN58BYM	LOT	161

Reg	Op	No	Reg	Op	No	Reg	Op	No
SN58BYO	LOT	162	SP04DCX	SREN	18100	SP06FVF	SREN	53253
SN58BYP	LOT	163	SP04EUZ	BCM		SP06FVG	SREN	53254
SN58BYR	LOT	164	SP04EVB	MOA		SP06FVH	SREN	53255
SN58BYS	LOT	165	SP04GZX	STAY	47250	SP06FVJ	SREN	53256
SN58BYT	LOT	166	SP05AUV	SAJ		SP07CAA	STAY	54018
SN58BYU	LOT	167	SP04CXX	BCM		SP07CAE	STAY	54019
SN58BYV	LOT	168	SP05CXY	JPM		SP07CAO	STAY	54020
SN58BYW	LOT	169	SP05ECF	SHIC	47252	SP07CAU	STAY	54021
SN58BYX	LOT	170	SP05ECJ	STAY	47253	SP07CAV	STAY	54022
SN58DVZ	DOI		SP05ECN	STAY	47254	SP07ENX	SMI	
SN58FXB	SCN		SP05EFF	SREN	47167	SP07ENY	SMI	
SN58JAU	PWW		SP05EFG	SREN	47168	SP07EWL	STAY	22502
SN59AXA	WLC		SP05EFH	SREN	47169	SP07FCX	STAY	54035
SN59AXB	WLC		SP05EFJ	SREN	47183	SP07FCY	SREN	53304
SN59AXC	WLC		SP05EKX	SREN	34725	SP07FCZ	SREN	53305
SN59BAA	GUM		SP05EKY	SREN	34726	SP07FHA	SMI	
SN59BBE	GUM		SP05EKZ	SREN	34727	SP07HHD	SREN	53277
SN59BFL	LOT	330	SP05ELC	SREN	34728	SP07HHE	SREN	53278
SN59BFM	LOT	331	SP05ELH	SREN	34729	SP07HHF	SREN	53279
SN59BFO	LOT	332	SP05ELJ	SREN	34730	SP07HHG	SREN	53280
SN59BFP	LOT	333	SP05EOH	SREN	47178	SP07HHJ	SREN	53281
SN59BFU	LOT	334	SP05EOJ	SREN	47179	SP07HHK	SREN	53282
SN59BFV	LOT	335	SP05FKG	STAY	16933	SP07HHL	SREN	53283
SN59BFX	LOT	336	SP05FKH	STAY	16934	SP07HHM	SREN	53284
SN59BFY	LOT	337	SP05FKJ	STAY	16935	SP07HHN	SREN	53285
SN59BFZ	LOT	338	SP05FKK	STAY	16936	SP07HHO	SREN	53286
SN59BGE	LOT	339	SP05FUJ	STAY	47255	SP07HHR	SREN	53287
SN59BGF	LOT	340	SP05FUM	STAY	47256	SP07HHS	SREN	53288
SN59BGK	LOT	341	SP06AEC	AMS	39	SP07HHT	SREN	53289
SN59BGO	LOT	342	SP06DAO	SREN	22400	SP07HHU	SREN	53290
SN59BGV	LOT	343	SP06DAU	SREN	22401	SP07HHV	SREN	53291
SN59BGX	LOT	344	SP06DBO	SREN	22402	SP07HHW	SREN	53292
SN59BGY	LOT	345	SP06DBU	SREN	22403	SP07HHX	SREN	53293
SN59BGZ	LOT	346	SP06DBV	SREN	22404	SP07HHY	SREN	53294
SN59BHA	LOT	347	SP06DBX	SREN	22405	SP07HHZ	SREN	53295
SN59BHD	LOT	348	SP06DBY	SREN	22406	SP07SOU	SOU	
SN59BHE	LOT	349	SP06DBZ	SREN	22407	SP08ADZ	SMI	
SN59BHF	LOT	350	SP06DFZ	DMC		SP08AET	SMI	
SN59CZR	MEX		SP06DGE	DMC		SP08DBY	STAY	22564
SN59DCE	BCD		SP06DGF	DMC		SP08DBZ	STAY	22565
SN60AEB	PWW		SP06EGK	STAY	18506	SP08DCE	STAY	22566
SN60AOF	DMC		SP06EGU	STAY	18507	SP08DCF	STAY	22567
SN60AOX	WHY		SP06EGV	STAY	18508	SP08DCO	STAY	22568
SN60AOY	WHY		SP06EGX	STAY	18509	SP08DCU	STAY	22569
SN60BFV	WHI		SP06EKA	AMS	38	SP08DCV	STAY	22570
SN60CNU	DMC		SP06FBG	SMI		SP08DCX	STAY	22571
SO06SOU	SOU		SP06FCF	SREN	47301	SP08DCY	STAY	22572
SP02HMV	HOR		SP06FCG	SREN	47302	SP08DCZ	STAY	22573
SP03GDJ	STAY	16929	SP06FCJ	SREN	47303	SP08DDA	BBD	22574
SP03GDK	STAY	16930	SP06FMY	SREN	35101	SP08DDE	STAY	22575
SP03GDU	STAY	16931	SP06FMZ	SREN	35102	SP08DDF	STAY	22576
SP04AKG	ACM		SP06FNA	SREN	47364	SP08DDJ	STAY	22577
SP04DBV	SREN	18092	SP06FNC	SREN	47366	SP08DDK	STAY	22578
SP04DBX	SREN	18093	SP06FND	SREN	47367	SP08DDL	STAY	22579
SP04DBY	SREN	18094	SP06FNE	SREN	47368	SP08DDN	SREN	22580
SP04DBZ	SREN	18095	SP06FVA	SREN	53248	SP08DDO	SREN	22581
SP04DCE	SREN	18096	SP06FVB	SREN	53249	SP08ENK	AMS	43
SP04DCF	SREN	18097	SP06FVC	SREN	53250	SP08ENL	AMS	42
SP04DCU	SREN	18098	SP06FVD	SREN	53251	SP08FJX	AMS	44
SP04DCV	SREN	18099	SP06FVE	SREN	53252	SP08FLZ	SREN	47607

Reg	Op	No	Reg	Op	No	Reg	Op	No
SP08FMA	SREN	47608	SP54CHJ	NXD	7004	SP57CNY	STAY	27524
SP08FMC	SREN	47609	SP54CHK	NXD	7005	SP57CNZ	STAY	27525
SP08FMD	SREN	47610	SP54CHL	NXD	7006	SP57COA	STAY	27526
SP08FME	SREN	47611	SP54CHN	NXD	7007	SP57COH	STAY	27527
SP08FPF	SWSC	54047	SP54CHO	NXD	7008	SP57COJ	STAY	27528
SP08FPJ	STAY	54048	SP54EGF	STAY	46690	SP57COU	STAY	27529
SP08FUV	SREN	53107	SP54EGJ	STAY	46691	SP57CPE	STAY	27530
SP09CWK	DMC		SP54ENO	STAY	47251	SP57DFD	STAY	27531
SP09DOH	SREN	22887	SP54ETX	STAY	46692	SP57FZZ	AYR	
SP09DOJ	SREN	22888	SP54FML	MFW		SP57XKL	SCN	
SP09DOU	SREN	22889	SP54FMM	MFW		SP58AZC	SREN	47657
SP09DPE	SREN	22890	SP55CXG	SREN	47228	SP58BYX	STAY	27545
SP09DPF	SREN	22872	SP55CXH	SREN	47229	SP58BYY	STAY	27546
SP09DPK	SREN	22873	SP55CXJ	SREN	47230	SP58BZA	STAY	27547
SP09DPN	SREN	22874	SP55CXK	SREN	47231	SP58BZB	STAY	27548
SP09DPO	SREN	22875	SP55CXL	SREN	47232	SP58BZC	STAY	27549
SP09DPU	SREN	22876	SP55CXM	SREN	47233	SP58BZD	STAY	27550
SP09DPV	SREN	22877	SP55CXN	SREN	47234	SP58BZE	STAY	27551
SP09DPX	SREN	22878	SP55CXO	SREN	47235	SP58BZF	STAY	27552
SP09DPY	SREN	22879	SP55DDE	BBD	47257	SP58CXV	STAY	19368
SP09DPZ	SREN	22880	SP55DND	STAY	47258	SP58CXW	STAY	19367
SP09DRO	SREN	22881	SP55EEA	SREN	47240	SP58CXX	STAY	19366
SP09DRV	SREN	22882	SP55EEF	MFW		SP58DPE	SMI	
SP09DRX	SREN	22883	SP55EGC	SREN	22369	SP58DPF	SMI	
SP09DRZ	SREN	22884	SP55EGD	SREN	22370	SP58DPK	SMI	
SP09DSE	SREN	22885	SP55EGE	SREN	22371	SP59AON	SREN	19554
SP09DSO	SREN	22886	SP55EGF	SREN	22372	SP59AOO	SREN	19555
SP10CWV	NXD	7029	SP55EGJ	SREN	22373	SP59AOR	SREN	19556
SP10CWW	NXD	7030	SP55EGK	SREN	22374	SP59AOS	SREN	19557
SP10CWX	NXD	7031	SP55EGU	SREN	22375	SP59AOT	BBD	19558
SP10CWY	NXD	7032	SP55EGV	SREN	22376	SP59AOU	SREN	19544
SP10CWZ	NXD	7033	SP55EGX	SREN	22377	SP59AOV	SREN	19545
SP10CXA	NXD	7019	SP55EGY	SREN	22378	SP59AOW	SREN	19546
SP10CXB	NXD	7020	SP55EHB	SREN	22367	SP59AOX	SREN	19547
SP10CXC	NXD	7021	SP55EHC	SREN	22368	SP59AOY	SREN	19548
SP10CXD	NXD	7022	SP56AGO	STAY	22506	SP59AOZ	SREN	19549
SP10CXE	NXD	7023	SP56AGU	STAY	22507	SP59APF	SREN	19550
SP10CXF	NXD	7024	SP56CXD	SHIC	47391	SP59APK	SREN	19551
SP10CXH	NXD	7026	SP56CXE	STAY	47392	SP59APO	SREN	19552
SP10CXJ	NXD	7027	SP56CXF	SREN	47393	SP59APU	SREN	19553
SP10CXK	NXD	7028	SP56EBL	SREN	53257	SP59APV	SREN	19541
SP10DWV	AMS	45	SP56EBM	SREN	53258	SP59APX	SREN	19542
SP51AWX	STAY	16923	SP56EBN	SREN	53259	SP59APY	SREN	19543
SP53EGY	STAY	42224	SP56EBO	SREN	53260	SP59BSX	MFW	
SP53EGZ	STAY	42225	SP56EBU	SREN	53261	SP59CTC	SREN	27612
SP53PYG	YUL		SP56FGO	STAY	22501	SP59CTF	SREN	27603
SP54AHX	MFW		SP56FGV	STAY	22503	SP59CTG	SREN	27613
SP54CGG	NXD	7009	SP56FGX	STAY	22504	SP59CTK	SREN	27604
SP54CGK	NXD	7010	SP56FGZ	STAY	22505	SP59CTO	SREN	27605
SP54CGO	NXD	7011	SP56VHY	SBO		SP59CTU	SREN	27606
SP54CGU	NXD	7012	SP57CNC	SREN	53296	SP59CTV	SREN	27607
SP54CGV	NXD	7013	SP57CNE	SREN	24001	SP59CTX	SREN	27608
SP54CGX	NXD	7014	SP57CNF	SREN	24002	SP59CTY	SREN	27609
SP54CGY	NXD	7015	SP57CNJ	SREN	24003	SP59CTZ	SREN	27610
SP54CGZ	NXD	7016	SP57CNK	SREN	24004	SP59CUA	SREN	27611
SP54CHC	NXD	7017	SP57CNN	SREN	24005	SP59DCE	MFW	
SP54CHD	NXD	7018	SP57CNO	SREN	24006	SR02NRN	PHO	
SP54CHF	NXD	7001	SP57CNU	SREN	24007	SR07SOU	SOU	
SP54CHG	NXD	7002	SP57CNV	SREN	24008	SRU410	HLO	
SP54CHH	NXD	7003	SP57CNX	SREN	24009	SS06PCH	DPC	

SS07JAY	SCJ		SV06GRX	FAB	69124	SV08FZN	BBD	47602
SS08PCH	DPC		SV06GUO	GIC		SV08FZO	BBD	47603
SS10PCH	DPC		SV06GUU	GIC		SV08FZP	BBD	47604
SS57PCH	DPC		SV07ACX	SHIC	54013	SV08FZR	BBD	47605
SSU727	OAD		SV07ACY	SHIC	54014	SV08FZS	BBD	47606
ST05LMO	KCO		SV07ACZ	SHIC	54015	SV08GUU	BBD	36046
ST09SOU	SOU		SV07ADO	SHIC	54016	SV08GUV	BBD	36047
ST52GZN	MFW		SV07ADU	SHIC	54017	SV08GUW	BBD	36048
ST52NTL	STAY	16924	SV07AZZ	BUT		SV08GUX	BBD	36049
ST52NTM	STAY	16925	SV07EHB	FAB	69125	SV08GVA	BBD	36050
ST52NTN	STAY	16926	SV07EHC	FAB	69126	SV08GXM	SHIC	53101
ST52NTO	STAY	16927	SV07EHD	FAB	69127	SV08GXN	SHIC	53102
ST52NTU	STAY	16928	SV07EHE	FAB	69128	SV08GXO	SHIC	53103
STG476Y	KOA		SV07EHF	FAB	69129	SV08GXP	SHIC	53104
SUI1480	SOK		SV07EHG	FAB	69130	SV08VUW	POH	
SUX476X	GCT		SV07EHH	FAB	69131	SV08VVE	POH	
SV03JZK	KIN		SV07EHJ	FAB	69132	SV08VVG	POH	
SV04DVK	STAY	47051	SV07EHK	FAB	69133	SV08VVH	POH	
SV04DVL	STAY	47052	SV07EHL	FAB	69134	SV09AEZ	MAY	26
SV04DVM	STAY	47053	SV07FCC	BBD	36031	SV09AOA	MAY	18
SV04DVN	STAY	47054	SV07FCD	BBD	36032	SV09AOB	MAY	28
SV04HLM	BBD	47078	SV07FCE	BBD	36033	SV09AOT	MAY	12
SV04HLN	BBD	47079	SV07FCF	BBD	36034	SV09AOU	MAY	14
SV04HLP	BBD	47080	SV07FCG	BBD	36035	SV09BHL	BBD	53321
SV05DJU	SHIC	47161	SV07FKY	SHIC	54036	SV09DNJ	MAY	9
SV05DJX	BBD	47162	SV08DHE	BBD	53306	SV09DNN	MAY	8
SV05DJY	SHIC	47180	SV08DHF	BBD	53307	SV09EFZ	BBD	53334
SV05DKA	SHIC	47181	SV08DHG	BBD	53308	SV09EGD	SHIC	53109
SV05DKD	SHIC	47182	SV08DHJ	BBD	53309	SV09EGE	SHIC	53110
SV05DXA	FAB	10154	SV08DHK	BBD	53310	SV09EGF	SHIC	53111
SV05DXC	FAB	10155	SV08DHL	BBD	53311	SV09EGJ	SHIC	53112
SV05DXD	FAB	10156	SV08DHM	BBD	53312	SV09EGK	BBD	53113
SV05DXE	FAB	10157	SV08DHN	BBD	53313	SV09EGY	SHIC	53108
SV05DXF	FAB	10158	SV08DHO	BBD	53314	SV09EGZ	SHIC	53331
SV05DXG	FAB	10159	SV08DHP	BBD	53315	SV09EHB	SHIC	53332
SV05DXH	FAB	10160	SV08DHU	BBD	53316	SV09EHC	SHIC	53333
SV05DXJ	FAB	10161	SV08DHX	BBD	53317	SV10CUK	D&B	
SV05DXK	FAB	10162	SV08DHY	SHIC	53318	SV10DDK	BBD	50231
SV05DXL	FAB	10163	SV08DHZ	SHIC	53319	SV10DDL	BBD	50232
SV05DXM	FAB	10164	SV08DJD	SHIC	53320	SV10DMZ	SHIC	27631
SV05DXO	FAB	10165	SV08FHA	FAB	69351	SV10DND	SHIC	27632
SV05DXP	FAB	10166	SV08FHB	FAB	69352	SV52VXA	HOR	
SV05DXR	FAB	10167	SV08FHC	FAB	69353	SV52VXB	HOR	
SV05DXS	FAB	10168	SV08FHD	FAB	69354	SV53DDJ	SHIC	34482
SV05DXT	FAB	10169	SV08FHE	FAB	69355	SV53DDK	SHIC	34483
SV05DXU	FAB	10170	SV08FHF	FAB	69356	SV53DDL	SHIC	34484
SV05DXW	FAB	10171	SV08FHG	FAB	69357	SV53DDN	SHIC	34485
SV05DXX	FAB	10172	SV08FXP	FAB	37633	SV53DDO	SHIC	34486
SV05DXY	FAB	10173	SV08FXR	FAB	37634	SV53DDU	SHIC	34487
SV05ZKT	WMC		SV08FXS	FAB	37635	SV53DDX	SHIC	34488
SV05ZPP	WMC		SV08FXT	FAB	37636	SV53DDY	SHIC	34489
SV06CEK	WHY		SV08FXV	FAB	37637	SV53DDZ	SHIC	34490
SV06CEN	APE		SV08FXW	FAB	37638	SV53ELJ	HUC	
SV06ESG	D&B		SV08FXX	FAB	37639	SV54BYM	BBD	47111
SV06ESN	D&B		SV08FXY	FAB	37640	SV54BYN	SHIC	47807
SV06FTF	BBD	53246	SV08FXZ	FAB	37641	SV54BYO	SHIC	53201
SV06FTJ	BBD	53247	SV08FYA	FAB	37642	SV54BYP	SHIC	53202
SV06GRF	FAB	69110	SV08FYB	FAB	37643	SV54BYR	SHIC	53203
SV06GRK	FAB	69122	SV08FYC	FAB	37644	SV54BYT	SWSC	53204
SV06GRU	FAB	69123	SV08FZM	BBD	47601	SV54BYU	SHIC	53205

SV54BYW	SHIC	53206	SV55CCY	BBD	22351	SV57BYX	BBD	27540
SV54BYY	SHIC	53207	SV55CCZ	BBD	22352	SV57BYY	BBD	27541
SV54BYZ	SWSC	53208	SV55EEJ	BBD	22363	SV58ASZ	FAB	23330
SV54CFV	FAB	68519	SV55EEM	BBD	22364	SV58BLN	SHIC	19369
SV54CFY	FAB	68518	SV55EEP	BBD	53221	SV58BLX	SHIC	19370
SV54EKP	SHIC	53209	SV55EER	BBD	53222	SV58BLZ	SHIC	19371
SV54EKR	SWSC	53210	SV55EES	BBD	53223	SV58BMO	SHIC	19372
SV54EKT	SHIC	53211	SV55EEU	BBD	53225	SV58BMU	SHIC	19373
SV54EKU	SHIC	53212	SV55FJN	BBD	53239	SV58BMY	BBD	19374
SV54EKW	SWSC	53213	SV55FJO	BBD	53240	SV58BMZ	BBD	19375
SV54EKX	SHIC	53214	SV55FJP	BBD	53241	SV58BNA	BBD	19376
SV54EKY	SWSC	53215	SV55FJU	BBD	53242	SV58BNB	SHIC	19377
SV54EKZ	SWSC	53216	SV55FJX	BBD	53243	SV58BND	BBD	19378
SV54ELC	SWSC	50126	SV55FJY	BBD	53244	SV58JJZ	D&B	
SV54ELX	SWSC	50132	SV55FJZ	BBD	53245	SV59CGG	BBD	50227
SV54EMF	SWSC	53217	SV55FKA	BBD	53226	SV59CGK	BBD	50228
SV54EMJ	SWSC	53218	SV55FKB	SHIC	53227	SV59CGO	BBD	50229
SV54EMK	SWSC	53219	SV55FKD	SHIC	53228	SV59CGU	BBD	50230
SV54ENC	SHIC	53220	SV55FKE	SHIC	53229	SV59CGX	BBD	54062
SV54EPJ	WMC		SV55FKF	SHIC	53230	SV59CGY	BBD	54063
SV54FRZ	FAB	23401	SV55FKG	SHIC	53231	SV59CGZ	BBD	54064
SV54FTA	FAB	23402	SV55FKH	BBD	53232	SV59CHC	BBD	54065
SV55BZB	STAY	47219	SV55FKJ	BBD	53233	SV59CHD	BBD	54066
SV55BZC	STAY	47220	SV55FKK	BBD	53234	SV59CHF	BBD	54067
SV55BZD	STAY	47221	SV55FKL	BBD	53235	SV59CHG	BBD	54068
SV55BZE	STAY	47222	SV55FKM	BBD	53236	SV59CHJ	SWSC	54069
SV55BZF	SHIC	34731	SV55FKN	BBD	53237	SV59CHK	BBD	54070
SV55BZG	SHIC	34732	SV55FKO	BBD	53238	SV59CHL	SWSC	54071
SV55BZH	SHIC	34733	SV55GWJ	SHIC	34795	SV59CHN	BBD	54072
SV55BZJ	SHIC	34734	SV55GWK	SHIC	34796	SV59CHO	BBD	54073
SV55BZL	SHIC	34735	SV56BVR	BBD	53262	SV59CHX	BBD	54074
SV55BZM	SHIC	34736	SV56BVS	BBD	53263	SV59CHY	BBD	54075
SV55BZN	SHIC	34737	SV56BVT	BBD	53264	SV59DDZ	BBD	27601
SV55BZO	STAY	47212	SV56BVU	BBD	53265	SV59DEU	BBD	27602
SV55BZP	BBD	47213	SV56BVW	BBD	53266	SW02VFX	WMC	
SV55BZR	BBD	47214	SV56BVX	BBD	53267	SW02VGY	WMC	
SV55BZU	STAY	47215	SV56BVY	BBD	53268	SW02VTP	ABO	
SV55BZW	BBD	47216	SV56BVZ	BBD	53269	SW03OYE	SWSC	60004
SV55BZX	STAY	47217	SV56BWA	BBD	53270	SW03OYF	SWSC	60005
SV55BZY	STAY	47218	SV56BWB	BBD	54008	SW03OYL	BBD	60010
SV55CAA	BBD	22353	SV56BWC	BBD	54009	SW03VCX	SAA	
SV55CAE	BBD	22354	SV56BWD	BBD	54010	SW52FCF	MCC	
SV55CAO	BBD	22355	SV56BWE	BBD	54011	SXF615	GEM	
SV55CAU	BBD	22356	SV56BWF	SHIC	54012	SXI2887	MAT	
SV55CAX	BBD	22357	SV57BFP	SHIC	19169	SY05DRX	MLC	
SV55CBF	BBD	22358	SV57BFU	SHIC	19170	SY07CEX	SHIC	21203
SV55CBO	BBD	22359	SV57BFX	SHIC	19171	SY07CFA	SHIC	21204
SV55CBU	BBD	22360	SV57BFY	SHIC	19172	SY07CFD	SHIC	21205
SV55CBX	BBD	22361	SV57BFZ	SHIC	19173	SY07CFU	SHIC	21206
SV55CBY	BBD	22362	SV57BGE	SHIC	19174	SY07CNJ	SHIC	21207
SV55CCA	STAY	47223	SV57BGF	SHIC	19175	SY07CUW	SHIC	16947
SV55CCD	SREN	47224	SV57BGK	SHIC	19176	SY07CUX	SHIC	16948
SV55CCE	STAY	47225	SV57BYM	BBD	27532	SY07CVA	SHIC	16945
SV55CCF	STAY	47226	SV57BYN	BBD	27533	SY07CVB	SHIC	16946
SV55CCJ	STAY	47227	SV57BYP	BBD	27534	SY51EHT	SHIC	27051
SV55CCK	SHIC	34738	SV57BYR	BBD	27535	SY51EHU	SHIC	27052
SV55CCN	BBD	34739	SV57BYS	BBD	27536	SY51EHV	SHIC	27053
SV55CCO	BBD	34740	SV57BYT	BBD	27537	SY51EHX	SHIC	27054
SV55CCU	SREN	22349	SV57BYU	BBD	27538	SY51EHZ	SHIC	27055
SV55CCX	SREN	22350	SV57BYW	BBD	27539	SY52UMS	SCB	

SY54BMV	SCD		T280TSF	APE		T504EUB	MLS	
SY57AXR	SHIC	36066	T288JLD	FG	41288	T504SSG	LOT	504
SY57AXU	SHIC	36067	T298LCH	CSA		T504TOL	MCO	2032
SY57AYF	SHIC	36068	T299BNN	PTW		T505SSG	LOT	505
SY57AYG	SHIC	36069	T299LCH	CSA		T505TOL	MCO	
SY57AYH	SHIC	36070	T301JLD	FG	41301	T506SSG	LOT	506
SY57EYH	FAB	69265	T301UOX	NXD	0301	T507SSG	LOT	507
SY57EYJ	FAB	69266	T302JLD	FG	41302	T508SSG	LOT	508
SY57EYK	FAB	69267	T303JLD	FG	41303	T509SSG	LOT	509
SYJ961X	MEW		T304JLD	FG	41304	T510SSG	LOT	510
T3APT	MLS		T304UOX	NXD	7200	T517EUB	GUM	600
T3DOT	DOT		T305JLD	FG	41305	T520EUB	GUM	601
T6DOF	DWF		T306JLD	FG	41306	T523GSR	SMI	
T7DOF	DWF		T307UOX	NXD	7309	T527EUB	MLS	
T8DOF	DWF		T307VYG	FG	40558	T534EUB	GUM	604
T8OVA	SAZ		T308VYG	FG	40559	T535EUB	SHIC	52519
T9DOF	DWF		T309VYG	FG	40560	T536EUB	SHIC	52518
T9TAP	KIN		T310VYG	FG	40561	T552ADN	BBD	47160
T10HAY	FIT		T311VYG	FG	40562	T566BSS	FED	60220
T10MCT	MCM		T312VYG	FG	40563	T567BSS	FED	60221
T11OUR	MOA		T331BNL	MCS		T572GSL	SAQ	
T12DEV	DEV		T333BUS	MLC		T577ASN	NXD	7308
T13ECL	ECL		T337ALR	FED	41337	T594JLS	HQL	
T13GDR	EAR		T339ALR	FED	41339	T599BRG	MLS	
T20JLS	LSK		T341LGB	JMC		T600WCM	WCM	
T20MCT	MCM		T342ALR	FED	41342	T608DGD	BCM	
T25ERS	SMI		T347AGR	MCM		T609DGD	ARC	
T30JLS	LSK		T373JWA	GEM		T640KCS	SWSC	51092
T34JBA	MLI		T381RFL	SHI		T641KCS	SWSC	51093
T35CNN	LID		T401JSL	GUM	602	T642BSS	SPA	
T36VCS	SWSC	33089	T402UCS	SWSC	33772	T642KCS	SWSC	51094
T37JBA	PTW		T403EGD	CNV		T660KPU	SREN	17060
T40JLS	LSK		T403UCS	SWSC	33773	T661KPU	STAY	17061
T50JLS	LSK		T404EGD	CNV		T676ASN	CFT	
T50TPB	JTK		T408BSS	BLY		T702BGB	GIC	
T52JBA	GUM	411	T409BGB	STK		T705TCS	PUM	
T52MOA	SAW		T420JNE	SHI		T709UOS	ACM	
T53JBA	GUM	412	T420UUB	AYR		T710SUT	MCM	
T56RJL	SHB		T421GUG	FG	61022	T712TCS	PUM	
T70JLS	LSK		T422GUG	FG	61023	T716TCS	MEW	
T75JBA	HOR		T423GUG	FG	61024	T717UOS	TEL	
T80LRT	STK		T423TGA	ALA	AT112	T721KFJ	LID	
T90WJC	WJC	XV02	T424GUG	FG	61025	T732JGB	FG	
T95JHN	SWSC	51095	T425GUG	FG	61026	T735JGB	FG	62935
T96JHN	SWSC	51096	T426GUG	FG	61027	T736JGB	FG	62936
T97JHN	SWSC	51097	T427GUG	FG	61028	T782TSF	GSM	GS70
T99HAL	HAO		T428AGP	CNV		T794TWX	MUN	794
T110JBC	MFW		T430JLD	FG	41300	T796BGD	ESB	
T111WCS	WMC		T431LGP	SMP		T798FRU	CFT	
T130UOX	NXD	300	T432EBD	MUN	432	T802FRU	DEV	
T136ARE	MEW		T435EBD	MUN	435	T805LLC	FG	32805
T167ATS	STAY	42237	T443KAW	BEK		T811LLC	FG	32811
T168ATS	STAY	42238	T460JRH	SAM		T813LLC	FG	32813
T190AUA	GCB		T469BCN	SBQ		T814LLC	FG	32814
T191AUA	GCB		T469GPS	BBD	33469	T815LLC	FG	32815
T200OCT	SAP		T470GPS	SHIC	33470	T816LLC	FG	32816
T206OWG	MFW		T471GPS	SHIC	33471	T820LLC	FG	32820
T272RMY	CNV		T501SSG	LOT	501	T821LLC	FG	32821
T278JLD	FG	41278	T502SSG	LOT	502	T823LLC	FG	32823
T279JLD	FG	41279	T503SSG	LOT	503	T824LLC	FG	32824

T825LLC	FG	32825	TJI4022	BRW		V1PEO	ROW	
T826LLC	FG	32826	TJI4024	SMP		V1PHC	HUC	
T827LLC	FG	32827	TJI5392	DOT		V2AMS	ABK	
T828LLC	FG	32828	TJI5393	DOT		V9DOT	DOT	
T829LLC	FG	32829	TJI5394	DOT		V10CBC	GUM	119
T830LLC	FG	32830	TJI6264	HOU		V34ESC	FED	62391
T831LLC	FG	32831	TJN505R	HOR		V35ESC	FED	62392
T832LLC	FG	32832	TJT196X	MCC		V40JLS	LSK	
T833LLC	FG	32833	TMS407X	KOA		V58KWO	GSM	GS68
T834LLC	FG	32834	TND423X	DCA		V86LYS	SAA	
T835LLC	FG	32835	TOF694S	ESB		V90CBC	JJT	
T836LLC	FG	32836	TRM144	SHIC	52049	V90JLS	LSK	
T837LLC	FG	32837	TRR814R	WJC	W1	V91LYS	BRW	
T838LLC	FG	32838	TSJ71S	KOA		V93LYS	BRW	
T839LLC	FG	32839	TSJ61S	APE		V100OJW	SAP	
T840LLC	FG	32840	TSU638	SWSC	13624	V100WCM	WCM	
T841LLC	FG	32841	TSU642	BBD	51063	V103DBB	SBO	
T842LLC	FG	32842	TSV677	DJI		V110ESF	GUM	200
T843LLC	FG	32843	TSV718	STAY	33434	V116FSF	FG	61667
T844LLC	FG	32844	TSV719	BBD	50135	V117FSF	FG	61668
T845LLC	FG	32845	TSV720	SREN	34086	V118FSF	FG	61669
T848LLC	FG	32848	TSV721	SWSC	50140	V119FSF	FG	61670
T865KLF	FG	32865	TSV722	BBD	33438	V120FSF	FG	61671
T866KLF	FG	32866	TSV778	BBD	50142	V122FSF	FG	61672
T868KLF	FG	32868	TSV781	BBD	50147	V126DND	FED	60178
T870KLF	FG	32870	TSV956	MOA		V127DND	FED	60179
T871KLF	FG	32871	TU07SOU	SOU		V128DND	FED	60180
T872MKL	LID		TVP863S	ESB	7	V129DND	FED	60181
T874TGD	MCO	3040	TVS619	EAR		V130DND	FED	60182
T877SSF	STP		TXI2251	MCO		V133ESF	SBP	
T881JBC	M&C		TXI4242	MCO	4001	V134DND	FED	60186
T900WCM	WCM		UAX891	MPC		V135DND	FED	60187
T919OWB	BLS		UCD528	HQL		V136DND	FED	60188
T945BNN	HOR		UCS659	SWSC	19959	V139DND	FED	60191
T947BNN	HOR		UCZ3032	HEB		V140DND	FED	60192
T948BNN	HOR		UDL453	YUL		V142ESC	FG	61043
T949BAK	MCD		UGE471	AUS		V142MVX	SWSC	34142
T976OGA	STP		UHG354Y	SCB		V143ESC	FG	61044
T980OGA	SMI		UHG741R	ESB		V143FOS	JTK	
T981WPN	BUT		UHR412	SPA		V143MVX	SWSC	34143
T993PFH	SHIC	59661	UIL1250	RSS		V146MVX	SWSC	34146
TDC854X	FIT		UIL1270	RSS		V151MVX	SWSC	34151
TDZ1960	PWW		UIL4223	WTB		V154EFS	HOR	
TFX966	SHIC	52048	UIL7808	SHIC	52679	V162EFS	HOR	
TIB2865	LID		UIL7816	DEV		V165ESL	NXD	7165
TIB5004	WMC		UIL7828	JJT		V166ESL	NXD	7166
TIB7836	CAM		UIW2135	D&B		V167ESL	NXD	7167
TIL2360	WTB		UJI4521	LID		V167MYS	MCO	2018
TIL4032	FIT		UKZ7822	HLO		V168ESL	NXD	7168
TIL4034	FIT		ULS658T	WJC	DD658	V168MYS	MCO	2020
TIL5416	PHO		URN168Y	SCB		V169ESL	NXD	7169
TIW2316	VIC		URN170Y	SCB		V169MYS	MCO	2021
TIW4227	GUM	605	URS318X	FAB	31528	V169NGE	WMC	
TIW5725	MAT		URS321X	GCT		V170ESL	NXD	7170
TIW7700	KIN		USU643	AUS		V170MYS	MCO	2019
TIW8406	VIC		USU662	NXD	7270	V171EPS	GCB	
TIW9829	KOA		USV981	HQL		V171ESL	NXD	7171
TJI1328	KOA		USY858	PWW		V172ESL	NXD	7172
TJI1700	CSA		UU08SOU	SOU		V172FFS	CFT	
TJI3140	SMK		UVS158	STU		V173ESL	NXD	7173

V173FFS	CFT		V518ESC	LOT	518	V618LGC	ASW	1488
V174ESL	NXD	7174	V519ESC	LOT	519	V619LGC	ASW	1489
V175EPS	GCB		V520ESC	LOT	520	V620LGC	ASW	1490
V175ESL	NXD	7175	V521ESC	LOT	521	V621LGC	ASW	1491
V176ESL	NXD	7176	V522ESC	LOT	522	V622LGC	ASW	1492
V177ESL	NXD	7177	V523ESC	LOT	523	V649PHJ	WCG	
V178ESL	NXD	7178	V524ESC	LOT	524	V671EDK	DOT	
V179ESL	NXD	7179	V525ESC	LOT	525	V676FPO	FG	42376
V217DSS	DIC		V526ESC	LOT	526	V691EWB	ALA	AT 95
V221GLS	FG	61673	V527ESC	LOT	527	V701DSA	BBD	22701
V246BNV	MUN	472	V527ESH	FED	62385	V701LWT	ASW	1471
V252ESX	STAY	22252	V528ESC	LOT	528	V702DSA	BBD	22702
V255ESX	BBD	22255	V528ESH	FED	62386	V703DSA	BBD	22703
V258DPS	LSK		V529ESC	LOT	529	V704DSA	BBD	22704
V258ESX	SWSC	22258	V529ESH	FED	62387	V705DSA	BBD	22705
V259ESX	STAY	22259	V530ESC	LOT	530	V706DSA	BBD	22706
V262ESX	SREN	22262	V530ESH	FED	62388	V707DSA	BBD	22707
V263ESX	SREN	22263	V531ESC	LOT	531	V708DSA	BBD	22708
V264ESX	STAY	22264	V531ESH	FED	62389	V709DSA	BBD	22709
V266ESX	SREN	22266	V532ESC	LOT	532	V710DSA	BBD	22710
V267ESX	SREN	22267	V532ESH	FED	62390	V711DSA	BBD	22711
V268ESX	SREN	22268	V533ESC	LOT	533	V712DSA	STAY	22712
V277DRC	PTW		V534ESC	LOT	534	V713DSA	SWSC	22713
V307GBY	FG	41307	V535ESC	LOT	535	V725GGE	SBZ	
V308GBY	FG	41308	V536ESC	LOT	536	V772GCS	SHIC	42019
V309GBY	FG	41309	V537ESC	LOT	537	V773GCS	SWSC	42020
V310GBY	FG	41310	V538ESC	LOT	538	V774GCS	SHIC	42021
V311GBY	FG	41311	V539ESC	LOT	539	V802DFV	BBD	22802
V311NGD	ASW	1408	V540DYA	KIN		V803DFV	BBD	22803
V312GBY	FG	41312	V540ESC	LOT	540	V828GGA	HTR	
V312NGD	ASW	1409	V541ESC	LOT	541	V829GGA	MEW	
V313GBY	FG	41313	V542ESC	LOT	542	V867HBY	FG	32867
V313NGD	ASW	1410	V543ESC	LOT	543	V869HBY	FG	32869
V314DSL	BBD	33264	V544ESC	LOT	544	V889HLH	FG	32889
V314GBY	FG	41314	V545ESC	LOT	545	V890HLH	FG	32890
V316DSL	STAY	33266	V601GCS	SWSC	22601	V891HLH	FG	32891
V317DSL	STAY	33267	V601GGB	FG	10044	V892HLH	FG	32892
V326XDO	KIN		V602GCS	SWSC	22602	V898DNB	CBC	
V349DLH	FED	41349	V602GGB	FG	10045	V899HLH	FG	32899
V350EKY	DEV		V603GCS	STAY	22603	V906DPN	STAY	52656
V357DLH	FED	41357	V603GGB	FG	10103	V956HEB	HTR	
V359DLH	FED	41359	V604GCS	STAY	22604	V958DSO	BUT	
V362CNH	FED	65662	V604GGB	FG	10104	V974DRM	SWSC	33074
V363CNH	FED	65663	V605GCS	SWSC	22605	V975DRM	SWSC	33075
V364CNH	FED	65664	V605GGB	FG	10105	V988HLH	FG	32888
V388KVY	HQD		V606GCS	SWSC	22606	VAV15	A&B	
V401SVV	JTK		V606GGB	FG	10106	VAV552	SBZ	
V451NGA	JJT		V607GGB	FG	10107	VAZ2534	MCR	
V452NGA	SMP		V608GGB	FG	10108	VAZ4859	MCL	
V490FSF	JJT		V609GGB	FG	10109	VAZ4918	MCO	4003
V500CBC	GUM	118	V609LGC	ASW	1479	VCS391	SWSC	50131
V501FSF	NIC		V610GGB	FG	10110	VCU303T	ACM	
V502FSF	NIC		V610LGC	ASW	1480	VEF151Y	MCD	
V511ESC	LOT	511	V611LGC	ASW	1481	VEL374	SPA	
V512ESC	LOT	512	V612LGC	ASW	1482	VIA230	SBQ	
V513ESC	LOT	513	V613LGC	ASW	1483	VIA488	KIN	
V514ESC	LOT	514	V614LGC	ASW	1484	VIA508	KIN	
V515ESC	LOT	515	V615LGC	ASW	1485	VIA963	KIN	
V516ESC	LOT	516	V616LGC	ASW	1486	VIB3264	ESB	
V517ESC	LOT	517	V617LGC	ASW	1487	VIB9485	DEV	

VIL4027	STU		W60JLS	LSK		W556BOV	LID	
VIL6350	JPM		W77BUS	KOA		W556RSG	LOT	556
VIL6685	PHO		W78PRG	ASW	1918	W557RSG	LOT	557
VIL6686	PHO		W79PRG	ASW	1919	W558RSG	LOT	558
VIL8250	WTB		W82PRG	ASW	1921	W559RSG	LOT	559
VIL 8578	WLC		W90JLS	LSK		W561RSG	LOT	561
VIL9330	CCG		W100WCM	WCM		W562JVV	MUN	471
VIL9331	MDO		W116CWR	FG	10033	W562RSG	LOT	562
VIL9332	CCG		W117CWR	FG	10034	W563JVV	DPG	
VIW7191	MOB		W131WPO	FG	10131	W563RSG	LOT	563
VJI1995	BLY		W132VLO	FG	32950	W564RSG	LOT	564
VJI3002	ROW		W132WPO	FG	10132	W566JVV	DCA	
VJI5885	SBQ		W133WPO	FG	10133	W566RSG	LOT	566
VJI9410	HQD		W137OSM	MEW		W567RSG	LOT	567
VJI9413	ROW		W153RYB	SBP		W568RSG	LOT	568
VJI9414	ROW		W158WTA	MEW		W569RSG	LOT	569
VKS910V	SBZ		W173CDN	OAD		W571RSG	LOT	571
VLT143	LOT	7	W174MWF	ORD		W572RSG	LOT	572
VLT163	LOT	2	W212DNO	SREN	34212	W573RSG	LOT	573
VLT235	LOT	3	W213DNO	SREN	34213	W574RSG	LOT	574
VLT237	LOT	8	W216DNO	SREN	34216	W575RSG	LOT	575
VLT242	LOT	9	W234DNO	SREN	34217	W576RSG	LOT	576
VLT281	LOT	10	W251GSE	SPA		W577RFS	FAB	62170
VMP10G	WJC		W252KDO	LID		W577RSG	LOT	577
VNU328	CFM		W262EWU	SAQ		W578RFS	FAB	62171
VO02VHN	D&B		W272MKY	MCC		W579RFS	FAB	62172
VRY357	WMC		W281EYG	BBD	47425	W581RFS	FAB	62173
VSB246T	HEB		W291PFS	LOT	291	W582RFS	FAB	62174
VSR591	NXD	7271	W292PFS	LOT	292	W583RFS	FAB	62175
VSV632	PWW		W293PFS	LOT	293	W584RFS	FAB	62176
VU02TSO	AVD		W294EYG	BBD	47426	W585RFS	FAB	62184
VU02TTE	AYR		W294PFS	LOT	294	W586RFS	FAB	62185
VU02TTO	AVD		W295PFS	LOT	295	W587RFS	FAB	62186
VU06KEJ	MCD		W296PFS	LOT	296	W588RFS	FAB	62187
VU06KFG	MCD		W297EYG	BBD	47427	W589RFS	FAB	62188
VU06XKX	WMC		W297UGX	WTB		W591PFS	SHB	
VU08SOU	SOU		W303EYG	BBD	47428	W591RFS	FAB	62189
VU52UEG	PTW		W314DWX	FED	50283	W591SNG	FG	65591
VU52UEH	PTW	11	W317OSA	DEV		W592PFS	APE	
VX08HZU	SBO		W333NOB	DCA		W592RFS	FAB	62190
VX53AVC	JPM		W343GSS	NIC		W592SNG	FG	65592
VX54CKL	GMC		W362ABD	MUN	473	W593RFS	FAB	62205
VX55FWN	MCD		W386WGE	GIB		W593SNG	FG	65593
VX57GYU	MCD		W409OSS	WMC		W594PFS	HOR	
VXI8302	TTA		W425CWX	HVB		W594RFS	FAB	62206
W2FAL	FAB	10047	W451PSG	HOU		W594SNG	FED	65594
W3FAL	FAB	10048	W462RSX	NIC		W595PFS	HOR	
W4FAL	FAB	10049	W463RSX	NIC		W595RFS	FAB	62207
W5FAL	FAB	10050	W464RSX	NIC		W595SNG	FED	65595
W6FAL	FAB	10051	W494PLS	MEW		W596PFS	HOR	
W7FAL	FAB	10052	W511PSF	CFT		W596RFS	FAB	62208
W7JDS	DMC		W537XNS	WHI		W596SNG	FG	65596
W8OVA	ACM		W546RSG	LOT	546	W597PFS	HOR	
W10CAE	STP		W547RSG	LOT	547	W597RFS	FAB	62209
W10CAT	JPM		W548RSG	LOT	548	W597SNG	FED	65597
W18RED	LAK		W549RSG	LOT	549	W598RFS	FAB	62210
W20JLS	LSK		W551RSG	LOT	551	W598SNG	FED	65598
W30JLS	LSK		W552RSG	LOT	552	W599RFS	FAB	62211
W49WDS	FG	62949	W553RSG	LOT	553	W599SNG	FED	65599
W52WDS	FG	62952	W554RSG	LOT	554	W600SOU	GUM	603

X103NSS	FAB	31560	X439JHS	BCD		X608NSS	FAB	62129
X104NSS	FAB	31561	X439NSE	SREN	33439	X609NSS	FAB	62130
X109RGG	RTT		X439UMS	FG	61688	X611NSS	FAB	62132
X132NSS	FAB	31558	X441JHS	ESB		X612HLT	FG	32960
X134FPO	FG	10134	X441NSE	BBD	33430	X612NSS	FAB	62133
X136FPO	FG	10136	X441UMS	FG	61689	X613JCS	SWSC	33443
X136NSS	FG	31562	X442JHS	ESB		X613NSS	FAB	62134
X137FPO	FG	10137	X442UMS	FG	61690	X614HLT	FG	32980
X137NSS	FG	31563	X443UMS	FG	61691	X614JCS	SWSC	33444
X138FPO	FG	10138	X445UMS	FG	61692	X614NSS	FAB	62135
X139FPO	FG	10139	X446UMS	FG	61693	X615JCS	SWSC	33445
X141FPO	FG	10141	X447UMS	FG	61694	X615NSS	FAB	62136
X142FPO	FG	10142	X448UMS	FG	61695	X616JCS	SWSC	33446
X143FPO	FG	10143	X449UMS	FG	61696	X616NSS	FAB	62137
X144FPO	FG	10144	X451UMS	FG	61697	X617JCS	SWSC	33447
X146FPO	FG	10146	X452UMS	FG	61698	X617NSS	FAB	62138
X163ENJ	SAP		X453UMS	FG	61699	X618NSS	FAB	62139
X174BNA	BNA	B131	X454UMS	FG	61700	X619NSS	FAB	62140
X178BNH	JTK		X457UMS	FG	61701	X621NSS	FAB	62149
X192HFB	FAB	20462	X458UMS	FG	61702	X622CWN	WHY	
X221RGD	HOR		X459UMS	FG	61703	X622NSS	FAB	62150
X223HCD	DEV		X461UKS	SHIC	33186	X623NSS	FAB	62151
X224USC	CHE		X461UMS	FG	61704	X624NSS	FAB	62152
X228RCS	LSK		X462UKS	SHIC	33187	X626DYB	AVD	
X235RGD	HOR		X463UKS	SHIC	33188	X675USX	NIC	
X256USH	FED	60199	X466SAS	SHIC	52525	X676NSE	STAY	52666
X271MTS	STAY	22271	X476XVG	GUM	116	X678NSE	STAY	52668
X272MTS	BBD	22272	X477NSS	FAB	62153	X683ADK	FAB	62182
X272USH	FED	60204	X477XVG	GUM	117	X684ADK	FAB	62183
X273MTS	BBD	22273	X508JGB	A&B		X685ADK	FAB	62191
X276MTS	SREN	22276	X523SHH	SWSC	33077	X686ADK	FAB	62192
X277MTS	SREN	22277	X534JGB	HOR		X689ADK	FAB	62195
X303JGE	FG	66233	X555EMH	HOR		X691ADK	FAB	62196
X304JGE	FG	66234	X578USC	LOT	578	X692ADK	FAB	62197
X311ABU	SHB		X579USC	LOT	579	X693ADK	FAB	62198
X331ABU	SMP		X581USC	LOT	581	X694ADK	FAB	62199
X366GWH	MFW		X582USC	LOT	582	X695ADK	FAB	62200
X415CSC	HOR		X583USC	LOT	583	X696ADK	FAB	62201
X416CSC	HOR		X584USC	LOT	584	X697ADK	FAB	62202
X424UMS	FG	61675	X585USC	LOT	585	X698ADK	FAB	62203
X425UMS	FG	61676	X586USC	LOT	586	X705UKS	STU	
X426UMS	FG	61677	X587USC	LOT	587	X714NSE	STAY	22714
X427UMS	FG	61678	X588USC	LOT	588	X715NSE	STAY	22715
X428NSE	SHIC	33428	X589USC	LOT	589	X716NSE	STAY	22716
X429NSE	SHIC	33429	X591USC	LOT	591	X717NSE	STAY	22717
X429UMS	FG	61679	X592USC	LOT	592	X718NSE	STAY	22718
X431NSE	BBD	33431	X593USC	LOT	593	X719NSE	STAY	22719
X431UMS	FG	61680	X594USC	LOT	594	X722NSE	SREN	22722
X432NSE	BBD	33432	X595USC	LOT	595	X739JCS	SWSC	33775
X432UMS	FG	61681	X596USC	LOT	596	X741JCS	SWSC	33776
X433NSE	SREN	33433	X597UKS	LOT	597	X742JCS	SWSC	33777
X433UMS	FG	61682	X598USC	LOT	598	X743JCS	SWSC	33778
X434UMS	FG	61683	X601NSS	FAB	62122	X744JCS	SWSC	33779
X435NSE	SREN	33435	X602NSS	FAB	62123	X771NSO	FAB	31559
X435UMS	FG	61684	X603NSS	FAB	62124	X777EMH	HOR	
X436NSE	SREN	33436	X604NSS	FAB	62125	X807KBO	CAM	
X436UMS	FG	61685	X605NSS	FAB	62126	X937MSP	SBJ	
X437NSE	BBD	33437	X606RFS	FAB	62224	X944NSO	FAB	62141
X437UMS	FG	61686	X606NSS	FAB	62127	X958HLT	FG	32958
X438UMS	FG	61687	X607NSS	FAB	62128	X959HLT	FG	32959

Reg	Code	No		Reg	Code	No		Reg	Code	No
YEZ2366	MCC			YJ06LDX	GCB			YJ51XSK	HOR	
YEZ2427	MCC			YJ06YRG	PWW			YJ51XSL	HOR	
YEZ2486	MCC			YJ06YSD	WCM			YJ51XSM	HOR	
YEZ2505	MCC			YJ06YSE	HVB	306		YJ51XSN	HOR	
YEZ3754	MCC			YJ06YSF	HVB	406		YJ51XSO	HOR	
YEZ5539	MCC			YJ06YSG	HVB			YJ54BSV	FG	53201
YF02SKX	SLA			YJ06YSH	HVB	206		YJ54CKG	ASW	1951
YF02SKZ	SLA			YJ07EHB	HOU			YJ54CKK	ASW	1952
YFS438	MOA			YJ07EHV	HVB	701		YJ54EXH	PHO	
YIJ351	SAW			YJ07EHW	HVB	702		YJ54UBY	IRB	
YIJ3053	KOA			YJ07JSU	ASW	1955		YJ54UXB	HVB	154
YIL1206	GEC			YJ07JSV	ASW	1956		YJ54UXD	HVB	354
YIL1207	GEC			YJ07JSX	ASW	1957		YJ54UXE	HVB	554
YIL1208	GEC			YJ07JSY	ASW	1958		YJ54ZXZ	HOU	
YIL2180	JPM			YJ07JSZ	ASW	1959		YJ54ZYK	WCM	
YIL2860	SOK			YJ07VRK	HVB	607		YJ54ZYL	WCM	
YIL2041	WTB			YJ07VRL	JTK			YJ54ZYM	WCM	
YIL4029	WTB			YJ07VRM	JTK			YJ55BGY	GIB	
YIL5456	MUN			YJ07VRN	ABK			YJ55BGZ	GIB	
YIL6691	GEC			YJ07VRO	JTK			YJ55BHA	GIB	
YIL7775	STP			YJ07VRR	STU			YJ55BHD	GIB	
YIL8799	BLY			YJ07VRX	IRB			YJ55BHE	GIB	
YJ03PGF	GCB			YJ08DXC	CIC	17		YJ55BHK	GIB	
YJ04BYB	WHI			YJ08DXD	CIC	18		YJ55BHW	STAY	47260
YJ04HJC	ASW	2011		YJ08DXE	CIC	19		YJ55BKD	STP	
YJ04HJD	ASW	2012		YJ08DXF	CIC	20		YJ55WRA	IRB	
YJ04HJE	ASW	2013		YJ08PGE	HVB	408		YJ55WRC	IRB	
YJ04HJF	ASW	2014		YJ08PHK	HVB	308		YJ55YGD	WCG	
YJ04HUU	GCB			YJ08PKA	HVB	208		YJ55YHC	IRB	
YJ05JWX	SHI			YJ08PKV	HVB	108		YJ55YHG	STU	
YJ05JXT	JTK			YJ09CUV	ASW	2004		YJ55YHH	STP	
YJ05PVF	WCM			YJ09CUW	ASW	2009		YJ55YHL	STP	
YJ05PVK	WCM			YJ09CUX	ASW	2010		YJ56JYC	OAD	
YJ05PVL	WCM			YJ09CVH	ASW	2001		YJ56JYD	OAD	
YJ05PWU	WCM			YJ09CVK	ASW	2002		YJ56WTW	PWW	
YJ05PYT	OAD			YJ09CVL	ASW	2003		YJ56WVE	SHIC	47574
YJ05PYY	BUT			YJ09CVM	ASW	2005		YJ56WVH	HVB	156
YJ05VVN	FG	66770		YJ09CVN	ASW	2006		YJ56YOD	APE	
YJ05VVO	FG	66771		YJ09CVO	ASW	2007		YJ57EGV	WRH	
YJ05WCT	NIC			YJ09CVR	ASW	2008		YJ57EHL	WRH	
YJ05XNP	AVD			YJ09CZY	CIC			YJ57EJA	EVE	
YJ05XNR	AVD			YJ09EVJ	HVB	309		YJ57XXC	HVB	257
YJ05XNS	AVD			YJ09EVL	HVB	409		YJ58CBX	HVB	
YJ05XOA	SHIC	47563		YJ09HRC	HVB	509		YJ58CBY	HVB	
YJ05XOB	SHIC	47564		YJ09HRD	HVB	609		YJ58CCV	HQD	
YJ05XOC	SHIC	47565		YJ09HRE	HVB	709		YJ58PKY	HVB	
YJ05XOD	SHIC	47566		YJ09OUP	SHB	10		YJ58PKZ	HVB	
YJ05XOE	SHIC	47567		YJ09OUV	IRB			YJ59GHZ	EVE	
YJ05XOF	SHIC	47568		YJ10EXX	WRH			YJ59NNX	WRH	
YJ05XOG	SHIC	47569		YJ10EXZ	WRH			YJ59NOF	SMI	
YJ05XOH	SHIC	47570		YJ10MGX	HVB	310		YJ59NOH	SMI	
YJ05XOK	SHIC	47571		YJ10MHF	GMC			YJ60KBM	IRB	
YJ05XOL	SHIC	47572		YJ10OAA	KIN			YJI1309	MCL	
YJ05XOM	SHIC	47573		YJ10OAB	KIN			YJU694	STAY	52432
YJ06FXO	HQD			YJ10OAC	KIN			YK04KWH	SHIC	47562
YJ06FXZ	HQD			YJ10OAD	KIN			YK04KWJ	MCD	
YJ06HRN	HOR			YJ10OAE	KIN			YK05BAO	SLA	
YJ06HRP	HOR			YJ51EKO	IRB			YK05BAV	SLA	
YJ06LDU	GCB			YJ51EKP	IRB			YK05CDE	MFW	
YJ06LDV	GCB			YJ51XSH	HOR			YK05CDF	MFW	

YK05EMV	HOR		YN06URA	FG	37147	YN53EFR	FG	31797
YK05EOY	HOR		YN06URB	FG	37148	YN53EFT	FG	31798
YKJ798	STU		YN06URC	FG	37149	YN53EFU	FG	31799
YL02FKZ	NIC		YN06URD	FG	37150	YN53EFV	FG	31800
YM08MPU	MIT		YN06URE	FG	37151	YN53EFW	FG	31801
YM52TOV	HOR		YN06URF	FG	37152	YN53EFX	FG	31802
YM52UVK	FED	61214	YN06URG	FG	37153	YN53EFZ	FG	31803
YM52UVL	FED	61215	YN06URH	FG	37154	YN53EGC	FG	31804
YM52UVN	FED	61216	YN06URJ	FG	37155	YN53EJC	WMC	
YM52UVO	FED	61217	YN07EAJ	PWW		YN53VBL	DEV	
YM52UVP	FED	61218	YN07EAY	PWW		YN53VBP	MLS	
YM52UVR	FED	61219	YN07KHH	AAA		YN53VBT	FAB	56001
YM52UVS	FED	61220	YN07KHK	AAA		YN53VBU	FAB	56002
YM52UVT	FED	61221	YN07LHR	CSS		YN53VBV	FAB	56003
YM52UVU	FED	61222	YN07LHV	GCB		YN53VCD	MFW	
YM52UVW	FED	61223	YN07LHY	CSS		YN53WZJ	MUN	502
YM52UVZ	FED	61224	YN07NWD	HUC		YN53YGZ	STP	
YM52UWA	FED	61225	YN07OPF	MFW		YN53YHJ	IRB	
YM52UWB	FED	61226	YN07OPG	MFW		YN54AGO	STU	
YM52UWD	FED	61227	YN08LCT	FG	37238	YN54WCM	MFW	
YM52UWF	FED	61228	YN08LCU	FG	37239	YN54WVX	KIN	
YM52UWG	FED	61229	YN08LCV	FG	37240	YN54XYK	BNA	B125
YM52UWH	FED	61230	YN08LCW	FG	37241	YN55KND	SREN	47259
YM52UWJ	FED	61231	YN08LCY	FG	37242	YN55KWJ	AAM	
YM52UWK	FED	61232	YN08LCZ	FG	37243	YN55LMO	WMC	
YM52UWN	FED	61233	YN08LDA	FG	37244	YN55UDZ	ACN	
YN03NDX	STP		YN08LDC	FG	37245	YN56DZF	TEL	
YN03NDY	HOR		YN08LDD	FG	37278	YN56ORW	CFT	
YN03NDZ	HOR		YN08NXP	OAD		YN56ORX	CFT	
YN03NJF	CFT		YN08NXW	WRH		YN56OSK	SEC	
YN03WPZ	IRB		YN08OWX	JTK		YN56OSM	MFW	
YN04HHR	MFW		YN08OWY	AUS		YN57AEZ	CIC	16
YN04HHW	FG	DR3	YN08OWZ	AUS		YN57DXH	EVE	
YN04HJX	HTR		YN09AOP	D&E		YN57MEU	KIN	
YN04LXS	MCR		YN09AOV	WRH		YN57MFK	KIN	
YN04PNL	FG	DR2	YN09BXW	WHY		YN57OTV	DPC	
YN04WTG	MFW		YN09EXC	WRH		YN57TVF	AAA	
YN04WTT	MFW		YN09EZD	WRH		YN58FXO	WRH	
YN04WTV	MFW		YN09EZE	AAA		YN58OKU	CIC	22
YN05GYZ	MEX		YN09EZG	RAB	19	YN58OKW	CIC	24
YN05GZA	IRB		YN09EZH	RAB	20	YN59BNA	SEC	
YN05HUZ	AAA		YN09HDX	MLS		YN59GOX	MFW	
YN05HVF	BCD		YN09HEJ	PSK		YO06TXF	MFW	
YN05HVT	MFW		YN09LCM	RTT		YO53OVA	MUN	503
YN05UVL	A&B		YN09LLK	HOU		YO53OVB	MUN	504
YN05WEC	SWSC	50145	YN09LMK	MCD		YOI890	SAW	
YN05WEF	SWSC	50146	YN10ABX	MFW		YP02AAY	MEW	
YN05WEK	SWSC	50150	YN10ABZ	MFW		YP02AAZ	MEW	
YN06AYL	ETN		YN10FLB	CIC		YP02LCE	NXD	7345
YN06CYG	SBO		YN52TOV	HOR		YP09NRF	DOI	
YN06CYH	SBO		YN53EFE	FG	31787	YP52KRG	WMC	
YN06CYJ	SBO		YN53EFF	FG	31788	YP52KSJ	SHC	
YN06CYV	APE		YN53EFG	FG	31789	YPJ207Y	JMC	
YN06MXR	MFW		YN53EFH	FG	31790	YR02YTD	GIC	
YN06OPK	MFW		YN53EFJ	FG	31791	YR02ZKY	POC	
YN06PCY	SHI		YN53EFK	FG	31792	YR02ZLX	CFM	
YN06PDX	MFW		YN53EFL	FG	31793	YR03UMR	MUN	501
YN06PFA	SHI		YN53EFM	FG	31794	YR52MBX	FIR	
YN06RVX	BCM		YN53EFO	FG	31795	YR52VEX	GUM	210
YN06RVY	BCM		YN53EFP	FG	31796	YR52XPA	DEV	

YR58SUH	ASW	4665	YX10EAO	GCB	
YR58SUO	ASW	4666	YX10EAP	GCB	
YR58SUU	ASW	4667	YX55ABF	CHE	
YR58SUV	ASW	4668	YX55ABU	CHE	
YR58SUX	ASW	4669	YX59AAE	SLA	
YR58SUY	ASW	4670	YX59AAV	SLA	
YRR436	PWW		YX59AAY	SLA	
YS02WVY	BBD	47281	YX59ABK	SLA	
YS51JVD	FAB	62228	YX59DZC	SHB	13
YSD350L	SWSC	59950	YXI7906	DOT	
YSU196	ECL	603	YY52SSU	SBZ	
YSU572	PWW				
YSU882	SHIC	52429			
YSU921	BUT				
YSU989	MAY	20			
YSU990	MAY	19			
YSV125	PWW				
YSV607	PWW				
YSV608	PWW				
YSV618	PWW				
YSV730	SWSC	50130			
YSV735	SWSC	52026			
YT51EBC	NXD	321			
YT51EBD	NXD	322			
YT57EJC	APE				
YU04HJD	BNA	B120			
YU04HJE	BNA	B121			
YU04HJF	BNA	B122			
YU04HJK	BNA	B123			
YU07KGU	BNA	B128			
YU07SOU	SOU				
YX03LKY	HEB				
YX04DLY	MCO	1009			
YX04FYF	BCM				
YX05AVT	SBZ				
YX05AVV	FAB	56501			
YX05FEK	BBD	27057			
YX05HHA	LID				
YX06AWM	NXD	7353			
YX06AXS	HUC				
YX07DXC	BBD	49756			
YX07EED	POC				
YX07JPF	HVB				
YX08AOP	DOI				
YX08AUA	DOI				
YX08HGC	DPC				
YX08HGD	DOI				
YX09EVG	ASW	2802			
YX09EVH	ASW	2803			
YX09HRF	SHB	8			
YX09HRG	SHB	9			
YX09HRW	SLA				
YX09HRZ	SLA				
YX09HSA	SLA				
YX10AXM	SHB				
YX10AXN	SHB				
YX10EAJ	GCB				
YX10EAK	GCB				
YX10EAM	GCB				

2GRT	L65UOU		1709AC	W293DYG
81CBK	V435EAL		2133PL	M36TRR
84HER	D608MVR		2154K	SA02RZB
101RTD	LSK827		2367AT	SA02EUP
109ASV	HC04CHS		2396FH	P930KYC/2396FH/P930KYC
121ASV	W877VGT		2433AT	OO02TEN
123TRL	01-D-60725/Y798GDV-ULZ1819		2450PP	ST02GDA
127ASV	P199OSE/WLT809/P199OSE		2625ED	C645KDS
128ASV	P671LWB/UIB3543/P671LWB		2767WF	FJ04ERU
128NNU	SP51AWW		3289AT	SK07FVE
138ASV	F171RJF		3401AC	DE52ONW
143CLT	R453MSL		3935AC	E688UNE
151EWU	E608SSD		4143AT	R96HUA
162EKH	95-G-955/M105VRA		4464RU	B238VGS
200UWX	M873GYS/VRG939/M973GYS		4670AT	SF06NEJ
246AJF	C331DND		5287FM	X154ENJ
283URB	N145XSA/VLT37		5397LJ	M5HWD
361EKH	K669SFE		5414PH	P972KTS
367NHA	JSV440/JHZ4805/N505CVW		5692FM	G164ECS
408UFC	C115DWR		5909D	UCS897S
410KGG	SWW125R		6292SC	K21OUY
439BUS	NX03MVL		6491ED	CCS243T
444VNX	W746NAS		7617SM	M959XST/B2YST/YST738/
448GWL	SV08GXL			M860KVU
479DKH	B183FDM		7722SR	YN03AXG
536ATT	W901MDT		7726AT	Y58THS
540FFX	P649NST/4234NT/540FFX/		7921AT	SF05NRY
	P869SSK		8578AT	SF06NEO
542GRT	R5FAL		9237AT	SF06NEN
611LFM	A334/UFE/51425C/A384XGG		A1VOL	C176LWB
641RHU	Y800SOU		A2XXH	K563GSA/TSV720/K563GSA
650GXJ	N764CAS		A2XXW	K565GSA/TSV722/K565GSA
671YWC	A608UGD/GIL7364/GIL3575/		A4JYT	R76VVP
	A842OSJ		A5MWN	C324DND
673EXA	M540RSO		A8AAA	R413EOS/LSK503
679JPU	YX54BJV		A8TPT	T434GSP
688EYV	L36CAY		A10TBT	WCU823T
699NAE	YX54BGZ		A12MWN	C534DND
703DYE	P92URG		A15MWN	D606MVR
719CEL	L232BUT		A15RBL	B947ASU
730UXG	2085KX/T727JHE/		A16RNY	N75CSX
731AFD	X444GSM		A17PHO	FX55YWH
755ABL	W657FUM		A17RNY	P78OSC
825BGE	unknown		A19MWN	F548TMH
828EWB	K594VBC		A19NCR	W989WDS
832DVV	M213UYD		A19RNY	N74BFS
835BUS	Y159KDP		A20HOF	J290NNC
837XHW	D556MVR		A20JPT	M1AGB
869SVX	A179MKE		A20MWN	H197DVM
875YYA	DCH359T		A201MFR	A201MFR/GSU551
887TTT	L37CAY		A221XDS	SXF615
900HKU	P492FAS		A286LLS	OBA695
900RWX	X48CNY		A565WAV	A262BTY/898NK/A465WAV/
935BRU	OO05HCC/S26HCC/HCC100			TFG154
937BUS	S27HCC/HCC974/S21HCC/		A717ASJ	NVY148
	OO04HCC/SJ04LLE		AA05DOT	FJ07VKL
953HBU	D800EST		AAZ3305	A654UGD/7173WW/A249JSA
9637EL	SV09EGC		AHZ9360	J440UFS
1528RU	KM03GSM		AIG6240	S333NSN/S77JDS

AJZ9204	F490WPR	BSK756	V261ESX
AM02NYC	Y11EAD	BSK790	J331LLK
AT2472	AK02LSJ	BSV216	SPR35
ATV24Y	W58WGA/SBM464	BU51DEC	YN09AOP
B1YST	M662KVU	BU53DEC	SN08GFA
B2YST	SF03AUH	BUI5220	L29ABB
B3VOL	LSK844	BVS118	YR02UOF
B3YST	P2GVT	BX53OLE	S22SPA/BX53OLE
B4VOL	M652KVU	BX56VUM	BX56VUM/NKH819
B5VOL	M648KVU	BXI7437	F159DET
B5YST	T2LEC	C3CHT	T843NBV
B6YST	V11BUS	C3POC	01-D-69366/Y797GDV
B7YST	N18OVA	C6POC	01-D-69361/Y87GDV
B8OVA	P658UDL	C7OST	F599EEA
B8YST	M408OKM	C7POC	W301GCW
B9YST	YJ07DVX	C8POC	R133XWF
B10MBC	F553TMH	C9POC	M127UWY
B10MGR	L320FLJ	C10EMH	N369TJT
B10MKF	EG7583	C10POC	LSK831
B10MSC	EA1844	C11MMM	JJZ6562/C100DWR/HIL2366/
B10MSE	DY8312		C100DWR
B10PSV	SF10BYU	C11POC	L708PHE
B10SBP	L11BUS	C12POC	Y286TSU
B10VOL	E641UNE	C12RNY	P76KSC
B10YST	P801AWR	C13POC	L709PHE
B11DWA	M77JCM	C13RNY	S584ACT
B12ABT	FC04UXW	C14POC	R134XWF
B12GEC	2WR/SG03ZER	C16EMH	YN08NXH
B12YST	J782KHD	C18EMH	S51KNW
B13YST	F113TML	C19EMH	T281DUY
B14PCH	YM03EOU	C20EMH	N370TJT
B14YST	F134PHM	C158HBA	DJ3429
B15KCT	M291RVS	C160HBA	DH9306
B15YST	B9YST/,404OKM	C170HBA	DH8737
B16AFC	R83RBY/ROI2929/R83RBY	C212PPE	C212PPE/9757VC/C212PPE/
B17YST	T87JBA		HIL3934/C212PPE/XIL7876
B19WCS	YR3939	C408HVH	MIL4890/C408HVH
B496MFS	SL8207	C640UNV	RBW396
B852OSB	B409OSB	C892WKS	C188WFS
B899RSH	TSD285	CAZ6833	F30UHN
BAZ7912	1716WW/T464GDG	CCZ2221	J23VVO
BAZ7916	WAY877	CCZ5837	98-KK-1562/R442LSC
BAZ7918	GW4343	CEZ8152	R100STL
BB05DOT	FJ07VKM	CEZ8153	J239NNC
BHZ1255	82-KF-05	CHZ1761	F640SAY
BHZ1256	87-KF-09/E261MWD	CKL1Y	P66MNM
BHZ1257	82-KF-08/D63MEA	CKZ8184	J130GNP
BHZ8809	C405LRP/XCD108	CKZ8186	M116XLV
BHZ9543	75-KK-04/K914SUS	CLZ1838	B627JRC
BHZ9546	J509LRY/WIJ297/J509LRY	CNZ2263	F277WAF
BHZ9548	R710TRV	CNZ3830	V22CCH
BHZ9549	CX-47-AA/M933ROS	CSU920	P198OSE/WLT978/P198OSE
BIG6153	G778HOV	CSU923	M535RSO
BIG9871	5645CEV/FC7233 (Hong Kong)	CSV651	P825XGD
BJI6863	SA02RYZ	CTO5T	NUI7559
BJZ6602	S618LWN	D5DOT	HSK656
BLZ589	HSK648	D6BUS	75-KK-34/K327PHT/439BUS
BLZ8582	F489YSC/PSU620	D11DOT	M641KVU
BMC2T	SV09EVM	D20DOT	M642KVU
BS8362	X563CNY	D53VSO	RJI2718/D53VSO

D131UGB	D219NCS	ESK985	L673OHL
D146ENV	D36ENH	EUE512	P432KSX
D349ESC	D349ESC/CRS61T	EV07EVE	SK07LNO
D453DWP	D79APC	EV08EVE	YN08NXV
D780FVT	4614RU/D780FVT/4614RU/	EVE4	YN07DVL
	D255HFX	EYN165	N701UVR
D825YCH	D609MVR	F1MMM	KSK982/L715ADS/L5BCL/L689UMB
DAZ4298	D210MDS	F11MMM	L955NWW
DBZ696	X20NAT	F49MCA	F999HGE
DCZ7109	S103KJF	F73GYB	PSU614
DCZ7588	M160WTJ	F106TML	F107TML
DEZ4258	P764VDS	F107TML	F111TML
DEZ4259	N870MSU	F109TML	F106TML
DEZ9611	B761KRB	F202FHH	WLT794/F202FHH
DFC568	G226EHD/EFC221/G372RHG	F357MGB	F980XSJ
DJZ4676	63-KG-97/E813NOU	F523UVW	F541PSL
DLS520Y	CLS709Y	F651GNT	F760ENE
DSU355	Y767TSJ	F737FDV	F727FDV
DSU707	X47CNY	F854LTU	F511NFW
DSV246	B15GOO/SG03ZEW/15RWM	F869TLJ	IUI466/F869TLJ/YIL3144/F869TLJ/
DSV707	LSK832		TIL1259/F869TLJ
DSV943	P670LWB/WLT720/P670LWB	F935ENV	MIL3606/F935ENV
E7WJC	E865RCS	F956HWB	F33VAC
E9WJC	E99AAK/XMM99	F969RSE	GSU950/DDZ8844/F27LTO
E11MMM	F46LCH	FC04UZK	04-LH-3752
E32HSH	E824MSG/DSK589	FCZ9700	K293GDT
E68EKG	L68EKG	FE02FBK	FE02RBK
E100LBC	935BRU	FHJ83Y	FHJ83Y/6306FH/KIJ117
E173FRA	E311OPR	FHZ2188	03-KE-3078/SL52DGV
E278YPS	E278YPS/WRC751	FHZ3530	M144KJF
E444ANN	P932TFE	FHZ3531	K16BUS
E711CDS	E420LLE/E444ANN	FHZ4134	W646FUM
E775NVT	3601RU	FHZ4170	M6WEB
E937XSB	IIL3504/E937XSB/GIL2967/	FHZ4171	M574JBC
	E626UNE	FHZ4190	A4XEL/N995THO
E949JJN	E892KYW/A8AAA	FHZ4191	A3XEL/N996THO
E996FRA	E310OPR	FHZ6882	03-KE-3077/SL52DGX
EAZ6207	F224RJX	FHZ8395	P608NJN
EAZ8407	E640NEL	FHZ9593	K15BUS
ECZ9120	L381RYC	FHZ9599	L935NWW
ECZ9122	L383RYC	FIG8241	Y336CJT/MLZ2370/Y336CJT
EDS50A	WLT560	FIG8242	99-D-74497/V289JTO
EGB60T	SV06CEN	FIL4166	A145RMJ
EIG1433	JJG907P	FIL7615	7391MH/A334MRB
EIG1434	JDT437N	FIL8613	A297RSU
EIG1435	BYW361V	FJZ9714	F170XLJ
EIG1436	AYR354T	FLZ6854	F424DU/B518HAM/F424DUG/
EIG1437	HPF313W		UO6929
EIG4966	N204DYB	FNZ2300	N445PYS/HSK644
EIG6554	V475HET	FNZ5671	N698AHL
EIG9345	W251WTA/00-KY-4020	FNZ5672	M213NHP
EIL584	G259RNS	FSU318	7092RU
EKS69X	TSO29X	FSU319	SF06OEB
EKZ469	BX04NCD	FSU331	K567GSA/127ASV
EPK1V	W154RYB	FSU335	V370XDO
ESK880	D562MVR	FSU371	EC-50-AA
ESK932	LX05BWM	FSU375	T645JWB
ESK934	SV54ELO	FSU382	T707JLD/HSU247
ESK981	L9TCC/CXP742	FSU394	S718MGB
ESK983	M115UWY	FSU718	R413YWJ

FSU739	P626NSE	H494LNA	ES 1963
FSU797	K571DFS	H511FRP	ES4877/WLT439/H511FRP
FSV864	SL02CPY	H522FRP	ER 9169
FXI194	SN55FOD	H603LNA	ES 8820
FXI249	SN55FPU	H606LNA	EV 3020
FXI253	SN55SPE	H617LNA	EF 8967
FXI457	SN04GZY	H625LNA	EF 8850
FXI724	V333ASH	H627LNA	ET 1190
FXI782	P531RGG/FXI690/P531RGG	H699PVW	91-D-1071
G5LAT	Y783THS	H708PVW	91-D-1061
G5WJC	G452FFX/EJ 1293	H709PVW	91-D-1064
G7BUS	PSU698/G436JSG	H718PVW	91-D-1073
G7WJC	G863FVX/EJ 4800	H778VHL	ET 160
G9WJC	G97PES	H912JVR	H169EJU
G21RHG	G778CSB	HCC100	SC02LVE
G95YFW	A17MWN/G95YFW	HCC296	Y287TSU
G107NGN	EUE512/G107NGN	HCC440	W285WCS
G128WGX	ET 1613	HCC551	S283JGA
G189YRJ	EL8119	HCC882	S282JGA
G194PAO	G194PAO/D19KEY	HDZ8349	SC02KVF
G278YRJ	EF 9671	HDZ8352	F77XUY
G280YRJ	EF 9412/G280YRJ/MSU463	HF53GVJ	HF53CVJ
G326PEW	G326PEW/920GTA/G326PEW	HIG2461	P512MBD
G452FVX	EJ 1293	HIG2462	YP52KRK
G504SFT	G504FST	HIG7793	SF57JRU
G557XAE	/PWV698G557XAE	HIG7814	P318VWR
G813GSX	G831GSX	HIL2148	P826KES
G932TVO	G879VNA/XTW359/G792YND	HIL2160	B402CMC
	B6WER/G316OKW/A9EBT/ACZ13	HIL2464	A610UGD/4294CR/A515JSA
G934TTV	G390PNV	HIL2702	E221JJF
G973KTX	G973KTX/610LYB	HIL2720	Y551BKS
G999SJR	G999SJR/TJI8785	HIL3318	X411UOE
GBZ8812	R23JSG	HIL4336	E216JJF
GCS38V	K488FFS	HIL5063	A433VDS/SRU41
GDZ3363	X679NSE	HIL5184	XRA4Y
GEZ1277	VOI189	HIL5345	T212NUB
GFA955	SK07FTV	HIL5346	S5SOU
GFV152W	GFW152W	HIL5347	R590USJ
GHZ8752	V94LYS/KSK977	HIL5348	SF03AXX
GIB6135	D392TAU	HIL5349	SN03THK
GIL1685	N113NYS	HIL6256	P314UWR
GIL2754	D342KVE	HIL6462	A915MKS
GIL5407	F253MGB/XJF448/F253MGB/	HIL6570	E654UNE
	LSK508/F764ENE	HIL7590	CSM915X
GIL6540	L351MKU	HIL8129	C774MVH
GJI627	M75FGG	HIL8441	E694NNH
GJI926	LSK835	HIL8617	E426EVS
GNZ9360	R784WSB	HIL9155	D614SJX
GS54EVE	YN05GXZ	HJI565	SJ03AOR
GSO84V	WA04TYT	HJZ3949	J798KHD
GSU341	N618USS	HMU118	FJ05AOT
GSU347	M943LYR	HOI365	G92VMM
GSU370	P431KSK	HSK735	H251XDS
GSU551	M721LJR	HSK857	W207EAG
GSU950	V254ESX	HSL660	WLT981
GXI53	W212EAG	HSU247	T706JLD/FSU382
H3KFC	W869VGY	HSU983	R357KSG/ABZ857/R357KSC/
H4KDY	R991ANB/CNZ1532/R199ANB		B15GOO/R357KSG
H223VKU	OSK784/H445PPU/EK258	HSV725	YD02PXN/378BNG/YD01PXN/
H445EGU	ER 1374/H455EGU/WLT794		TKU717/YD02PXN

HSV782	SF04SXX	JIL2159	PUK643R
HUI6828	J531JNH	JIL2161	HWC87N
HUI8156	P722RWU/2450PP/P722RWU	JIL2165	JOX516P
HV01PAO	HV02PAO	JIL2566	B705WUA
IIB379	N203HWX/403OWA/N575ACP	JIL2949	WSV553/G882VNA
IIB457	2HAN/T583DGD/GIL1685/T583DGD	JIL3757	E265OMT
IIL3481	E33MKV	JIL3961	R974EHS
IIL3504	P153ASA	JIL5623	FNM860Y
IJI336	E89VWA	JIL7656	Y162HMX
IUI2129	YRR436/J120NJR/YBK159/J2DTS	JIL8206	D350KVE
IUI9890	F793NNL	JIL8207	P612UGE
IXI1337	A336YDT/GSU388/A546RNW	JIL8256	C301JNS
J3EGT	P571HKM	JIL8560	J39HSU
J5EGT	YG52XGA	JIL8561	D864PGB
J7EGT	R904YBA	JIL8562	E129BSU
J8LWC	K265SSD/K5HWD/K265SSD	JJI3316	B910UPW
J10WCM	J13853	JSJ746	VLT90
J15GEC	Y998TGG	JSJ747	VLT84
J20JPT	J615PNE	JSJ748	VLT80
J20WCM	J74393	JSJ749	VLT94
J30WCM	J69267	JSU384	F782UJS
J40WCM	J86370	JSU542	P973KTS
J50WCM	J86372	JSU550	W512PSF
J55BUS	F954RCH	JSV362	L971KDT
J60WCM	J61334	JSV440	SN05FDU
J70WCM	J64744	JSV486	99-C-50980
J77GEC	W444GSM	JW02BUS	MX54KLE
J80WCM	J64745	JXI317	BC51NAT
J90WCM	J85325	K1WGD	N204HWX
J100WCM	J11467	K5KFC	W452AKN
J119DUV	J199DUV	K7SKY	P600TCC
J127MTY	J211NNC	K10EVE	R903FYS/N1EVE
J222BER	M303YWE/EC-43-AA	K14AMC	93-D-8002/K881GSG
J229NNC	DVS52/J229NNC	K14BUS	L853MYB
J249LLB	J249LLB/JIB9496/MBZ8509	K20JCM	M777JCM/W77JDS
J642CWJ	8827LG	K30SBL	SC02SOU
J701HMY	WW8656	K40SBL	SN04WYF
J773HMX	J365DPL/CSU907	K60BSL	Y20BGS
J864XFS	J867YLS	K70AYR	SV02CUK
J880RHA	J414AWF	K400WCM	K400WCM
J882UNA	J5BUS	K85DTM	K8BUS
J938MHC	EW9757	K100AYR	R870MRD
J999BER	M304YWE/EC-51-AA	K101UJR	74-KK-34
J3PUB	Y633TYS	K174EUX	SBS7204J
JAZ3285	E567UHS	K200AYR	R910ULA
JAZ4886	C340DND	K200WCM	YJ03PDZ
JAZ9850	N90TGM/850RFX/N90TGM/3692NT	K222AYR	LSK506/R416EOS
JAZ9852	S494UAK/KFO809/S494UAK	K226BJA	BUS1N
JAZ9855	S495UAK/WFO311/S495UAK	K240EUX	K5HWD/K240EUX/K870ANT
JBZ3675	NCH868/F905YNV	K244SUS	93-D-8011
JBZ4910	37-KC-52	K300AYR	P27TTX
JCZ2065	K671SBV	K300WCM	YJ03PFA
JDS77J	248D433/L318HYP	K333AYR	N95SKG
JEZ4096	FXI405	K400AYR	N318BYA
JEZ8980	FXI406	K400JCD	M764CWS/M11AFC/M764CWS
JHZ4804	383DVF/YSV607/H822AVK/H5DTS/	K400WCM	K400WCM
	H822AVK/P23KWA	K434DRW	K534DRW
JIB82	M25XSC	K498PGN	135D 242
JIB292	C661KDS	K500AYR	XEL4
JIB3032	GN53HOL	K500WCM	R94GNW

K579PHU	74-KK-40	L345ERU	XEL31
K600AYR	M631KVU	L374BGA	94-D-2020
K600JLS	K106TCP	L375BGA	94-D-2018
K600SOU	K909RGE/K600SOU/B1AFC/	L376BGA	94-D-2019
	K600SOU/C9WGC	L388YNV	A8CLN
K662BGA	FIG8241/K132FKW/LAZ5876/	L395BGA	93-D-10010
	K662OBA/K9EFT/K662GBA	L400WCM	R177GNW
K688CBA	FJ4674	L416BGA	93-D-10004
K700AYR	M731KJU	L421ORS	DAZ1566
K700BUL	K326ANC	L464BGA	94-D-2014
K764CSG	93-W-1150	L465BGA	94-D-2015
K800AYR	M863TYC	L481BGA	94-D-2013
K918RGE	K918RGE/K10EVE/K918RGE	L493BGA	93-D-8012
K966SUS	75-KK-08/K966SUS/BHZ9545	L583JSA	L583JSA/FSU739/L583JSA/WLT415
K977XND	K977XND/J7EGT	L586JSA	XRC487/L586JSA
K987SUS	74-KK-92	L619SESC	L6DMC
KAO238V	PIJ2799/USU641/MDS238V	L628AYS	LSK841
KBZ4631	LSK875/LSK473/N527PYS	L637AYS	LSK876
KC02BUS	LC54BVY	L643DNA	B88BUS/L643DNA
KC51BUS	SA03WFZ	L700JPC	M763CWS/M1GRT/M763CWS
KCT50	WSC571/R132JGA	L710ADS	KSK986
KDZ6277	E635UNE	L717ERU	A19XEL
KIW1102	E302OMG	L776AUS	L2BUS
KKG109W	NIB2796/KKG109W	L906ANS	L855WDS
KLZ2317	X465SAS/MXI694	L946LBV	VJI9411/RIL2576/L942LBV/1PSV
KSK933	SA02PAO	L990ASU	L300WCM
KSK934	SJ05ACX	LAZ4120	E593UHS
KSK979	LSK511	LAZ4470	216TYC/A335XOS
KSK980	LSK512	LAZ7403	E896KYW
KSK985	SF07OSE	LAZ9205	SA52CTF/MIL7793/SA52CTF
KSU175	YJ09FHW	LB10BUS	SN10DLJ
KSV803	87-KF-13/E812NOU	LCA381	P355VWR
KUI2759	F981HGE	LCN36	T765JYB
KUI3849	L93GAX	LCZ1890	G649WFE
KX08HDE	KX07HDE	LCZ3677	E638UNE
KXG661	E375HSH	LEZ3945	ND54KCF
KXI244	V10NAT	LEZ9446	87-KF-49/E116MPV/HUI1580
KXI599	D571FBK	LIB8921	G701XFB
L1PPN	V720GGE	LIJ595	M972NFU
L3OBS	L350RDO	LIL2173	H151DVM
L4PPN	S312DLG	LIL4398	MFE504
L8PPN	X319RSD	LIL8050	A211DPB
L11JDT	L748YGE	LIL8970	F325DCL
L11PPN	P530UGA	LIL9814	G340HSC
L15YUL	Y222GSM	LIL9970	E973NMK
L17ATS	M580JBC	LIW4270	G931TUS/XUF456/G42VHS
L18TVL	R636FCT	LIW4290	C671KDS
L82RHL	00-RN-38	LJ04JFZ	LJ04FJZ
L98WSW	L906LFS	LJI978	SF03AVM
L100JLB	L110JSA	LJZ6056	B764UHG/TOP11N/B153NKB
L100WCM	YJ05PYP	LKU618	D366RHS
L125DRN	K125XHG	LKZ4453	6280RU/P193HNT
L128DRN	K128XHG	LOI1454	G448BVT
L188SUB	L921NWW	LSG27N	UPT6N
L200WCM	YJ05PYO	LSK478	M627KVU
L215GJO	L214GJO	LSK479	M624ORJ
L252YOD	L752YUD	LSK495	LSK444
L270ULX	L4NCP	LSK496	LSK555
L297ORS	L5TCC/PSU609	LSK507	LSK511
L300WCM	R180GNW	LSK530	F369MUT

LSK545	R153HHK	M808ASL	FSU393/M808ASL/00-RN-45
LSK570	K3GRT	M821YSC	XSV270
LSK571	K4GRT	M823ASL	FSU395/M823ASL/00-RN-44
LSU689	M30CLA	M831HNS	HJI565/M831HNS/M5END/
LSV380	W899VRE		M831HNS/LSK503
LTU284	R792PAO	M846DUS	M846DUS/WLT357
LUI1727	MoD	M937JGB	95-D-206
LUI3026	T104GSE/2367AT/T104GSE	M994HHS	KSK978
LUI5800	J712BAO	MAZ6509	MIL1846/E404LTR
LUI6840	X646AKW/1359UP	MAZ8433	M332GFW
LUI7857	E113RBO	MAZ8439	P7WMS/P455KFC
LUI9240	J731KBC	MBZ1758	L273YCW
LVG263	T435GSP	MBZ9374	G551KET
M1MCT	LSK832	MDM371	P571BAY
M1PCV	X88CCH	MIL1053	E649KCK
M2CLL	M336JGB/M384WET	MIL1085	G337PAO
M8KFC	W453AKN	MIL1846	MAZ6509/E515YGC
M10DVS	M75WYG	MIL1920	H852AHS
M10MCT	WV52HSX	MIL2410	LUI3026/M134GAP/M5CLE/
M59LBB	FCU190/M59LBB		M134GAP/PRD34/M134GAP/
M100WCM	Y485HUA		M222CDY
M141TMS	M407XSL	MIL2515	H203CRH
M151FGB	M1ABO	MIL2979	E911AFM/M8SKY
M203VSX	M203VSXM	MIL3218	T734JHE
M251XWS	16-RN-63	MIL3606	JHZ4805/367NHA/K103UFP/
M258JGB	95-D-213		REL135/K103UFP
M271JGB	95-D-231	MIL3725	G912XAS
M274JGB	95-D-229	MIL4314	H853AHS
M275JGB	95-D-215	MIL5016	F442SOU
M277JGB	95-D-227	MIL5573	R775PST/WXI878
M302JGB	95-D-237	MIL5575	D22EFS
M321RAW	M321RAW/3408NT	MIL5830	WA53FDJ
M328TJA	M8JPT	MIL6548	E241BMA
M345JGB	95-D-233	MIL6676	TOE490N
M346JGB	95-D-232	MIL7620	TOE512N
M381JGB	95-D-236	MIL7622	ROK469M
M396JGB	95-D-2087	MIL7795	K300SOU
M438ECS	LSK444	MIL8028	WA53FDG
M516TVM	CX61AA	MIL9145	C807FMC
M527RSO	M527RSO/HSV194	MIL9587	B379PAJ
M528RSO	M528RSO/TSV778	MJI6254	J709CWT
M529RSO	M529RSO/TSV779	MKZ585	K956UAG/YSU914/NCZ1912/
M530RSO	M530RSO/TSV780		K524EHE
M534CEY	M744KJU	MKZ1878	JL-62-AA
M534NCG	A13XEL	MKZ7183	R5FWM
M544RSO	M544RSO/145CLT	MKZ7184	R6FWM
M600WCM	Y486HUA	MM54GSM	SF54COA
M611YSF	95-MH-410	MNZ9303	HF03HOF
M623RCP	196FCG/M623RCP	MSL276X	KES305X
M658ROS	PSV223	MSU466	SV54ELJ
M685MRP	A17CLN	MSV452	SP03ANV
M700WCM	M837RCP	MUD490	R952RCH
M760ASL	94-RN-07	MUI4134	LSK870
M778XHW	00-RN-39	MUI5346	L206JSX
M780XHW	64-RN-28	MUI5348	N502FSL
M783ASL	EC-48-AA	MV08CNN	LSK483
M788ASL	EC-49-AA	MX04BVL	MX04VBL
M796ASL	EC-47-AA	MX56YNU	T11GAJ
M800WCM	M838RCP	MX56YOV	T12GAJ
M802ASL	EC-46-AA	MXI694	SY51EZU

N1GRT	N600TCC/PSU629/N600TCC	NHG551	05-G-503/FB05HXR
N2CLL	N1CLL	NIB2796	W585PFS
N3CLL	R788WSB	NIB4138	L28JSA
N5SBL	YJ54ZXU	NIB5233	B93WUV
N6SBL	YJ54ZXV	NIB6535	A230RNS
N7CTL	LSK839	NIL1235	K57BAX
N7SBL	YJ54ZXW	NIL2266	E600WDV
N11JCR	SB05GME	NIL3296	M126UWY
N18OVA	RM02GSM	NIL3416	YBK159
N22CLL	N2CLL	NIL3792	N589SJS
N30BUS	97-KY-1022/P133FTA/MJI66/	NIL4979	R743HWU
	P133FTA	NIL5906	H71PWO
N33CLL	N3CLL	NIL7707	E980LRN
N77JDS	P511UUG	NIL8646	A11XEL/J115NJT/NIL8647
N86FHL	ES-15-AA	NIW252	2RWM/T587DGD/FPN259/
N87FHL	MoD/M964VGS		T587DGD/VIL1533/T587DGD
N88WJC	N597BRH	NIW525	SN04WLWMIL5169/SN04WLW/
N93HSJ	N73HSJ		04-LH-3136
N195RGD	GW18AA	NIW1422	K992OHS
N200CHA	T100SOU	NIW1951	7994WW/N329RGB/VIL1532/
N200WCM	P720RWU		N329RGB
N224THO	A13EXC/N224THO/YJY316	NIW2531	LSK839
N245RGD	unknown	NIW6712	YN04AHF
N289RGD	ER-40-AA	NIW8920	B312UNB
N926YOA	N926YOA/MBZ8509	NM02AUJ	AG02WMS
N332HGK	N332HGK/WLT512	NNF922	MX06ONZ
N400CHA	PN05BNZ	NSK919	FX51BNN
N401LTL	N401LTL/NHE340	NSK920	OO05HCC
N465AAO	ER-97-AA	NSK921	unknown
N474PYS	PSU98/N474PYS/KSK951/LSK444	NSU132	V265ESX
N500CHA	PN57CVH	NSU133	V905DPN
N500TCC	N500TCC/PSU627/N500TCC/	NSV224	H226ACK
	KSU391	NSV621	V74DSN
N501LCD	N501KCD	NSV622	V73DSN
N530KCD	N503KCD	NT05MXL	GO05WMS
N536SJF	N536SJF/YAF65	NUI1247	B764GSC
N561SJF	N561SJF/YSV730	NUI1582	S496UAK
N562SJF	N562SJF/VCS391	NUI2416	M256CDE
N600CHA	FX04EEN	NUI2420	N883JRG
N620USS	N620USS/703DYE	NUI2572	L234BUT
N627RGD	KSK933	NUI4223	N87FWU
N700CHA	W913MDT	NUI6046	N5APT
N728HSX	95-D-5033	NX04MCL	SF04WMX
N731RGD	95-D-245	NXI9004	F756ENE
N732RGD	95-D-286	NXX451	EC-56-AA/N84RGD
N781PEC	N781PEC/WX7622	OAZ1372	G806XAS/ESK9985/G253UAS
N800CHA	SN06KBY	OAZ9372	K823HUM
N801RGD	KSK934	OBA695	R858SRY
N887HSX	EC-57-AA/BHZ9542	OBX51	WA04TYU
N905AAS	NXI327/N905AAS/YBZ818/	OBZ2241	C335DND
	N905AAS	OFA990	M542RSO
N920RGD	96-D-284	OIB3519	D108HLJ
N931RGD	95-D-252	OIL2946	J418HDS
N993THO	A2XEL	OIL5079	F960ASD/7062WW/F101CBD
NBZ1357	E660UWU	OIL5265	C136GSD
NCC745	M700SOU	OIL5315	D910RBU
NCH868	JBZ3675/383DVF/S919CSX	OIW7025	GLP427T
NDZ3026	E793BTV	OJI5506	D566MVR
NGH456	P98VGD	OJI7161	WVT887X
NHG550	YN51MHJ	OJU106	M31TRR

ONR314	R356KSG	PIB277	R801YBK
OO03HCC	SJ03HMY	PIB9211	X677NSE
OO05HCC	YJ05FXC	PIJ601	T807TSC
OO05HCC	SN05FBB	PIJ2799	YN03WYL
OO06EVE	SK07OXR/YN07DVL/EVE4	PIL2167	A999GLD
OOB32X	SA52OCX	PIL2172	H721YYS
OSU638	L1NNC	PIL3750	E506YSU
OTC950	R609CJS	PIL3752	F365TSX
OUI3813	02-RN-59	PIL6351	M444GSM
OUJ969	T51BBW	PIL7835	K595VBC
OUR610	PN08CMF	PIL9740	B679FCA
OWW618	F412DUG/FSU315	PIW2633	P58KWG
OXI413	V943JST/TRM144/V943JST	PJI5631	BDV866Y
OXI459	V944JST	PJI7756	MRU551W
P1MCT	LSK509	PJY534	F785UCV
P2KLT	P307VWR/8665WA/P307VWR	PNB800W	PNB800W/ALZ4555
P3KON	P291URW	PNR723	96-C-14344/N669EYD
P8OVA	R412GWU	PP04BUS	AR04AAA
P9MCT	LSK444	PP06BUS	SN06AZB
P10MCT	WK52SVU	PR06PET	YN06RUW
P11RVN	P59XNL	PSU314	H104TSH
P17LJE	P931KYC	PSU315	H105TSH
P17PHO	SE53SOU	PSU317	H103TSH
P20GSG	LSK499	PSU374	R127HNK
P20WJC	P20SOU	PSU375	R521TWR
P22GSG	R296PTF	PSU376	R522TWR
P66BUS	R842DVF	PSU610	02-KK-2088/SL2OXG
P80BMC	SV54CKU	PSU611	03-D-37075/SK03FCE
P127FRS	N3CLL	PSU612	HY06EJX/06-D-38299
P157XNW	AT2472/P157XNW	PSU613	01-D-50257/Y474KSF
P159ASA	P159ASA/13CLT	PSU614	03-KK-1870/SN03AXF
P279VUS	DBZ696	PSU615	03-KK-2078/SK03DWW
P301VWR	YCZ8703/P301VWR	PSU616	FX06EWY
P331LCC	JN-94-AA	PSU617	04-KK-2412/SN04UMB
P349ASO	P348ASO	PSU618	03-KK-2418
P364JJU	97-D-7825	PSU619	03-W-1830
P451LSR	JL-77-AA	PSU620	05-D-7799/SN54LWW
P459LSR	JL-85-AA	PSU621	05-D-7792/SN54LWT
P492LSR	unknown	PSU623	D52VSO
P532RGG	FXI214/P532RGG	PSU627	R3FAL/R527RSS
P600WCM	YJ07EHC	PSU628	P2GRT/P578FRS
P678GNV	PLF567/P678HNV	PSU629	P4GRT/P579FRS
P683HND	P682HND	PSU698	05-D-47695
P686JBD	P692JBD	PSU755	HSK647
P720ESA	P9CHT	PSU954	KSK980/N415PYS
P782WOS	JL-71-AA	PSV223	T733JGB
P840HRM	P24TTX	PV55GNX	PX55GNX
P896EEC	P896EEC/7121RU	PVY569	L256UCV/PSV323/L256UCV
P974WOS	97-C-8212	PWV693	YR02ZMU
P984JBC	97-D-7916	PY52PHN	JH52BUS
P994VOS	JL-79-AA	PYJ136	P10TAY
PAZ2535	97-C-8212/L96NWW	R3JNK	R980GUB/827APT/R980GUB
PAZ6344	C775MVH	R8OVA	Y38TSJ
PDZ5772	J989JNS	R15SCC	R907ULA
PDZ6277	TPE161S	R16DAB	ND09YJH
PEZ4338	S825TCL	R17CGT	98-D-20443
PEZ4562	S508RWP	R27HNS	SIL9995
PEZ4563	R485EDW	R100DJD	R95XHL
PFG362	J19BUS	R101PWR	TIJ929/R101PWR
PH54PCH	SN54FNL	R111WJC	R380XYD/XVV380

R137LNR	R137LNR/OET309/R137LNR	S20FMC	SK07FYU
R182LBC	HJZ3949/R182LBC	S22SPA	BX05AJV
R261OFJ	KSU617/R261OFJ/LSK498/	S33AAM	ST57LWF
	R261OFJ	S55ECH	S884SVK/TTC86/S2TSH
R263JHL	R263JHL/OFA590	S174SVK	2JVK
R341KGG	XIL6471/R341KGG	S200WCM	YJ54ZYM
R376DJN	WSV341	S240CSF	S241CSF
R402EOS	WAW367/R402EOS/LSK512	S273LGA	C11MMM/S273LGA
R478SSA	R126LKS	S300WCM	YJ54ZYL
R484GNB	R1BLU	S400EVE	YN56SDX
R685WRN	XAT11X/R685WRN/R761GUA/	S555JSE	S655JSE
	NLE145/R761GUA	S555WCM	YJ54ZYH
R687TTS	MoD	S600WCM	YJ54ZYK
R694OYS	DMN35R (I.O.M.)	S690RWG	S690RWG/LTU284/S690RWG/
R888WMC	R651RSE		WXI878
R900WCM	YD02RJU	S751SCJ	S751SCJ/FSU797
R913GFF	R766DUM	S869OGB	S869OGB/HIL2148
R951RCH	R951RCH/660CUH	S900WCM	YD02RJV
R971XBC	R971XBC/CRS62T	S961BBV	S44ABC
R984SSA	97-D-59002	S962BBV	S111ABC
R985SSA	97-D-59003	S963BBV	S33ABC
R986SSA	97-D-59004	S964BBV	S22ABC
R993SSA	97-D-59005	SA02CJO	SA02CJU
RDZ4286	L95GAX	SA04AGT	WCZ2201
RG02NMN	OO02TEN	SA51CTF	MIL7793/SA52CTF
RG03BSY	C5OXF/BKZ70/YJ03GXP	SC03WJC	FN03DXJ
RG03BVK	C3OXF/NBZ70/YJ03GXM	SE02TWJ	MUI5608
RG03BVW	C4OXF/NDZ70/YJ03GXN	SF05XDG	LSK502
RIB2901	M657KVU	SF06WDZ	KSK980
RIB6563	C175LWB	SF06WKE	2HAN
RIB7742	F812XSG	SF08VVE	LSK497
RIB8036	B472UNB	SF08VVG	2WR
RIB8847	J272WFS	SF54CFO	SP54CFO
RIB8848	F133UMD	SF54KHP	SF54HKP
RIJ774	P809GBA	SF54OVB	SF52GET
RIL2576	M133SKY	SG03ZEL	KSK949
RIL3690	C270TPL	SG03ZEX	HSK656
RIL3693	D641ALR	SIA637	W534WPO
RIL3998	D102BNV	SIB2284	W503WCA/W583WCA
RJI2612	B634OEC	SIB3933	L735RUM
RJI2719	D55VSO	SIB4458	C179LWB
RJI5715	G867RNC	SIB6297	M103WKA
RJI5716	C342GSD	SIB7357	YN04YJB/L14NNC
RJI6395	F765ENE	SIL1075	M623ORJ
RJI8711	M670KVU	SIL1103	HSK657
RO06ART	YJ57BTO	SIL1104	HSK658
RRS303X	TND429X	SIL1598	N313BYA
RRY342	T211NUB	SIL1895	J261NNC
RSU585	SF04SXY	SIL2292	GKN116Y
RSV533	F46TMU	SIL4860	L804SAE
RUI2184	L120BPH	SIL6715	F753ENE
RUI2185	H423DVM	SIL7566	KSK953
RUI9469	J721KBC/J928FPS	SIL8013	T496LCS
RUI9470	R626FCT	SIL8572	M328KRY
RUI9480	R991EWU	SIL8697	LSK844
RUI9481	R992EWU	SIL8753	A315XHE/GSU368
RX06WPT	RX06WPY	SIL8761	C86HCX
S1YST	PG51GAR/WA51JYN	SIL9637	M10FTG
S4DPC	S913BSF	SIL9988	Y832NAY
S10MCT	SN57EHH	SIL9991	YD02PWZ

SIL9993	YJ03GXL	T333BUS	T734JGB
SIL9994	SP04EVB	T401JSL	T77JDS
SIL9996	M865TYC	T403EGD	99-KE-111
SIL9997	N755CYA	T404EGD	99-KE-11
SIW1940	UWJ52Y	T469BCN	T321BUS/T469BCN
SIW9154	L62YJF	T535EUB	T535EUB/TRM144
SJ56BFL	225BMR	T536EUB	T536EUB/319DHR
SJI8112	E515KNV	T594JLS	99-KY-2587
SK03FDL	03-D-28869/PSU616-SK03DFL/	T600WCM	MF52KCO
	PSU616	T608DGD	LSK444
SK05BYX	V20AFC	T609DGD	T3EVE/T609DGD/KSK980/12HM
SK07FCF	SK07DCF	T709UOS	LSK841
SK08FYO	S20FML/SK07FYU	T717UOS	2603HP/T717UOS/HSK648
SM04GSM	GM04GSM	T721KFJ	T3RED
SN03AXM	SN03NXM	T782TSF	T782TSF
SN02TOA	SN03TOA	T794TWX	T116AUA
SN04VUR	04-WH-2101	T798FRU	A15XEL/T798FRU/B1MGR
SN08BXR	SN08BXS	T802FRU	A18XEL
SN08BXS	SN08BXT	T875TGD	99-D-541
SN08CNJ	SN08CNU	T900WCM	YD02RJY
SN09CVV	SN09CVT	T949BAK	2367AT/T949BAK
SN53KYO	L5BUS	TDZ1960	M308BAV
SN54GWV	SN54GWV/USU643	TFX966	9396WW/N330RGB
SP07HHO	SP07HHP	TIB2865	G284BEL
SP58CXV	SP58CXX	TIB5004	R550MSS
SP58CXX	SP58CXV	TIB7836	G800CRW
SN02NRN	K17PHO/SN01NRN	TIL2360	F296RMH
SRU410	SN51NFR	TIL4032	E656UNE
SSU727	YN54DDA	TIL4034	F805TMD
STG476Y	ECK880E	TIW2316	YU02HXH
SUI1480	R109AKP	TIW4227	Y376BFS
SUX476X	LEC197X	TIW5725	SF03AWC
SV08VUW	2HAN	TIW7700	WAC828
SV08VVE	LSK497	TIW8406	Y546CDS
SV08VVG	2WR	TIW9829	H192DVM
SV08VVH	3HWS	TJI1328	C486HAK
SW02VFX	MoD	TJI1700	F471WAD
SW02VGY	MoD	TJI3140	J41VWO
SW02VTP	KSK953	TJI4022	B482UNB
SXF615	G961UKL/A18KFC/KCZ5663/	TJI4024	A612UGD
	A12APT/G962FYX	TJI5392	E314OPR
SXI2887	W222GSM	TJI5393	C519DND
SY54BMV	BU54DEC/SY54BMV	TJI5394	C520DND
T3DOT	AA05DOT	TJI6264	J241NNC
T6DOF	SF54OUP	TRM144	N658EWJ
T7DOF	T641BSS	TRR814R	RTO1R
T8DOF	SN03OAJ	TSJ61S	SV04CVA
T9DOF	LSK555	TSU638	ES 3771/H987RKG
T10MCT	YN09HDU	TSU642	P563MSX
T11OUR	Y557MES	TSV677	M254FYS
T12DEV	T297ROF	TSV718	X434NSE
T13ECL	T418KAG	TSV719	CN05APY
T13GDR	TM06ONE	TSV720	S486BWC
T20JLS	YJ03PDX	TSV721	CN05FVV
T25ERS	W2JAY	TSV722	X438NSE
T50TPB	TFO532	TSV778	KX05HVF
T52MOA	T52MOA/HST11	TSV781	MX05BWP
T90WJC	HJ02XVN	TSV956	N71EAK/YNJ214/N71EAK/SIW1937
T99HAL	T643BSS	TU07SOU	SK07FUY
T272RMY	101CLT	TXI2251	J7FTG/J779MJK

TXI4242	P23TTX	VIL9332	R70ACE
UAX891	R204MGA	VIW7191	A308RSU
UCD528	T160AUA	VJI1995	G545LWU
UDL453	K491VVR	VJI3002	99-D-41314/T391UCH
UGE471	SK07FSN	VJI5885	E502KNV
UHR412	F719ENE	VJI9410	T79RJL
UIL1250	J513LRY	VJI9413	M309KRY
UIL1270	F399KTU	VJI9414	WIA20
UIL4223	DG52WJM	VRY357	N85LSE
UIL7808	J22PJT/UIL7808	VSR591	N128YRW
UIL7816	D111BNV	VSV632	W653FUM
UIL7828	F439LTU/NIL9777/3810VT/	VXI8302	B834AUS
	F439LTU/7052VT/9975VT/F994KFM	W7JDS	W491HOB
UIW2135	D538MVR	W8OVA	W153RYB
UJI4521	C46WLL	W20JLS	YN05CUY
UKZ7822	N973EUG	W77BUS	W211/BUS/77BUS
USU643	BN08OBW	W100WCM	Y845HUA
USU662	R92GTM	W153RYB	W8OVA/W153RYB
USV981	T53AUA	W158WTA	00-D-41917
USY858	SN05FBE	W173CDN	W17CDN
UVS158	W247OCC	W294PFS	W294PFS/W122DOP
V1PEO	W636YSB/W1JAY	W297UGX	YIL2941/W297UGX
V1PHC	YN56NRJ	W333NOB	W42BGB
V9DOT	BB05DOT	W409OSS	W358GSE
V86LYS	LSK497	W548RSG	W548RSG/LSK548
V90JLS	YJ57BSX	W785BCF	W785BCF/YJL693
V91LYS	KSK949	WAY877	N475PYS/SIL9541/N475PYS/
V93LYS	KSK976		KSK981
V100WCM	SF57OTG	WAZ7316	M724KPD
V133ESF	BXI 850/V133ESF	WDF297	00-D-31073/X683RDA
V167MYS	99-D-60005	WDS343V	GCS38V
V168MYS	99-D-60017	WDZ4724	K822HUM
V169MYS	99-D-60004	WIB7186	D101BNV
V170MYS	99-D-60006	WIB9256	G98PCK
V311NGD	V311NGD/WSU475	WIL3629	F105SEU
V312NGD	V312NGD/WSU476	WIL6457	P398FEA
V313NGD	V313NGD/GSU347	WIL6957	E688NNH
V601GCS	V601GCS/B10PSV	WIL6981	M101WKA
V649PHJ	94-D-60018/WIL9216	WIL7215	C860PSM
VAV15	F830NNF	WIL9217	94-D-60020
VAV552	N936RBC/NJI1189/TSV956/	WJ08BUS	MW08BUS
	N936RBC	WJI2321	F672TFH
VAZ2534	H62XBD	WJI6650	E299UHE
VAZ4918	M100TPT	WJI6730	C192RVV
VCS391	SV54ELW	WLT408	M842DUS
VEL374	MSU614Y	WLT415	S487BWC
VIA230	A516NCL	WLT416	ER 9289
VIA488	S750XYA	WLT427	SP51AVV
VIA508	M827HNS/LSK499	WLT447	N616USS
VIA963	P500GSM	WLT546	TBC1X
VIB3264	D614FSL	WLT720	SV54ELH
VIB9485	N921DWJ	WLT741	M844DUS
VIL4027	G154TYT	WLT743	SP03GDV/SP03EUJ
VIL6350	F37PKV	WLT809	N871MSU/VJI9411/N871MSU
VIL6685	G51VMM	WLT915	R83SEF
VIL6686	C245RSF	WLT978	M406BFG
VIL8250	C734TJF	WNB604	N708CYC
VIL8578	H258AAS/XIB3473	WNR536	N77JDS
VIL9330	K714TSD	WRC751	FN52GUC
VIL9331	G47RGG	WSC267	W200SOU

WSC471	S752CKO
WSC700	SC02LVD
WSD827	TSD285
WSU476	M947LYR
WSU487	T704JLD
WSU489	T705JLD
WSU557	R3PCL
WSU857	G93PBG
WSU858	PX07GXS
WSU859	G586KKU
WSU860	FJ07AAV
WSU864	KM02GSM
WSU871	SN04VVF/04-KY-2600
WSU892	M635KVU
WSU982	T14HCT
WSV238	JW02BUS
WSV713	SA02PBF
WUH704	EC-44-AA
WXI2245	NES483Y
X7DCR	LN51AZA
X7DKR	LN51AZB
X22BUS	HX51LPU
X23BUS	HX51LPO
X23MCG	HX51LPV
X23MGL	HX51LPZ
X23OUR	HX51LPK
X23SLF	HX51LPL
X23SPT	HX51LPJ
X23TOP	HX51LPY
X429NSE	X429NSE/NSU132
X431NSE	X431NSE/BSK756
X432NSE	X432NSE/TSV719
X437NSE	X437NSE/TSV721
X441NSE	X441NSE/GSU950
X466SAS	W745NAS
X606RFS	W606RFS
X626DYB	704BYL
X937MSP	X937MSP/GNT184
XAM124A	E420LOU
XAM826A	OTC711Y
XAT11X	Y658HWY
XCS961	F480WFX
XCZ4150	P348WHS/L300NGS
XCZ7782	F381MUT/PPY238/F381MUT/ A5UNF/F381MUT
XIB2453	G167RBD
XIB3473	K750UJO
XIB9829	XTU771W
XIJ602	W744NAS
XIL1257	E316UUB
XIL1540	M317RSO
XIL4668	H43VNH
XIL5755	971OHT/J888BST
XIL6215	G770GOP
XIL6465	N945MGG
XIL6467	L467DNA
XIL6468	M713FMR
XIL6471	R321EHS
XIL6472	L964JFU
XIL6473	W382OSN
XIL6474	J410PRW
XIL7241	K698RNR
XIL7307	E633UNE/GIL1685/LSK615/ E633UNE
XIL8125	J694CEV/LSK607/J597CEV/FC9356
XIL8788	P309VWR
XIL9007	J306UKG
XIW1182	J209NNC
XJF448	FN04JZM
XJI5891	A586WNY/LIB7134/A586WNY
XLM923	N197DYB/HCC882/N197DYB
XRY278	SF05KWN
XSU913	C101OTW/823NMC/ C259MWJ/4475WE
XSV893	P503VUS
XWA907	F888GWD
Y3WJC	Y336VST
Y6SPA	Y241RSO
Y7NES	Y202XAS
Y10DPC	Y556KSC
Y10EVE	B18DWA
Y173CGC	Y4HCT
Y178KCS	T8DOF/Y178KCS/GIL1685/ Y178KCS/LSK655
Y603JSH	B17DWA
YAZ6510	H653UWR
YBL526	J20BUS
YBZ818	R272FBX/719CEL/R272FBX
YC02DHV	EGB60T/YC02DHV
YC02DHZ	TSJ61S/YC02DHZ
YCX320	PN02LZE
YEZ2366	T509EUB
YEZ2427	N121RJF
YEZ2486	P337CEP
YEZ2505	N554SJF
YEZ3754	K95UFP/LIB3899/NIL1503/K95UFP
YEZ5539	P316UHS
YFS438	L424LLS
YIJ351	M683KVU/7345FM/M683KVU
YIJ3053	63-KG-96/E818NOU
YIL1206	N985ODS
YIL1207	P763VDS
YIL1208	G879ARO/OYY3-G879ARO
YIL2180	M881WFA/TSV798
YIL2860	FY02WHE
YIL2941	N220WDO
YIL4029	J459HCA
YIL5456	T120AUA
YIL6691	75-KK-24
YIL7775	L807FRD
YIL8799	C347GSD
YJ09HRC	YJ09EZP
YJI1309	BAJ630Y
YJU694	R452MSL
YKJ798	W304SBC
YN06MXR	B7WTN
YN09LCM	PC58PCC
YN58FXO	YSV695/YN58FXO
YO06TXF	J600JFJ
YOI890	Y2JBT/Y958RKW

YR03UMR	YJ03UMR
YRR436	IUI2129/T60UBE
YSU196	00-C-17992
YSU572	FC03KZT/03-G-6853
YSU882	R872RST/NFL881
YSU921	N702UVR
YSV125	BT05LCT
YSV607	SF03AXJ
YSV608	AT05LCT
YSV618	FN04CZZ
YSV730	SV54ELU
YSV735	M103XBW/GSU341/M103XBW
YX04DLY	TXI2251/YX04DLY
YXI7906	F744ENE

Garage Codes

A	Stagecoach in Fife	Methilhaven Road, Aberhill KY8 4??
A	West Coast Motors Ltd	GlenburnRoad, Ardrishaig PA30 8EU
AB	First Aberdeen	395 King Street, Aberdeen AB9 1SP
AB	Stagecoach Bluebird	East Tullos Industrial Estate, Aberdeen AB12 3HL
AH	Stagecoach Strathtay	Peasehill Road, Elliot Industrial Estate, Arbroath DD11 2NJ
AL	Stagecoach Bluebird	Montgarrie Road, Alford, Aberdeen AB33 8AE
AN	Stagecoach West Scotland	The Pier, Brodick, Isle of Arran KA27 8AY
AS	Stagecoach West Scotland	Harbour Road, Ardrossan KA22 8BZ
AV	Stagecoach Highlands	Myrtlefield Industrial Estate, Aviemore PH22 1SB
AY	Stagecoach West Scotland	48 Waggon Road, Ayr KA8 8BB
BF	First Edinburgh	11 Dunmore Street, Balfron G63 0TU
BK	First Edinburgh	Cowie Road, Bannockburn FK7 8JW
BL	Stagecoach Strathtay	Haugh Road, Blairgowrie PH10 7BJ
BT	First Glasgow	Glasgow Road, Blantyre
BU	Stagecoach Bluebird	Dykeshead Garage, Blackhall, Banchory AB31 6PS
C	First Glasgow	4 Glencyran Road, Cumbernauld G67 2UL
C	Lothian Buses	55 Annandale Street, Edinburgh EH7 4AZ(Central)
C	Stagecoach in Fife	250 Broad Street, Cowdenbeath KY4 8JE
C	West Coast Motors Ltd	Saddell Street, Campbeltown PA28 6DN
CK	Stagecoach West Scotland	Ayr Road, Cumnock KA18 3HD
CT	Stagecoach Highlands	Caithness
D	First Edinburgh	Eskbank Road, Dalkeith EH22 1HH
D	Stagecoach in Fife	St Leonards Street, Dunfermline KY11 3AL
D	West Coast Motors Ltd	14 Argyll Road, Dunoon PA23 8EL
DE	Stagecoach Strathtay	Seagate, Dundee DD1 2HR
DS	Stagecoach West Scotland	Eastfield Road, Dumfries DG1 2EQ
DU	First Glasgow	Birch Road, Dumbarton G82 2RE
DU	Travel Dundee	44 East Dock Street, Dundee DD1 3JS
FR	Travel Dundee	Station Road, (Wishart) Friockhiem DD11 4SF
FR	Stagecoach Strathtay	Prior Road, Forfar DD8 3DP
FW	Stagecoach Highlands	Ardgour Road, Coal, Fort William PH33 7PH
G	Stagecoach in Fife	2 Flemington Road, Glenrothes KY7 5QF
G	West Coast Motors Ltd	528 Blochairn Road, Glasgow G21 2DZ
GS	First Edinburgh	Duke Street, Galashiels TD1 1QA
GW	Stagecoach Glasgow	528 Blochairn Road, Glasgow G21 2DZ
IN	Arriva Scotland West	24 Greenock Road, Inchinnan PA4 9PG
IS	Stagecoach Highlands	1 Seafield Road, Inverness IV2 1TN
TN	Stagecoach Bluebird	Insch Business Park, Muiryheadless, Insch AB52 6TJ
J	Arriva Scotland West	Cochranemill Road, Johnstone PA5 8PY
K	Stagecoach West Scotland	33a McKinlay Place, Kilmarnock KA1 3DN
KY	Stagecoach in Fife	Esplanade, Kirkcaldy KY1 1SP
L	First Glasgow	197 Victoria Road, Larkfield, Glasgow G42 7AD
L	Lothian Buses	50 Longstone Road, Edinburgh EH14 2BH
LN	First Edinburgh	Deans Road Industrial Estate, Livingston EH54 8JY
LT	First Edinburgh	300 Stirling Road, Larbert FK5 3NJ
LW	First Edinburgh	87 High Street, Linlithgow EH49 7AB
M	First Edinburgh	The Mall, Musselburgh EH21 7DY
M	Lothian Buses	18 Seafield Road East, Edinburgh EH15 1ED (Marine)
M	Stagecoach Strathtay	Rossie Island Road, Parkend, Kirriemuir DD8 4PD
MY	Stagecoach Bluebird	Moray
NB	First Edinburgh	Tantallon, North Berwick EH39 5NF
O	First Glasgow	5 Castlehill Road, Overtown ML2 5QS
O	West Coast Motors Ltd	Unit2, 7a GlengallanRoad, GlenshellachIndustrial Estate, Oban PA34 4HG
OY	Stagecoach Highlands	Scott's Road, Hatson Industrial Estate, Kirkwall, Orkney KW15 1GR
P	Stagecoach Scotland	Ruthvenfield Road, Perth PH1 3EE
PH	First Glasgow	252 Tollcross Road, Parkhead G31 4UZ
PO	Stagecoach Highlands	Park Road, Portree IV51 9EP

Notes

Notes

HB Publications Ltd

All our books are A5 laminated Spiral Bound and made up with 90gm paper
Full details of all our Publications can be found at www.hbpub.co.uk

UK Sighting Files
PU01 Combined Volume 2011.....£11.99
PU02 Wagons 2011.......................£11.99
PU03 Engineer's Stock 2011........£11.99
IU08 Internal Users.......................£6.99
IU09 Pre-nat Departmental Stock .£7.99
IU10 Dep Coaching Stock.............£4.99
PD02 2009 Pocket Datafile...........£5.00

2011 Preserved Datafiles
IP01 Standard Gauge Loco's £11.99
IP02 Wagons................................£11.99
IP03 Coaching Stock £11.99
IP04 Non-Standard Gauge £11.99

European Datafiles
IE01 **Germany 2011**.................£12.99
IE02 German PO 2010 ....£10.99
IE03 France 2011 ....£13.99
IE04 **Benelux 2011** £10.99
IE05 **Switzerland 2011**..........£10.99
IE06 **Austria 2011** £7.99
IE07 Iberia 2010 ....£9.99
IE08 **Italy 2011** £9.99
IE09 Scandanavia 2011 ....£10.99
IE10 Czech & Slovakia 2010 .....£10.99
IE11 Hungary 2010 ....£6.99
IE12 Poland 2010 ....£6.99
IE14 **Balkans 2011** £12.99
IE15 *Russia 2007*....................£12.99
IE16 Preserved Loco's & Units.. £10.99

Non-European Datafiles
NE1 Australia & New Zeal. 2009..£7.99
NE2 North Africa 2010 ....£4.99

2011 Tram & Light Rail
IT01 Western Europe £10.99
IT02 Eastern Europe £11.99
IT03 Metro Systems......................£9.99
IT04 European Trolleybuses -2010 £11.99

Miscellaneous
IM3 Locolog................................£7.99
IM4 Traction Engines...................£7.99

BR Wagons Numerical History

HW01 Vol 1 Directory.................................£5.99
HW02 Vol 2 Engineers' Stock.....................£6.99
HW03 Vol 3 Vans.......................................£10.99
HW04 Vol 4 Flat Wagons B5xxxx/B7xxxxx £7.99
HW05 Vol 5 Flat Wagons B9xxxxx £8.99
HW06 Vol 6 Brakes Vans & Pre-Nationalisation Vans..£6.99
HW07 Vol 7 Hopper Wagons......................£9.99

HW08 Vol 8 Open Wagons (A) (Mineral) £11.99
HW09 Vol 9 Open Wagons (B) (Mineral) £11.99
HW10 Vol 10 Open Wagons (Goods)...................£8.99
HW11 Vol 11 Track Machines......................£4.99
HW12 Vol 12 Private Owner Wagons.........................£10.99
HW13 Vol 13 BR Box Containers £10.99
HW14 Vol 14 Air Braked Wagons...............................£10.99

Foreign Railway Wagons

2011 Editions
FW01 Germany Type 0xxx , 1xxx & 2xxx £11.99
FW02 Germany Type 3xxx £11.99
FW03 Germany Type 4xxx £11.99
FW04 Germany Type 5xxx & 6xxx £11.99
FW05 Germany Type 7xxx, 8xxx & 9xxx £13.99

2010 Editions
FW09 Private Operator...............................£11.00
FW10 Scandanavia £12.00
FW11 Belgium..£12.00
FW12 Luxembourg & Netherlands £10.00
FW13 France Type 0xxx - 2xxx £11.00
FW14 France Type 3xxx £12.00
FW15 France Type 4xxx & 5xxx £13.00
FW16 France Type 6xxx & 7xxx £13.00
FW17 France Type 8xxx & 9xxx £12.00

FW18 Spain & Portugal.............................£12.00
FW19 Hungary £14.00
FW20 Adriatic, Turkey & Greece £10.00
FW21 Austria Type 0xxx-4xxx £11.00
FW22 Austria Type 5xxx-9xxx £11.00
FW23 Switzerland £13.00
FW24 Italy Type 0xxx-3xxx £13.00
FW25 Italy Type 4xxx-9xxx £13.00
FW26 Czech Republic Types 0xxx-2xxx,8xxx & 9xxx...£13.00
FW27 Czech Republic Types 3xxx, 4xxx & 7xxx £11.00
FW28 Czech Republic Types 5xxx & 6xxx £13.00
FW29 Slovakia Types 0xxx-4xxx £11.00
FW30 Slovakia Types 5xxx-9xxx £11.00
FW31 Poland Types 0xxx-4xxx £13.00
FW32 Poland Type 5xxx..............................£13.00
FW33 Poland Type 6xxx, 7xxx & 9xxx.......£11.00
FW34 Bulgaria & Romania £12.00

Road Haulage 2010

RH01 Fleets A to C £13.00
RH02 DHL Fleet...£13.00
RH03 Fleets D to G £12.00
RH04 Fleets H to L £12.00
RH05 Fleets M to O £12.00

RH06 Fleets P to R £13.00
RH07 Fleets S..£12.00
RH08 Fleets T to Z......................................£12.00
RH09 European Fleets.................................£14.00
RH10 Road Haulage Register £13.00

HB Publications

HB1	South West of England 2011	£13.00	HB11 Ireland 2011 .... £14.00
HB2	South East of England 2011	£13.00	HB12 National Express 2011 .... £11.00
HB3	London 2011	£15.00	HB13 Preserved Buses 2011 .... £15.00
HB4	Central England 2011	£12.00	HB14 UK Regional Registration List 2011 .... £15.00
HB5	Eastern Counties 2011	£13.00	HB17 Hong Kong & Singapore 2010 .... £14.00
HB6	East Midlands 2011	£12.00	HB21 Budget Stagecoach Fleet 2011 .... £8.00
HB7	North East of England & Yorkshire 2011	£15.00	HB22 Budget First Fleet 2011 .... £8.00
HB8	North West of England 2011	£14.00	HB23 Budget Arriva Fleet 2011 .... £8.00
HB9	Wales 2011	£13.00	HB24 Budget Municipal & Other Major Fleets 2011 .... £8.00
HB10	Scotland 2011	£15.00	HB31 North of England Bus Garages & Stations £6.00

Name _____

Address _____

_____

_____

All orders are post free from
HB Publications Ltd, 3 Ingham Grove, Hartlepool TS25 2LH
24 Hour Sales Line 01429 293611 or Order on line at http://hbpub.co.uk

Code	Desciption	Quantity	Cost

Payment Details - Credit / Debit Card or Cheque
payable to **HB Publications Ltd**

Sub-Total	
Discount	
Total	

Credit / Debit Card Number

Expiry Date   CV2 No   Valid from date   Issue No

————Maestro Cards Only————

Signature..